Series editor: Keith Pledger

Author team:
Amanda Bearne
Sharon Bolger
Ian Boote
Gwenllian Burns
Greg Byrd
Meryl Carter
Gareth Cole
Crawford Craig
Jackie Fairchild
Freda Gardiner
June Hall
Mark Haslam
Phil Marshall
Avnee Morjaria
Catherine Murphy
Keith Pledger
Harry Smith
Robert Ward-Penny
Angela Wheeler

Heinemann

Heinemann is an imprint of Pearson Education Limited, a company incorporated in England and Wales, having its registered office at Edinburgh Gate, Harlow, Essex, CM20 2JE. Registered company number: 872828

www.heinemann.co.uk

Heinemann is a registered trademark of Pearson Education Ltd

First published 2008

12 11 10 09 08
10 9 8 7 6 5 4 3 2 1

British Library Cataloguing in Publication Data is available from the British Library on request.

ISBN 978 0 435537 32 6

Edited by Gwenllian Burns, Jane Glendening, Nicola Morgan and Jim Newall

Designed by Tom Cole (Seamonster design) and Debbie Oatley (room9design)

Typeset by Tech-Set Ltd, Gateshead

Original illustrations © Pearson Education Limited, 2008

Illustrated by Tech-Set Ltd, Shane Clester (Advocate), Paul McCaffrey (Sylvie Poggio), Matt Buckley (Chrome Dome Design), Peter Lubach (Beehive Illustration), Mark Beech, Richard Duckett (NB Illustration), Jonathan Edwards, Andy Hammond, Tom Cole (Seamonster design)

Cover design by Tom Cole (Seamonster design)

Cover illustration © Pearson Education Limited

Printed in China

Acknowledgements

We would like to thank all of those schools who provided invaluable help in the development and trialling of this course.

The author and publisher would like to thank the following individuals and organisations for permission to reproduce photographs and images: AKG-Images/British Library p68 top; Alamy/Atmosphere Picture Library p150; Alamy/Franck Fotos p162; Alamy/Image Source Pink p220; Alamy/Imagezebra p272; Alamy/John Henshall p166; Alamy/Mary Evans Picture Library p280; Alamy/MedioImages p194; Alamy/Paw-Print.com Photography p70 (background); Alamy/PHOTOTAKE Inc. p52 (background); Alamy/Sally & Richard Greenhill p50; Alamy/Smart MAGNA p240; Alamy/The London Art Archive p184; Alamy/Transtock Inc p228; Author p52 (census form); Ben Colman, South Boats Special Projects Ltd pp186 top, 186 bottom; Comstock Images p303; Corbis p168; Corbis/Eye Ubiquitous, David Batterbury p182 (pirate ship); Corbis/Patric Giardino p14 (background); Corbis/Tim De Waele/TDWsport.com p60; Creatas p10; Digital Stock p210; Digital Vision pp2, 14 (concept art), 244; Dreamstime/Antonio Nunez p300; Dreamstime/Michael Osterrieder p260; Getty Images/PhotoDisc pp12, 14 (shredded document), 42, 54, 64, 71 (surfer), 92, 96, 98, 100, 106, 124 top, 124 bottom, 128, 136, 140, 192, 196, 206, 215, 276, 284, 286, 294 top, 298; Getty Images/Photonica p126 (background); Getty Images/Taxi p236; Illustrated London News p292; iStockPhoto p218 (background); iStockPhoto/Achim Prill p120 (hand); iStockPhoto/Acilo p74; iStockPhoto/Alexander Shalamov p104; iStockPhoto/Andrea Manciu p214; iStockPhoto/Andreas Kaspar p30; iStockPhoto/Andres Balcazar p232; iStockPhoto/Andrew Lewis p120; iStockPhoto/Bart Coenders p110; iStockPhoto/Bartek Nowak p94; iStockPhoto/bluestocking p216; iStockPhoto/Carmen Martinez Banus p112; iStockPhoto/Carol Woodcock pp48-49 (cards); iStockPhoto/Chris Hutchison p256; iStockPhoto/Christian Nasca p136 (background); iStockPhoto/Christine Balderas p84 (background); iStockPhoto/Dan Barnes p154; iStockPhoto/Daniel Padavona p278; iStockPhoto/David Dawson p182 (background); iStockPhoto/David Freund pp8, 176; iStockPhoto/David Marchal p130; iStockPhoto/Diego Cervo p160; iStockPhoto/Duncan Walker p114; iStockPhoto/Emrah Turudu p224; iStockPhoto/Emre Tildiz p120 (background); iStockPhoto/Eric Hood p178; iStockPhoto/Fabphoto p246; iStockPhoto/Firina p122; iStockPhoto/Freddie Vargas p247; iStockPhoto/Gavin Hellier p230; iStockPhoto/Graeme Whittle p38; iStockPhoto/iLexx p164; iStockPhoto/iofoto p170; iStockPhoto/Izvotinka Jankovic p44; iStockPhoto/Jack Puccio p254; iStockPhoto/James Steidl p152; iStockPhoto/Janne Ahvo p252; iStockPhoto/Jesse Karjalainen p90; iStockPhoto/Jim Jurica p76; iStockPhoto/Karl Blessing p19; iStockPhoto/Marco Testa p102; iStockPhoto/Michael Braun p78; iStockPhoto/Michael Cox p180; iStockPhoto/Michael Jay p226; iStockPhoto/Michael Krinke p294 bottom; iStockPhoto/Michael Zysman p195; iStockPhoto/Mikael Damkier p22; iStockPhoto/Mike Dabell p158; iStockPhoto/Nicola Keegan p32; iStockPhoto/Nikola Spasenoski p121; iStockPhoto/Paulus Rusyanto p174; iStockPhoto/Pawel Talajkowski p103; iStockPhoto/Philpell p4; iStockPhoto/Pwei p40; iStockPhoto/Ralph25 p80; iStockPhoto/Rampersad Pamautar p102 (orange drips); iStockPhoto/Sean Locke p49; iStockPhoto/Sean Nel p82; iStockPhoto/Sherwin McGehee p238; iStockPhoto/Siuman pp48-49 (back of playing cards); iStockPhoto/Spencer Doane p26; iStockPhoto/Stephanie Horrocks p248; iStockPhoto/Steve Dibblee p64 (scroll); iStockPhoto/Steve Geer p167; iStockPhoto/Suan Godfrey p172; iStockPhoto/Tan Kian Khoon p208; iStockPhoto/Uzinusa p212; iStockPhoto/Webking p64 (background); iStockPhoto/William D Fergus McNeill p258; iStockPhoto/Winhorse p24; Jackie Fairchild p168 (beach huts); Jupiter Images/Photos.com p65 (treasure chest); London 2012 p269 bottom; Lonely Planet Images Maps p269 top; Lonely Planet Images Maps p268 bottom; Mahogany Hair p242 top; National Sea Life Centre, Birmingham p88 (background); PA Photos/Gareth Fuller/PA Archive p282 top; PA Photos/Matthwe Fearn/PA Archive p68 bottom; PA Wire/Ian Nicholson p297 bottom; Pearson Education Ltd/Arnos Design pp72, 190; Pearson Education Ltd/Carlos Reyes Manzo p132; Pearson Education Ltd/Debbie Rowe pp142, 188, 290; Pearson Education Ltd/Gareth Boden p58, 134; Pearson Education Ltd/Jules Selmes p144; Pearson Education Ltd/Lord and Leverett p146; Pearson Education Ltd/Malcolm Harris p36 bottom; Pearson Education Ltd/Peter Gould p234; Pearson Education Ltd/Peter Morris p62; Pearson Education Ltd/Tudor Photography pp6, 28, 204 (background); Photolibrary p18 (background); Rare pp222 top, 222 bottom; Rex Features/Steve Alexander p150; Science Photo Library p126; Science Photo Library/Royal Astronomical Society p260; Shutterstock/Aliciahh p288; Shutterstock/Amlet p 102 (background); Shutterstock/Andrea Danti p108 (background); Shutterstock/ARTEKI p282 (background); Shutterstock/Daniela Schrami p36 top; Shutterstock/Guy Erwood p296 (Sterling); Shutterstock/Harris Shiffman p268; Shutterstock/Ian Scott p46; Shutterstock/John Evans p34 (background); Shutterstock/Kmita p116; Shutterstock/Lebanmax p270; Shutterstock/Lisa F Young p274; Shutterstock/Lucian Comn p137 top; Shutterstock/Manfred Steinbach p250; Shutterstock/Marcin Bakerzak p264; Shutterstock/Markus Gana p296 (background); Shutterstock/Olena Savytska p118; Shutterstock/Pchemyan Georgig p262; Shutterstock/Peter Clark p102; Shutterstock/Peter Elvidge p56; Shutterstock/Richard Seymour p182 (carousel); Shutterstock/Stefan Jovanovic p266; Shutterstock/Xavier Pironet p183 (Rollercoaster); Shutterstock/Yakov Bloch p242 (background); Topfoto/Fortean p150; www.imagesource.com p148.

Every effort has been made to contact copyright holders of material reproduced in this book. Any omissions will be rectified in subsequent printings if notice is given to the publishers.

Contents

Expanded contents

Unit 6 Measure up – Geometry and measures 2

Unit 7 Into the unknown – Algebra 3

Unit 8 Clever calculations – Number 3

Unit 9 Tons of transformations – Geometry and measures 3

Unit 10 Under construction – Algebra 4

Unit 15 Back to the drawing board – Geometry and measures 4

Unit 16 Statistically speaking – Statistics 3

Welcome to Level Up Maths!

Level Up Maths is an inspirational new course for today's classroom. With stunning textbooks and amazing software, Key Stage 3 Maths has simply never looked this good!

This textbook is divided into 16 units. Here are the main features.

Unit introduction

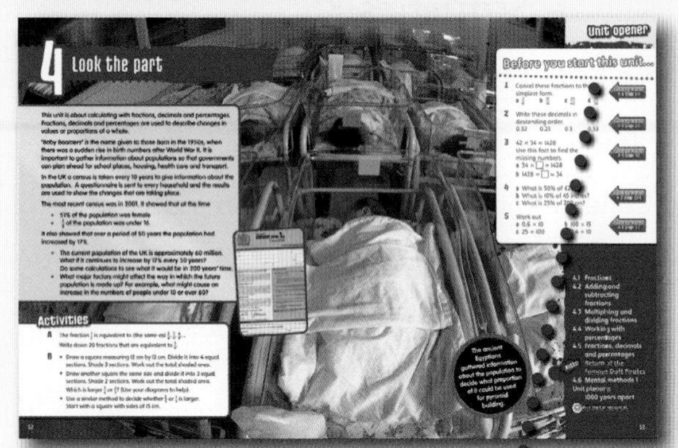

Each unit begins with an introduction. These include a striking background image to set the scene and short activities to check what you know.

Here's a quick quiz to see how much you already know. The arrows tell you where to look for help.

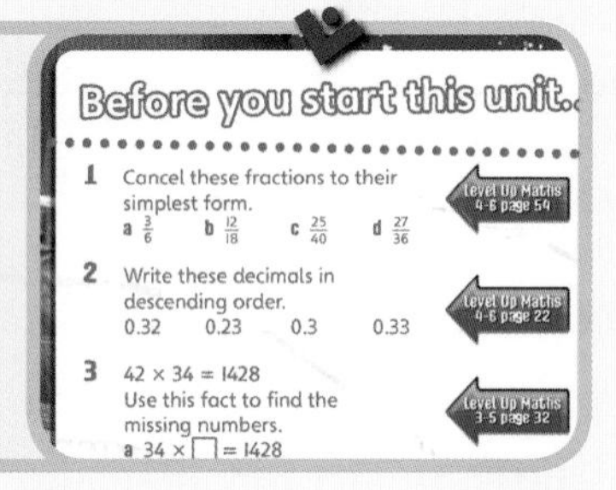

Before you start this unit...

1 Cancel these fractions to their simplest form.
a $\frac{3}{6}$ b $\frac{12}{18}$ c $\frac{25}{40}$ d $\frac{27}{36}$

Level Up Maths 4–6 page 54

2 Write these decimals in descending order.
0.32 0.23 0.3 0.33

Level Up Maths 4–6 page 22

3 $42 \times 34 = 1428$
Use this fact to find the missing numbers.
a $34 \times \square = 1428$

Level Up Maths 3–5 page 32

Twelve sets of special activities highlight some intriguing **applications and implications of maths**. Where in history and culture does today's maths come from? How does it affect our lives? Why is it so important to get it right?

Main content

Why learn this?

Understanding fractio
to understand musical
A crotchet is a quarter
quarter notes last the s

Why are you learning this? For each topic there's a reason why it is useful.

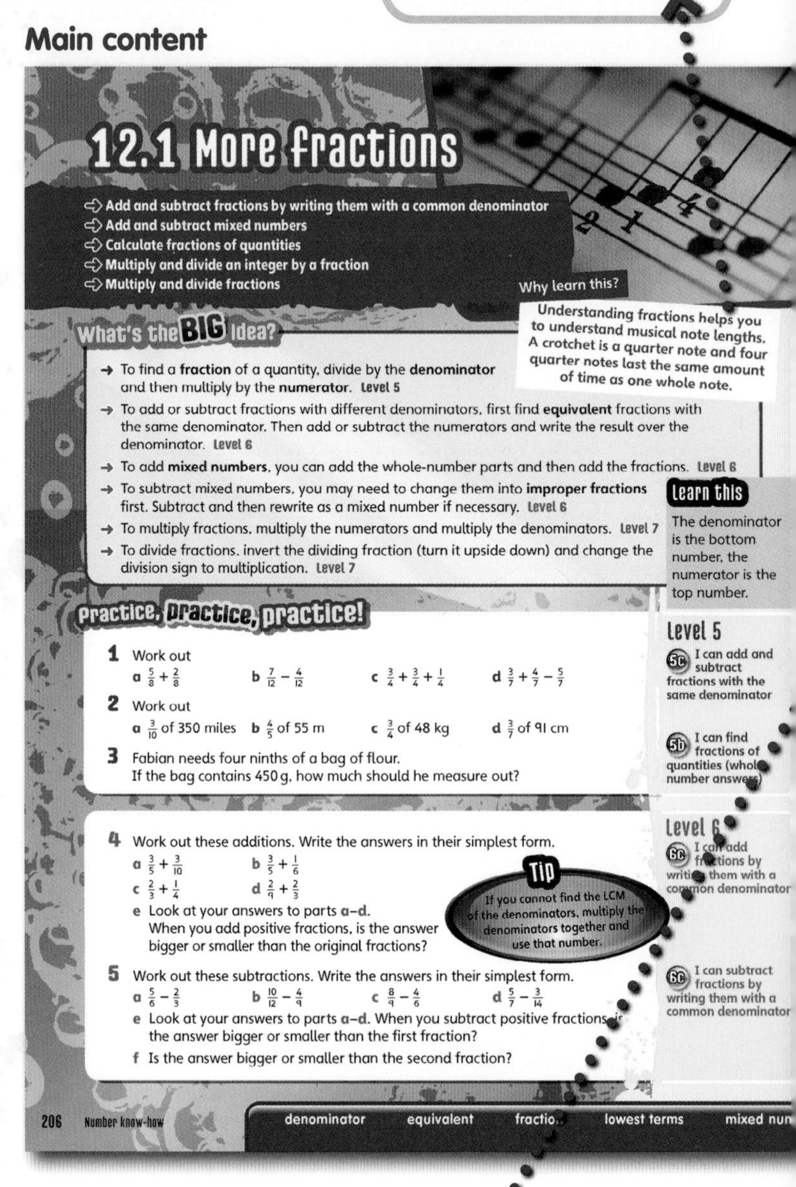

12.1 More fractions

- Add and subtract fractions by writing them with a common denominator
- Add and subtract mixed numbers
- Calculate fractions of quantities
- Multiply and divide an integer by a fraction
- Multiply and divide fractions

Why learn this?
Understanding fractions helps you to understand musical note lengths. A crotchet is a quarter note and four quarter notes last the same amount of time as one whole note.

What's the BIG idea?

- To find a **fraction** of a quantity, divide by the **denominator** and then multiply by the **numerator**. Level 5
- To add or subtract fractions with different denominators, first find **equivalent** fractions with the same denominator. Then add or subtract the numerators and write the result over the denominator. Level 6
- To add **mixed numbers**, you can add the whole-number parts and then add the fractions. Level 6
- To subtract mixed numbers, you may need to change them into **improper fractions** first. Subtract and then rewrite as a mixed number if necessary. Level 6
- To multiply fractions, multiply the numerators and multiply the denominators. Level 7
- To divide fractions, invert the dividing fraction (turn it upside down) and change the division sign to multiplication. Level 7

Learn this
The denominator is the bottom number, the numerator is the top number.

Practice, practice, practice!

1 Work out
a $\frac{5}{8}+\frac{2}{8}$ b $\frac{7}{12}-\frac{4}{12}$ c $\frac{3}{4}+\frac{3}{4}+\frac{1}{4}$ d $\frac{3}{7}+\frac{4}{7}-\frac{5}{7}$

2 Work out
a $\frac{3}{10}$ of 350 miles b $\frac{4}{5}$ of 55 m c $\frac{3}{4}$ of 48 kg d $\frac{3}{7}$ of 91 cm

3 Fabian needs four ninths of a bag of flour.
If the bag contains 450 g, how much should he measure out?

4 Work out these additions. Write the answers in their simplest form.
a $\frac{3}{5}+\frac{3}{10}$ b $\frac{3}{5}+\frac{1}{6}$
c $\frac{2}{3}+\frac{1}{4}$ d $\frac{2}{9}+\frac{2}{3}$
e Look at your answers to parts a–d.
When you add positive fractions, is the answer bigger or smaller than the original fractions?

Tip
If you cannot find the LCM of the denominators, multiply the denominators together and use that number.

5 Work out these subtractions. Write the answers in their simplest form.
a $\frac{5}{6}-\frac{2}{3}$ b $\frac{10}{12}-\frac{4}{9}$ c $\frac{8}{9}-\frac{4}{6}$ d $\frac{5}{7}-\frac{3}{14}$
e Look at your answers to parts a–d. When you subtract positive fractions, is the answer bigger or smaller than the first fraction?
f Is the answer bigger or smaller than the second fraction?

Level 5
5c I can add and subtract fractions with the same denominator
5b I can find fractions of quantities (whole number answers)

Level 6
6c I can add fractions by writing them with a common denominator
6c I can subtract fractions by writing them with a common denominator

206 Number know-how
denominator equivalent fractio... lowest terms mixed num...

There are plenty of questions for you to practise on.
All the questions have been **levelled** and **sublevelled**, so you can see how well you are doing. The '**I can ...**' statements confirm what you can do.

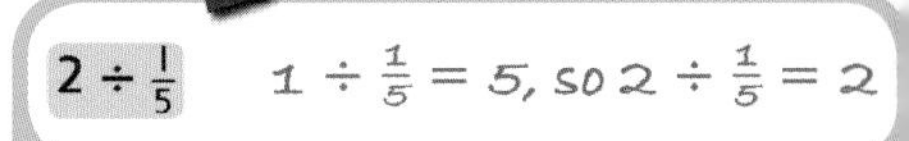

Highlighted sample questions show you how to set out your working.

This shows that the questions are at Level 6.

- 'c' questions are easiest.
- 'b' questions are of medium difficulty.
- 'a' questions are hardest.

Level 6

6c I can add and subtract several fractions by writing them with a common denominator

6c I can use inverse operations

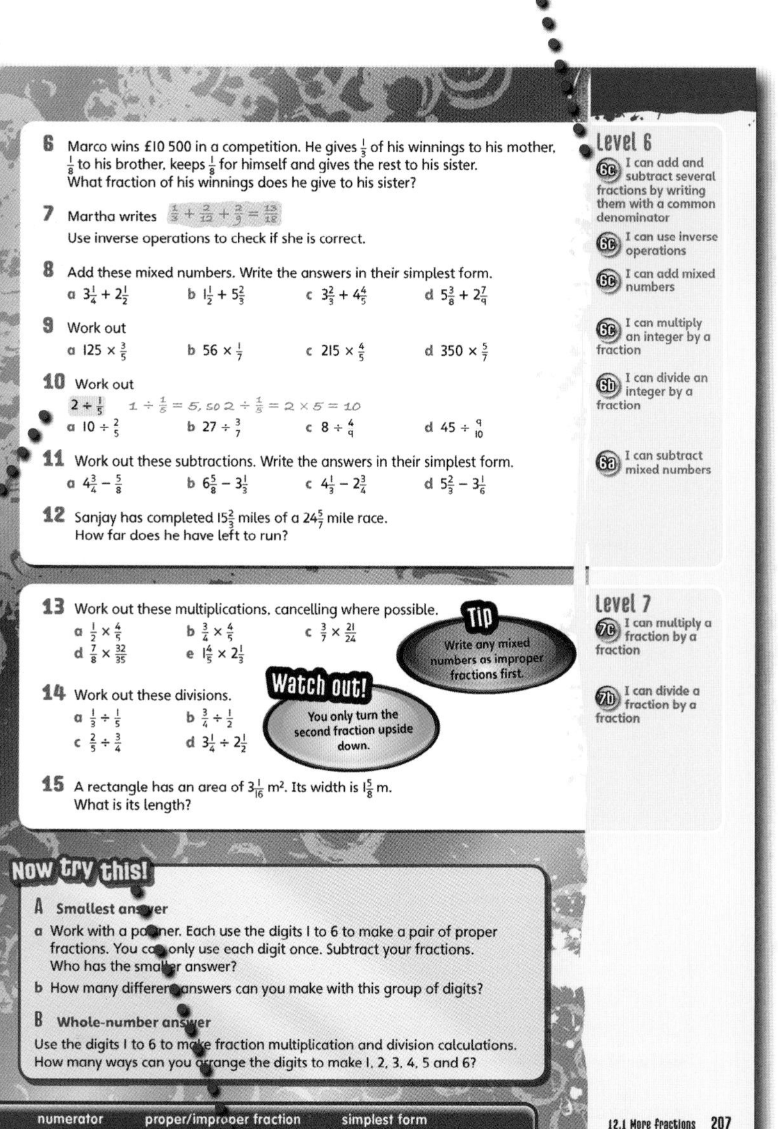

6 Marco wins £10 500 in a competition. He gives $\frac{1}{3}$ of his winnings to his mother, $\frac{1}{6}$ to his brother, keeps $\frac{1}{8}$ for himself and gives the rest to his sister. What fraction of his winnings does he give to his sister?

7 Martha writes $\frac{1}{3} + \frac{2}{12} + \frac{2}{9} = \frac{13}{18}$
Use inverse operations to check if she is correct.

8 Add these mixed numbers. Write the answers in their simplest form.
a $3\frac{1}{4} + 2\frac{1}{2}$ b $1\frac{1}{2} + 5\frac{2}{3}$ c $3\frac{2}{3} + 4\frac{4}{5}$ d $5\frac{3}{8} + 2\frac{7}{9}$

9 Work out
a $125 \times \frac{3}{5}$ b $56 \times \frac{1}{7}$ c $215 \times \frac{4}{5}$ d $350 \times \frac{5}{7}$

10 Work out
$2 \div \frac{1}{5}$ $1 \div \frac{1}{5} = 5$, so $2 \div \frac{1}{5} = 2 \times 5 = 10$
a $10 \div \frac{2}{5}$ b $27 \div \frac{3}{7}$ c $8 \div \frac{4}{9}$ d $45 \div \frac{9}{10}$

11 Work out these subtractions. Write the answers in their simplest form.
a $4\frac{3}{4} - \frac{5}{8}$ b $6\frac{5}{8} - 3\frac{1}{3}$ c $4\frac{1}{3} - 2\frac{3}{4}$ d $5\frac{2}{3} - 3\frac{1}{6}$

12 Sanjay has completed $15\frac{2}{3}$ miles of a $24\frac{5}{7}$ mile race.
How far does he have left to run?

Level 6
6c I can add and subtract several fractions by writing them with a common denominator
6c I can use inverse operations
6c I can add mixed numbers
6c I can multiply an integer by a fraction
6b I can divide an integer by a fraction
6a I can subtract mixed numbers

13 Work out these multiplications, cancelling where possible.
a $\frac{1}{2} \times \frac{4}{5}$ b $\frac{3}{4} \times \frac{4}{5}$ c $\frac{3}{7} \times \frac{21}{24}$
d $\frac{7}{8} \times \frac{32}{35}$ e $1\frac{4}{5} \times 2\frac{1}{3}$

Tip
Write any mixed numbers as improper fractions first.

14 Work out these divisions.
a $\frac{1}{3} \div \frac{1}{5}$ b $\frac{3}{4} \div \frac{1}{2}$
c $\frac{2}{5} \div \frac{3}{4}$ d $3\frac{1}{4} \div 2\frac{1}{2}$

Watch out!
You only turn the second fraction upside down.

15 A rectangle has an area of $3\frac{1}{16}$ m². Its width is $1\frac{5}{8}$ m.
What is its length?

Level 7
7c I can multiply a fraction by a fraction
7b I can divide a fraction by a fraction

Now try this!

A Smallest answer
a Work with a partner. Each use the digits 1 to 6 to make a pair of proper fractions. You can only use each digit once. Subtract your fractions. Who has the smaller answer?
b How many different answers can you make with this group of digits?

B Whole-number answer
Use the digits 1 to 6 to make fraction multiplication and division calculations. How many ways can you arrange the digits to make 1, 2, 3, 4, 5 and 6?

numerator proper/improper fraction simplest form

12.1 More fractions 207

Now try this!

A Smallest answer

a Work with a partner. Each use the digits 1 t
fractions. You can only use each digit once

Two '**Now try this!**' activities give you the chance to **solve problems** and explore the maths further, sometimes with a partner. Activity B is generally more challenging than Activity A.

We've scoured the planet to find examples of the World's greatest maths for you to try. You may find yourself helping to build a starship, designing a paper aeroplane, organising a music festival or knocking down skittles with a catapult!

Unit plenary

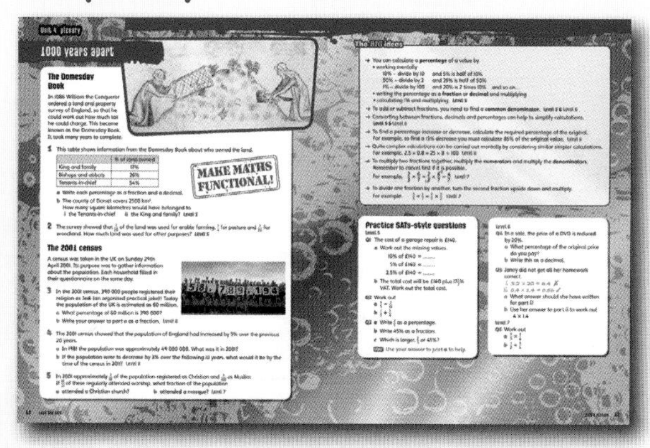

Each unit ends with an extended, levelled activity to help you practise **functional maths** and demonstrate your understanding. There are also SATs-style questions to try.

Revision activities

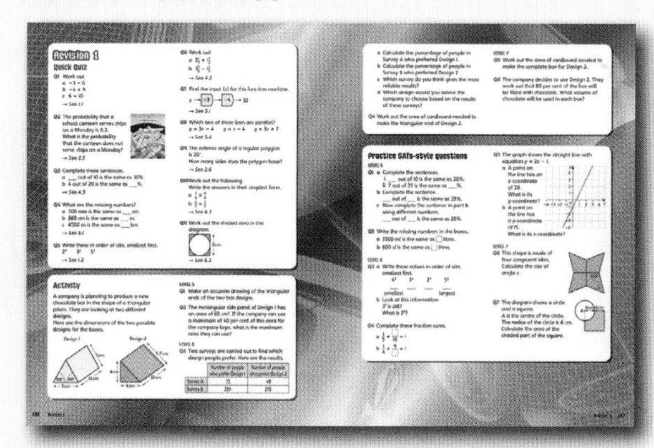

Three revision sections (one for each term) give you the chance to double-check your understanding of previous units. Each consists of a quick quiz, an extended activity and SATs-style questions.

LiveText software

The LiveText software gives you a wide range of additional materials – interactive explanations, games, activities and extra questions.

Simply turn the pages of the electronic book to the page you need, and explore!

Interactive explanations

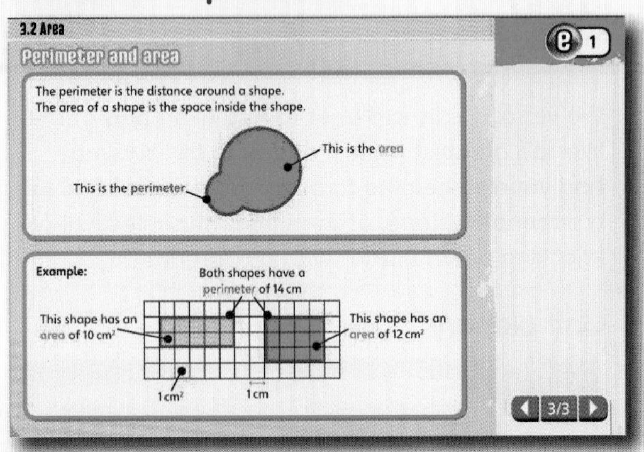

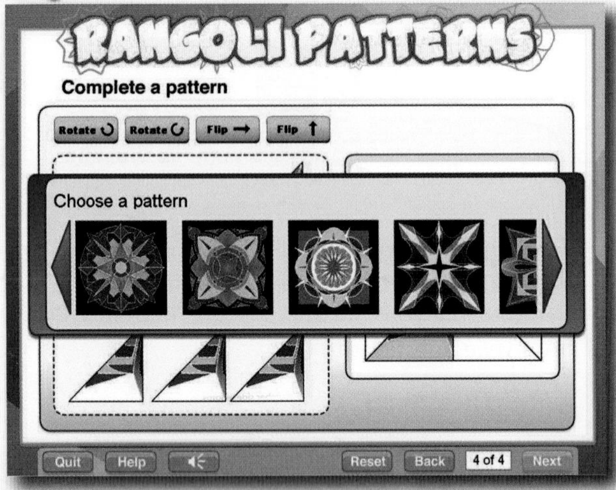

Competitive maths games

➪ Draw an angle accurately using a protractor
➪ Construct a triangle using a protractor and a ruler
➪ Construct a triangle using compasses and a ruler
➪ Draw a right-angled triangle using compasses

Zoom in on any part of the page with a single click.

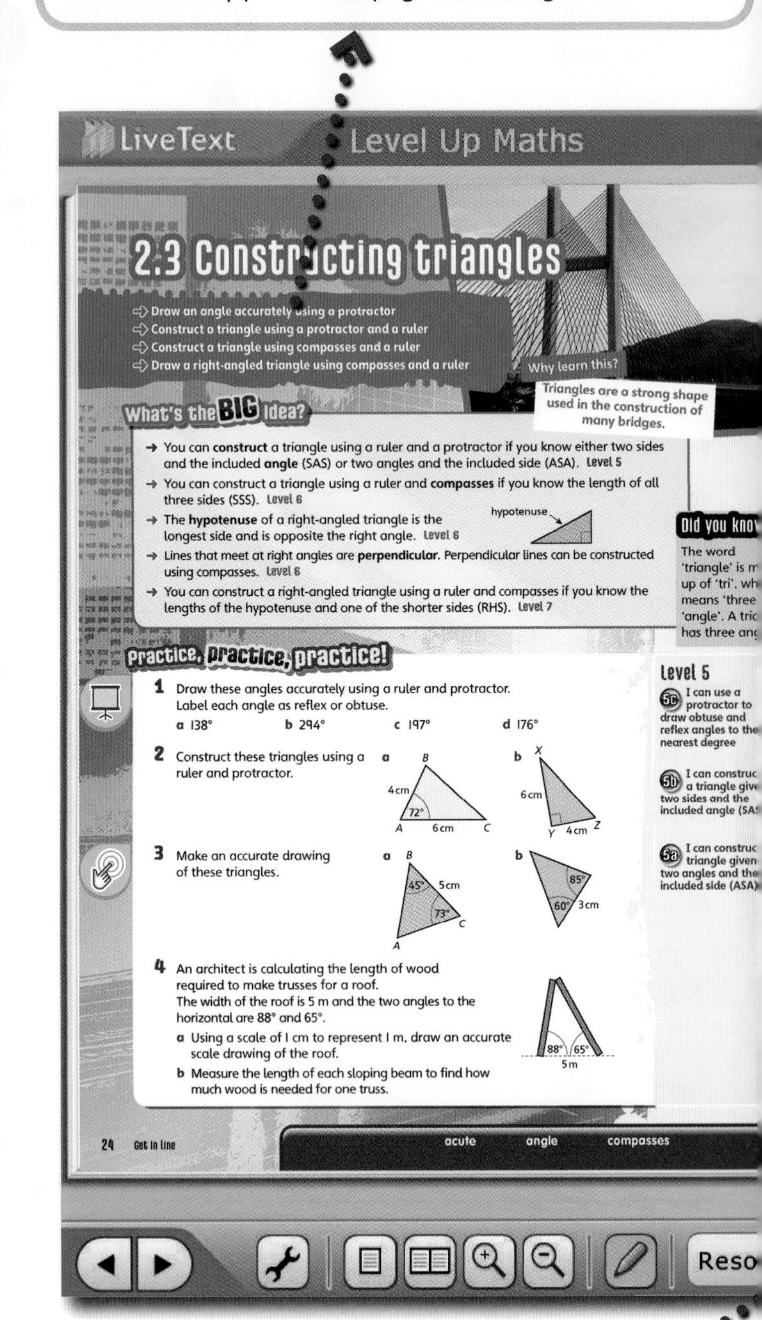

Resources – a comprehensive list of all relevant resources plus lesson plans.

Glossary – contains definitions of key terms. Play audio to hear translations in Bengali, Gujarati, Punjabi, Turkish and Urdu.

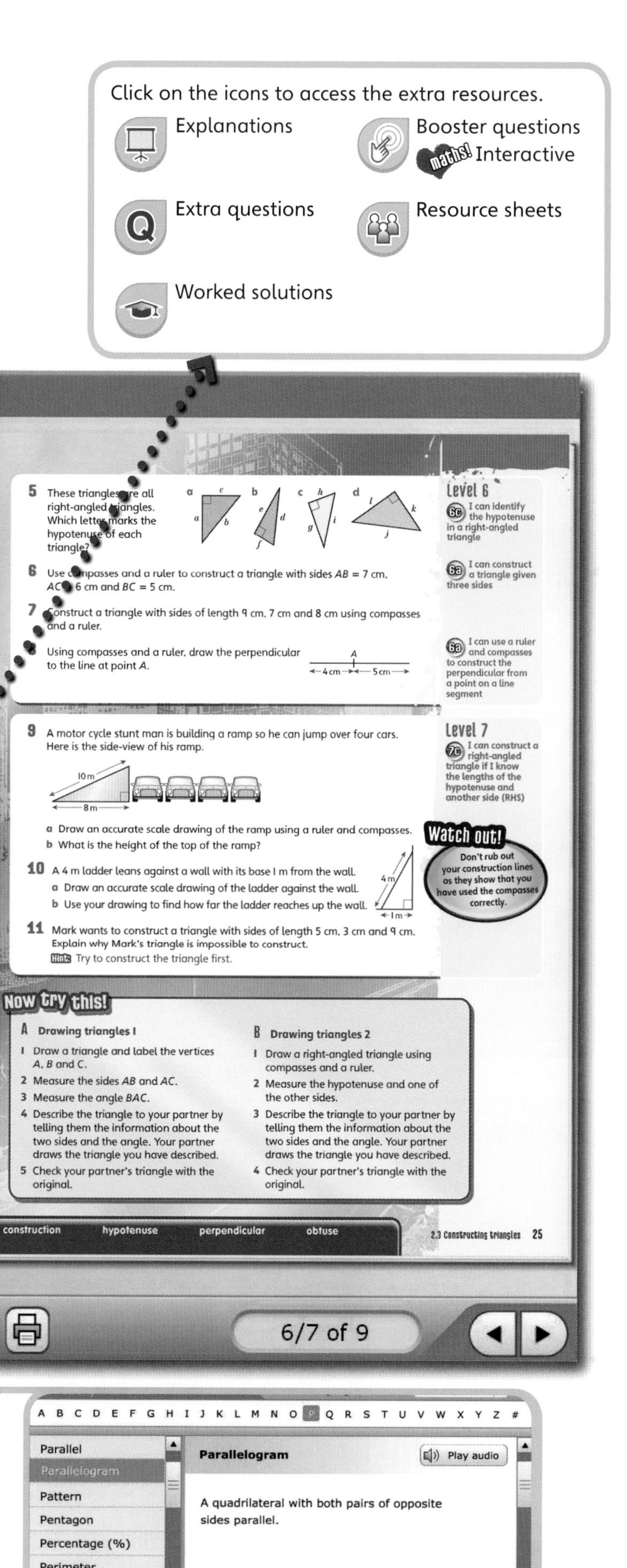

Interactive

Boosters

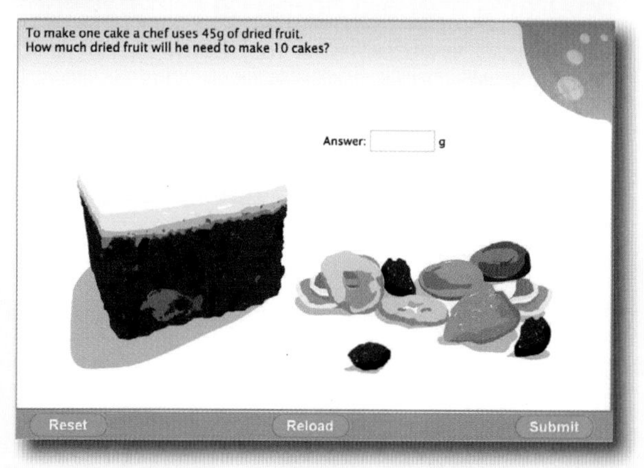

Extra practice questions

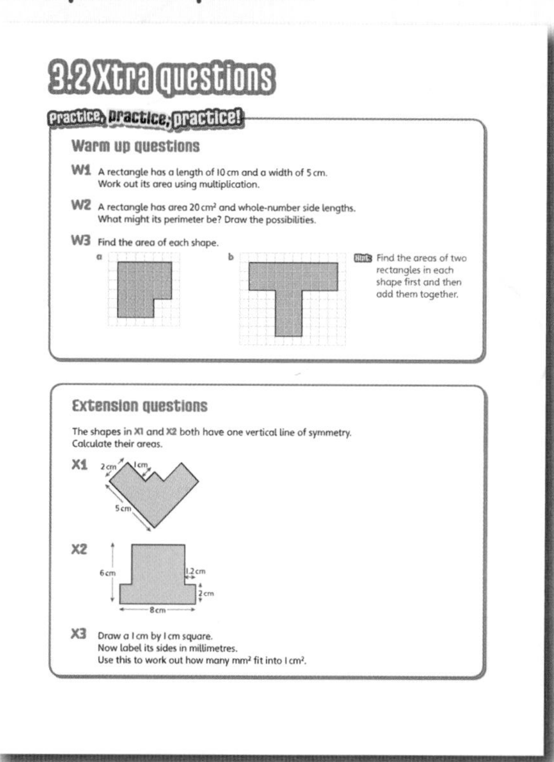

1 Getting things in order

In 2007 it was estimated that 1.244 billion people worldwide use the internet. Every day millions of private conversations and business transactions take place without people ever having to meet. However, these communications must be kept private.

To keep information secure, many companies use encryption programs that are based on prime numbers. To crack such a code, you would need to break down a large number into its prime factors – factors that are also prime numbers.

As part of this unit, you will learn about prime numbers, why they are so special, and how you can factorise a larger number into its prime factors.

Activities

A A prime number p is called a Sophie Germain prime (after the French mathematician Marie-Sophie Germain) if $2p + 1$ is also prime.

For example,

2 is a prime number
$2 \times 2 + 1 = 5$ is a prime number
So, 2 is a Sophie Germain prime.

- Find the next five Sophie Germain primes.

B
- How many whole-number sequences can you find with a second term of 4 and a third term of 9?

Hint: You can use negative numbers.

- For each sequence, write down the first five terms and the rule for finding the next term.

Did you know?

The largest known prime number, at the time of writing this book, is 9 808 358 digits long. One American organisation is offering a $100 000 prize to the first person who discovers a prime number with more than 10 million digits!

1 The starting temperature is −4°C. What is the new temperature if it

a rises by 3°

b falls by 8°

c rises by 12°?

Level Up Maths 4–6 page 24

2 Write down the first five square numbers.

Level Up Maths 4–6 page 32

3 Identify the prime numbers in this list.

11, 21, 14, 31, 19

Level Up Maths 4–6 page 256

4 Write down all the factors of each number.

a 21

b 24

c 100

Level Up Maths 4–6 page 256

5 Write down the next two numbers in each sequence.

a 4, 9, 14, 19…

b 3, 14, 25, 36…

c 13, 10, 7, 4…

Level Up Maths 4–6 page 4

The Greek mathematician Euclid showed that there is no largest prime number. Euclid proved that if p is a prime, it is always possible to find another prime which is larger than p.

Plus digital resources

1.1 Using negative numbers

- Add, subtract, multiply and divide positive and negative integers
- Use the sign change key to input negative numbers into a calculator

What's the BIG idea?

- You can understand **adding** or **subtracting** numbers by imagining them on a number line. **Level 5**

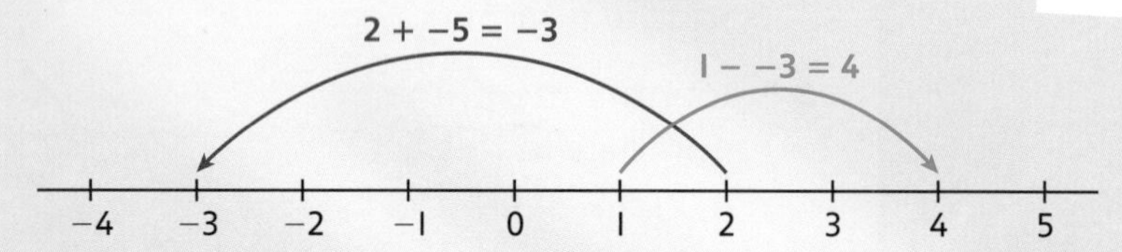

- If you add a **negative** number, the result is smaller. So, adding a negative number is the same as subtracting a **positive** number. **Level 5**
- If you subtract a negative number, the result is bigger. So, subtracting a negative number is the same as adding a positive number. **Level 5**
- You can use the **sign change key**, [+/−] or [(−)], to enter negative numbers into your calculator. **Level 5**
- When you **multiply** or **divide** a positive number by a negative number, the answer is negative. **Level 6**
- When you multiply or divide a negative number by a positive number, the answer is negative. **Level 6**
- When you multiply or divide a negative number by a negative number, the answer is positive. **Level 6**

Why learn this?

Manipulating negative numbers is a crucial skill for anyone working in finance.

Did you know?

The earliest known written use of negative numbers is in an Indian manuscript from the seventh century CE – but, confusingly, it uses '+' as a symbol to mean negative!

Practice, practice, practice!

1 Work out

a $-2 - 5$ **b** $-8 + 4$ **c** $-8 - 4$ **d** $-5 + 7$

e $-5 - 7$ **f** $-1 - 1$ **g** $-1 + 1$ **h** $-3 + 10 - 2$

2 Use the sign change key on your calculator to help with these calculations.

a $-303 + -61$ **b** $-48 - -211$ **c** -13×-5 **d** $-481.1 \div 28.3$

e Hannah's bank statement shows her balance as −£585 at the end of January. In February, she makes a deposit of £1200 and withdraws £725. What is her bank balance at the end of February?

3 Work out

$-2 \times 5 = -10$

a 2×-5 **b** 3×-4 **c** $-12 \div 3$ **d** $12 \div -3$

e $15 \div -5$ **f** 12×-6 **g** $-24 \div 3$ **h** $-3 \times 12 \div 4$

Level 5

5c I can add and subtract positive integers to/from negative integers

5c I can use the sign change key to enter negative numbers into a calculator

5b I can multiply and divide a negative number by a positive number

add divide integer multiply negative

4 Work out

a $13 - -3$ b $4 + -5$ c $-1 + -5$ d $-19 - -11$

e $3 + -8$ f $-15 + -16$ g $-2 - -2$ h $-5 + 11 - -2$

5 On Monday night the temperature was −2°C. By 4.30 am Tuesday, the temperature had dropped by 4 degrees. At 8 am Tuesday, the temperature was 1°C.

a What was the temperature at 4.30 am?

b What was the temperature change between 4.30 am and 8 am?

Level 5

5a I can add or subtract any integers

6 Work out

$-8 \div -2$ = 4

a -5×-3 b -4×8 c $-20 \div -5$ d $39 \div -3$

e -11×-7 f $12 \div -1$ g $-9 \div -9$ h $-3 \times -4 \div -2$

7 Copy and complete.

a $4 \times$ ____ $= -16$ b ____ $\times 8 = -48$

c $-72 \div 8 =$ ____ d $-21 \div$ ____ $= 7$

e $-19 \div$ ____ $= -9.5$ f $-12 \times$ ____ $= 60$

8 Find two different pairs of numbers that multiply to make 28 and have a difference of 3.

9 Work out these

i by evaluating the brackets first, and

ii by expanding the brackets first.

Do you get the same solution each time?

$-2 \times (3 + 5)$

i $-2 \times (3 + 5) = -2 \times 8 = -16$

ii $-2 \times (3 + 5) = -2 \times 3 + -2 \times 5 = -6 + -10 = -16$

a $-3 \times (4 + 7)$ b $-2 \times (10 - 3)$ c $5 \times (-2 + -4)$ d $(3 - -8) \times 7$

Level 6

6c I can multiply and divide any integers

Learn this

When multiplying or dividing with two integers:

- if the signs are the same, the answer is positive
- if the signs are different, the answer is negative.

6b I can evaluate expressions with negative numbers and brackets

Now try this!

A Pattern spotting

Copy and continue this pattern to find the answer to $3 - -4$.

$3 - 2 = 1$
$3 - 1 = 2$
$3 - 0 = \ldots$

Write another pattern to help you work out $5 + -3$.

B Power play

$(-1)^2 = -1 \times -1 = 1$

Work out

a $(-1)^3$ b $(-1)^4$ c $(-1)^7$ d $(-1)^{10}$ e $(-1)^{17}$

Look for a rule for the value of $(-1)^n$, where n is any positive integer. Write down your rule.

positive sign sign change key subtract

1.2 Indices and powers

- Find square numbers, square roots, cube numbers and cube roots
- Write numbers using index notation
- Use the square, square root, cube and cube root keys on a calculator
- Understand and use the index laws for multiplication and division of numbers in index form
- Use the index laws for positive powers of letters

Why learn this?

Indices are used in formulae to measure the amount of space in shapes. Square numbers are used to calculate areas, and cube numbers are used to calculate volumes.

What's the BIG idea?

- When you multiply a number by itself, you are 'squaring' it. For example $4^2 = 4 \times 4 = 16$. 16 is a **square number**. **Level 5**
- Finding the **square root** of a number is the **inverse**, or opposite, of squaring. $\sqrt{16} = 4$ because $4^2 = 16$. 4 is a square root of 16. **Level 5**
- 5^3 is 'five **cubed**' which means $5 \times 5 \times 5 = 125$. 125 is a **cube number**. **Level 6**
- The inverse of cubing is finding the **cube root**. $\sqrt[3]{125}$ is 5 because $5^3 = 125$. 5 is the cube root of 125. **Level 6**
- You can write repeated multiplication of numbers using **index notation**. $4 \times 4 \times 4 \times 4 \times 4 = 4^5$ and $3 \times 3 \times 5 \times 5 \times 5 = 3^2 \times 5^3$. **Level 6**
- There are special rules (or 'laws') for working with numbers written using index notation.
  - When multiplying, you add the **powers**: $3^2 \times 3^3 = 3^{2+3} = 3^5$.
  - When dividing, you subtract the powers: $5^8 \div 5^4 = 5^{8-4} = 5^4$. **Level 6 & Level 7**

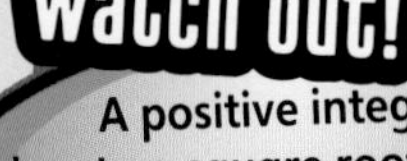

A positive integer has two square roots, one positive and one negative, but by convention the square root sign $\sqrt{}$ refers to the positive root only.

Joke!

Why are the numbers floating? Because they're in-da-seas!

Did you know?

A 16th-century writer suggested that the 4th power should be called 'zenzizenzic', and the 8th power should be called 'zenzizenzizenzic'!

Practice, practice, practice!

Level 5

5c I can recall the first twelve square numbers and their square roots

5a I can use the squares I know to calculate others mentally

5a I can estimate the square roots of non-square numbers

1 Without using a calculator, write these squares and square roots.

a $\sqrt{64}$　b $\sqrt{25}$　c 3^2　d 11^2　e $\sqrt{100}$

f 9^2　g $\sqrt{1}$　h $\sqrt{36}$　i 7^2　j $\sqrt{25}$

2 Use the squares you know to mentally calculate these.

15^2　$15 = 3 \times 5$, so $15^2 = 3^2 \times 5^2 = 9 \times 25 = 225$

a 14^2　b 16^2　c 20^2　d 21^2

3 Estimate these square roots.
Use the square root key on your calculator to check the exact answer.

$\sqrt{8}$　$2^2 = 4$ and $3^2 = 9$, so $\sqrt{8}$ lies between 2 and 3 and is closer to 3.
Estimate: $\sqrt{8} = 2.8$.

a $\sqrt{11}$　b $\sqrt{17}$　c $\sqrt{32}$　d $\sqrt{74}$

cube　cubed　cube number (e.g. 2^3)　cube root (e.g. $\sqrt[3]{8}$)　index (indices)

4 Write these numbers as squares, cubes or powers of 10.

100 $= 10^2$ because $10 \times 10 = 100$

a 8 **b** 64 **c** 1000 **d** 10 000 **e** 1 000 000

5 Work out

a $\sqrt{121}$ **b** the square roots of 81

c the square roots of 4 **d** $\sqrt{49}$

6 Rewrite these using index notation.

a $2 \times 2 \times 2 \times 2 \times 2 \times 2 \times 2 \times 2$ **b** $3 \times 3 \times 3 \times 3$

c $7 \times 7 \times 7 \times 7 \times 8 \times 8 \times 8$ **d** $5 \times 5 \times 5 \times 2$

7 Work out

a 4^3 **b** 2^3 **c** $\sqrt[3]{27}$ **d** 10^3 **e** $\sqrt[3]{1}$

8 Use the cube numbers you know to mentally calculate these.

a 6^3 **b** 8^3 **c** -9^3 **d** $(0.1)^3$

9 Estimate these cube roots.

a $\sqrt[3]{9}$ **b** $\sqrt[3]{21}$ **c** $\sqrt[3]{50}$ **d** $\sqrt[3]{90}$

10 Simplify, leaving your answers in index form.

a $3^2 \times 3^3$ **b** $7^2 \times 7^5$ **c** $6^4 \times 6^2$ **d** $9^3 \times 9$

e $5^5 \div 5^2$ **f** $7^9 \div 7^4$ **g** $6^3 \div 6^2$ **h** $4^2 \div 4^2$

11 Use a calculator to write these in order, smallest first.

$\sqrt[3]{12\,167}$ 18^2 $(-5)^3$ $\sqrt{18^2 \div \sqrt{16}}$

Level 6

6c I can use index notation to write squares, cubes and powers of 10

6c I can give the positive and negative square roots of a number

6c I can rewrite numbers using index notation

6c I can recall the cubes of 1 to 5 and 10, and their roots

6c I can use the cube numbers I know to calculate others mentally

6b I can estimate the cube roots of non-cube numbers

6b I can use the index laws for multiplying and dividing numbers in index form

6a I can use a calculator to find squares, square roots, cubes and cube roots

12 Simplify these, leaving your answers in index form.

a $c^6 \times c^5$ **b** $d^8 \div d^2$ **c** $z^3 \times z^4$

d $t^5 \times t^3 \times t^6$ **e** $(r^3 \times r^5) \div r^2$ **f** $(u^9 \div u^4) \times u^2$

Level 7

7b I can use the index laws for multiplying and dividing letters in index form

Now try this!

A Squared away

Keith writes the numbers 1 to 16 on cards and begins to lay them out.

Two cards next to each other always add up to make a square number.

$8 + 1 = 9$ $1 + 15 = 16$ $15 + 10 = 25$ etc.

Lay out the rest of the cards so that this rule continues.

B Binary

Computers often use binary strings to store and process information. A binary string uses only the digits 0 and 1, for example 0011000101.

How many different binary strings are there with

a one digit **b** two digits **c** three digits?

List them in each case.

d How many different binary strings are there with n digits?

index law index notation inverse power square number square root

1.3 Prime factor decomposition

- Find the lowest common multiple and the highest common factor
- Find and use the prime factor decomposition of a number
- Understand and use the index laws for multiplication and division of numbers in index form
- Use the index laws for numbers

Why learn this?

Just like the elements in chemistry, prime numbers are the building blocks that combine to make every other number.

What's the BIG idea?

- The **lowest common multiple (LCM)** of two numbers is the lowest number that is a multiple of them both. **Level 5 & Level 6**
- The **highest common factor (HCF)** of two numbers is the highest number that is a **factor** of them both. **Level 5 & Level 6**
- You can write any number as the product of its **prime factors**. For example $90 = 2 \times 3 \times 3 \times 5$ or $2 \times 3^2 \times 5$. **Level 6**
- You can use the **prime factor decomposition** to find the HCF and LCM of two numbers quickly. **Level 6**
- To multiply powers of the same number, add the **indices**. $3^2 \times 3^4 = 3^{2+4} = 3^6$
  To divide powers of the same number, subtract the indices. $3^4 \div 3^2 = 3^{4-2} = 3^2$
  Level 6 & Level 7
- Any number to the power zero is 1. For example $3^0 = 1$, $5^0 = 1$, $35^0 = 1$. **Level 7**
- Negative powers can be written as unit fractions or decimals.
  For example $10^{-1} = \frac{1}{10} = 0.1$, $10^{-2} = \frac{1}{100} = 0.01$, $10^{-3} = \frac{1}{1000} = 0.001$. **Level 7**

Did you know?

The 20th-century composer Messiaen wrote a piece of music that used prime numbers to create unpredictable rhythms.

Practice, practice, practice!

Level 5

5c I can find all the factor pairs for any whole number

5a I can find the HCF of two numbers

5a I can find the LCM of two numbers

1 Find all the factor pairs for these numbers.

a 56 **b** 72 **c** 48 **d** 120

2 Find the highest common factor (HCF) of these numbers.

a 30 and 42 **b** 27 and 45 **c** 18 and 66 **d** 96 and 144

3 Find the lowest common multiple (LCM) of these numbers.

7 and 9 — *Multiples of 7: 7, 14, 21, 28, 35, 42, 49, 56, (63), …*
Multiples of 9: 9, 18, 27, 36, 45, 54, (63), …
LCM = 63

a 12 and 20 **b** 15 and 25 **c** 30 and 42 **d** 33 and 121

Level 6

6b I can find the prime factor decomposition of a whole number

4 Find the prime factor decomposition of these numbers.

180 — factor tree: 180 → 18 and 10; 18 → (3) and 6; 6 → (2) and (3); 10 → (2) and (5)

Look for a pair of factors, neither of which is 1.
Circle the factor if it is a prime number.
Continue until no further factor pairs are possible.
$180 = 2 \times 2 \times 3 \times 3 \times 5$ or $2^2 \times 3^2 \times 5$

a 30 **b** 42
c 72 **d** 99

Tip

Check a prime factorisation by multiplying the factors back together.

factor highest common factor (HCF) index (indices) index law index form

5 Simplify these, leaving your answers in index form.

a $4^5 \times 4^6$ b $8^9 \div 8^3$ c $6^5 \times 6$ d $(4^3 \times 4^5) \div 4^2$

e $3^4 \times 3^5$ f $7^2 \times 7^3$ g $5^6 \div 5^4$ h $2^5 \div 2^2$

6 Use prime factor decomposition to find the HCF of these numbers.

42 and 154 *Complete prime factor decomposition:* $42 = 2 \times 3 \times 7$

$154 = 2 \times 7 \times 11$

Identify common factors, and multiply them: $HCF = 2 \times 7 = 14$

a 30 and 48 b 30 and 100 c 180 and 210 d 176 and 350

7 Use prime factor decomposition to find the LCM of these numbers.

84 and 308 *Complete prime factor decomposition:* $84 = 2 \times 2 \times 3 \times 7$

$308 = 2 \times 2 \times 7 \times 11$

Multiply together all the factors but only include overlaps once:

$2 \times 2 \times 3 \times 7 \times 11 = 924$

a 35 and 42 b 30 and 100 c 180 and 810 d 176 and 350

8 a Write down the value of 2^3. What is the value of $2^3 \div 2^3$?

b Use an index law to simplify $2^3 \div 2^3$.

c What is the value of 2^0?

Level 6

6b I can use the index laws for multiplying and dividing numbers in index form

6a I can find the HCF of two numbers using their prime factor decompositions

6a I can find the LCM of two numbers using their prime factor decompositions

6a I can prove that any number to the power zero is 1

9 Work these out, writing your answers as decimals.

a $10^3 \div 10^4$ b $10^7 \div 10^{10}$ c $10^{-2} \times 10^{-1}$ d $10 \div 10^2$

10 a Use an index law to simplify $2^2 \div 2^3$.

b What is the value of 2^{-1}?

c A whole number raised to a negative power is smaller than 1. True or false?

11 Use prime factor decomposition to simplify these.
Give your answers in index form.

45 × 48 $45 = 3^2 \times 5$ *and* $48 = 2^4 \times 3$

so $45 \times 48 = 3^2 \times 5 \times 2^4 \times 3 = 2^4 \times 3^3 \times 5$

a 24 × 32 b 60 × 21 c 1500 ÷ 75 d 126 × 30

Level 7

7c I can understand and use negative indices

7c I can use the index laws to simplify multiplication and division calculations

Now try this!

A Factor line

1 Calculate the HCF of 12 and 20.

2 Draw a pair of axes and join the points (0, 0) and (12, 20) with a straight line. How many points with whole-number coordinates (not including (0, 0)) does the line pass through? What do you notice?

3 Make a prediction: how many points with whole-number coordinates (not including (0, 0)) will the line connecting (0, 0) to (12, 15) pass through? Test your prediction to see if you are correct.

B Highest common formula

Using your answers from Q6 and Q7, or otherwise, copy and complete this table.

Number a	Number b	HCF	$a \times b$	LCM
30	42			
30	100			
180	210			

Write down a formula for the LCM.
Can you explain why it works?

lowest common multiple (LCM) prime factor prime factor decomposition

1.4 Sequences

➩ Generate and describe integer sequences
➩ Generate and predict terms from practical contexts

Why learn this?

Sequences can describe in numbers how things grow or develop – from the size of an insect population to the spread of a forest fire.

What's the BIG idea?

- → A mathematical **sequence** is a list of numbers which follow a rule or pattern. The numbers in a sequence are called the **terms** of the sequence. **Level 5**
- → A **term-to-term rule** tells you what to do to each term to obtain the next term in a sequence. **Level 5**
- → An **arithmetic sequence** starts with a number, a, and adds on or subtracts a constant difference, d, each time. The numbers change in equal-sized steps **Level 5**
- → To find the rule for a sequence, look at the differences between consecutive terms – the **difference pattern**. **Level 5**
- → Not all sequences have equal-sized steps.
  For example 1 4 9 16 … **Level 6**

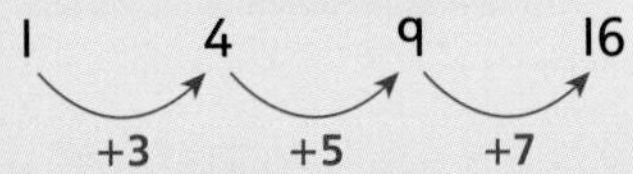

Super fact!

The Fibonacci sequence is a set of numbers which appears all over nature. It can be used to express the arrangement of a pine cone or how fast some species reproduce.

Practice, practice, practice!

Level 5

5c I can continue or generate a sequence and use a term-to-term rule

1 For each sequence, identify the term-to-term rule and write the next two terms.

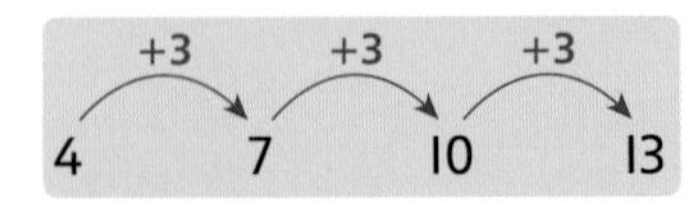

Term-to-term rule: add 3
The next two terms are 13 + 3 = 16
and 16 + 3 = 19

a 11, 15, 19, 23, … **b** 19, 16, 13, 10, …
c 5, 6.5, 8, 9.5, … **d** 2.5, 2.6, 2.7, 2.8, …
e 2, 4, 8, 16, … **f** 1, −1, 1, −1, …
g 200, 100, 50, 25, … **h** 9, 3, 1, $\frac{1}{3}$, …

Watch out!

A term-to-term rule could contain 'add', 'subtract', 'multiply' or 'divide'.

2 Look at these growing rectangles.

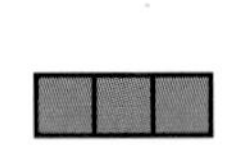

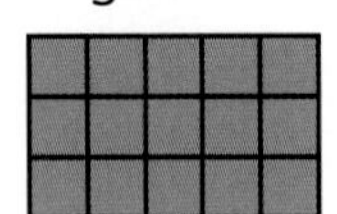

a Draw the next rectangle in the sequence.
b Write down the number of squares in each rectangle.
c Does this sequence increase in equal steps?
Describe what is happening each time.
d How many squares will be in the 5th and 6th rectangles?

3 The first term of a sequence is 3, and the term-to-term rule is 'square the number and add 1'. What are the next two terms in the sequence?

arithmetic sequence difference pattern flow chart

4 Which of these sequences are arithmetic sequences? Copy them and identify the values of a and d for each sequence.

a 3, 5, 7, 9, … **b** 1, 4, 9, 16, …

c 10, 7, 4, 1, … **d** 7, 17, 27, 37, …

Learn this

In an arithmetic sequence, a is the first term and d is the constant difference that is added on each time. If the sequence is decreasing, d is a negative number.

5 Write the sequence generated by this flow chart. Is it an arithmetic sequence?

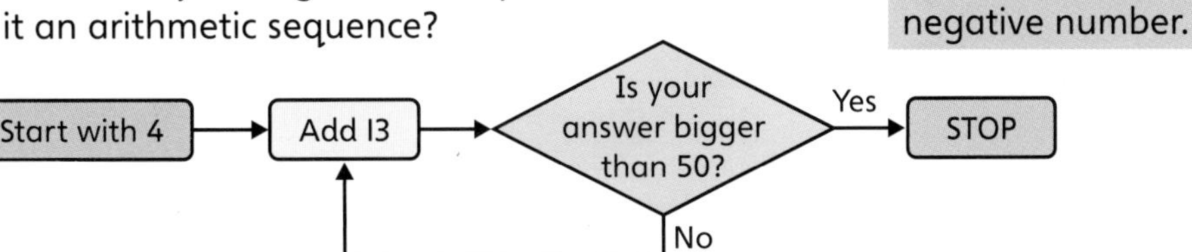

6 Steph is making some terraced houses out of rods.

a Draw the next picture.

b Copy and complete the table.

Number of houses	1	2	3	4	5	6
Number of rods	6					

c Describe this sequence with a term-to-term rule.

d Is this sequence arithmetic? If so, write down the values of a and d.

7 George wants to model the spread of a forest fire. He starts by colouring in one square in his book. The fire will spread to another square if it shares an edge with a square that is already on fire.

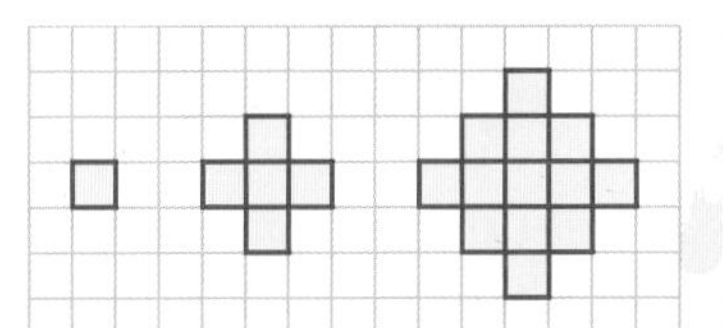

a Copy and complete the table.

Term number	1	2	3
Squares on fire	1		

b Predict the number of 'squares on fire' for the 4th and 5th terms.

c Draw the fourth term to test your prediction.

d What is happening each time? Explain your answer.

e Describe this sequence with a term-to-term rule.

f Is this sequence arithmetic? If so, write down the values of a and d.

Level 5

5b I can recognise and describe an arithmetic sequence

5b I can generate a sequence from a flow chart

5a I can generate a sequence from a practical context

5a I can predict and test the next term in a practical sequence

8 Copy these sequences and write the next two terms.

a 3, 4, 6, 9, … **b** 100, 99, 97, 94, … **c** 5, 7, 11, 17, …

d 2, 8, 18, 36, … **e** 49, 36, 25, 16, … **f** 1, 8, 20, 37, …

Level 6

6b I can continue a non-arithmetic sequence

Now try this!

A Look and say

A sequence begins like this.

1, 11, 21, 1211, 111221, …

What is the next number in the sequence?

Hint There is a clue in the title.

B Fired up

George used a square-based system to model a forest fire in Q7. Repeat his experiment using equilateral triangles. (You may like to use isometric paper.) Does the fire spread faster or slower? What real-world situations might this model?

generate predict sequence term term-to-term rule

1.5 Generating sequences using rules

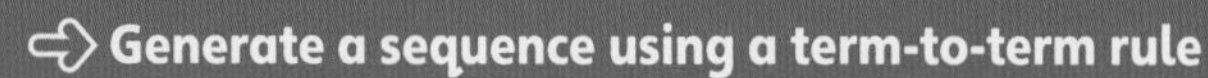

- Generate a sequence using a term-to-term rule
- Generate a sequence using a position-to-term rule

Why learn this?

Position-to-term rules can help you predict future instances of events that follow sequences – such as solar eclipses.

What's the BIG idea?

→ The **term** number tells you the position of that term in the **sequence**. Level 5

→ A **position-to-term rule** tells you what to do to the term number to obtain that term in the sequence. Level 5 & Level 6

→ A position-to-term rule can be written in words or in algebra. For example, $3n + 5$: n is the term number, so to find a term multiply its term number by 3 and add 5. Level 5 & Level 6

Practice, practice, practice!

Level 5

5b I can recognise and describe an arithmetic sequence

1 Each of the arithmetic sequences below has one mistake. Rewrite the sequence correctly and identify a (the first term) and d (the constant difference).

a 3, 7, 11, 16, …

b

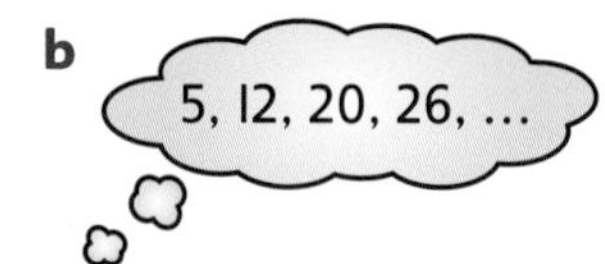

c

2 In an arithmetic sequence, the 3rd term is 15 and the 5th term is 23. What are the values of a and d for this sequence?

3 In another arithmetic sequence, the 3rd term is 18 and the 7th term is 10. What are the values of a and d for this sequence?

5a I can find a term given its position and a position-to-term rule

4 Use the position-to-term rules to find the 1st, 2nd, 3rd and 10th terms of these sequences.

Multiply the term number by 2.

When term number = 1, term = $1 \times 2 = 2$.
When term number = 2, term = $2 \times 2 = 4$.
When term number = 3, term = $3 \times 2 = 6$.
When term number = 10, term = $10 \times 2 = 20$.

a Multiply the term number by 5.
b Multiply the term number by 3 and add 2.
c Multiply the term number by 7 and subtract 4.
d Divide the term number by 2 and add 5.

Watch out! Don't confuse term-to-term and position-to-term rules!

arithmetic sequence decrease generate

Level 6

6c I can find a term given its position and a position-to-term rule using positive and negative numbers

5 Use the position-to-term rules to find the 1st, 2nd, 3rd and 100th terms of these sequences.

a Multiply the term number by −3.

b Multiply the term number by 2 and subtract 7.

c Subtract 3 from the term number and then multiply by 8.

d Subtract the term number from 10.

e Divide the term number by 4.

6b I can find a term given its position and an algebraic position-to-term rule

6 Use the position-to-term rules to find the 1st, 2nd, 3rd and 7th terms of these sequences.

$5n + 2$

1st term $= 5 \times 1 + 2 = 7$
2nd term $= 5 \times 2 + 2 = 12$
3rd term $= 5 \times 3 + 2 = 17$
7th term $= 5 \times 7 + 2 = 37$

a $4n - 3$ **b** $100 - n$ **c** $7n + 99$

d $6n - 8$ **e** $3 - 2n$ **f** $n \div 2$

Tip
If the number before n is positive, the sequence is increasing. If it is negative, the sequence is decreasing.

7 **a** For each of these position-to-term rules, write the first five terms.

$5n + 7$ $4n - 2$ $6n + 1$ $-3n + 2$

b What do you notice about the term-to-term rule and the position-to-term rule in each case?

8 Match each term-to-term definition to a position-to-term definition.

Term-to-term	Position-to-term
a Start at 3, add 2 each time.	Multiply the term number by 4 and subtract 2.
b Start at 4, subtract 3 each time.	Multiply the term number by −3 and add 7.
c Start at 2, add 4 each time.	Double the term number and add 1.

Tip
Find the first few terms of each sequence.

6b I can understand and use algebraic position-to-term rules

9 True or false?

a The sequence $7n$ produces the multiples of 7.

b Every term in the sequence $2n + 3$ is odd.

c The sequence $5 - n$ is a decreasing sequence.

d The sequences $2(n + 4)$ and $2n + 8$ are not the same.

e Every term in the sequence $3(100 - n)$ is positive.

Now try this!

A Can you digit?

The digits 1 to 8 can be arranged as an arithmetic sequence of two-digit numbers like this.

12, 34, 56, 78 (start at 12, add 22 each time)

Find another way to arrange the digits 1 to 8 as an arithmetic sequence of two-digit numbers.

B Rows by any other name

Calculate the first five terms of the sequence with the position-to-term rule $\frac{1}{2}n(n + 1)$. By what name are these numbers better known?

increase position-to-term rule sequence term

World's Greatest Maths!

1.6 Awards ceremony

Roll out the red carpets! It's time for the first annual British Awards For Tricky Algebra (or BAFTAs for short).

Carpet capers

You need to buy a red carpet for the ceremony.
The carpet costs £10 per metre plus a delivery charge of £15.

- What is the total cost of a 5 metre carpet, including delivery?
- Copy and complete this table for the cost of different lengths of carpet.

Length in metres	1	2	3	4	5	6	7	8
Total cost of carpet	25							

- What do you notice about the numbers on the bottom row of your table? Write down the term-to-term rule for this sequence of numbers.
- You have a budget of £150. What is the longest carpet you can buy? Will you have any money left over?
- Write down an expression for the cost of a carpet that is x metres long.

Seating plan

There are six possible seating plans for the ceremony.
For each seating plan:

- Copy this table for the number of guests and fill in the first three columns.

Number of tables	1	2	3	4	5	6	7	8
Number of guests								

- Write down what you notice about the numbers on the bottom row of your table. Give a reason for your answer.
- Write down the term-to-term rule for this sequence of numbers.
- Write down the position-to-term rule for your sequence.
- Complete the rest of the table.

1
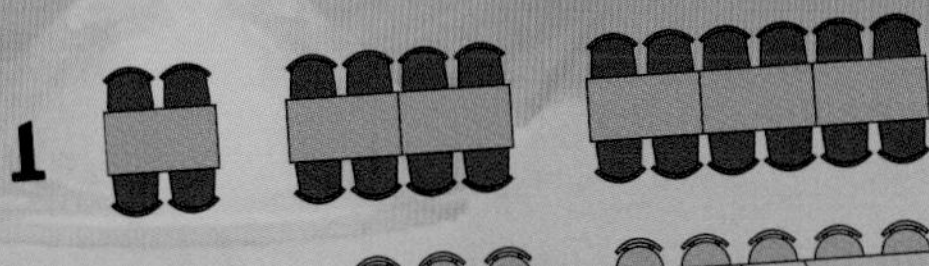
2

3
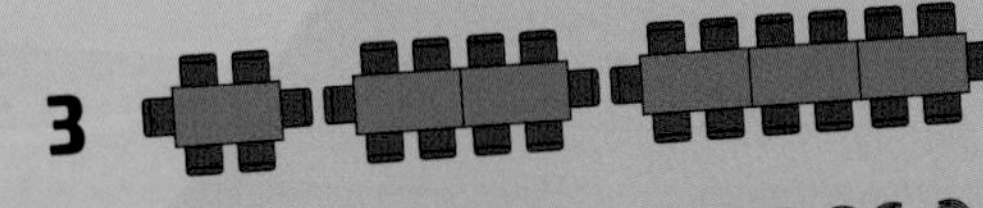
4

5

6

Trophy-tastic

The BAFTA trophies come in different sizes, depending on how clever the winner is.

- Complete this table for the numbers of squares and triangles needed for each size of award.

Size of award	1	2	3
Number of squares (S_n)			
Number of triangles (T_n)			

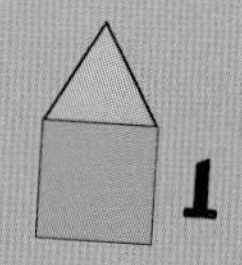

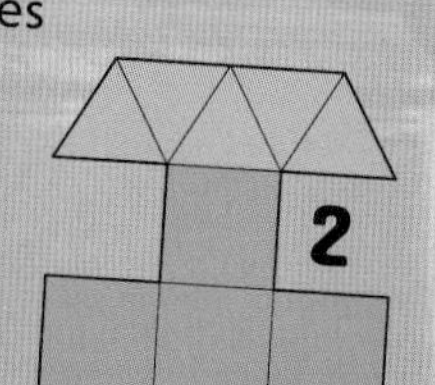

- Write down an expression for the number of squares in a trophy of size n.
- Write down an expression for the number of triangles in a trophy of size n.
- You are being awarded a trophy of size 12. How many squares and triangles are there in your trophy?

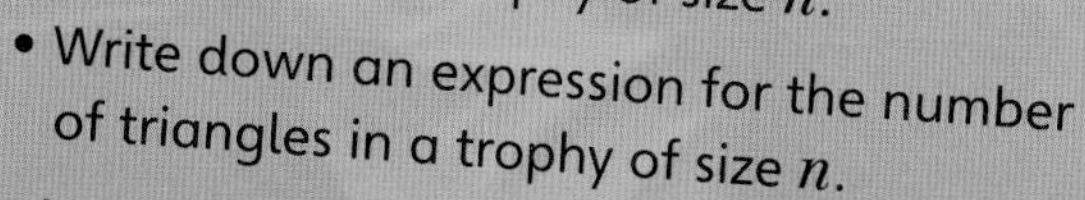

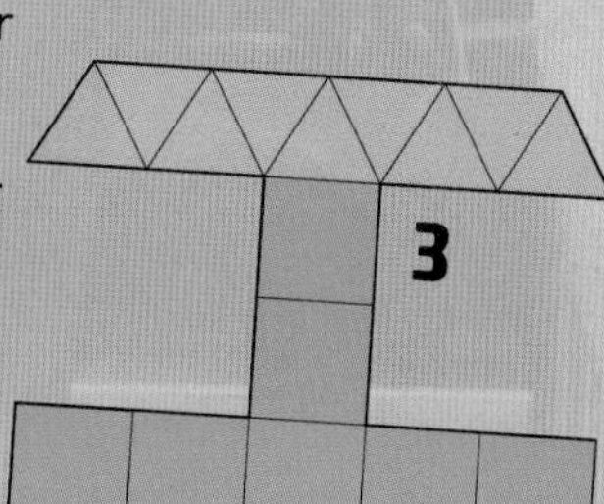

A new award is being created, and you need to design the trophy. You can use squares or triangles, or just different coloured squares. Here are some ideas:

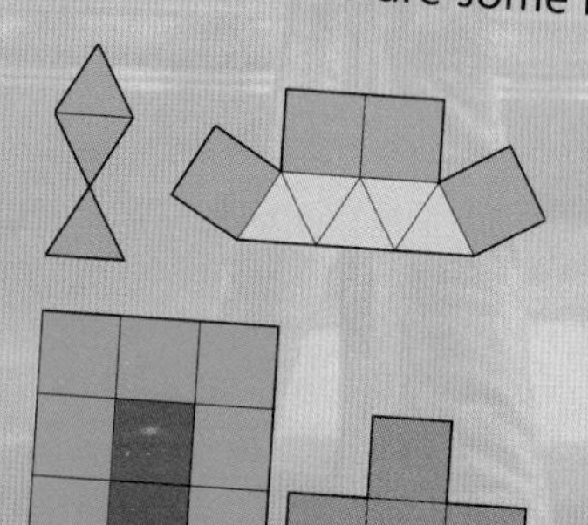

Make sure you show clearly how you can make the trophy in different sizes. Draw your trophy in sizes 1, 2, 3 and 4. Describe the sequences formed by the numbers of squares or triangles in your trophy.

And the winner is ...

Oh no! The names of all the winners are locked in a safe, but the combination is missing. You need to find arithmetic sequences of three or more numbers in this grid to open the door.

You can start anywhere, and you can move up, down, left or right (but not diagonally). A sequence of length 3 is highlighted.

Complete these challenges to open the safe:

- Find a sequence of length 10
- Find a sequence starting on the number 60
- Find a sequence with term-to-term rule 'add 9'
- Find a sequence with position-to-term rule $36 - 5n$

For each sequence you find, write down the sequence, the term-to-term rule and the nth term.

- How many sequences of length 3 or more can you find in the grid?

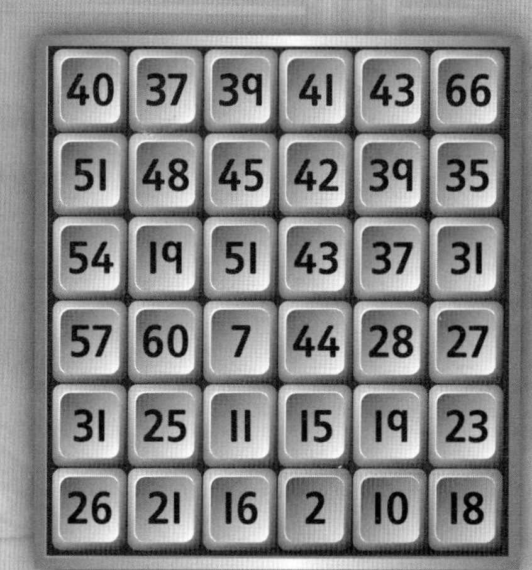

40	37	39	41	43	66
51	48	45	42	39	35
54	19	51	43	37	31
57	60	7	44	28	27
31	25	11	15	19	23
26	21	16	2	10	18

You can use the same number in different sequences. Remember that sequences can go down as well as up.

You've opened the safe, and have been awarded a special BAFTA for saving the ceremony. Keep next year's results safe by creating your own sequence grid.

- Draw a 5 × 5 grid using squared paper.
- Choose a sequence of length 8 and write it on the grid. Fill in the rest of the grid to hide your sequence.
- Challenge a partner to find the sequence in your grid. To win, they must write down the nth term for the sequence.

You can make your sequence harder to find by including other shorter sequences in the grid. Your partner has to find the sequence of length 8.

Unit 1 plenary

Break the bank

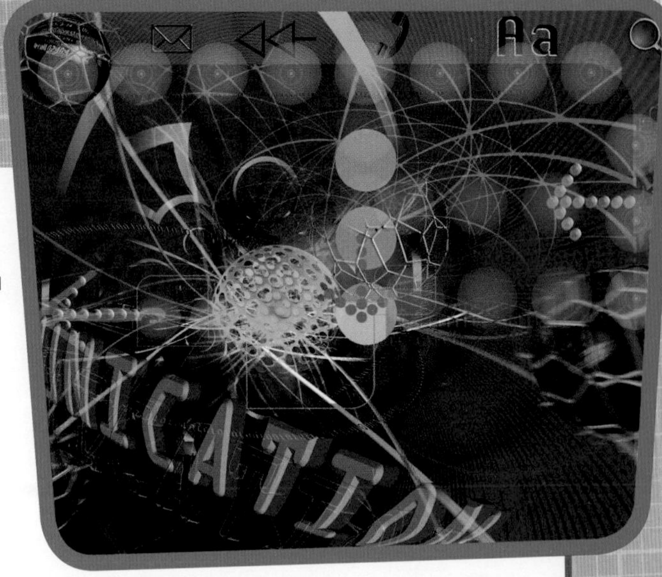

You are a secret agent. Your mission is to investigate the bank accounts of Mr E Mann to find out when he is going to run out of money and leave the country. To do this, you must find and hack into his bank accounts.

1 You have intercepted the following calculations. Work out which could be Mr E Mann's accounts by seeing which answers are negative.
Data Stream A: ... $-2 + -3$ ...
Data Stream B: ... $4 \times (-1 + 5)$ ...
Data Stream C: ... $(14 - -2) \div -4$ ...
Data Stream D: ...-5×-7 ... **Level 5 & Level 6**

2 Having narrowed down the possible accounts, you now need to crack his key code.
A spy gives you these clues:

- The key code uses four of the digits 2, 3, 4, 5 and 6.
- The first two digits form a cube number.
- The last two digits form a square number.

MAKE MATHS FUNCTIONAL!

What is his key code? **Level 5**

3 Now you have his code you need to factorise it.
Find the prime factor decomposition of your answer to Q2. **Level 6**
Hint: You may need a calculator!

4 Mr E Mann has two bank accounts. The weekly statement on the first account follows a position-to-term rule of 'multiply the term number by -2 and add 15'.

a Write down the first five terms on his account statement.
b Write down the term-to-term rule for this sequence.
c Which is the first term to go below 0? **Level 5 & Level 6**

5 The weekly statement on the second account reads as follows:
89 77 65

a Write down the next two terms on his account statement.
b The algebraic position-to-term rule for this sequence is $101 - \square$
Complete the position-to-term rule.
c Which is the first term to go below 0? **Level 6**

6 Look at your answers to Q4 and Q5.
In which week will Mr E Mann run out of money in both accounts and flee the country?

The BIG ideas

- If you add a **negative** number, the result is smaller. So, adding a negative number is the same as subtracting a **positive** number. **Level 5**
- If you subtract a negative number, the result is bigger. So, subtracting a negative number is the same as adding a positive number. **Level 5**
- A mathematical **sequence** is a list of numbers which follow a rule or pattern. **Level 5**
- The numbers in a sequence are called the **terms** of the sequence. **Level 5**
- A **term-to-term** rule tells you what to do to each term to obtain the next term in a sequence. **Level 5**
- The term number tells you the position of that term in the sequence. **Level 5**
- When you multiply a number by itself, you are 'squaring' it. For example, $4^2 = 4 \times 4 = 16$. 16 is a **square number**. **Level 5 & Level 6**
- 3^3 is 'three **cubed**' which means $3 \times 3 \times 3 = 27$. 27 is a cube number. **Level 5 & Level 6**
- A **position-to-term** rule tells you what to do to the term number to obtain that term in the sequence. **Level 5 & Level 6**
- A position-to-term rule can be written in words or in algebra. For example, $3n + 5$: n is the term number, so this means multiply the term number by 3 and add 5. **Level 5 & Level 6**
- If you **multiply** or **divide** a positive number by a negative number, the answer is negative. **Level 5 & Level 6**
- If you multiply or divide a negative number by a negative number, the answer is positive. **Level 6**
- Any number can be written as the product of its **prime factors**. For example, $90 = 2 \times 3 \times 3 \times 5$ or $2 \times 3^2 \times 5$. **Level 6**
- When finding the prime decomposition of a number, you can use a 'factor tree'. Begin by looking for a pair of factors, neither of which is 1. Highlight the factor if it is a prime number. Continue until no further factor pairs are possible.

Practice SATs-style questions

Level 5

Q1 Complete the magic square so that every row, column and shaded diagonal adds up to 3.

−2	3	
	1	

Q2 Put these cards in order from the smallest to the largest.

2^3 1^4 3^2 3^3 $\sqrt{25}$

Q3 Daryl thinks of a number.
The number is a factor of 20.
Olwen thinks the number must be even.
Is Olwen correct? Explain your answer.

Level 6

Q4 The nth term for a number sequence is $3n - 4$. What is the ninth term?

Q5 Look at these pairs of number sequences. Write down the missing nth terms.

7, 10, 13, 16… nth term = $3n + 4$
8, 11, 14, 17… nth term = …

2, 6, 10, 14… nth term = $4n - 2$
4, 12, 20, 28… nth term = …

10, 16, 22, 28… nth term = $6n + 4$
5, 8, 11, 14… nth term = …

Level 7

Q6 Simplify as fully as possible.

a $p^2 \times p^{-4}$

b $a^2b^3 \times ab^6$

c $\frac{6d^4e^{-5}}{3d^2e^{-8}}$

Q7 What is the value of x?

$$\frac{y^2}{y^3} \times y^4 = y^x$$

2 Get in line

This unit is about 2-D geometric shapes and their properties.

Geometric puzzles have intrigued mathematicians, young and old, for centuries. Solving them and setting fresh challenges can lead to new mathematical discoveries and understanding.

Dissection (or transformation) puzzles involve cutting one geometric shape into pieces that can be rearranged to make other geometric shapes. One of these puzzles (known to the Ancient Greeks) involved dissecting two small squares into pieces which, when fitted together, made a large square.

The Haberdasher's puzzle was created just over 100 years ago by Henry Dudeney. He showed how to cut an equilateral triangle into four pieces that could be arranged to form a square. What's more, the pieces can be hinged to make a chain, so that the triangle unfolds to become the square.

Mathematicians across the world then started to investigate whether this could be done with other polygons. (The answer is it can!)

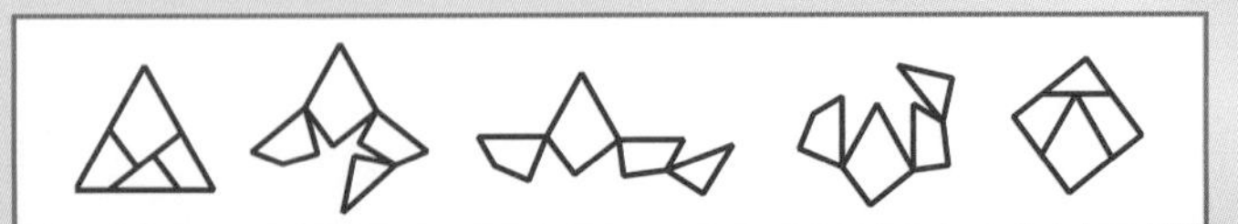

Activities

A Copy this shape onto squared paper and cut it into four pieces as shown by the solid lines.

Rearrange the pieces to form a

a trapezium
b rhombus

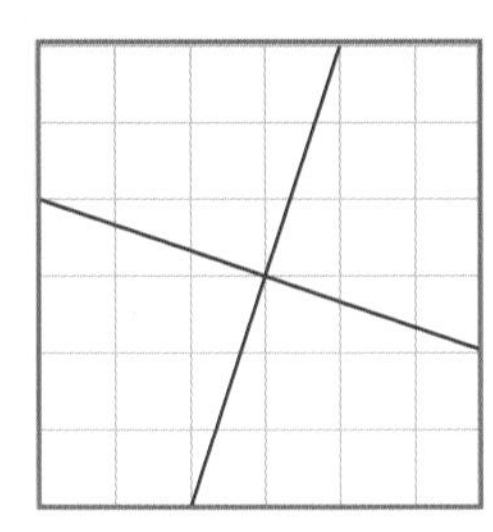

B Copy this shape onto squared paper and cut it into five pieces as shown by the solid lines.

Rearrange the pieces to form a

a rectangle
b right-angled triangle
c parallelogram

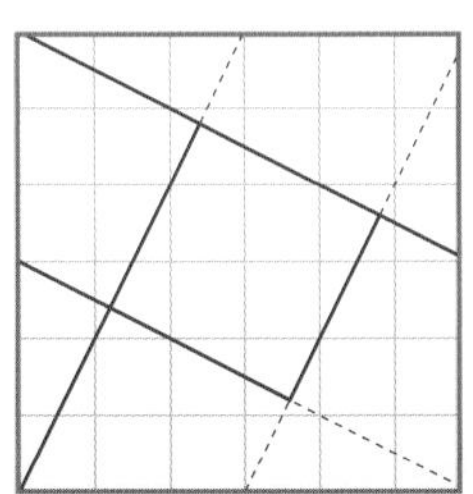

Did you know?
Tangram puzzles use a standard dissection of a square into seven pieces. The pieces are called tans and the objective is to form a shape with all seven pieces, which must not overlap.

Before you start this unit...

1. Draw a line that is exactly 6.3 cm long. Level Up Maths 4-6 page 48
2. Use a protractor to measure this angle to the nearest degree. Level Up Maths 4-6 page 170
3. Draw an angle of 87°. What type of angle is this? Level Up Maths 4-6 page 170
4. Choose the word to complete each sentence: Level Up Maths 4-6 page 176

   square, scalene triangle, rectangle, equilateral triangle

   a A ___ has four right angles and two lines of symmetry.
   b An ___ has angles of 60°.
   c A ___ has sides of equal length and four lines of symmetry.
   d A ___ has no lines of symmetry.
5. Name as many different types of quadrilateral as you can. Level Up Maths 4-6 page 176

Did you know?
The dissection in Activity B was created by Sam Loyd, another famous creator of puzzles. Loyd was also an enthusiast of tangram puzzles – he published a book containing 700 unique tangram designs.

Plus digital resources

World's Greatest Maths!

2.1 Paper planes

It's the paper aeroplane world championships! Can you help the competitors find the missing angles in their designs? If you can, maybe you could build a world-beater!

Folding practice 1

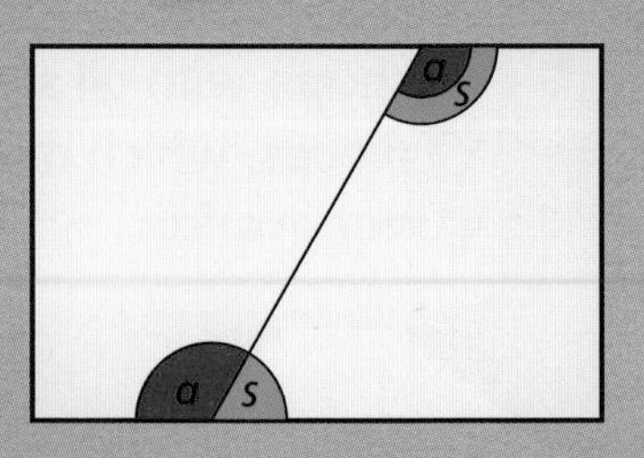

- Fold and unfold a rectangular piece of paper so that the fold line touches opposite sides.
- Measure the alternate angles (labelled a) with a protractor.
- Measure the supplementary angles (labelled s) with a protractor.
- Fold the paper at a different angle and repeat your measurements.
- Record your results in a table like this one.

Alternate angles		Supplementary angles	

- Write down two things that you notice.

Make sure your fold lines always touch opposite sides of the paper.

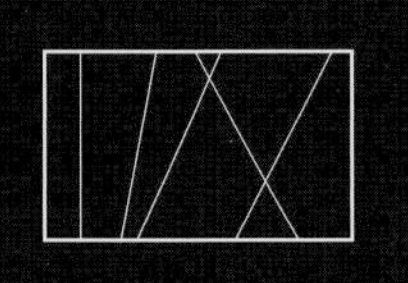

Second place

This aeroplane design came in second place. It would have won, but the designer couldn't remember how he worked out any of the angles!

- Angles round a point add up to 360°.
- Angles on a straight line add up to 180°.
- Angles in a triangle add up to 180°.
- Alternate angles are equal.
- Supplementary angles add up to 180°.
- Base angles of an isosceles triangle are equal.
- Angles in an equilateral triangle are 60°.
- Corresponding angles are equal.

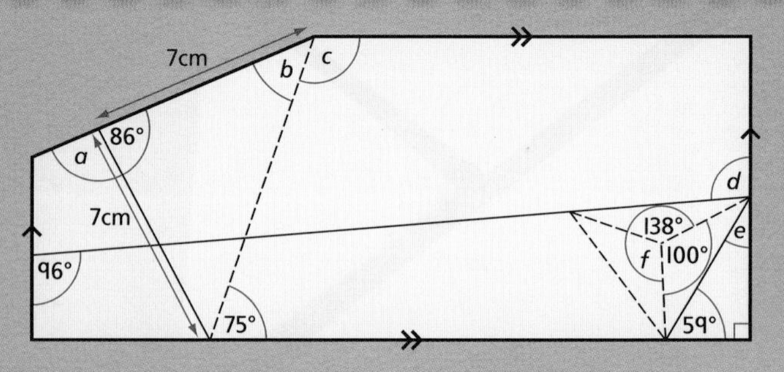

Use the statements in the blue box to give a reason for each answer.

a Angle a is 94°
b Angle b is 47°
c Angle c is 105°
d Angle d is 96°
e Angle e is 31°
f Angle f is 122°

Missing angles 1

Find the missing angles in these aeroplane designs. Use the statements in the blue box to give reasons for your answers.

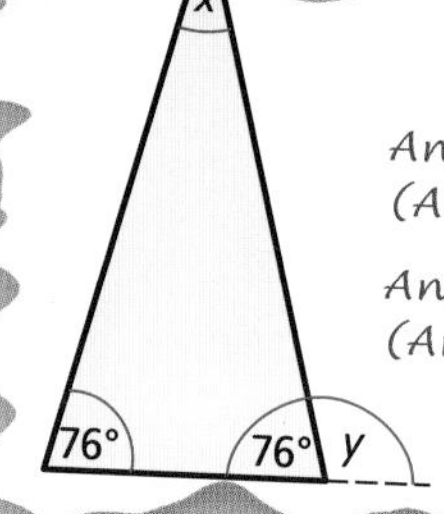

Angle x is 180° - 76° - 76° = 28°
(Angles in a triangle add up to 180°)
Angle y is 180° - 76° = 104°
(Angles on a straight line add up to 180°)

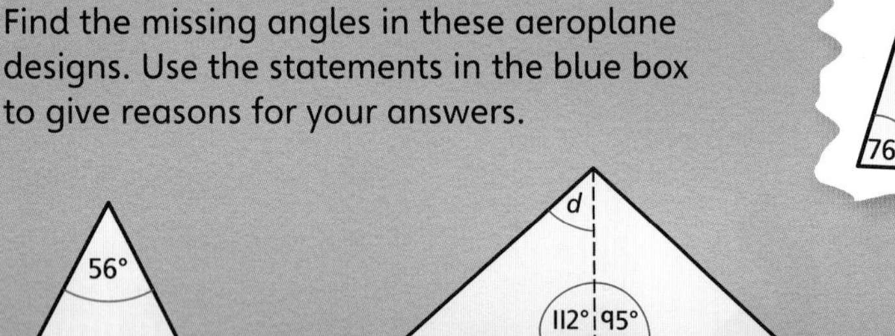

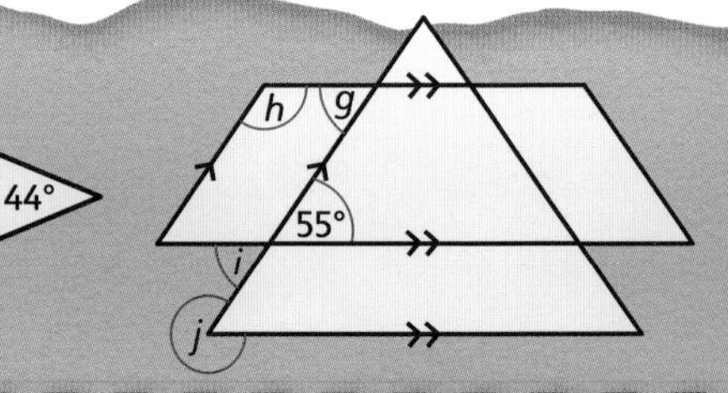

Folding practice 2

- Fold and unfold a rectangular piece of paper so that the fold line touches adjacent sides.
- Measure angles a, b, c and d with a protractor.
- Fold the paper at a different angle and repeat your measurements. Record your results in a table like this.
- Write down what you notice about a and b.
- Write down what you notice about c and d.
- Prove your two statements.

a	b	c	d

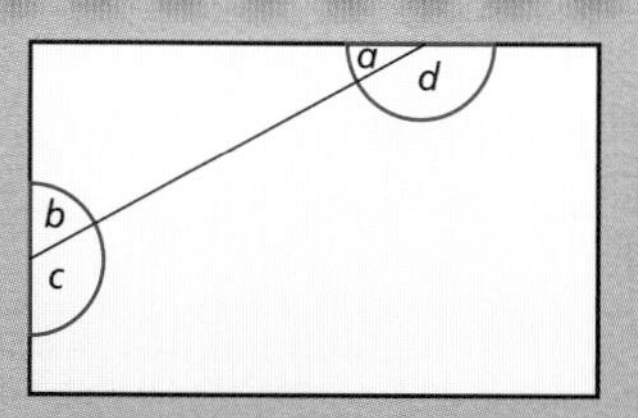

'Prove' means explain why the statements will be true for *any* fold.

Missing angles 2

These two advanced designs have reflection symmetry.

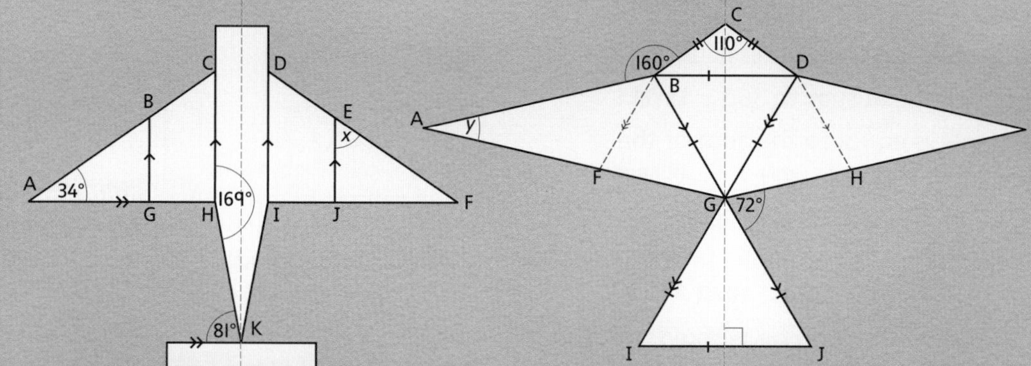

Your first proof might start like this:

Angle GHK = 99°
(Supplementary angles add up to 180°)
Angle CHG = 92°
(Angles round a point add up to 360°)

a Prove that $x = 54°$
b Prove that $y = 27°$

Grand final

Here are the instructions for making the winning aeroplane. You will need a sheet of A4.

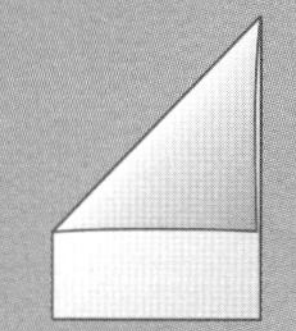

1 Fold the corner over

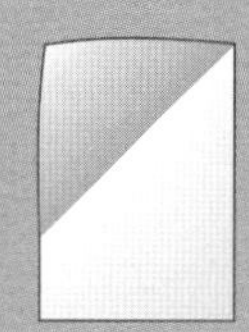

2 Unfold the paper

3 Fold the other corner over

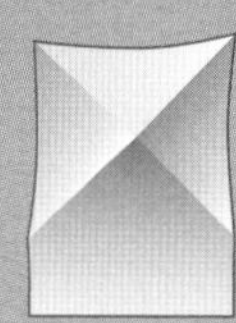

4 Unfold and turn over

5 Fold down to make a triangle

6 Unfold and turn over

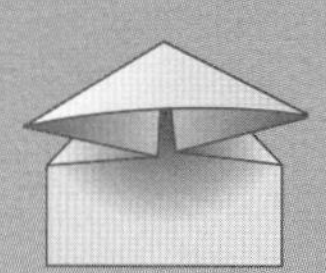

7 Press the middle and fold the sides in

8 Fold these triangles up

9 Fold the small triangles in to meet the centre

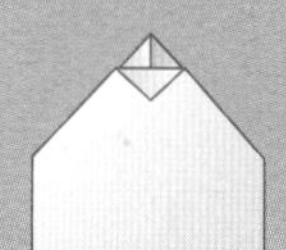

10 Turn over and fold down the flap

11 Fold in half, then fold the wings down on both sides

Before you're allowed to fly your plane, you have to find each of the angles shown. Give reasons for your answers.

Hint: $a = 2b$ and $d = e$.

How far can you make your plane fly? Try adjusting your plane to make it fly better. You can cut small flaps in the back of the wings. Folding the edges of the wings up makes the plane more stable.

2.2 Angles and proof

- ⇨ Identify interior and exterior angles in triangles and quadrilaterals
- ⇨ Calculate interior and exterior angles of triangles and quadrilaterals
- ⇨ Understand the idea of proof
- ⇨ Recognise the difference between conventions, definitions and derived properties

Why learn this?

Angles can be crucially important in some extreme sports.

What's the BIG idea?

interior angle

exterior angle

- → **Interior** and **exterior angles** sum to 180°. **Level 5**
- → The interior angles in a **triangle** sum to 180°. **Level 5**
- → The interior angles in a **quadrilateral** sum to 360°. **Level 6**
- → The exterior angle of a triangle is equal to the sum of the two interior opposite angles. For example, $a + b = e$. **Level 6**
- → A **convention** is an accepted mathematical way to show some information. **Level 7**

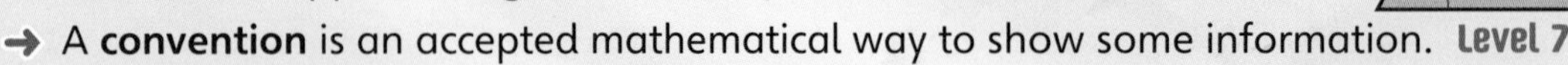

- → A **definition** is a precise description. For example, the definition of a square is: a shape with exactly four equal sides and four equal angles. **Level 7**
- → A **derived property** is information that can be worked out from a definition. For example, each angle of a square is 90° because they sum to 360° and are all equal. **Level 7**

Did you know?

The word 'angle' comes from the Latin word 'angulus', which means 'a corner'.

Practice, practice, practice!

Level 5

5c I can use interior and exterior angles to calculate angles

1 Work out the size of angle q.

q is an interior angle.

q and 52° lie on a straight line, so they sum to 180°.

q = 180 − 52 = 128°

Work out the size of angle p.

2 **a** Copy and complete these sentences to identify the interior and exterior angles.

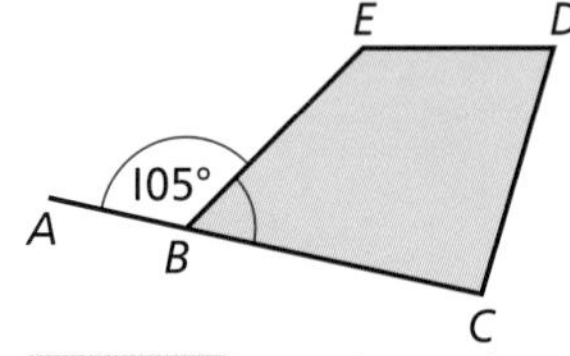

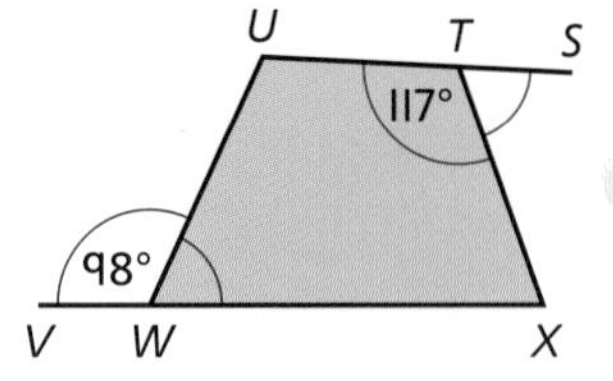

∠EBC is *an interior angle.*

i ∠ZYW is ____. **ii** ∠UWX is ____. **iii** ∠XTS is ____.

b Calculate the missing angles marked on the diagrams.

Tip

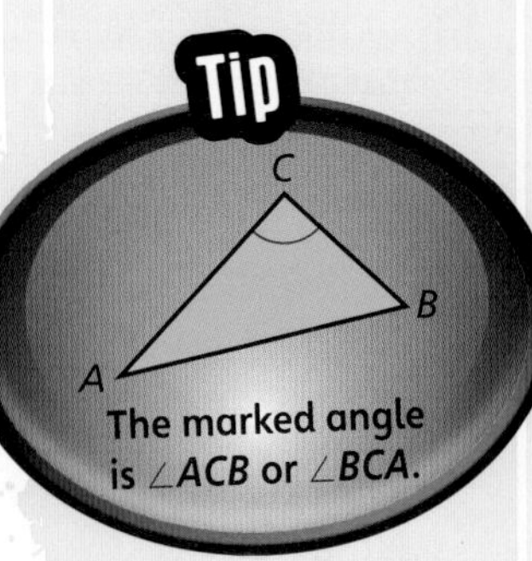

The marked angle is ∠ACB or ∠BCA.

Level 6

6c I can calculate interior and exterior angles of triangles and quadrilaterals

3 Calculate the size of the lettered angles, stating any angle facts that you use.

a

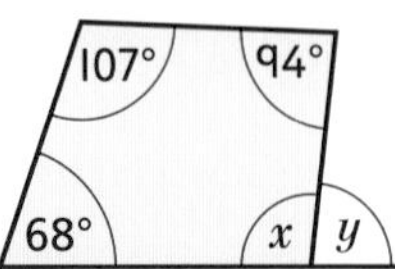

b

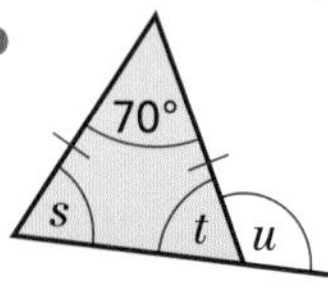

c

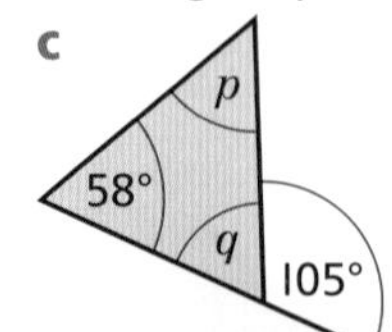

d

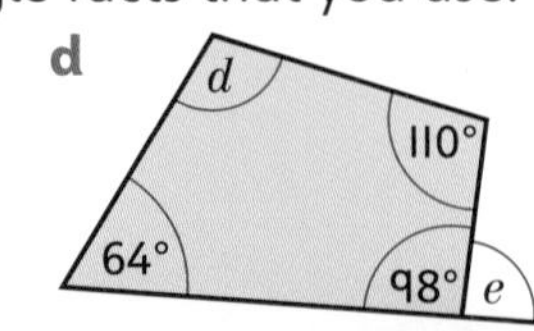

convention definition derived property exterior angle

4 Sketch this diagram.

Then copy and complete these sentences.

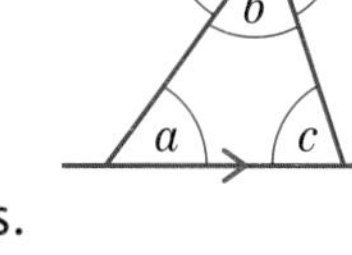

a Angle x is equal to angle a because they are ____ angles.

b Angle y is equal to angle ____ because they are ____ angles.

$x + b + y =$ ____ because they lie on a ____.

c Since $x = a$ and $y =$ ____,

$a + b + c =$ ____ $+ b +$ ____.

This proves that angles in a triangle sum to ____.

Learn this

Angles in a triangle sum to 180°. Angles in a quadrilateral sum to 360°.

5 Sketch this diagram.

The quadrilateral has been split into two triangles.

$a + b + c = 180°$

Continue the proof to show that angles in a quadrilateral sum to 360°.

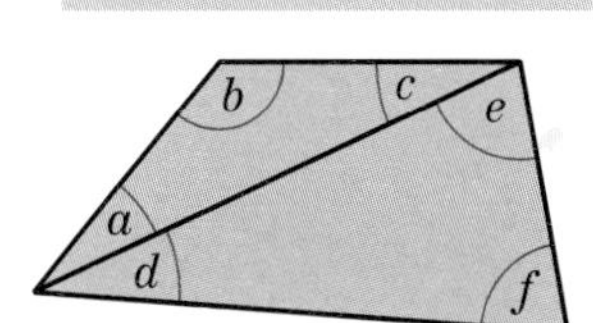

6 Sketch this diagram.

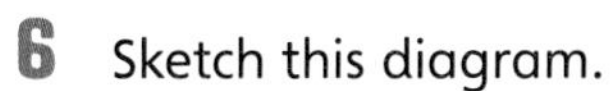

Then copy and complete this proof.

a $a + b +$ ____ $= 180°$ because angles in a triangle sum to ____.

b $c + x =$ ____ because they lie on a ____ ____.

c So $a + b + c = c +$ ____.

So $a + b = x$.

Level 6

6c I can follow a proof that the sum of angles in a triangle is 180°

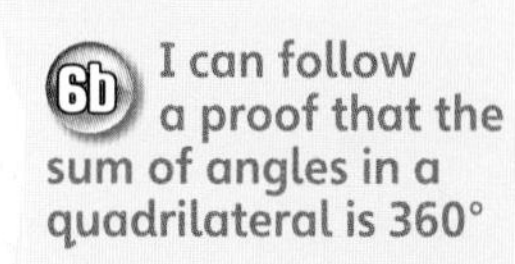

6b I can follow a proof that the sum of angles in a quadrilateral is 360°

6a I can follow a proof that the exterior angle of a triangle is equal to the sum of the two interior opposite angles

7 Decide whether each statement is a definition, a convention or a derived property.

Angles on a straight line sum to 180°. *Derived property*

An interior angle is an angle inside a shape. *Definition*

a The exterior angle of a triangle is equal to the sum of the two interior opposite angles.

b The dashes on opposite sides of a rectangle show that the sides are the same length.

c A triangle has three sides and three interior angles.

d Parallel lines are marked with arrows pointing in the same direction.

Level 7

7c I can recognise the difference between conventions, definitions and derived properties

Now try this!

A Angle problems

Work with a partner. Each draw a triangle with the interior and exterior angles marked.
Tell your partner two of the interior angles from your triangle.
Challenge them to work out the other interior angle and the exterior angles.
Check their answers to see if they are correct.

B Triangle properties

Use a dynamic geometry program to construct a triangle with a line going through one vertex that is parallel to the opposite side.
Drag any of the vertices to explore what happens.

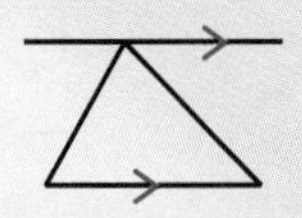

interior angle proof quadrilateral triangle

2.3 Constructing triangles

- Draw an angle accurately using a protractor
- Construct a triangle using a protractor and a ruler
- Construct a triangle using compasses and a ruler
- Draw a right-angled triangle using compasses and a ruler

Why learn this?

Triangles are a strong shape used in the construction of many bridges.

What's the BIG idea?

- You can **construct** a triangle using a ruler and a protractor if you know either two sides and the included **angle** (SAS) or two angles and the included side (ASA). **Level 5**
- You can construct a triangle using a ruler and **compasses** if you know the length of all three sides (SSS). **Level 6**
- The **hypotenuse** of a right-angled triangle is the longest side and is opposite the right angle. **Level 6**

hypotenuse

- Lines that meet at right angles are **perpendicular**. Perpendicular lines can be constructed using compasses. **Level 6**
- You can construct a right-angled triangle using a ruler and compasses if you know the lengths of the hypotenuse and one of the shorter sides (RHS). **Level 7**

Did you know?

The word 'triangle' is made up of 'tri', which means 'three' and 'angle'. A triangle has three angles.

Practice, practice, practice!

1 Draw these angles accurately using a ruler and protractor.
Label each angle as reflex or obtuse.

a 138° **b** 294° **c** 197° **d** 176°

2 Construct these triangles using a ruler and protractor.

a

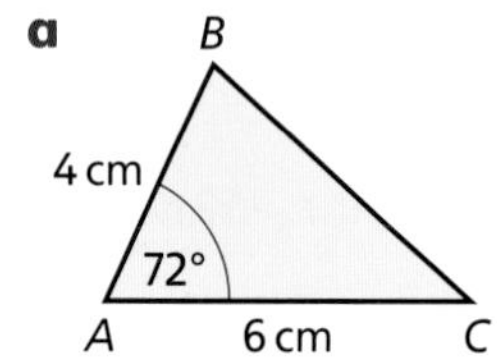

b

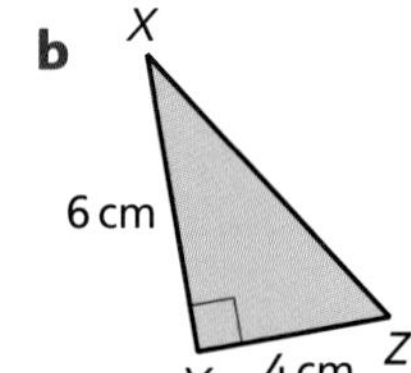

3 Make an accurate drawing of these triangles.

a

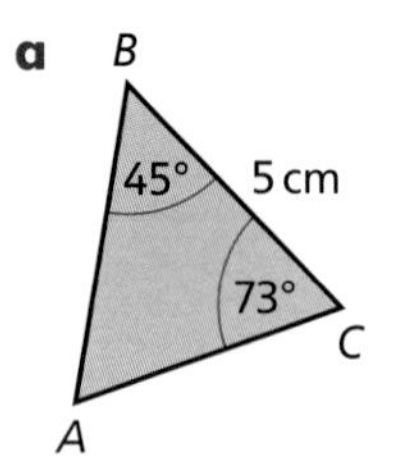

b

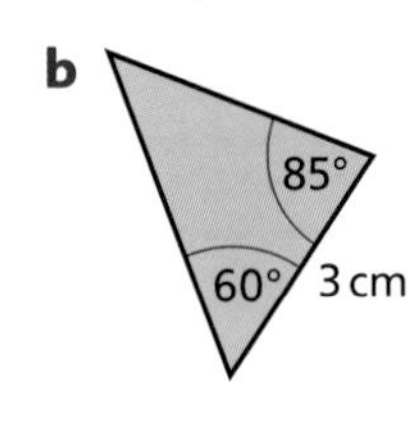

4 An architect is calculating the length of wood required to make trusses for a roof.
The width of the roof is 5 m and the two angles to the horizontal are 88° and 65°.

a Using a scale of 1 cm to represent 1 m, draw an accurate scale drawing of the roof.

b Measure the length of each sloping beam to find how much wood is needed for one truss.

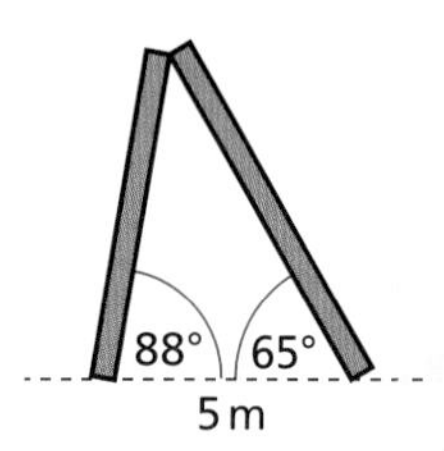

Level 5

5c I can use a protractor to draw obtuse and reflex angles to the nearest degree

5b I can construct a triangle given two sides and the included angle (SAS)

5a I can construct a triangle given two angles and the included side (ASA)

acute angle compasses

5 These triangles are all right-angled triangles. Which letter marks the hypotenuse of each triangle?

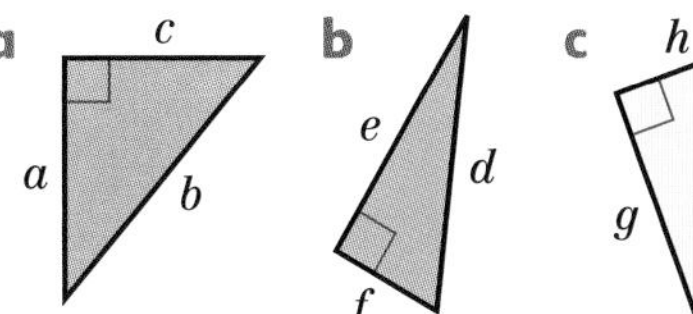

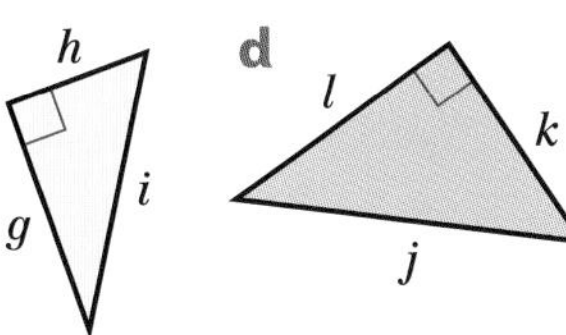

6 Use compasses and a ruler to construct a triangle with sides $AB = 7$ cm, $AC = 6$ cm and $BC = 5$ cm.

7 Construct a triangle with sides of length 9 cm, 7 cm and 8 cm using compasses and a ruler.

8 Using compasses and a ruler, draw the perpendicular to the line at point A.

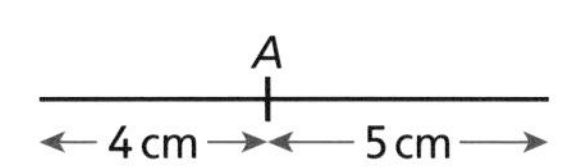

Level 6

6c I can identify the hypotenuse in a right-angled triangle

6a I can construct a triangle given three sides

6a I can use a ruler and compasses to construct the perpendicular from a point on a line segment

9 A motor cycle stunt man is building a ramp so he can jump over four cars. Here is the side-view of his ramp.

a Draw an accurate scale drawing of the ramp using a ruler and compasses.

b What is the height of the top of the ramp?

10 A 4 m ladder leans against a wall with its base 1 m from the wall.

a Draw an accurate scale drawing of the ladder against the wall.

b Use your drawing to find how far the ladder reaches up the wall.

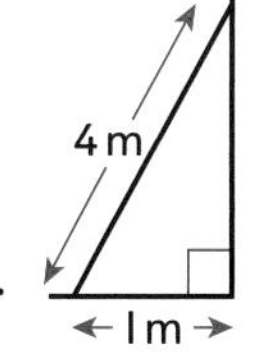

11 Mark wants to construct a triangle with sides of length 5 cm, 3 cm and 9 cm. Explain why Mark's triangle is impossible to construct.

Hint: Try to construct the triangle first.

Level 7

7c I can construct a right-angled triangle if I know the lengths of the hypotenuse and another side (RHS)

Watch out!

Don't rub out your construction lines as they show that you have used the compasses correctly.

Now try this!

A Drawing triangles 1

1. Draw a triangle and label the vertices A, B and C.
2. Measure the sides AB and AC.
3. Measure the angle BAC.
4. Describe the triangle to your partner by telling them the information about the two sides and the angle. Your partner draws the triangle you have described.
5. Check your partner's triangle with the original.

B Drawing triangles 2

1. Draw a right-angled triangle using compasses and a ruler.
2. Measure the hypotenuse and one of the other sides.
3. Describe the triangle to your partner by telling them the information about the two sides and the angle. Your partner draws the triangle you have described.
4. Check your partner's triangle with the original.

construction hypotenuse perpendicular obtuse

2.4 Special quadrilaterals

- Know the properties of quadrilaterals
- Solve geometrical problems involving quadrilaterals and explain the reasons

Why learn this?

Many buildings are made of rectangles and other quadrilaterals. How many different shapes can you see in this photo?

What's the BIG idea?

→ **Quadrilateral** properties:

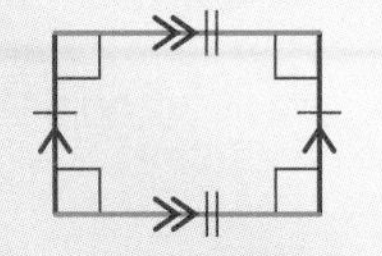
rectangle

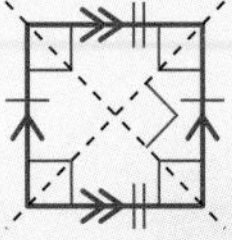
square

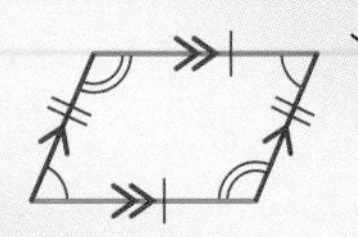
parallelogram

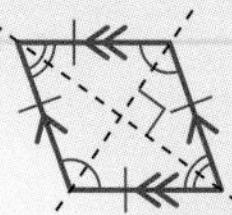
rhombus

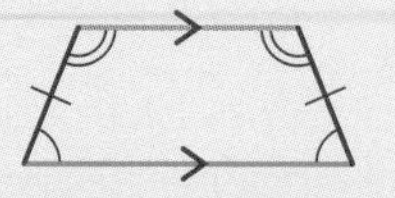
isosceles trapezium

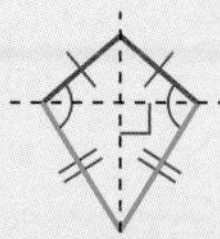
kite

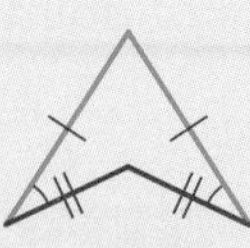
arrowhead
Level 6

→ When solving problems using the properties of shapes it is important to explain your reasoning. Level 6 & Level 7

Practice, practice, practice!

Level 6

6C I can identify angle, side and symmetry properties of simple quadrilaterals

1 Nathaniel said 'A square is a rectangle'. Is this true? Explain your answer.

2 Which of these statements are always true for a rectangle?
A All its sides are equal.
B It has four lines of symmetry.
C It has four right angles.

3 Copy this table. Complete it by writing each shape name in the correct position.

Number of pairs of parallel sides	Number of lines of symmetry			
	0	1	2	4
0				
1				
2				

a rectangle **b** square **c** parallelogram
d rhombus **e** kite **f** arrowhead
g isosceles trapezium

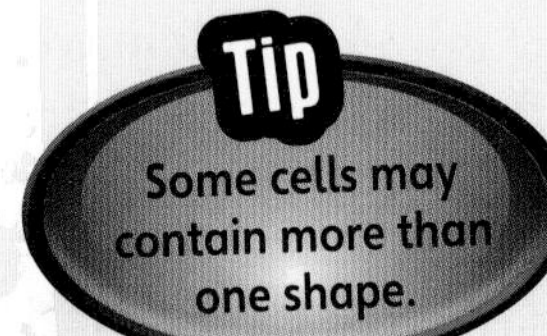
Tip
Some cells may contain more than one shape.

Did you know?

The prefix 'quadri-' comes from the Latin word for four. Can you think of any other words that begin with 'quad'?

6C I can identify and begin to use angle, side and symmetry properties of quadrilaterals

4 Draw a rectangle and cut it out.

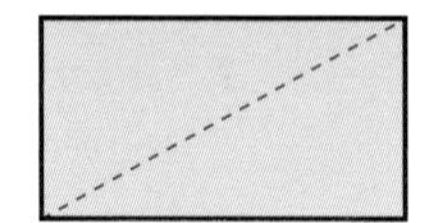

a Cut along one of the diagonals. Rearrange the pieces to make another quadrilateral.
b Write the name of the new quadrilateral that you have made.
c Write one geometrical fact about this shape.

arrowhead isosceles trapezium kite parallelogram

5 Sketch an equilateral triangle. Reflect it along one of its sides.

a Write the name of the quadrilateral that is formed.

b Which of these statements are always true for this special quadrilateral?

A The diagonals bisect at right angles.
B The angles are all equal.
C It has two pairs of parallel sides.
D It has four lines of symmetry.

Level 6

6c I can identify and begin to use angle, side and symmetry properties of quadrilaterals

6 Look at this rectangle. One of the diagonals is drawn. Work out the sizes of angles a, b and c.

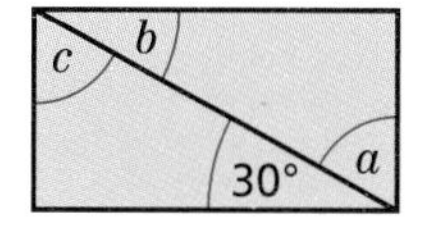

6c I can solve simple geometrical problems using properties of quadrilaterals

7 In a rhombus, one of the angles is 40°. Work out the sizes of the other angles.

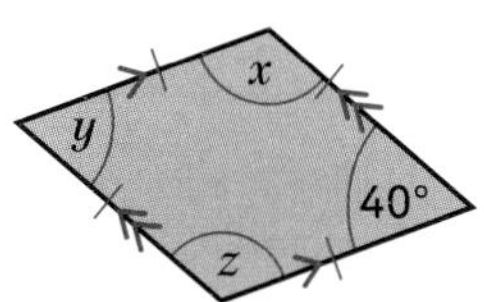

Learn this

The square and rhombus are quadrilaterals with equal length sides.

8 Look at this arrowhead.
$\angle TSV = 45°$, $\angle STV = 30°$

Calculate

a $\angle TUV$ **b** $\angle TVU$ **c** $\angle SVU$

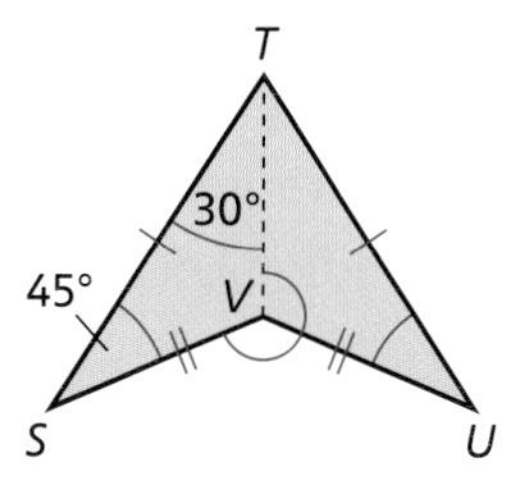

6b I can solve geometrical problems using properties of triangles and quadrilaterals

9 In this rectangle, calculate angle EBD.
Show your steps for solving this problem and explain your reasoning.

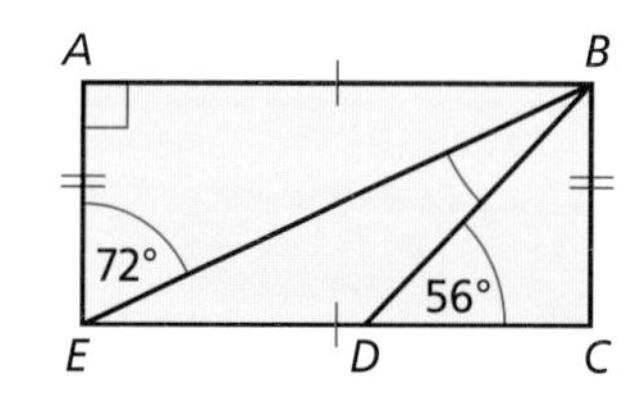

6a I can use reasoning to solve geometrical problems

Level 7

10 Work out the sizes of these angles.
Explain your reasoning.

a $\angle FAB$ **b** $\angle ABE$ **c** $\angle CBE$ **d** $\angle BCD$

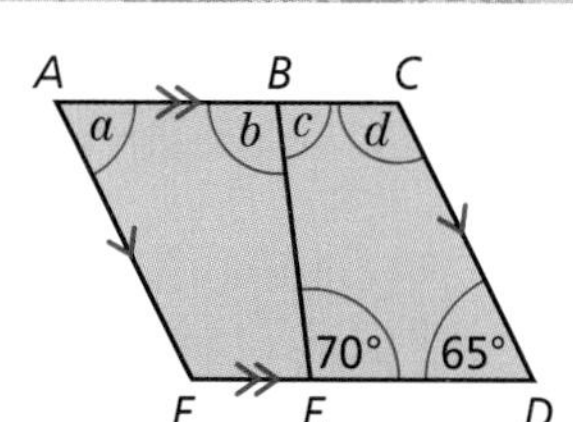

7c I can use reasoning to solve more complex geometrical problems

Now try this!

A Special quadrilaterals

A game for two players. Each secretly draw a special quadrilateral. Take turns to tell each other one property of your shape. Try to guess each other's shape. Score 1 point if you guess correctly from one property, 2 points from two properties, and so on. The player with the lowest score wins.

B Parallelograms

Draw a parallelogram like this.
Label three angles with their sizes.
Challenge your partner to work out the missing angles and explain their reasons.
Use what you know about the properties of parallelograms to check their answers.

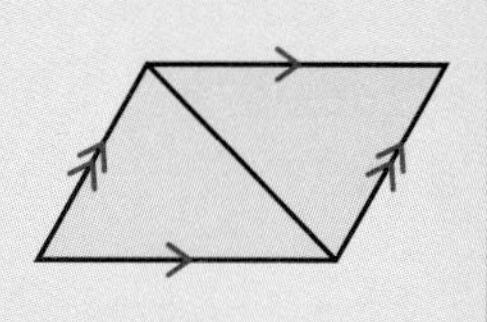

quadrilateral rectangle rhombus square symmetry

2.5 More constructions

- Know the names of parts of a circle
- Use a straight edge and compasses to construct the perpendicular bisector of a line and an angle, and the perpendicular to a line
- Use a straight edge and compasses to investigate the properties of overlapping circles

Why learn this?

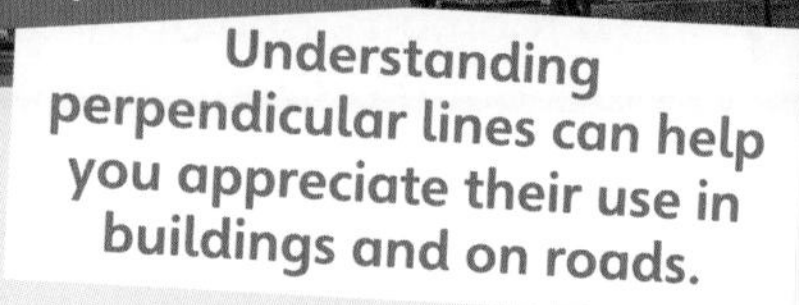

What's the BIG idea?

- Lines that meet at **right angles** are **perpendicular**. Perpendicular lines can be constructed using compasses. **Level 6**
- The angle **bisector** cuts the angle in half. The perpendicular bisector cuts the line in half at right angles. Both can be constructed using compasses. **Level 6**
- The perpendicular from a point to a line segment is the shortest distance to the line. **Level 6**
- When the points of intersection of two identical overlapping **circles** are joined to the centres, a rhombus is formed. **Level 7**
- A right-angled triangle can be constructed using a ruler and **compasses** if you know the length of the hypotenuse and one of the shorter sides. **Level 7**

Practice, practice, practice!

Level 6

6c I can construct the mid-point and perpendicular bisector of a line segment

1 Using only a ruler and compasses, draw the perpendicular bisectors of these line segments. Mark the mid-point of each line segment.

a a straight line segment AB of length 6 cm

b a straight line segment BD of length 8 cm

2 A construction company is building two houses, 10 m apart. The architect's plans look like this.

10 m

a Copy the plan, using a scale of 1 cm to represent 1 m.

b Construct the perpendicular bisector of the 10 m line.

c A fence will be built on the perpendicular bisector. What can you say about the position of the fence?

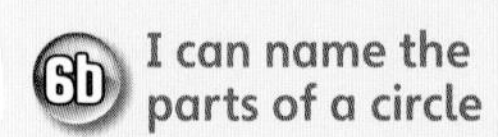

3 Copy this circle with radius 4 cm. Add these labels.

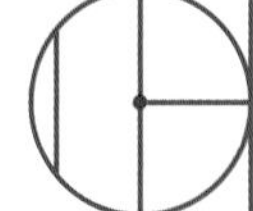

a radius	**b** diameter	**c** chord
d arc	**e** tangent	**f** circumference

6b I can construct the bisector of an angle

4 Use compasses and a ruler to draw the bisector of these angles.

a an acute angle of your choice

b an angle of 90° drawn with a protractor

c an obtuse angle of your choice

Learn this

'Bisect' means to cut something into two equal parts.

arc | bisector (bisect) | chord | circle | compasses

5 Make a copy of this diagram. Construct the perpendicular from point A to the line.

6 Copy the diagram. Using compasses and a ruler, draw the perpendicular at X.

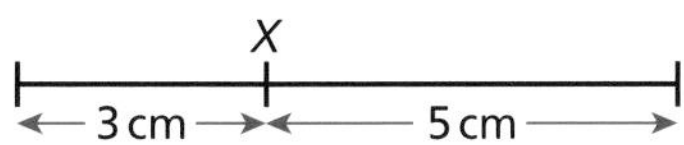

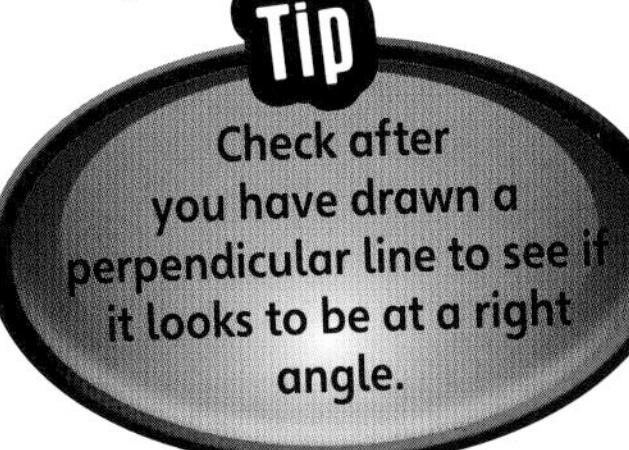

7 A construction company is building a bridge across a river.
Copy the diagram and draw the perpendicular from point S across the river to show where the bridge should be built.

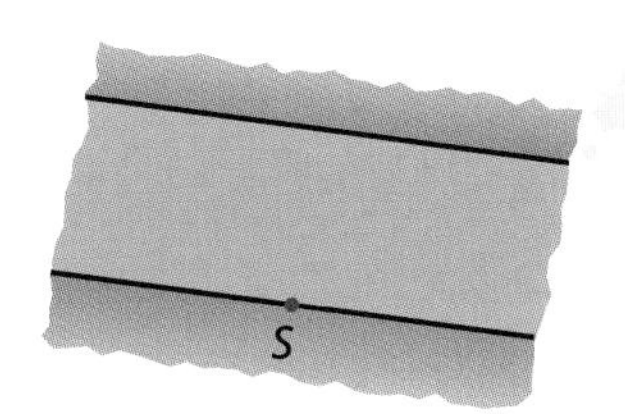

Level 6

6a I can construct the perpendicular from a point to a line segment

8 **a** Using compasses, draw two circles of radius 4 cm that overlap.
b Join the centres of the circles with a straight line and draw the chord that is common to both circles.
c Join the centres of the circles to the points where the circles intersect.
What do you notice about the quadrilateral that is formed?

Level 7

7a I can explain how standard constructions using a ruler and compasses relate to the properties of two intersecting circles with equal radii

A Triangles in circles

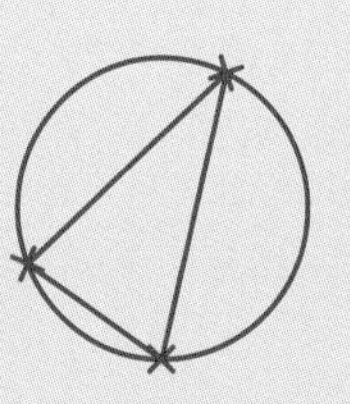

1. Draw a circle, using compasses or dynamic geometry software.
2. Mark three points on the circumference of the circle.
3. Join up these points to make a triangle.
4. Construct the perpendicular bisector of each side of your triangle.
5. What do you notice?
6. What happens when the vertices of the triangle are moved to different points on the circumference?

B Polygons in circles

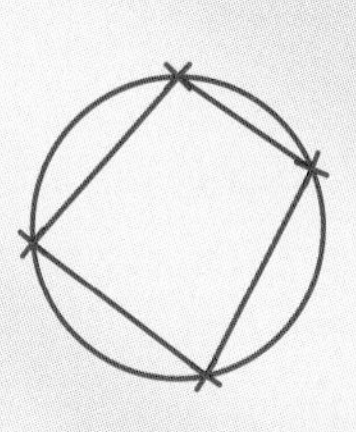

1. Draw a circle, using compasses or dynamic geometry software.
2. Mark four points on the circumference of the circle.
3. Join up these points to make a quadrilateral.
4. Construct the perpendicular bisector of each side of your quadrilateral.
5. What do you notice?
6. Investigate other polygons inside a circle.

diameter perpendicular radius right angle tangent

2.6 Angles in polygons

- Find the sum of the interior and exterior angles of polygons
- Find an interior and exterior angle of a regular polygon
- Use the interior and exterior angles of regular and irregular polygons to solve problems

Why learn this?

Polygons are found in many places in nature. When lava cools it can form columns in the shape of polygons.

What's the BIG idea?

- An **interior angle** and its corresponding **exterior angle** sum to 180°. **Level 5**
- The sum of the interior angles in an n-sided polygon is $(n - 2) \times 180°$. **Level 6**
- The sum of the exterior angles in any polygon is always 360°. **Level 6**
- A **regular polygon** has all sides of equal length and all angles equal. **Level 6**
- The interior angle of a regular polygon $= \frac{\text{sum of interior angles}}{\text{number of sides}}$. **Level 6**
- You can use interior and exterior angles in polygons to solve problems. **Level 7**

Practice, practice, practice!

1 Explain how you calculate the sum of the interior angles in

a a quadrilateral

b a pentagon.

2 **a** Explain how you find the size of an interior angle in a regular pentagon.

b Explain how you find the size of an exterior angle in a regular pentagon.

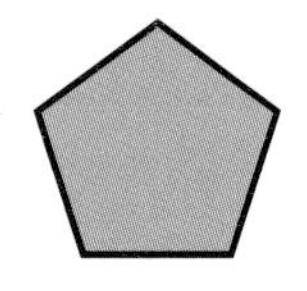

3 **a** What is the sum of the interior angles in

i a quadrilateral **ii** a pentagon **iii** a hexagon?

b Calculate the sum of the interior angles in a 10-sided polygon.

4 Look at this quadrilateral.
At each vertex the sum of the interior and exterior angles is 180°.

$I + E = 180°$

Explain why this is true.

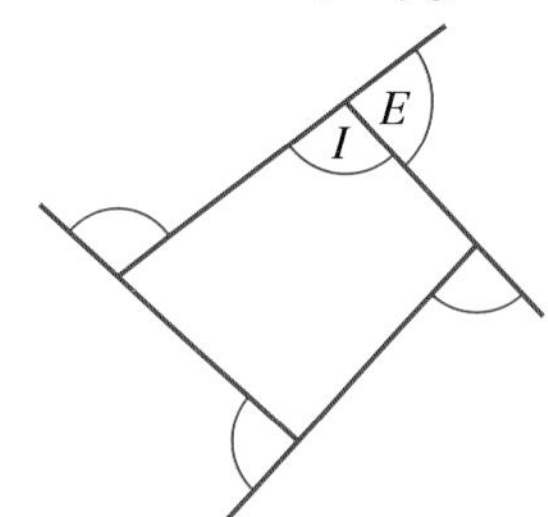

5 **a** Draw a quadrilateral with the exterior angles marked, like the one in Q4.

b Use a protractor to measure each exterior angle.
Find the sum of the exterior angles.

c Repeat parts **a** and **b** for a pentagon and a hexagon.

d What do you notice about the sum of the exterior angles of a polygon?

Level 6

6c I can explain how to find the interior angle sum of a polygon

6b I can explain how to calculate the interior and exterior angles of regular polygons

6b I can calculate the sums of the interior and exterior angles of irregular polygons

exterior angle hexagon interior angle irregular polygon

6 a Calculate the exterior angle of a regular hexagon.

b Calculate the size of each interior angle in a regular hexagon.

7 Copy and complete this table.

Regular polygon	Number of sides	Sum of interior angles	Size of each interior angle	Sum of exterior angles	Size of each exterior angle
equilateral triangle	3	180°		360°	
square	4				
regular pentagon	5				
regular hexagon					
regular octagon					

8 a How do you find the sum of the interior angles in an n-sided polygon?

b Calculate the size of the interior and exterior angles in a regular 16-sided shape.

Level 6

6a I can calculate the interior and exterior angles of regular polygons

9 a The exterior angle of a regular polygon is 18°.

i How many sides does the polygon have?

ii Calculate the size of each interior angle.

b The interior angle of a regular polygon is 156°. How many sides does the polygon have?

Learn this

The exterior angles of a polygon always add up to 360°.

10 Is it possible to draw a polygon that has interior angles that sum to 1300°? Explain your reasoning.

11 The diagram shows a regular octagon. The line *BC* is parallel to the line *AD*.

Calculate the size of

a $\angle BCD$

b $\angle CDA$

c $\angle ADH$

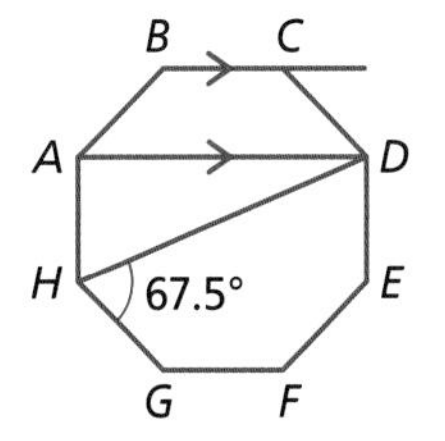

Level 7

7c I can use the interior and exterior angles of regular polygons to solve problems

7c I can solve harder problems using properties of angles, parallel and intersecting lines, and triangles and other polygons

Now try this!

A Polygon poster

Make a poster of all the facts you know about the interior and exterior angles of polygons.

B Tessellating polygons

Investigate which regular polygons tessellate. Look at the interior angles. How can you tell by looking at the interior angles whether a shape will tessellate? Why will a regular hexagon and a square tessellate?

Did you know?

Polygons are used to create complex-shaped computer graphics. Next time you play a computer game, see how many polygons you can spot.

octagon pentagon quadrilateral regular polygon triangle

Puzzle time

In the opener to this unit you were introduced to Henry Dudeney, a puzzle creator.
Henry Dudeney also published the first known crossnumber puzzle (a crossword with numbers instead of words) in 1926.

Step 1: Solve the problems by finding the values of the missing angles. Give reasons for your answers, e.g. the interior angles of a triangle sum to 180°.

Step 2: Copy the crossnumber grid on squared paper and slot in your answers. One solution is given to start you off.

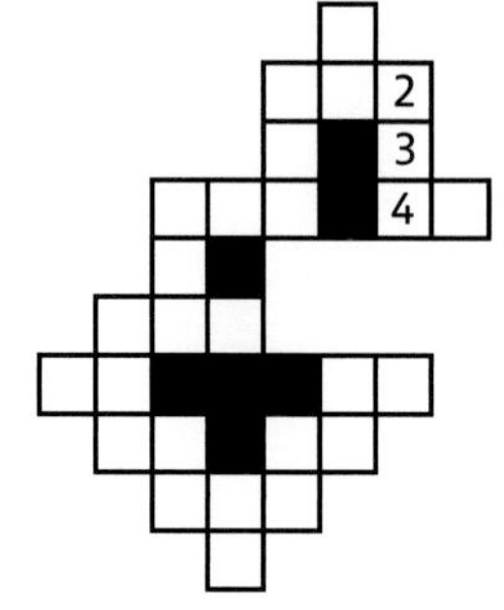

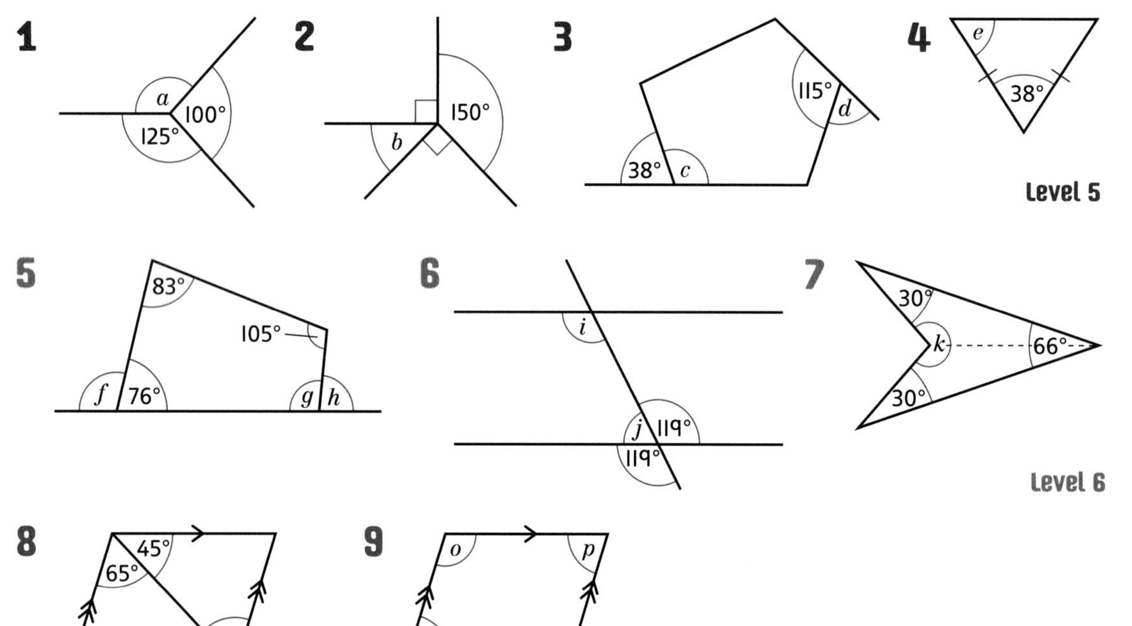

10 A nonagon is a nine-sided polygon. Its interior angles are 155°, 140°, 125°, 115°, 105°, 145°, 135°, r and s. If $r = s$, what is the value of r? **Level 7**

The BIG ideas

- **Interior angles** are the angles inside a shape. **Level 5**
- An **exterior angle** is the angle outside the shape. **Level 5**
- Interior and exterior angles add up to 180°. **Level 5**
- An exterior angle is made by extending one of the edges of the shape. **Level 5**
- The interior angles in a **triangle** sum to 180°. **Level 5 & Level 6**
- **Alternate angles** are equal. **Level 6**
- **Corresponding angles** are equal. **Level 6**
- The interior angles in a **quadrilateral** sum to 360°. **Level 6**
- When solving problems using the properties of shapes it is important to explain your reasoning. **Level 6 & Level 7**
- The sum of the interior angles in an n-sided **polygon** is $(n - 2) \times 180°$. **Level 6 & Level 7**

interior angle

exterior angle

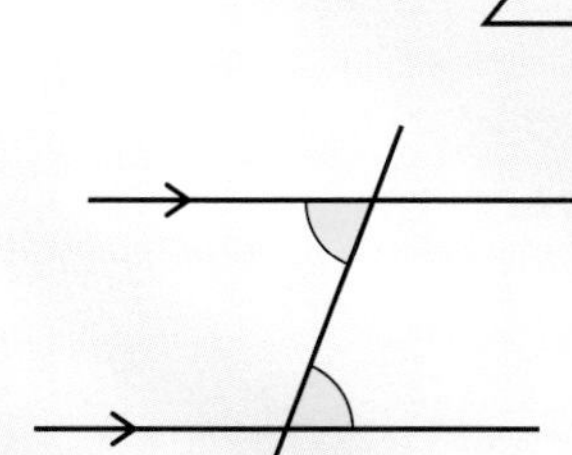
alternate angles

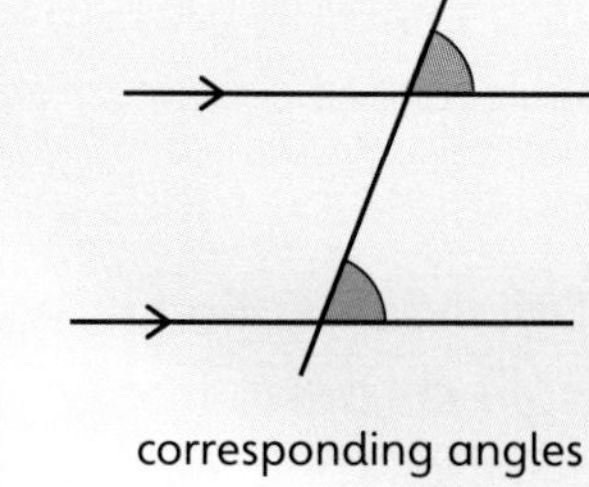
corresponding angles

Practice SATs-style questions

Level 5

Q1 Look at the diagram.
Sally writes:
Angle b is equal to 110°.

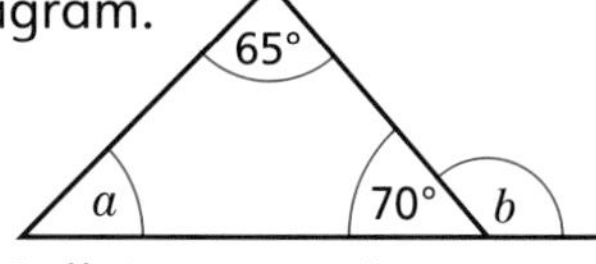

a Explain why Sally's answer is correct.
b Find the value of angle a.

Q2 Look at the diagram. Work out the sizes of the angles marked with the letters a, b and c.

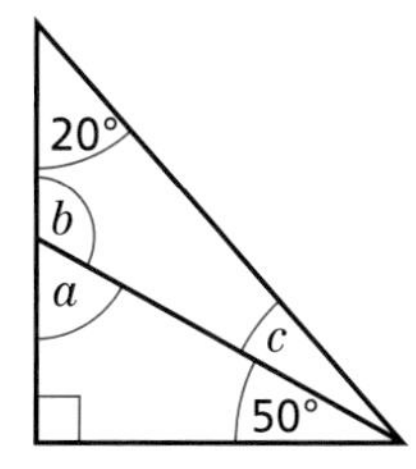

Level 6

Q3 $ABCD$ is a trapezium.
$BA = CD$
Angle ABC is 105°.

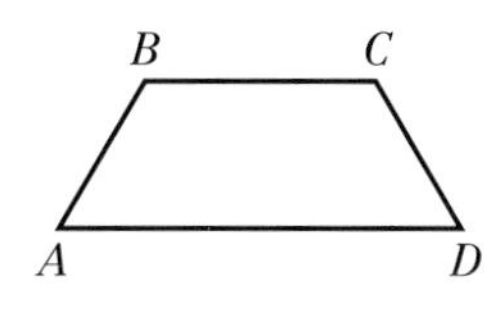

a) Calculate the size of angle BCD.
b) Calculate the size of angle BAD.

Q4 Use compasses to construct two different isosceles triangles.
One side must be 6 cm. Another side must be 8 cm.

Q5 Look at the triangle.
a Work out the value of angle y.
b Work out the value of angle x.

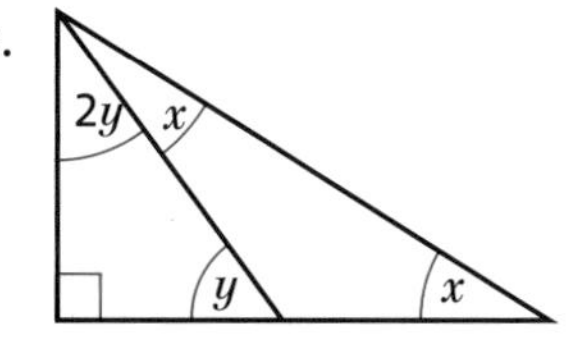

Level 7

Q6 The diagram shows a quadrilateral $ABCD$. Line DE bisects angle ADC.

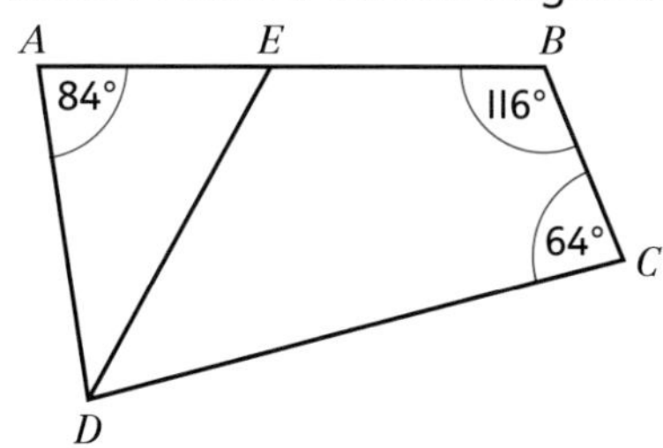

a Find angle EDC. Explain your answer.
b Find angle DEB.
c What type of triangle is DAE? Explain your answer.

Q7 This pattern has rotational symmetry of order 6.
a Calculate the size of angle s.

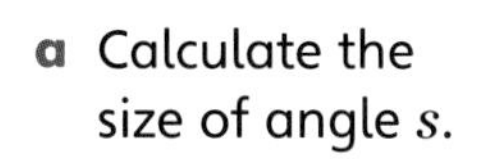

Each quadrilateral in the pattern is an arrowhead made up of two congruent isosceles triangles.
b Calculate the size of angle t.

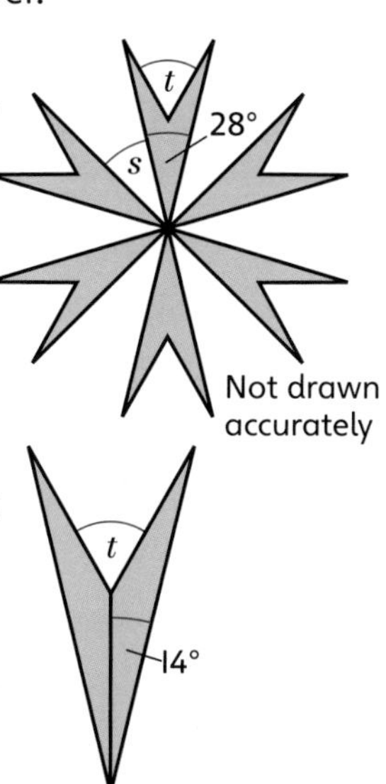

3 Definitely maybe

This unit is about probability and working out the chance or likelihood of different events occurring.

Do you think the roads are getting busier?

The Office for National Statistics (ONS) carries out surveys and collects data, from people in the UK, about all aspects of daily life. Their transport data shows that in 1993 an average of 58.2 thousand vehicles used the motorways each day. By 2005, the figure was 75.5 thousand vehicles.

The ONS also collects data on road accidents. Despite the increase in the levels of traffic, the number of road deaths in Great Britain fell by 60 per cent between 1980 and 2004. Why do you think this is?

Data on accidents is used to calculate the risk of passenger death for different modes of transport, as shown in the table.

Great Britain: Passenger death rates per billion passenger kilometres

	1981	1996	2004
Bus or coach	0.3	0.2	0.4
Walk	76.9	55.9	36.7
Car	6.1	3	2.5
Rail	1.0	0.4	0.2
Van	3.7	1.0	0.8
Water	0.4	0.8	0.0
Motorcycle	115.8	108.4	105.0
Air	0.2	0.0	0.0
Bicycle	56.9	49.8	34.7

Activities

A Look at the data in the table.

In 2004, which method of transport had the highest death rate?

Which had the highest death rates in 1981 and 1996?

Why do you think this might be? Consider factors such as age, training and vehicle design.

B Public transport is the safest option!

Use the data in the table to help you decide whether this statement is true.

Give reasons for your answer.

Before you start this unit...

1 Copy and complete the probability scale.

Unlikely — Certain

Level Up Maths 4–6 page 76

2 Mark these outcomes on your probability scale.

Level Up Maths 4–6 page 76

a The next baby born will be male.

b April Fool's Day will be on 2 April next year.

c It will snow in Liverpool in June.

3 Copy and complete these equivalent fractions.

Level Up Maths 4–6 page 54

a $\frac{3}{4} = \frac{6}{\blacksquare} = \frac{\blacksquare}{16}$ b $\frac{5}{\blacksquare} = \frac{\blacksquare}{18} = \frac{45}{54}$

4 What are the missing fractions?

Level Up Maths 4–6 page 56

a $\frac{\blacksquare}{\blacksquare} + \frac{5}{8} = 1$ b $1 - \frac{1}{3} = \frac{\blacksquare}{\blacksquare}$

5 Work out these in your head.

Level Up Maths 4–6 page 28

a 100 – 37 b 1 – 0.3

Did you know?

According to a 'trivia' website, you are more likely to be killed by a snake than in an plane crash. The website claims that you have a 1 in 3 000 000 chance of being killed by a snake, and a 1 in 6 000 000 chance of being killed in a plane crash.

3.1 What are your chances?

➪ Use probability words to describe the results of an experiment and the chances of something happening
➪ Understand that random events are unpredictable
➪ Use fractions to compare the chances that events will happen

Why learn this?

We need to be able to understand information about the risk of something happening.

What's the BIG idea?

→ All **probabilities** have a value from 0 to 1. **Level 5**

→ You can use a probability scale to show the outcome of an event in words or in values between 0 and 1. The probability of the **outcome** of an **event** can be described as impossible, possible, certain, even chance, likely or unlikely. **Level 5**

→ The probability of something happpening

$$= \frac{\text{total number of successful outcomes}}{\text{total number of possible outcomes}}$$ **Level 5**

→ You can write a probability as a fraction, a decimal or a percentage. **Level 5**

Did you know?

You have a 1 in 10 chance of dying from lung cancer if you are a moderate smoker and almost a 1 in 5 chance if you are a heavy smoker (more than 15 cigarettes a day).

Practice, practice, practice!

Level 5

5c I can use the probability scale

1 In a game you have to match a letter with any number containing that letter. For example, the letter 't' matches numbers 2, 3 and 8 ('**t**wo', '**t**hree' and 'eigh**t**').

a Work out and mark on a probability scale the likelihood of matching each letter with the number cards shown.

7	5	3	9	8	1

i 'i' **ii** 'e' **iii** 'x'

b What probability word best describes your chance of matching the letter 'g' with one of these numbers?

impossible	unlikely	even chance	likely	certain

5b I can explain why random events are unpredictable

2 Zoe deals 13 cards from a normal 52-card pack. They are all hearts or diamonds.

a Is it possible to deal a red card next? Explain your answer.

b Zoe says, 'The next card will definitely be a black card'.
Sabrina says, 'The next card is likely to be black'.
Who is correct?

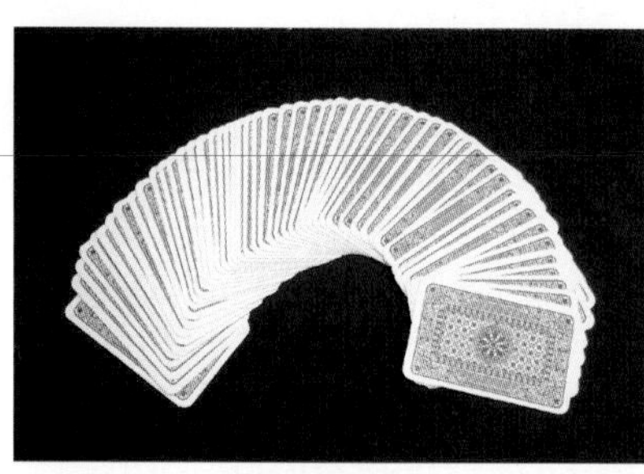

biased event fair likelihood

3 On a scratch card you win if you find a 'sun' in the first square you scratch off.
Here are the scratch cards before the suns are covered.

a Which card gives you the greatest chance of winning?

b Design a scratch card that would give an even chance of winning.

A

B

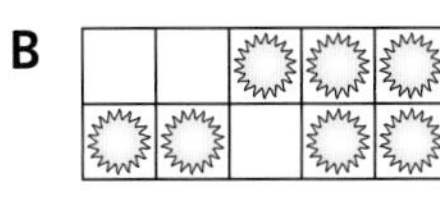

C

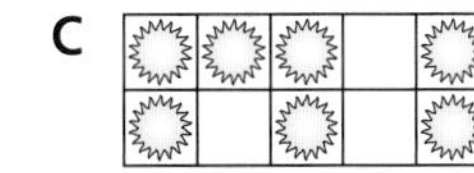

Level 5

5a I can compare probabilities using simple fractions

4 Here are the results of a football tournament.

a In which round was a 0–0 result most likely?

b Was a win more likely in the quarter-finals or the semi-finals?

Round	0–0	Score draw	Win
1	2	9	5
2	2	3	3
Quarter-finals	2	0	2
Semi-finals	0	0	2
Final	0	0	1

Level 6

6c I can compare probabilities using fractions with the same numerator

5 Use the results table in Q4 to answer these questions.

a Was a win in Round 1 more likely than a score draw in Round 2?

b In which round was a win least likely?

6b I can compare probabilities using equivalent fractions

6 Jim has two bags.
Bag A contains 18 balls. 15 of them are red.
Bag B contains 40 balls. 32 of them are red.
Jim picks a ball at random from each bag. From which bag is he most likely to pick a red ball?

6b I can compare probabilities using decimal conversions of fractions

7 Three friends compare how many MP3 tracks they have by the band 'Wow!' and how many tracks they have in total. 34 out of Tirone's 914 tracks are by 'Wow!', Tariq has 29 out of a total of 833, and Trisha has 18 out of 547.
They each play a track at random.

a Who is most likely to play a track by 'Wow!'?

b Trisha adds another 'Wow!' track to her MP3 player. Will she now be more likely than Tariq to play a track by 'Wow!'? Explain your answer.

6a I can use probability to find the likelihood of a complex event happening

Tip
To compare probabilities given as fractions use your calculator to change them into decimals (top divided by bottom).

Now try this!

A Raise three

A game for 2 players. You need a complete suit (e.g. hearts) from a pack of cards.
Shuffle the cards and deal six cards each, face down. Place the remaining card face up on the table. Take turns to predict whether your next card will be higher, or lower, than the card in the middle. Bet 1, 2 or 3 points on the outcome, then turn up your cards. If your prediction is correct, add the points to your score – if not, subtract them. Then place your card in the middle for the other player to bet against.

B Fraction cards

A game for two players. Each design five fraction cards, using single-digit numerators and denominators (make the numerator smaller than the denominator). Swap cards and order your partner's cards, from smallest to largest. Check with a calculator. The person with the most cards in order wins. Repeat with different sets of fractions.

outcome probability random

3.2 Representing probability

- Represent the likelihood of something happening on a probability scale
- Understand the term 'mutually exclusive'
- Identify all possible outcomes for one, or two successive events
- Use diagrams and tables to represent probability

Why learn this?

When you've got choices to make it helps to be able to work out the range of options available.

What's the BIG idea?

→ You can use a **probability scale** to show the **outcome** of an event.

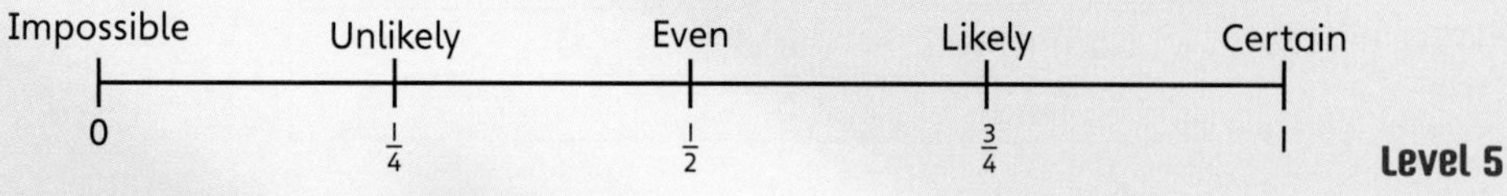

Level 5

→ If one **outcome** is equally as likely as another, it is possible to work out the probability of an event happening.
For example, every ball is equally likely to be selected from a set of lottery balls numbered 1 to 49. The probability that the first ball is even is $\frac{24}{49}$. **Level 5**

→ **Mutually exclusive** outcomes are things that cannot happen together.
For example, the two outcomes for tossing a coin are mutually exclusive – either heads or tails **Level 6**

→ You can use a **sample space diagram** to list all the possible outcomes of two combined events. The total number of possible outcomes is equal to the number of possible outcomes in the first event, multiplied by the number of possible outcomes in the second event. **Level 6**

Did you know?

You have roughly a 1 in 14 000 000 chance of winning the lottery.

Practice, practice, practice!

Level 5

5c I can understand and use a probability scale

1 Match each cross on these probability scales with one of the probabilities.

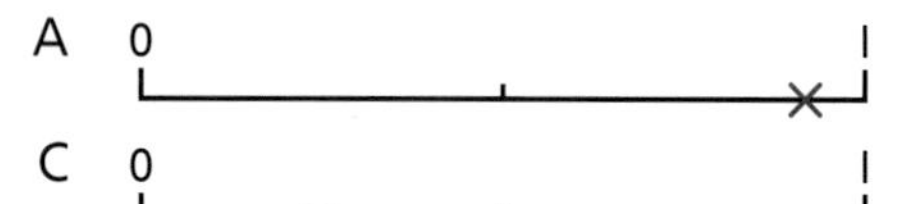

B 0 1

D 0 1

a the probability that a number chosen at random between 1 and 100 is even

b the probability that a page opened at random in a calendar is not in your birthday month

c the probability that a number chosen at random from 1 to 20 is 1 or 8

d the probability that a season chosen at random is Spring

5b I can work out the probability of an event occurring, based on an understanding of equally likely outcomes

2 Look at this list of tracks from an album.

Hey you	Wild one	Tonight	Too right	Yeah babe	Awesome
Maybe	Never	Let's dance	Why me	Groove it	Tac-a-back

A random function is used to play a track.
What is the probability that the track will

a start with the letter 't'

b end with the letter 'e'

c have only one word in the title

d begin and end with the same letter?

mutually exclusive outcome

3 These charts show information collected from a group of pupils about their main holiday last year.

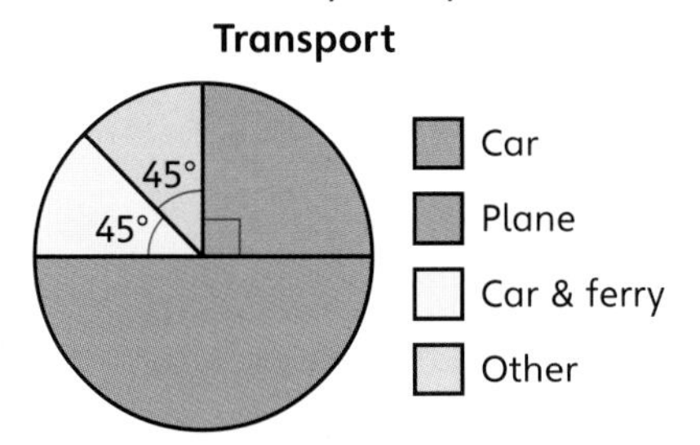

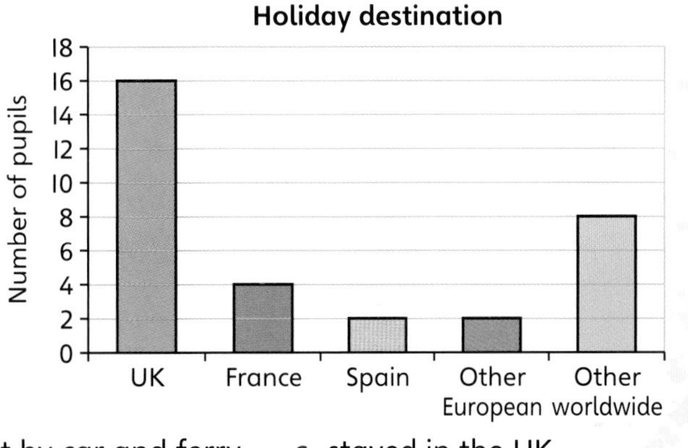

What is the probability that a pupil picked at random

a went by plane **b** went by car and ferry **c** stayed in the UK

d went to a country in Europe other than the UK **e** went to Spain?

Level 5

5b I can work out the probability of an event occurring, based on an understanding of equally likely outcomes

4 Here are some ways to describe the numbers in the box.

even | under 20 | product of two odd numbers | over 40 | over 50 | multiple of 3 | multiple of 8 | cube | multiple of 7

a Find pairs of descriptions that are mutually exclusive for these numbers.

b For each pair, which of the two outcomes is more likely to occur if a number is chosen at random from the box?

99 3 42 45 16 64

c Calculate the probability of the more likely outcome in each case.

5 In each of the final two levels of a computer game you are randomly given one of these things to help you win.

a code-breaker £1000 a banana

a Draw a sample space diagram to show all the possible outcomes.

b What is the probability that you get a banana

i in both levels **ii** in at least one level?

6 Imagine you roll a four-sided dice and a six-sided dice and add the scores together. Are you more likely to get a score greater or less than 5? Explain how you found your answer.

Level 6

6c I can identify mutually exclusive outcomes for a single event

6b I can identify all the possible outcomes for two successive events

Watch out!

Order matters – getting a head first and then a tail is a different outcome from getting the tail first, then the head.

Now try this!

A Fruit machines

A game for two players. Make a 'fruit machine' like this, with the same three fruits on both strips. Player 1 secretly slides the strips to set a combination of fruits and Player 2 guesses the combination. Swap roles and repeat several times.
How likely are you to get it right?

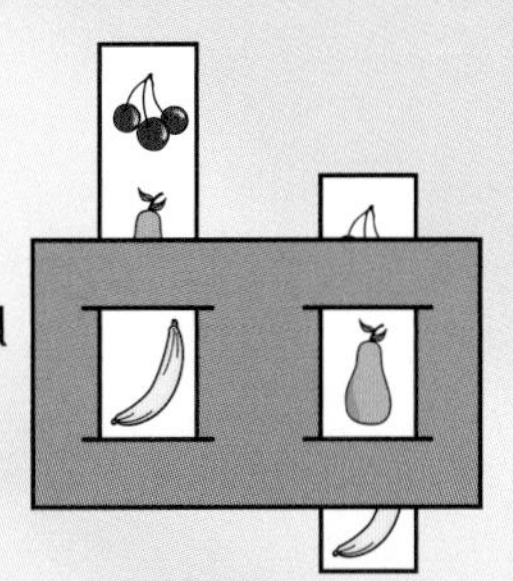

B Race to five

A game for two players. You need an ordinary dice and a pack of cards. Take turns to roll the dice and pick a card at random. If the dice score is more than 3 and the card is not a picture card, you win 1 point. The first to five points wins. How many turns do you expect it to take to find a winner?

probability scale **sample space diagram**

3.3 It all adds up to 1

- If the probability of an outcome occurring is P then the probability of it not occurring is $1 - P$
- Identify all the mutually exclusive outcomes of an experiment; know that the sum of the probabilities of all mutually exclusive outcomes is 1 and use this when solving problems

Why learn this?

You may want to know the chances of a card *not* being drawn if you think it will strengthen someone else's hand in poker.

What's the BIG idea?

- Probability of outcome *not* occurring = 1 − probability of outcome occurring **Level 5**
- **P(n)** is mathematical shorthand for 'the probability of outcome n occurring'. **Level 6**
- Probability of outcome A *or* outcome B happening
  = probability of outcome A happening + probability of outcome B happening
  P(A or B) = P(A) + P(B) **Level 6**
- When experiments are **independent**, the outcome of the first experiment does not have any effect on the outcome of the second experiment.
  For example, if you get a head first when spinning a coin, your chance of getting a head the next time is still $\frac{1}{2}$. **Level 7**
- Probability of a combined event occurring
  = 1 − the sum of the probabilities for all other combinations **Level 7**
- A **tree diagram** helps you work out probabilities of combined events. **Level 7**

Super fact!

There is a higher chance of a baby being born a boy than a girl. In 1994 the chance of a baby being a boy was 51.35% in the UK.

Practice, practice, practice!

Level 5

5a I can work out the probability of an event not occurring

1 Use the probabilities on the scales to write down the probability of each of these events.

- **a** It will rain next Monday.
- **b** It will rain next Tuesday.
- **c** It will rain at the weekend.
- **d** It will not rain next Tuesday.
- **e** It will not rain next Monday.
- **f** It will not rain at the weekend.
- **g** What is the sum of the answers to parts **c** and **f**?

0 rain next Tuesday 1

0 rain next Monday 1

0 rain at the weekend 1

2 Hayley wants to meet Sam and Taj. She has estimated the chances of them turning up at either her party or the youth group.
Based on her estimates, what is the probability that

- **a** Sam goes to the youth group
- **b** Taj doesn't go to the youth group
- **c** Sam doesn't go to the party
- **d** Sam doesn't go to the youth group?

	At the party	At the youth group
Sam	$\frac{2}{5}$	$\frac{1}{5}$
Taj	$\frac{1}{8}$	$\frac{5}{8}$

exhaustive independent

3 The school canteen has to serve a vegetable with every main meal choice. However, some vegetables seem to be served more often than others.

P(sweetcorn) = 0.15 P(tomatoes) = 0.1 P(green beans) = 0.2
P(peas) = 0.3 P(cabbage) = 0.1 P(carrots) = 0.15

What is the probability that these are served?

a tomatoes or cabbage

b any vegetable other than tomatoes or cabbage

c a vegetable that is not green

d a vegetable that doesn't begin with the letter 'c'.

4 Here is a summary table for a week's weather predictions last winter. However, parts of the table cannot be read! Copy and complete the table.

Predicted weather	Mon	Tue	Wed	Thur	Fri	Sat	Sun
Dry	45%	60%	80%		10%		60%
Rain		40%	20%	80%	80%	65%	
Snow/sleet/hail	0%		0%	5%		10%	30%

Level 6

6a I can work out the probability of an outcome occurring if I know the probabilities of all other possible outcomes

5 **a** Draw a tree diagram to show all the possible outcomes when the spinner is spun twice and each time it is recorded whether the number is 'a square number', or 'not a square number'.

b Sophie says there is a 50–50 chance of it landing on a square number both times. Is she correct? Explain your answer.

6 This tree diagram shows the possible outcomes when a six-sided dice is rolled three times.
What is the probability of getting an even number

a every time

b in none of the rolls

c in both the first and last rolls

d in at least one of the three rolls?

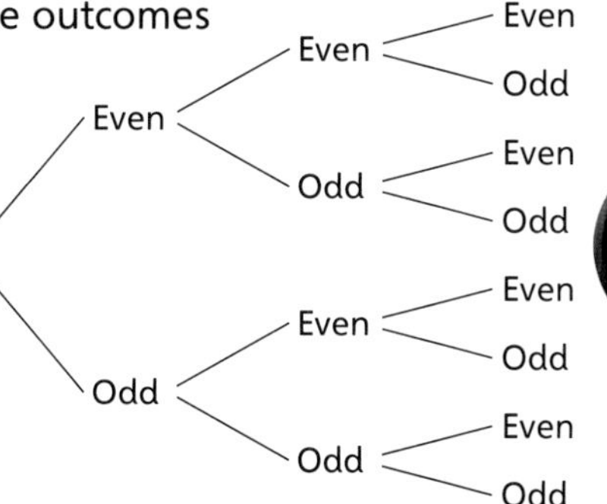

Level 7

7c I can work out the probability of combined outcomes if I know the probabilities of all other possible outcomes

Tip
The quickest way to find the total number of outcomes for two or more successive events is to multiply the number of possible outcomes for each event together.

Now try this!

A Which card?

A game for two players. You need a pack of cards. Shuffle the cards and deal six cards each. Take turns to ask your partner probability questions about their cards (10 questions each). For example "What is the probability that if I choose one of your cards it is a picture card?" Then guess your partner's cards – you score 1 point for each correct guess.

B Menus

Work with a partner. Each design a menu with two starters, three main meals and two desserts. Secretly write down prices for every option so there is a 25% chance that the bill for three courses is exactly £15. Show each other your menus and take turns to select a three-course meal from your partner's menu. You score 1 point every time your bill is £15.
The first to score 3 points wins.

Tip
Write down your questions and answers.

P(n) for 'probability of event n'   tree diagram

3.4 Experimental probability

- Know what a frequency table is and how to use it to collect data
- Use data collected in an experiment to make predictions about what might happen if the experiment is repeated
- Understand that if you carry out an experiment several times it is likely to have different outcomes each time
- Realise that predictions made from the results of an experiment become more reliable when you increase the number of times you do the experiment

Why learn this?

Experimental probability can help you predict what might happen in similar circumstances another time.

What's the BIG idea?

- A **frequency table** uses **tallying** to count the number of times a particular outcome happens. The results can be used to estimate the probability of a particular outcome if the experiment is repeated. **Level 5**
- Each time an experiment is repeated you can expect different outcomes. The more times you repeat an experiment, the greater the accuracy of predictions made from the results. **Level 5**
- The **estimated probability** of an **outcome** can be calculated after an experiment has been completed.

  $$\text{Estimated probability} = \frac{\text{number of times the outcome happened}}{\text{total number of times the experiment was carried out}}$$ **Level 5**
- The estimated probability is the **relative frequency** of the event happening. **Level 5**
- Once you have worked out the probabilities for a combined experiment you can use them to estimate the number of times a combined event would be expected to occur. **Level 6**

Did you know?

You are three times more likely to have an accident indoors than outdoors!

Practice, practice, practice!

Level 5

5b I can estimate probabilities from experimental data collected in a frequency table

1 Dan has been given a biased dice and asked to investigate it. He recorded the results of 200 rolls.

Score	1	2	3	4	5	6
Frequency	29	60	30	32	20	29

a Which number is most likely to come up?

b Which number is least likely to come up?

c He says the number 2 is likely to come up 30% of the time. Is he correct? Explain your answer.

5b I can explain why an experiment may have different outcomes each time it is repeated

2 A raffle is drawn every night for a week. Any ticket ending in 5 or 0 wins a prize. Kirsty bought five tickets on Sunday and won two prizes. On Monday, she bought 10 tickets but only won one prize.

a On Tuesday, she buys another 10 tickets. Is she more likely to win one prize or two prizes?

b She continues to win a prize every draw. Is she less likely to win a prize on the last night?

estimated probability experimental probability frequency

3 Pupils were asked to collect enough data to enable them to estimate the probability of an egg breaking when dropped from a height of 10 cm. Suzie broke the first egg she dropped and didn't try any more. She estimated the probability of it breaking was 100%. Tamsin bought 12 eggs and it took 96 goes before she had broken every one.

a Explain why Tamsin's estimate is likely to be more reliable than Suzie's.

b Estimate the probability of breaking an egg under these circumstances using Tamsin's data.

Level 5

5b I can explain why predictions from experimental results are better when the experiment is repeated lots of times

4 Darryl rolled two four-sided dice and calculated the difference between the numbers on the dice. He did this many times and recorded his results in a frequency table.

Difference	0	1	2	3
Tally	𝍸 𝍸 𝍸 𝍸 𝍸	𝍸 𝍸 𝍸 𝍸 𝍸 𝍸 𝍸 I	𝍸 𝍸 𝍸 𝍸 𝍸 II	𝍸 𝍸 II
Frequency	25	36	27	12

a How many times did the difference equal 2?

b How many times was the experiment carried out?

c Which outcome is most likely?

d Estimate the chance of getting a difference of 2. Give your answer as a fraction.

Level 6

6c I can estimate the probabilities for the outcomes of a combined experiment from the experimental data

5 **a** Look again at Darryl's game in Q4. How many times would you expect to get a difference of 0 if you rolled the dice 1000 times?

b Imagine that a set of results shows there is 'a difference of 3' 30 times. Roughly how many times might the dice have been rolled?

6b I can use estimated probabilities to predict the outcomes of a combined experiment

6 Phil rolled two six-sided dice 80 times and added up the numbers each time. He got a total of 7 on 13 occasions.

a Use a calculator to decide whether $\frac{1}{4}$, $\frac{1}{5}$ or $\frac{1}{6}$ is the best estimate for the probability of rolling a total of 7.

b Imagine he rolled the dice 360 times.
Use your estimate to predict how many times he would expect a total of 7.

Watch out!

If an experiment has a large number of possible outcomes you will need to repeat it many times before you can calculate reliable estimates for the probabilities.

Now try this!

A Biased dice

Make a net of a cube with faces labelled 1 to 6. Stick a counter on the inside of one of the faces. Then fold and stick the net to make a biased dice. Now conduct an experiment to estimate the probability of your dice landing on each number.

B Prime or square?

A game for two players. You need two ordinary dice. Roll both dice and find the difference between the two numbers. Player 1 scores 1 point if the difference is a prime number, and Player 2 scores 1 point if it is a square number. The first to 10 points wins. Is it a fair game?

Tip

Make a sample space diagram of the outcomes

frequency table **outcome** **relative frequency** **tally** **trial**

3.5 Can you trust experimental probability?

- Review ways of identifying all possible outcomes for an experiment
- Appreciate that results of experiments in reality seldom fit in with the theory exactly
- Know that, in some situations, experimental data is the only basis for making estimates of the probability of an event
- Use theoretical probability to make games 'fair' but appreciate that a game may not be fair every time

Why learn this?

It is unwise to base a decision on a theoretical probability if any of the other outcomes could be disastrous.

What's the BIG idea?

- An experiment needs to be repeated many times to be the basis for reliable estimates of probability, so computer simulations or large databases are often used to work out **experimental probabilities**. **Level 5**
- The **theoretical probability** of an equally likely outcome is the predicted value.
  Theoretical probability $= \frac{\text{predicted number of successful outcomes}}{\text{total number of possible outcomes}}$ **Level 5**
- Probabilities based on experimental results may be different from those predicted from theory. **Level 6**
- You tend to only use experimental probability if you don't understand the theory, or if it is not possible to work out theoretical probabilities. **Level 6**
- You can make a game '**fair**' by combining outcomes to produce events that have a theoretically equal chance of occurring. **Level 6**
- Experiments can provide **evidence** for an estimate of probability but theory provides the **explanation** for a probability. **Level 6**

Practice, practice, practice!

Level 5

5a I can identify ways of improving the accuracy of probabilities based on experimental data

1 **a** Roll a dice 10 times and record whether the number is
  A equal to 3
  B greater than 3
  C less than 3.

b Calculate the probabilities for A, B and C, based on your results.

c Calculate the theoretical probabilities for A, B and C.

d How could you make your experimental probabilities closer to the theoretical probabilities?

2 A six-sided dice and a twelve-sided dice were rolled 100 times each. Experimental probabilities for rolling each number were calculated from the results. For which dice would you expect the experimental probabilities to be closest to the theoretical probabilities? Explain your answer.

biased experimental probability evidence

3 Zack put four 50p coins in a bag. He took one out, recorded the year it was minted and put it back in the bag. He did this 40 times.

1999	2001	2001	2002	2002	1999	2001	2001	2001	1999
2002	2001	1999	2002	2001	2002	2002	1999	2002	2002
2001	1999	2001	2001	2001	2001	2001	2001	1999	2001
2002	2001	2002	1999	1999	2001	1999	2001	2001	1999

a How many coins of each date do you think there were?

b Assuming your guess is correct, what is the theoretical probability of choosing a 2002 coin?

c How many different combinations are there if he chooses a coin, puts it back and then chooses another coin?

d Is it more likely that two coins chosen in **c** are both 1999 or both 2001?

Level 6

6c I can use estimated probabilities, based on experimental data, to make predictions for more complex events

4 A five-colour spinner and a coin are used in an experiment. The spinner is spun 200 times, and the coin is spun each time. Here are the results of the trials.

	Red	Blue	Green	Grey	Brown
Head	19	22	18	21	17
Tail	21	23	20	17	22

a Use the results to calculate the experimental probability of getting 'blue' and a head. Give your answer as a percentage.

b Calculate the theoretical probability of getting 'blue' and a head as a percentage.

c How many times would you expect to get 'blue' and a head after 200 trials?

d Do you think a game played with the spinner and coin would be fair? Why?

6b I can understand whether an experiment with simple outcomes is 'fair'

Watch out!
The chance of two events happening together is always much smaller than the chance of either event happening on its own.

5 A 12-sided dice has a month of the year on each side. Greg challenged Amy to play a game he invented called JAM FONDS. If he rolls two of these dice and both land with months beginning J, A or M on top he gets a point. If they both start with F, O, N, D or S Amy gets a point. Amy refused, saying the game wasn't fair.

a Explain why it isn't fair.

b Is it possible for Amy to win?

c How could the rules be changed to make it fair?

Now try this!

A Lady luck

A game for two players. You need two ordinary dice.
Take turns to predict the total on the two dice and then roll them.
If you are correct you score 1 point. The first to 10 points wins

Tip
Use a sample space diagram to help you make your bid.

B Gamer's paradise

Use a sample space diagram to work out the theoretical probabilities when you multiply the numbers on two six-sided dice. Make up your own game rules so that choosing particular results will give you an advantage.

explanation fair theoretical probability

3.6 The best holiday ever – probably

- Use lists, two-way tables or tree diagrams to identify the number of outcomes
- Use the idea that probabilities sum to 1 to solve probability problems
- Calculate probabilities
- Know how reliable probability estimates are when they have been based on experimental data

Why learn this?

You may consider probable risks relating to health and safety before taking part in some activities.

What's the BIG idea?

- If all outcomes are not equally likely, it may be possible to **estimate** the probability of an event using experimental results. **Level 5**
- **Estimated probabilities** become more reliable the more times you carry out an experiment. **Level 5**
- **Mutually exclusive** events cannot occur at the same time. The sum of the probabilities of all mutually exclusive events add up to 1. **Level 6**
- The probabilities of events can be used to decide if an experiment or game is fair, or not. **Level 6**
- You can work out the probability for a combined event if all the other probabilities are known because the total of all the probabilities is 1. **Level 7**

Practice, practice, practice!

Level 5

5b I can explain why predictions from experimental results are better when the experiment is repeated lots of times

Jing was on work experience in a travel agency last week.
She left on Friday, leaving the company with some problems to sort out!

1 Jing gathered data about the punctuality of flights arriving in New York from London to use to make predictions about next year's flights.

Airline	Percentage arriving within 15 minutes of scheduled time	Total flights analysed
BOS	68.76	1005
Omega	60.18	884
Flash	44.99	3236
MiniJet	34.05	232
Zoop	22.28	543

a Why does the data for Flash give the most reliable estimate of the punctuality probability for next year?

b Which airline has the worst probability estimate for punctuality?

c Why might it not be a good idea to make assumptions about the reliability of MiniJet planes next year based on this data?

Watch out!

An estimate of a probability is not a rough guess. It should be based on experimental data.

estimate estimated probability

2 Jing left a note that said 'Mr Williams is booked on the 7.30 plane to London.' The company uses three London airports and they didn't know whether the flight was in the morning or the evening.

a How many different combinations of airport and time of day are there?

b What is the probability of choosing the correct airport if they just guess?

c What is the probability of choosing the correct time *and* airport if they guess?

3 One day Jing suggested that some of the comments in the brochure were not very positive and should be rewritten. Rewrite these statements so they sound more positive.

There is a 20% chance of rain. *There is an 80% chance it will stay dry.*

a There is a 15% chance of being delayed on the outward flight.

b There is a 7% chance of being delayed on the return flight.

c The chance of there not being enough snow to ski in February is 28%.

Level 5

5b I can work out the probability of an event occurring, based on an understanding of equally likely outcomes

5a I can work out the probability of an event not occurring

4 All pupils who complete a work experience placement with this travel agency are entered into a prize draw. They always give four prizes – one to a boy and another to a girl from each of the two local schools.
Explain why this may not give everybody a fair chance of winning.

Level 6

6a I can understand whether a more complex experiment is 'fair'

5 400 customers were randomly telephoned in a follow-up satisfaction survey. Based on previous surveys

- the probability of calling someone aged 20–39 is $\frac{2}{5}$
- the probability of calling a completely satisfied customer aged over 60 is $\frac{1}{4}$
- the probability of calling a dissatisfied customer aged 40–59 is the same as that of contacting a generally satisfied customer aged 60 or over.

Copy and complete this table using the information given above.

	Completely satisfied	Generally satisfied	Dissatisfied
20–39	80	40	
40–59	60		12
60 or over			28

Level 7

7c I can work out the probability of combined outcomes if I know the probabilities of all other possible outcomes

Now try this!

A Favourite destination

Work with a partner. You each need eight blank cards. Each choose three holiday destinations and write one on each of your cards – your favourite destination should appear most often but each destination must appear at least once. Shuffle the cards and ask your partner to pick one. Repeat this 20 times and see if your partner can guess

a your favourite destination and

b the number of cards that show that destination.

B Sum it

A game for 2 players. You need four sets of 1–4 digit cards. Player 1 shuffles the cards and deals two face down. Player 2 predicts the sum of the two cards. If correct they keep the cards, if not the cards are replaced. Swap roles and repeat. The first person with six cards wins.

mutually exclusive sum to

Leader of the pack

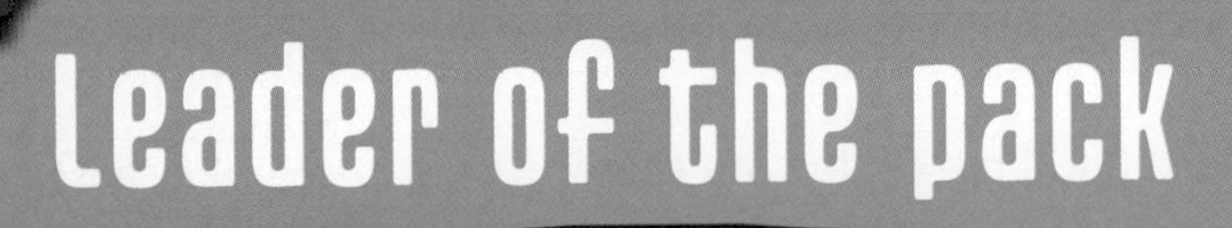

Higher or Lower?

In the game Higher or Lower a card is turned over and you have to guess whether the next card will be higher or lower than the previous card. Aces are said to be 'low' (they count as the number 1).

After the first card is drawn there are 51 cards left. If this card is the 6 of hearts then the probability of getting a lower card next is 20/51.

What is the probability of getting a higher card next?

If the first two cards drawn are the 6 of hearts and the jack of spades, what is the probability of the next card being higher than the jack?

What would be the probability that each of these guesses is correct?

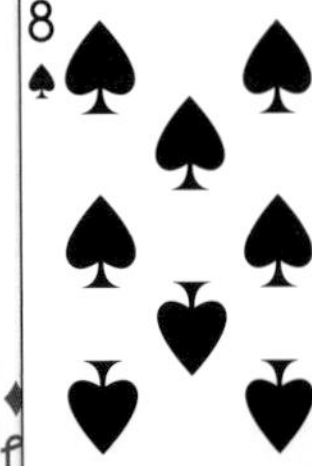

52 Card Pick-Up

Imagine a set of 52 cards spread out on a table face down.
You start turning the cards over one by one.

What is the probability of turning over all the queens before you turn over the ace of spades?

Simple Card Trick

Ask a friend to choose two different denominations of card without the suits (for example a 6 and a jack). Tell them that if they concentrate hard then those two cards will appear next to each other somewhere in the pack. Turn over the cards to see if it has worked.

Explain why this seems to work most of the time.
How many times does it work if you attempt it ten times?
Perhaps you are not concentrating hard enough!

Transport events

Ricky and Carmel are interested in the methods of transport used by people when travelling.
They have completed their research and their findings are shown in the tables below.

Table 1 Methods of transport used by children when travelling to school

	Walk	Car/van	Bus	Other
Proportion	$\frac{2}{5}$	$\frac{1}{5}$	$\frac{3}{10}$	$\frac{1}{10}$

Table 2 Methods of transport used by adults for all distances travelled in a year

	Walk	Car	Bus, coach or rail	Other
Proportion	$\frac{1}{10}$	$\frac{4}{5}$	$\frac{1}{20}$	?

1 Draw a probability scale from 0 to 1. Place the following events on your scale.
A: a child walks to school
B: a child travels by car/van to school **Level 5**

2 Mikey only travels by car to school if it is raining. If it is fine, he walks.
There is a 35% chance of rain on Wednesday. What is the probability that Mikey will walk to school on Wednesday? **Level 5**

3 Is a child more likely to travel by bus or 'other' method of transport to school? Give a full reason for your answer. **Level 5**

4 Which is the most popular method of travel to school? How can you tell? **Level 6**

5 What is the probability that a pupil travels by car or bus to school?
Give your answer as **a** a fraction and **b** a percentage. **Level 6**

6 What is the probability that Mr Wheeler will walk or drive the car to work? **Level 6**

7 What is the probability that Mrs Wheeler will not travel by bus or car? **Level 6**

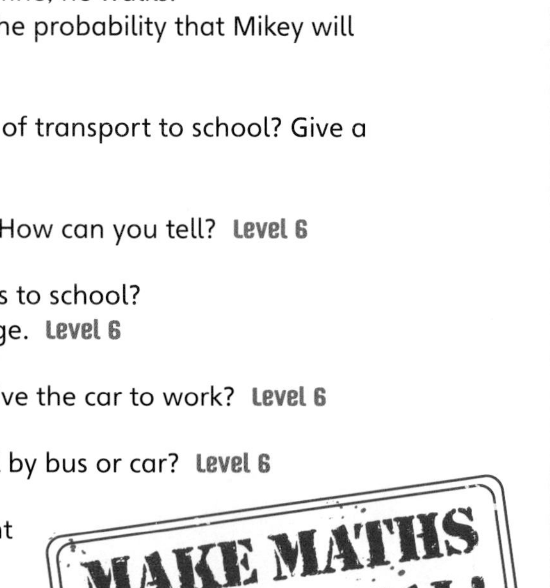

8 **a** What could the 'other' method of transport represent in Table 2?
b What is the probability of an adult using an 'other' method of transport?
c Is it possible to compare the tables and say that children are more likely to walk than adults? Explain your answer fully. **Level 7**

MAKE MATHS FUNCTIONAL!

The BIG ideas

- A **probability scale** is a line representing how likely something is to happen. An impossible **event** has the value 0; a certain event has the value 1. All other possible events have a value between 0 and 1. **Level 5**

0 ——————— 1
Impossible ——— Certain

- It is easy to use fractions to compare the chances of something happening if the **denominator** of each is the same – the fraction with the largest **numerator** is most likely.
For example, $\frac{7}{17}$ is more likely than $\frac{3}{17}$. **Level 5**
- Probability of an event **not** occurring = 1 – probability of event occurring. **Level 5**
- If the numerators of the fractions are the same, the event with the smallest denominator is more likely to happen. For example, $\frac{4}{18}$ is more likely to happen than $\frac{4}{23}$. **Level 6**
- If both numerators and denominators are different, you need to either find **equivalent fractions** with the same denominator, or convert the fractions into decimals to see which event is most likely. For example, $\frac{3}{8}$ is more likely than $\frac{1}{6}$ because $\frac{3}{8} = \frac{9}{24}$ is greater than $\frac{1}{6} = \frac{4}{24}$. **Level 6**
- Probability of event A or event B happening = probability of event A happening + probability of event B happening. **Level 6**
- If events are **mutually exclusive** and **exhaustive** then:
Probability of any one event = 1 – probability of all other possible outcomes. **Level 6**
- It is possible to work out the probability for a complex event if all the other probabilities are known because the total should be 1. **Level 7**

Practice SATs-style questions

Level 5

Q1 A twenty-sided dice, numbered from 1 to 20, is rolled.

0 ——————— 1

a Copy the probability scale. Add a cross labelled A to show the probability of the dice landing on a number that is **greater than 15**.

b Put a cross on your probability scale and label it B to show the probability of the dice landing on a number that is **more than 5**.

Q2 This information was collected in a survey about class 9E.

	Boys	Girls
Can swim	12	
Cannot swim	2	3
Total		18

a Copy and complete the table.

b A pupil from 9E is chosen at random. What is the probability that the pupil is a boy?

c If the teacher chooses a girl instead, what is the probability that the girl cannot swim?

Level 6

Q3 a Sharon puts 4 white balls and 1 black ball in a bag. She closes her eyes and takes a ball from the bag. What is the probability that the ball is black?

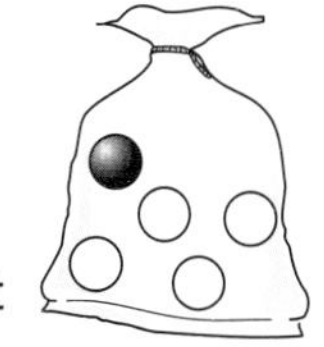

b She then adds some more black balls and says, 'The probability of getting a white ball is now two fifths'. How many black balls has she added?

Level 7

Q4 I have two fair spinners. One spinner is numbered 5, 6, 7 and 8. The other is numbered 2, 4, 6 and 8.

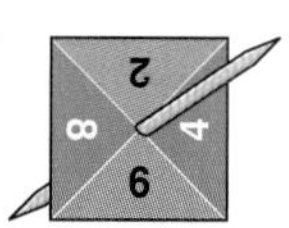

I spin each one and then add the numbers they land on.

a What is the probability that the total is less than 10?

b What is the probability that the total is more than 10?

c What is the probability that the total is exactly 10?

You must show your workings to explain your answers.

4 Look the part

This unit is about calculating with fractions, decimals and percentages. Fractions, decimals and percentages are used to describe changes in values or proportions of a whole.

'Baby Boomers' is the name given to those born in the 1950s, when there was a sudden rise in birth numbers after World War II. It is important to gather information about populations so that governments can plan ahead for school places, housing, health care and transport.

In the UK a census is taken every 10 years to give information about the population. A questionnaire is sent to every household and the results are used to show the changes that are taking place.

The most recent census was in 2001. It showed that at the time

- 51% of the population was female
- $\frac{1}{5}$ of the population was under 16.

It also showed that over a period of 50 years the population had increased by 17%.

- The current population of the UK is approximately 60 million. What if it continues to increase by 17% every 50 years? Do some calculations to see what it would be in 200 years' time.
- What major factors might affect the way in which the future population is made up? For example, what might cause an increase in the numbers of people under 10 or over 60?

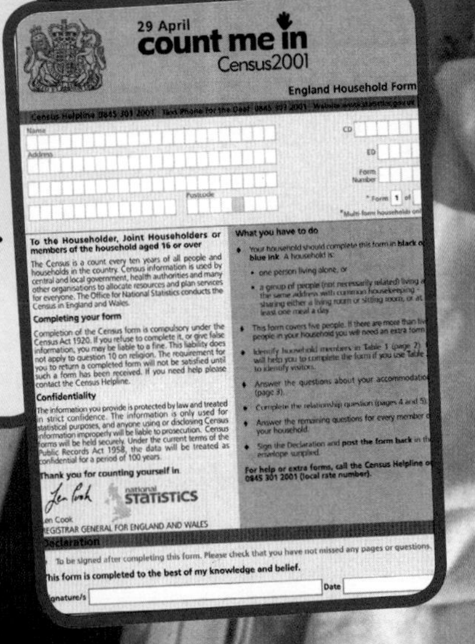

29 April
count me in
Census2001

England Household Form

Name

Address

Postcode

CD

ED

Form Number

To the Householder, Joint Householders or members of the household aged 16 or over

The Census is a count every ten years of all people and households in the country. Census information is used by central and local government, health authorities and many other organisations to allocate resources and plan services for everyone. The Office for National Statistics conducts the Census in England and Wales.

Completing your form

Completion of the Census form is compulsory under the Census Act 1920. If you refuse to complete it, or give false information, you may be liable to a fine. This liability does not apply to question 10 on religion. The requirement for you to return a completed form will not be satisfied until such a form has been received. If you need help please contact the Census Helpline.

Confidentiality

The information you provide is protected by law and treated in strict confidence. The information is only used for statistical purposes, and anyone using or disclosing Census information improperly will be liable to prosecution. Census forms will be held securely. Under the current terms of the Public Records Act 1958, the data will be treated as confidential for a period of 100 years.

Thank you for counting yourself in

Len Cook
REGISTRAR GENERAL FOR ENGLAND AND WALES

national statistics

What you have to do

- Your household should complete this form in **black or blue ink**. A household is:
  - one person living alone, or
  - a group of people (not necessarily related) living at the same address with common housekeeping – sharing either a living room or sitting room, or at least one meal a day.
- This form covers five people. If there are more than five people in your household you will need an extra form.
- Answer the questions about your accommodation (page 3).
- Complete the relationship question (pages 4 and 5).
- Answer the remaining questions for every member of your household.
- Sign the Declaration and **post the form back** in the envelope supplied.

For help or extra forms, call the Census Helpline on 0845 301 2001 (local rate number).

Declaration

To be signed after completing this form. Please check that you have not missed any pages or questions.

This form is completed to the best of my knowledge and belief.

Signature/s | Date

Activities

A The fraction $\frac{1}{2}$ is equivalent to (the same as) $\frac{2}{4}, \frac{3}{6}, \frac{4}{8}\ldots$

Write down 20 fractions that are equivalent to $\frac{3}{4}$.

B
- Draw a square measuring 12 cm by 12 cm. Divide it into 4 equal sections. Shade 3 sections. Work out the total shaded area.
- Draw another square the same size and divide it into 3 equal sections. Shade 2 sections. Work out the total shaded area.

  Which is larger $\frac{3}{4}$ or $\frac{2}{3}$? (Use your diagrams to help).
- Use a similar method to decide whether $\frac{2}{5}$ or $\frac{1}{3}$ is larger. Start with a square with sides of 15 cm.

Before you start this unit...

1 Cancel these fractions to their simplest form.

a $\frac{3}{6}$ **b** $\frac{12}{18}$ **c** $\frac{25}{40}$ **d** $\frac{27}{36}$

Level Up Maths 4-6 page 54

2 Write these decimals in descending order.

0.32 0.23 0.3 0.33

3 $42 \times 34 = 1428$

Use this fact to find the missing numbers.

a $34 \times \square = 1428$

b $1428 \div \square = 34$

Level Up Maths 3-5 page 32

4 **a** What is 50% of £20?

b What is 10% of 45 inches?

c What is 25% of 200 cm?

5 Work out

a 0.6×10 **b** 100×15

c $25 \div 100$ **d** $0.4 \div 10$

Level Up Maths 4-6 page 22

Plus digital resources

The ancient Egyptians gathered information about the population to decide what proportion of it could be used for pyramid building.

4.1 Fractions

- Express one number as a fraction of another
- Convert between fractions and decimals
- Compare and order fractions

What's the BIG idea?

- **Fractions** can be **simplified** by **cancelling** common factors. Level 5
- A fraction is in its **lowest terms** when it has been cancelled down to its **simplest form**. Level 5
- You can express one quantity as a fraction of another. For example, 75p as a fraction of £1 is $\frac{75}{100} = \frac{3}{4}$. Level 5 & Level 6
- You can **convert** a decimal to a fraction by writing it with **denominator** 10, 100 or 1000 and then cancelling. For example, 0.03 = 3 hundredths = $\frac{3}{100}$. Level 5 & Level 6
- A **terminating decimal** is one which has a finite number of digits. It has an exact decimal value. For example, 0.65. Level 5 & Level 6
- A **recurring decimal** contains a digit, or sequence of digits, which repeats itself forever. A dot ˙ over a digit shows that it recurs. For example, 0.333... = $0.\dot{3}$ Level 5 & Level 6
- You can convert a fraction to a decimal by dividing the **numerator** by the denominator. For example $\frac{3}{4} = 3 \div 4 = 0.75$ Level 6
- To order fractions you can convert them to decimals or **equivalent** fractions with a common denominator. Level 6

Why learn this?

Discounts in shops may be given as fractions. To decide which shop is offering the best deal, you need to be able to compare fractions.

Watch out!

When giving one quantity as a fraction of another, make sure that the units are the same for both.

Practice, practice, practice!

Level 5

5c I can use a diagram to compare two fractions

1 A bar of chocolate is split into 15 blocks as shown.
Pippa and Jude are arguing about which is the greater number of blocks, $\frac{1}{3}$ or $\frac{2}{5}$.
Pippa thinks $\frac{1}{3}$ is more blocks than $\frac{2}{5}$.

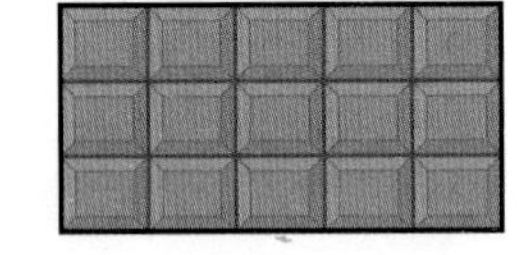

a Draw the chocolate bar and shade $\frac{1}{3}$ red and $\frac{2}{5}$ blue.

b Is Pippa right?

5b I can express one number as a fraction of another

2 Ali receives a weekly allowance of £15, Charlie receives £5 and Henry receives £7.50.

a What fraction of Ali's allowance does Charlie receive?

b What fraction of Henry's allowance does Charlie receive?

Give your answers in their lowest terms.

5a I can convert terminating decimals to fractions and simplify the answer

3 Convert these decimals to fractions.
Give your answers in their simplest form.

a 0.46 **b** 0.725 **c** 0.602 **d** 3.2

cancel convert denominator equivalent fraction lowest terms

4 Given that $0.\dot{3} = \frac{1}{3}$ and $0.\dot{1} = \frac{1}{9}$, write these as fractions.

a $0.\dot{6}$ **b** $0.\dot{2}$ **c** $0.\dot{7}$ **d** $0.\dot{5}$ **e** $0.\dot{8}$

5 Convert these fractions to decimals using written division.

$\frac{7}{5}$

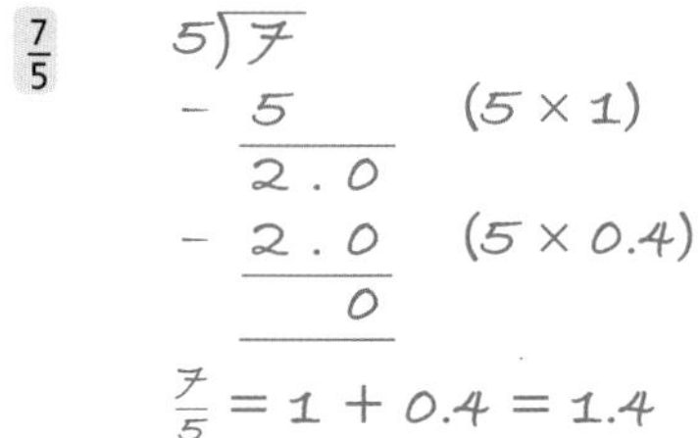

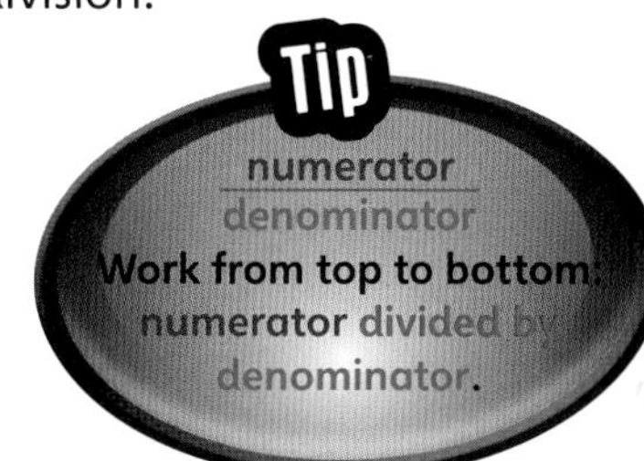

a $\frac{3}{5}$ **b** $\frac{7}{8}$ **c** $\frac{34}{8}$ **d** $\frac{1}{6}$

6 A fraction is equivalent to a terminating decimal if the only factors of the denominator of the fraction in its simplest form, apart from 1 and itself, are 2 and/or 5.

a Use this information to identify which of these fractions are equivalent to recurring decimals.
$\frac{4}{8}$ $\frac{2}{7}$ $\frac{3}{9}$ $\frac{3}{12}$

b Use a calculator to test your answer to part **a**.

c Which other denominators below 10 will give recurring decimals?

7 Express these savings as a fraction of the original selling price. Give each answer in its lowest terms.

a *save* £5.50 *originally* £10 **b** *save* 80p *originally* £4 **c** *save* 45p *originally* £2.40

8 By converting the fractions to decimals, write these in descending order.

$\frac{1}{2}$ $\frac{4}{5}$ $\frac{5}{8}$ $\frac{2}{3}$ $\frac{7}{12}$

9 Use equivalent fractions to put each set of fractions in order, starting with the smallest.

a $\frac{2}{5}$ $\frac{7}{8}$ $\frac{19}{20}$ $\frac{7}{10}$ **b** $\frac{11}{14}$ $\frac{3}{4}$ $\frac{1}{2}$ $\frac{3}{7}$ **c** $\frac{7}{10}$ $\frac{3}{5}$ $\frac{4}{6}$ $\frac{11}{15}$

10 Put the correct sign, > or <, between each pair of fractions.

Hint: Convert the fractions to decimals.

a $\frac{6}{21}$ ☐ $\frac{13}{17}$ **b** $\frac{4}{18}$ ☐ $\frac{2}{3}$ **c** $\frac{25}{30}$ ☐ $\frac{15}{80}$

d $\frac{11}{15}$ ☐ $\frac{7}{10}$ **e** $\frac{9}{20}$ ☐ $\frac{23}{50}$ **f** $\frac{5}{7}$ ☐ $\frac{17}{30}$

Level 6

6c I can write recurring decimals as fractions

6c I can use division to convert a fraction to a decimal

6c I can identify the denominator of fractions that give recurring decimals

6c I can express a smaller whole number as a fraction of a larger one

6b I can order fractions by converting them to decimals

6b I can use equivalent fractions to order fractions

6a I can use the > and < symbols to compare decimals and fractions

Now try this!

A Fraction dice

A game for two players. You need four dice.
Roll two dice each, at the same time.
Form a fraction by using your smaller score as the numerator and your larger score as the denominator. Convert your fraction to a decimal.
The player with the larger decimal scores 1 point.
First to 5 points wins.

B Recurring magic

a Write these as decimals: $\frac{1}{9}$, $\frac{2}{9}$, $\frac{11}{99}$, $\frac{22}{99}$.
Describe any patterns that you see.

b How would you expect $\frac{5}{9}$, $\frac{7}{9}$, $\frac{12}{99}$ and $\frac{33}{99}$ to be written as decimals?
What about $\frac{78}{99}$? Check your answers.

c Investigate fractions with denominator 999 and 9999. Is the pattern the same?

numerator recurring decimal simplest form simplify terminating decimal

4.2 Adding and subtracting fractions

- Add and subtract fractions with the same denominator
- Add and subtract fractions with different denominators
- Add and subtract mixed numbers
- Use inverse operations to check fraction calculations

Why learn this?

Distances are often given as fractional values. If you want to calculate part or total distances, you will need to add and subtract fractions.

What's the BIG idea?

→ To add or subtract fractions with a common **denominator**, add or subtract the **numerators.** Write the result over the same denominator. **Level 5**

→ To add or subtract fractions with different denominators, first find **equivalent** fractions with the same denominator. **Level 6**

→ To add or subtract **mixed numbers**, add or subtract the whole-number parts then add or subtract the fractions. **Level 6**

→ When subtracting mixed numbers, you may need to **convert** the first mixed number to an equivalent mixed number with an **improper fraction**. For example, $4\frac{1}{3}$ is equivalent to $3\frac{4}{3}$. **Level 6**

Did you know?

The Egyptians used fractions as early as 1800 BC. Since they only used hieroglyphs, their fractions were in pictures.
For example, $\frac{1}{5}$ looked like this.

Practice, practice, practice!

Level 5

5c I can add and subtract fractions with a common denominator

1 Work out

a $\frac{3}{7} + \frac{2}{7}$ **b** $\frac{4}{9} + \frac{5}{9} - \frac{3}{9}$ **c** $\frac{7}{15} - \frac{2}{15} + \frac{1}{15}$ **d** $\frac{23}{100} - \frac{15}{100} - \frac{8}{100}$

Level 6

6c I can add fractions by writing them with a common denominator

2 Work out these. Give your answers in their simplest form.

$\frac{1}{4} + \frac{1}{12}$ *The lowest common multiple of 4 and 12 is 12.*
Convert to equivalent fractions with denominator 12.

$= \frac{3}{12} + \frac{1}{12} = \frac{3+1}{12} = \frac{4}{12} = \frac{1}{3}$

a $\frac{3}{5} + \frac{3}{10}$ **b** $\frac{1}{3} + \frac{1}{2}$ **c** $\frac{3}{5} + \frac{1}{2}$ **d** $\frac{3}{4} + \frac{1}{6}$

3 **a** Copy and complete. **i** $\frac{1}{3} + \frac{1}{5} = \square$ **ii** $\frac{1}{3} + \frac{1}{4} = \square$

b True or false? When you add positive fractions, the answer is bigger than the original fractions.

6c I can subtract fractions by writing them with a common denominator

4 Work out these. Give your answers in their simplest form.

a $\frac{1}{3} - \frac{1}{6}$ **b** $\frac{3}{4} - \frac{1}{5}$ **c** $\frac{3}{5} - \frac{1}{7}$ **d** $\frac{2}{3} - \frac{1}{2}$

convert denominator equivalent improper fraction

5 **a** Copy and complete.

i $\frac{8}{9} - \frac{1}{3} = \square$ **ii** $\frac{8}{9} - \frac{2}{3} = \square$ **iii** $\frac{3}{5} - \frac{1}{4} = \square$

b True or false? When you subtract positive fractions, the answer is smaller than the first fraction.

c Is the answer smaller than the second fraction?

6 $\frac{5}{12}$ of the memory on Molly's computer stores music. A further $\frac{3}{7}$ is used by games software. How much memory is left on Molly's computer?

7 Isabelle, Iram and Olivia enter a competition. If they win, they agree to split the prize like this – Isabelle $\frac{1}{3}$, Iram $\frac{1}{5}$, Olivia $\frac{1}{12}$ – and to give the remainder to charity.

a If they won, what fraction of the prize would they give to charity?

Another girl, Aisha, joins their group and they agree to give her $\frac{1}{6}$ of the prize.

b How much more would Aisha receive than Olivia?

c How much would now go to charity?

8 $5\frac{1}{8} - 3\frac{2}{7} = 1\frac{47}{56}$ $5\frac{1}{8} + 3\frac{2}{7} = 8\frac{23}{56}$

Use the facts in the boxes to work out

a $1\frac{47}{56} + 3\frac{2}{7}$ **b** $8\frac{23}{56} - 5\frac{1}{8}$ **c** $8\frac{23}{56} - 3\frac{2}{7}$ **d** $1\frac{47}{56} - \left(5\frac{1}{8} - 3\frac{2}{7}\right)$

9 Add these mixed numbers.

$1\frac{2}{5} + 3\frac{9}{10}$ $= 4\frac{2}{5} + \frac{9}{10} = 4\frac{4}{10} + \frac{9}{10} = 4\frac{13}{10} = 5\frac{3}{10}$

a $2\frac{2}{3} + \frac{5}{6}$ **b** $5\frac{4}{5} + 2\frac{1}{3}$ **c** $3\frac{1}{8} + 7\frac{2}{5}$

Watch out!
When you add or subtract mixed numbers, the fraction parts must still have the same denominator.

10 Work out these subtractions.
Write each answer in its simplest form.

a $3\frac{4}{8} - 2\frac{1}{4}$ **b** $7\frac{2}{3} - 5\frac{1}{2}$ **c** $5\frac{3}{4} - 2\frac{1}{3}$ **d** $3\frac{1}{2} - 2\frac{1}{5}$

11 Work out these subtractions.

$4\frac{1}{2} - 1\frac{3}{4}$
$= 3\frac{1}{2} - \frac{3}{4}$ subtract whole number parts
$= 3\frac{2}{4} - \frac{3}{4}$ convert to equivalent fractions
$= 2\frac{6}{4} - \frac{3}{4}$ $\frac{2}{4} < \frac{3}{4}$, so rewrite $3\frac{2}{4}$ as $2\frac{6}{4}$
$= 2\frac{3}{4}$

a $2\frac{1}{3} - 1\frac{3}{4}$ **b** $3\frac{2}{5} - 2\frac{7}{10}$ **c** $8\frac{4}{9} - 5\frac{2}{3}$ **d** $5\frac{1}{3} - 2\frac{5}{6}$

Level 6

6c I can subtract fractions by writing them with a common denominator

6c I can add and subtract simple fractions

6c I can use inverse operations

6c I can add mixed numbers

6b I can subtract mixed numbers when the second fraction is smaller than the first

6a I can subtract mixed numbers when the second fraction is larger than the first

Now try this!

A Making 1

You can make the number 1 by adding two fractions with four different digits in many ways, for example $\frac{1}{3} + \frac{4}{6} = 1$.
Find as many other ways of doing this as you can.

B Fraction sequence

$\frac{1}{2}, \frac{1}{4}, \frac{1}{8}, \frac{1}{16}, \frac{1}{32}, \ldots$

a Continue this sequence by finding the next five terms.

b Add

i the first two terms **ii** the first three terms
iii the first four terms **iv** the first five terms.

c Use your answers to part **b** to predict the sum of

i the first six terms **ii** the first seven terms.

d Will the terms in your sequence ever add up to 1?

lowest common multiple mixed number numerator simplest form

4.3 Multiplying and dividing fractions

- Calculate fractions of quantities and measurements
- Multiply and divide integers by fractions
- Multiply and divide fractions by fractions

What's the BIG idea?

- To find a fraction of a quantity, **divide** by the **denominator** and then **multiply** by the **numerator**.
  $\frac{4}{5}$ of 80 kg, $\frac{4}{5} \times 80$ kg and 80 kg $\times \frac{4}{5}$ are all equivalent. **Level 5**
- To multiply a whole number by a fraction you can write the whole number as a fraction.
  $80 \times \frac{4}{5} = \frac{80}{1} \times \frac{4}{5}$
  Cancel, then multiply the numerators and multiply the denominators.
  $\frac{{}^{16}\cancel{80}}{1} \times \frac{4}{\cancel{5}_1} = \frac{64}{1} = 64$ **Level 6**
- To multiply a fraction by a fraction, multiply the numerators and multiply the denominators.
  $\frac{2}{3} \times \frac{3}{5} = \frac{2 \times 3}{3 \times 5} = \frac{6}{15}$ **Level 7**
- To divide fractions, invert the dividing fraction (turn it upside down) and change the **division** sign to **multiplication**.
  $\frac{2}{3} \div \frac{3}{5} = \frac{2}{3} \times \frac{5}{3} = \frac{2 \times 5}{3 \times 3} = \frac{10}{9}$ or $1\frac{1}{9}$ **Level 7**

Why learn this?

When decorating, you may need to calculate areas that involve fractional measurements.

Did you know?

In India fractions are written the same way you write fractions but without the line, for example $\frac{2}{3}$ is written as $\begin{matrix}2\\3\end{matrix}$.

Practice, practice, practice!

1 Work out

$\frac{2}{3}$ of £240 $= (£240 \div 3) \times 2 = £80 \times 2 = £160$

a $\frac{1}{5}$ of 15 inches **b** $\frac{2}{3}$ of £21 **c** $\frac{3}{8}$ of 480 miles
d $\frac{6}{7}$ of 77p **e** $\frac{5}{9}$ of 4500 km **f** $\frac{7}{12}$ of 132 m

2 Calculate the areas of the shapes.

a

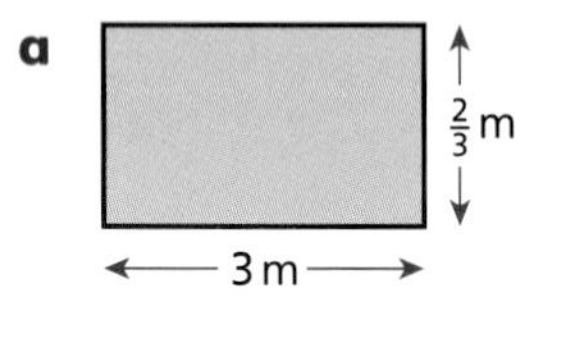

b

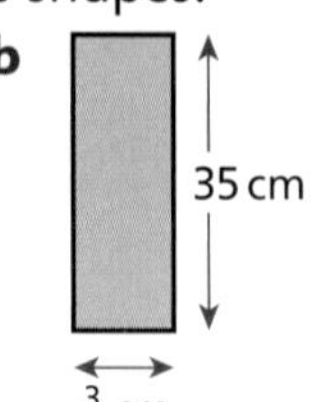

c

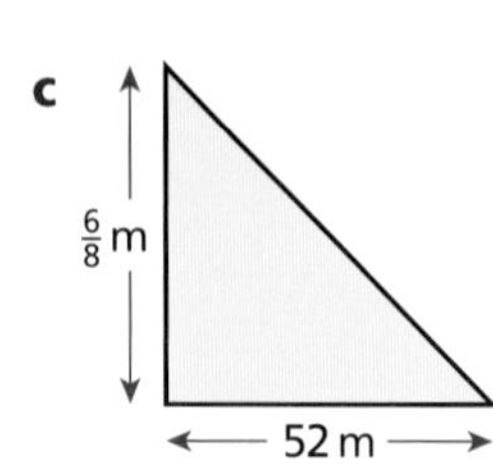

3 Flo has mixed 5 kg of concrete.
She uses two sevenths of the mix. How much concrete does she have left?

Level 5

5b I can find fractions of quantities (whole-number answers)

5a I can multiply a fraction by an integer

5a I can calculate fractions of amounts (fraction answers)

denominator divide division integer inverse

4 Work out

a $210 \times \frac{5}{6}$ b $44 \times \frac{3}{8}$ c $82 \times \frac{7}{8}$ d $284 \times \frac{3}{10}$ e $364 \times \frac{5}{6}$

5 Keiko is playing a game with Caroline. She multiples the number 90 by a fraction from the cloud and says the answer. Caroline has to work out which fraction she used.

Work out which fraction Keiko used if she says

a 60 b 18 c 15 d 45

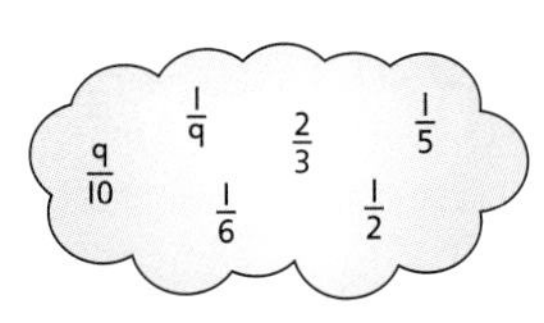

6 Calculate

a $8 \div \frac{2}{3}$ b $5 \div \frac{5}{7}$

c $22 \div \frac{2}{9}$ d $18 \div \frac{6}{11}$

change division to multiplication

$5 \div \frac{1}{4} = 5 \times \frac{4}{1} = \frac{20}{1} = 20$

turn upside down

7 Suri cycles 5 miles in $\frac{7}{12}$ hour. What is her speed?

8 Simplify these multiplications by cancelling common factors.

a $\frac{2}{3} \times \frac{9}{10}$ b $\frac{5}{8} \times \frac{4}{15}$ c $\frac{7}{12} \times \frac{6}{7}$ d $\frac{18}{19} \times \frac{2}{9}$ d $\frac{5}{24} \times \frac{6}{15}$

Level 6

6c I can multiply an integer by a fraction

6c I can interpret division as the inverse of multiplication

6b I can divide an integer by a fraction

6b I can cancel common factors in a fraction multiplication

9 Work out these, cancelling when possible.

a $\frac{1}{5} \times \frac{7}{8}$ b $\frac{4}{5} \times \frac{5}{12}$ c $\frac{3}{7} \times \frac{2}{7}$ d $\frac{3}{8} \times \frac{2}{7}$ e $\frac{6}{7} \times \frac{3}{14} \times \frac{7}{21}$

10 A rectangle is $3\frac{3}{5}$ cm long and $4\frac{5}{6}$ cm wide. Calculate its area.

11 Work out

a $\frac{3}{5} \div \frac{1}{4}$ b $\frac{2}{7} \div \frac{3}{4}$ c $\frac{3}{8} \div \frac{1}{2}$

d $\frac{2}{3} \div \frac{5}{6}$ e $7\frac{1}{2} \div \frac{1}{4}$ f $\frac{7}{9} \div \frac{5}{7}$

Watch out!
You only turn the second fraction upside down.

12 Find the length of the unmarked sides of these rectangles.

a area = $3\frac{1}{2}$ m^2 ; $\frac{3}{5}$ m

b area = $2\frac{2}{3}$ m^2 ; $\frac{1}{4}$ m

Level 7

7c I can multiply a fraction by a fraction

7b I can divide a fraction by a fraction

Now try this!

A Equal shares

Emily has bought 15 bars of chocolate. She wants to give lots of people a piece.

a How many pieces will she have if she breaks the bars into
 i halves ii quarters iii thirds?

b What fractions would she need to break the bars into if she wanted to give 75 people a piece?

c How many pieces would Emily have if she broke the bars into $n$ths?

B Making 10

A unit fraction is one whose numerator is 1 (e.g. $\frac{1}{2}$, $\frac{1}{3}$, $\frac{1}{4}$ etc). You can make the number 10 by multiplying a unit fraction by a whole number in many different ways, for example $\frac{1}{2} \times 20$, $\frac{1}{14} \times 140$.

a Find six other ways of making 10 by multiplying an integer by a unit fraction.

b Describe any patterns you notice.

You can also make the number 10 by multiplying integers by non-unit fractions.

c If the fraction you choose must have a denominator that is 1 more than the numerator, write down as many ways of making 10 as you can, for example $\frac{2}{3} \times 15$.

multiply multiplication numerator unit fraction

4.4 Working with percentages

- Know that percentage is the number of parts per 100
- Find percentages of quantities
- Express one number as a percentage of another
- Find the outcome of a percentage increase or decrease

Why learn this?

Percentages are used to describe proportions. For example, an Olympic gold medal is 92.5% silver, with only a thin covering of gold.

What's the BIG idea?

- You can convert a **percentage** to an equivalent fraction or decimal. 'Per cent' means 'out of 100', so 13% means '13 out of 100', which is $\frac{13}{100}$ or 0.13. **Level 5**
- To find a percentage of an amount you can first change the percentage to a fraction or decimal. You can also use a **unitary method**, that is find 1% first. **Level 5**
- To express one number as a percentage of another, write the number as a fraction of the other, find the equivalent fraction with denominator 100, then write down the percentage. **Level 6**
- To **increase** an amount by a percentage, you can find the percentage of the amount and add it to the original amount, or simply find (100 + increase)% of the amount. **Level 6**
- To **decrease** an amount by a percentage, you can find the percentage of the amount and subtract it from the original amount, or simply find (100 − decrease)% of the amount. **Level 6**

Did you know?

The sign ‰ means 'per thousand' and the sign ‱ means 'per ten thousand'.

Practice, practice, practice!

Level 5

- 5c I can convert a percentage to a fraction
- 5c I can use percentages to compare proportions
- 5b I can work out percentages mentally
- 5b I can calculate percentages by converting them to fractions

1 Convert each percentage into a fraction in its simplest form.

a 17% **b** 35% **c** 98% **d** 19% **e** 55%

2 In a survey on shopping habits, 4 out of 15 of those surveyed said they buy their clothes on the internet, 9 out of 15 shop on the high street and 2 out of 15 use catalogues.

a What percentage of those surveyed use the internet?

b What percentage of those surveyed don't shop on the high street?

3 Use a mental method to work out

a 50% of 34 **b** 10% of £60 **c** 25% of 300 cm **d** 5% of 50p

e 90% of 70 **f** 30% of £22 **g** 75% of 260 km **h** 15% of 300

4 Calculate these by converting the percentages to fractions.

15% of 120 $= \frac{15}{100} \times 120 = \frac{3}{20} \times 120 = 3 \times 6 = 18$

a 70% of £70 **b** 85% of 60 km **c** 42% of 250

decrease increase percentage (%) sale price

5 Check your solutions to Q4 by converting the percentage to a decimal and using a calculator.

15% of 120 $= 0.15 \times 120 = 18$ $(15\% = \frac{15}{100} = 15 \div 100 = 0.15)$

6 Use the unitary method to work out

52% of 400 $1\% = 400 \div 100 = 4$, so $52\% = 4 \times 52 = 208$

a 12% of 540 **b** 27% of £260 **c** 46% of 50 miles

Level 5

5b I can calculate percentages by converting them to decimals

5b I can use the unitary method to calculate percentages

Watch out! Make sure the units are the same for both quantities.

7 There are 250 g of cement, 700 g sand and 50 g lime in a 1 kg bag of mortar. What percentage of the bag is

a sand **b** lime **c** cement and lime?

8 The cost of clothing in a shop is changed as shown. Calculate the new price of each item.

Shirt £60
Reduced by 10%

The price is (100 − 10)% of the original price, so the new price is 90% of the original price.
90% of £60 $= 0.9 \times £60 = £54$

a Jeans £70 Reduced by 15%

b Shoes £40 Increased by 5%

c Jacket £115 Reduced by 18%

9 Maria bought a MP3 player on eBay for £40. She paid 20% of the retail price.

a If 20% is £40, what is 1%?

b Use your answer from part **a** to calculate the retail price of the MP3 player.

Hint: You need to find 100%.

Level 6

6c I can write one number as a percentage of another

6b I can find the outcome of a percentage increase or decrease

6a I can use the unitary method to solve percentage problems

10 There was a 20% discount in a sale. If a coat had a sale price of £38, what was the original selling price?

11 An adult hippo weighs 2000 kg. A newborn hippo weighs 50 kg. What percentage of the adult hippo's weight is this?

Level 7

7c I can solve percentage problems

Now try this!

A Christmas sale

LFS Sofas are offering a further discount of 20% in the Boxing Day sale. Their furniture was already reduced by 30%, so the store claims to be offering a total saving of 50%. Is this claim correct? Explain your answer.

Hint: Try it with a few different prices.

B Growing populations

In the middle of 2005, the UK population was approximately 60.2 million. The average annual growth rate of the population in the last few years has been 0.5%. If the average growth rate remains the same, what will the population be in 2025? Can this rate of growth continue? Explain your answer.

selling price simplest form unitary method

4.5 Fractions, decimals and percentages

- Recognise equivalent fractions, decimals and percentages
- Convert between fractions, decimals and percentages
- Use the equivalence of fractions, decimals and percentages to compare proportions

Why learn this?

Nutrition information on food labels is often given as proportions in fractions, decimals or percentages.

What's the BIG idea?

- You can use facts you know to derive unknown facts. For examle, $\frac{1}{5} = 0.2$, so $\frac{2}{5} = 0.2 \times 2 = 0.4$. **Level 5**
- To find 10% of an amount divide by 10. To find 1% of an amount divide by 100. **Level 5**
- A **proportion** of a whole can be written as a **fraction**, **decimal** or **percentage**. 'What proportion?' just means 'What fraction?' or 'What decimal?' or 'What percentage?'. **Level 5 & Level 6**
- To convert a fraction to a decimal, divide the numerator by the denominator. **Level 6**
- To express one number as a percentage of another, write the number as a fraction of the other, find the **equivalent fraction** with denominator 100, then write down the percentage. **Level 6**
- You can use doubling and halving strategies to derive unknown facts. For example, $\frac{1}{4} = 0.25$, so $\frac{1}{8} = 0.125$ because $\frac{1}{8}$ is half of $\frac{1}{4}$. **Level 6**

Learn this

$\frac{1}{4} = 0.25 = 25\%$

$\frac{1}{2} = 0.5 = 50\%$

$\frac{3}{4} = 0.75 = 75\%$

$\frac{1}{3} = 0.333... = 33\frac{1}{3}\%$

$\frac{1}{10} = 0.1 = 10\%$

$\frac{1}{5} = 0.2 = 20\%$

$\frac{1}{100} = 0.01 = 1\%$

Practice, practice, practice!

Level 5

5b I can work out percentages mentally

5a I can recall equivalent fractions, decimals and percentages

1 Use a mental method to work out these percentages of £650.

a 10% **b** 80% **c** 15% **d** 1% **e** 12%

2 These signs are used in a sale for maths students.

A

B Reduced by $\frac{2}{3}$

C SAVE 25%

D 10% off ALL prices

E All goods 0.25 off

F PRICE REDUCED BY 0.666...

G REDUCED BY 0.1

H $66\frac{2}{3}\%$ OFF

I Save $\frac{1}{10}$ on items with stickers

a Match them into sets of three equivalent signs.

b Meena has mislaid some signs.
Which equivalent signs are needed to complete these sets?

i 1% OFF **ii** 40% OFF **iii** SAVE 0.05 **iv** REDUCED BY $\frac{3}{8}$

5a I can recall and use known facts to convert fractions to decimals

3 a What is $\frac{1}{5}$ as a decimal?

b Use your answer to part **a** to write $\frac{3}{5}$ and $\frac{4}{5}$ as decimals.

decimal equivalent fraction fraction

4 Thomas, Iram and Lexi each win a prize in a lottery. Thomas wins 0.2 of the £6000 prize. Iram wins 30% and Lexi wins $\frac{1}{3}$ of the prize money. Who wins the most money?

5 Here are the nutrition information panels from two packets of biscuits.

Cranberry Bites *Per 200 g*	
Protein	14.1 g
Carbohydrate	137.8 g
Fat	37 g
Fibre	5.4 g
Sodium	5.7 g

Chocolate Crisps *percentage content*	
Protein	9.5%
Carbohydrate	62%
Fat	22.8%
Fibre	3.2%
Sodium	2.5%

a Write as a fraction, decimal and percentage the proportion of
i fat **ii** protein **iii** fibre in the Cranberry Bites.

b Which biscuit has the higher proportion of carbohydrates?

c Which biscuit would be better for a low sodium diet?

6 Given that $\frac{3}{25} = \frac{12}{100} = 12\% = 0.12$, write each fraction as a percentage and a decimal.

a $\frac{1}{25}$ **b** $\frac{12}{25}$ **c** $\frac{19}{25}$ **d** $\frac{21}{25}$ **e** $\frac{15}{25}$

7 **a** What is 36% as a decimal?

b Express 0.365 as a percentage.

8 **a** What is $\frac{1}{100}$ as a decimal? Use this fact to help you convert $\frac{1}{200}$ to a decimal.

b What is $\frac{1}{50}$ as a decimal?

Watch out!

$\frac{1}{8}$ is smaller than $\frac{1}{4}$.
$\frac{1}{50}$ is bigger than $\frac{1}{100}$.

9 **a** Given that $6.5\% = \frac{13}{200}$, write 19.5% as a fraction.

b Given that $\frac{4}{17} \approx 24\%$, write $\frac{2}{17}$ as a percentage.

c Given that $0.28 = \frac{14}{50}$, write $\frac{35}{50}$ as a decimal.

Level 6

6c I can use the equivalence of fractions, decimals and percentages to compare proportions

6c I can use equivalent fractions, decimals and percentages to calculate others mentally

6b I can use doubling and halving strategies to convert between fractions and decimals

6b I can use doubling and halving strategies to convert between fractions, decimals and percentages

Now try this!

A Healthy cake?

What proportion of the ingredients in the cake is

a nuts **b** sugar **c** dairy product?

Almond cake
6 oz flour
5 oz butter
4 oz sugar
3 oz milk
1 oz ground almonds
1 oz bicarbonate of soda

B VAT

Value Added Tax is charged on most goods and services in the UK. VAT is 17.5% of the value of a product. You can calculate VAT in your head like this:

- Calculate 10% – divide by 10.
- Calculate 5% – halve 10%.
- Calculate 2.5% – halve 5%.
- Add the values together.

Work out how much VAT would be charged on a product costing

a £560 **b** £1500 **c** £2.50

Round your answers to the nearest penny.

Did you know?

VAT was introduced in the UK in 1973. VAT is generally not charged on food (except confectionery and crisps).

percentage (%) proportion value added tax (VAT)

maths!

Return of the Famous Daft Pirates

The Famous Daft Pirates are after the legendary Isle of Vinculum treasure – but unless they solve these problems they'll only get a fraction of it! Can you help them?

A fruitful journey

The Vulgar Crone has promised Captain Jack Robin a map to find the long lost Isle of Vinculum if he can answer this riddle. Help him by finding the solution to the riddle.

The other day I came home with 100 kg of fruit that was 99% water. However, after a day in the sun, it was only 98% water. How much did my fruit weigh then?

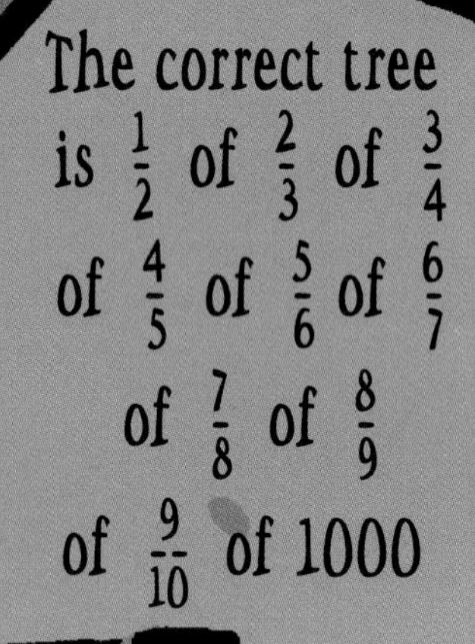

Barking up the right tree

On the island, there are 1000 numbered palm trees – but only one hides the next clue. Help Long Joan Silver solve this riddle to find the correct tree.

Sum of the parts

Black Beard isn't happy – he's found the clue in the tree, but it's in code. How far do the pirates need to travel to find the treasure?

Saving the chest 'til last

Nearly there – but to open the treasure chest, Wavy Jones has to work out what fraction of the design on the chest is coloured in red. Work through these steps to open the chest!

- The largest red triangle is a quarter of the design. Write this as a decimal.
- The next largest red triangle is a quarter of a quarter of the design. What fraction is this? Write this as a decimal and then add your two answers together.
- The next largest red triangle is a quarter of a quarter of a quarter of the design. What fraction is this? Write this as a decimal and add your three answers together.
- What fraction are you getting nearer and nearer to? Look again at the design and give Wavy her answer.

4.6 Mental methods 1

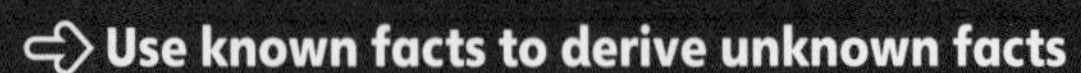

- Use known facts to derive unknown facts
- Multiply and divide mentally
- Carry out mental calculations with fractions, decimals and percentages

What's the BIG idea?

→ To **multiply** a **decimal** by a decimal in your head, look for an **equivalent** calculation.
$0.4 \times 0.03 = (4 \div 10) \times (3 \div 100) = 4 \times 3 \div 1000$
$= 12 \div 1000 = 0.012$ **Level 5 & Level 6**

→ You can also use an equivalent calculation to mentally **divide** a decimal by a decimal.
$0.8 \div 0.4 = 8 \div 4$ because both numbers have been multiplied by 10. **Level 6**

→ Multiplication and division problems can be simplified by using equivalent **fractions**.
$2.25 \times 12 = \frac{9}{4_1} \times 12^3 = 27$ **Level 6**

Why learn this?

Being able to calculate mentally means you can quickly calculate costs to ensure you don't get overcharged or short-changed!

Did you know?

The UK did not adopt decimal currency until 15 February 1971. Until then there were 240 pennies to the pound.

Practice, practice, practice!

Level 5

5a I can use given facts to derive unknown facts

1 Use the fact that $0.32 \times 5.5 = 1.76$ to work out these.

$32 \times 5.5 = 176$

$32 = 0.32 \times 100$ $\quad$ 1.76×100

a 0.32×55 **b** 32×55 **c** 0.32×0.55

Level 6

6c I can use known facts to derive unknown facts

2 Use the multiplication facts you know to find the missing numbers.

a $6 \times 0.7 =$ ______ **b** $0.08 \times 3 =$ ______ **c** $0.5 \times 0.3 =$ ______

d $0.4 \times$ ______ $= 3.6$ **e** $0.03 \times$ ______ $= 0.36$ **f** ______ $\times 0.8 = 0.072$

6b I can multiply two decimals mentally

3 Work out these using a mental method.

$0.5 \times 0.07 = (5 \div 10) \times (7 \div 100) = 5 \times 7 \div 1000 = 35 \div 1000 = 0.035$

a 0.08×0.7 **b** 0.32×0.2 **c** 0.17×0.4 **d** 0.09×0.09

4 What is the area of a rectangular field measuring 0.99 km by 0.3 km?

6b I can use known facts to calculate fractions of numbers mentally

5 Nice Town's population has increased by $\frac{5}{8}$.
If the original population numbered 3200, what is the increased population size?

6b I can use known facts to find decimals of a given number

6 0.125 of a number is 3. What is the number?

decimal divide equivalent fraction multiply

7 Use equivalent fractions to calculate these.

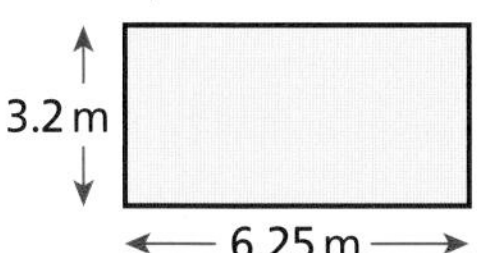

a 36 cm × 0.75 cm **b** 3.25 kg × 12 **c** 6.25 ÷ 5

d 7.5 ÷ 0.2 **e** 2.2 × 15 **f** 6.25 ÷ 1.25

8 Use equivalent fractions to find the area of the rectangle.

3.2 m

6.25 m

9 Use a mental method to work out

a 0.6 ÷ 0.3 **b** 6.25 ÷ 0.5 **c** 0.35 ÷ 0.05

d 7.5 ÷ 0.15 **e** 360 ÷ 0.03 **f** 0.02 ÷ 0.4

10 A rectangular area measures 9.75 km². One side measures 0.25 km. What is the length of the other side?

11 A pair of jeans was reduced by 35% in January. Prices were further reduced by $\frac{1}{5}$ in February. If the original selling price of the jeans was £50, what is the sale price in February?

12 Here are the numbers of defective products manufactured by three factories.

Factory A – 36 out of 300 products
Factory B – 15% of products
Factory C – 0.125 of products

a Based on these figures, which factory produces the smallest proportion of defects?

b If factory A makes 1200 products per day and factories B and C make 800 per day, which factory produces the most defects per day?

Level 6

6a I can use equivalent fractions to simplify multiplication and division calculations

6a I can divide decimals mentally

6a I can solve word problems mentally

Now try this!

A Paint it

One of the walls of a school hall needs to be redecorated. Use this information to work out the total cost of the paint.

- The dimensions of the wall are 6.7 m by 2.5 m.
- One tin of paint covers 5 m².
- Three coats of paint are required.
- One tin of paint normally costs £15.50, but there is a 20% reduction in the sale.

B Puzzles

a Find two numbers whose sum is 0.5 and whose product is 0.06.

b Find two numbers whose sum is 0.6 and when the larger is divided by the smaller the answer is 2.

c Find as many pairs of numbers as you can whose product is 0.1.

percentage (%) product simplify sum

1000 years apart

The Domesday Book

In 1086 William the Conqueror ordered a land and property survey of England, so that he could work out how much tax he could charge. This became known as the Domesday Book. It took many years to complete.

1 This table shows information from the Domesday Book about who owned the land.

	% of land owned
King and family	17%
Bishops and abbots	26%
Tenants-in-chief	54%

MAKE MATHS FUNCTIONAL!

a Write each percentage as a fraction and a decimal.

b The county of Dorset covers 2500 km^2.
How many square kilometres would have belonged to
i the Tenants-in-chief **ii** the King and family? **Level 5**

2 The survey showed that $\frac{7}{20}$ of the land was used for arable farming, $\frac{1}{4}$ for pasture and $\frac{3}{20}$ for woodland. How much land was used for other purposes? **Level 5**

The 2001 census

A census was taken in the UK on Sunday 29th April 2001. Its purpose was to gather information about the population. Each household filled in their questionnaire on the same day.

3 In the 2001 census, 390 000 people registered their religion as Jedi (an organised practical joke)! Today the population of the UK is estimated as 60 million.

a What percentage of 60 million is 390 000?

b Write your answer to part **a** as a fraction. **Level 6**

4 The 2001 census showed that the population of England had increased by 5% over the previous 20 years.

a In 1981 the population was approximately 49 000 000. What was it in 2001?

b If the population were to decrease by 3% over the following 10 years, what would it be by the time of the census in 2011? **Level 6**

5 In 2001 approximately $\frac{7}{10}$ of the population registered as Christian and $\frac{3}{100}$ as Muslim.
If $\frac{15}{21}$ of these regularly attended worship, what fraction of the population

a attended a Christian church? **b** attended a mosque? **Level 7**

The BIG ideas

- You can calculate a **percentage** of a value by
  - working mentally

    10% – divide by 10 and 5% is half of 10%

    50% – divide by 2 and 25% is half of 50%

    1% – divide by 100 and 20% is 2 times 10% and so on…
  - writing the percentage as a **fraction** or **decimal** and multiplying
  - calculating 1% and multiplying. **Level 5**
- To add or subtract fractions, you need to find a **common denominator**. **Level 5 & Level 6**
- Converting between fractions, decimals and percentages can help to simplify calculations. **Level 5 & Level 6**
- To find a percentage increase or decrease, calculate the required percentage of the original. For example, to find a 15% decrease you must calculate 85% of the original value. **Level 6**
- Quite complex calculations can be carried out mentally by considering similar simpler calculations. For example, $2.5 \times 0.8 = 25 \times 8 \div 100$ **Level 6**
- To multiply two fractions together, multiply the **numerators** and multiply the **denominators**. Remember to cancel first if it is possible.

  For example, $\frac{2}{3} \times \frac{6}{7} = \frac{2}{\cancel{3}_1} \times \frac{\cancel{6}^2}{7} = \frac{4}{7}$ **Level 7**
- To divide one fraction by another, turn the second fraction upside down and multiply.

  For example, $\frac{3}{5} \div \frac{2}{7} = \frac{3}{5} \times \frac{7}{2}$ **Level 7**

Practice SATs-style questions

Level 5

Q1 The cost of a garage repair is £140.

a Work out the missing values.

10% of £140 = ____

5% of £140 = ____

2.5% of £140 = ____

b The total cost will be £140 plus $17\frac{1}{2}$% VAT. Work out the total cost.

Q2 Work out

a $\frac{4}{5} - \frac{3}{10}$

b $\frac{1}{3} + \frac{3}{4}$

Q3 a Write $\frac{2}{5}$ as a percentage.

b Write 45% as a fraction.

c Which is larger, $\frac{2}{5}$ or 45%?

Hint: Use your answer to part **a** to help.

Level 6

Q4 In a sale, the price of a DVD is reduced by 20%.

a What percentage of the original price do you pay?

b Write this as a decimal.

Q5 Janey did not get all her homework correct.

i $3.2 \times 20 = 6.4$ ✗

ii $0.4 \times 1.4 = 0.56$ ✓

a What answer should she have written for part **i**?

b Use her answer to part **ii** to work out 4×1.4

Level 7

Q6 Work out

a $\frac{3}{5} \times \frac{3}{4}$

b $\frac{1}{2} \div \frac{3}{4}$

5 Function frenzy

This unit is about functions and graphs.

Sailors need to know about the tides before they set out to sea. At low tide they might not be able to sail in some shallow areas, or even get out of the harbour. They can find out about the tides for their port from a tide graph, which shows how the depth of water will change over a period of time. The vertical axis shows the depth of water and the horizontal axis shows the time.

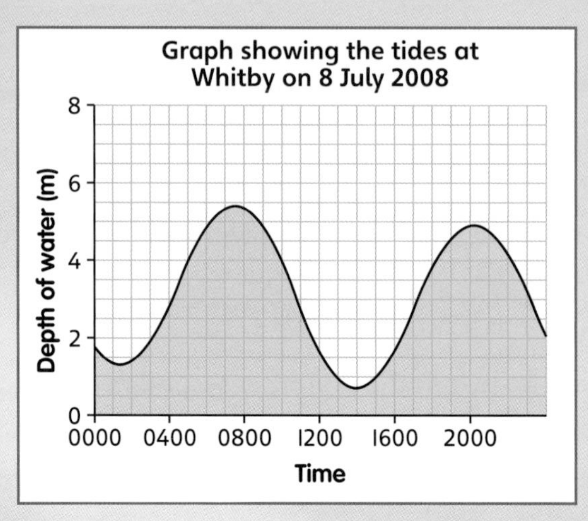

Tides are caused by the gravitational pull of the Moon and Sun on the oceans. There are two high tides and two low tides each day. The high tides are 12 hours and 25 minutes apart, so high tide is not at the same time each day.

The depth of water at high and low tide also varies. At spring tides, which happen just after the New and Full Moon, the water is deeper at high tide. At neap tides, the water level at high tide is lower.

Activities

A Look at the tidal graph for Whitby for 8 July 2008.

- At what times are the two high tides?
- At what times are the two low tides?
- What is the deepest water level over this 24-hour period?
- What is the shallowest water level?

B Captain Jack is taking some tourists out for a boat trip on 8 July. His boat needs at least 3 metres of water to enter and leave the harbour.

- Use the graph to work out the range of times when Captain Jack can leave the harbour in the morning.
- Between what times must he return in the afternoon?

Did you know?
The Bristol Channel has the second highest tidal range in the world, with ranges in excess of 15 metres just above Avonmouth.

Before you start this unit...

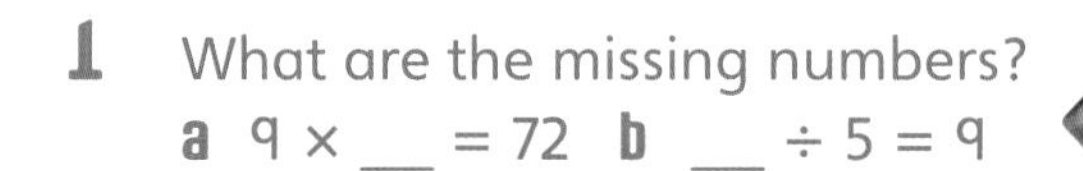

1. What are the missing numbers?
   a $9 \times \_\_ = 72$ **b** $\_\_ \div 5 = 9$

Level Up Maths 4-6 page 30

2. Find the missing inputs.

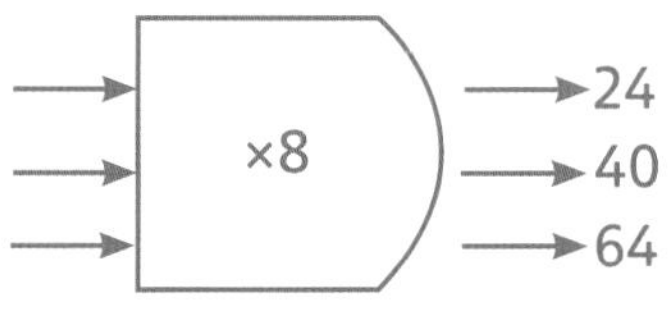

Level Up Maths 4-6 page 160

3. Plot these points on a set of axes: (4, 3), (8, 9), (5, 5)

Level Up Maths 4-6 page 162

4. What is the rule for each sequence?
   a 15, 13, 11, ... **b** 54, 18, 6, ...

page 10

5. Write down the first three terms of each sequence.
   a Start at 2, multiply by 3 and add 4
   b Start at 16, divide by 2 and add 2

page 12

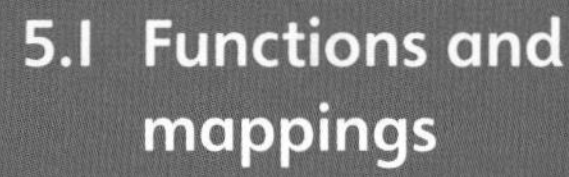

Plus digital resources

Did you know?
As the tide falls, it can create a strong current out to sea. Surfers need to know about the tides so they don't surf when the currents are dangerous.

5.1 Functions and mappings

- Use function machines to describe mappings
- Find the outputs and inputs of functions expressed in words and symbols using inverse operations
- Draw mapping diagrams for simple functions involving positive and negative numbers, and fractions

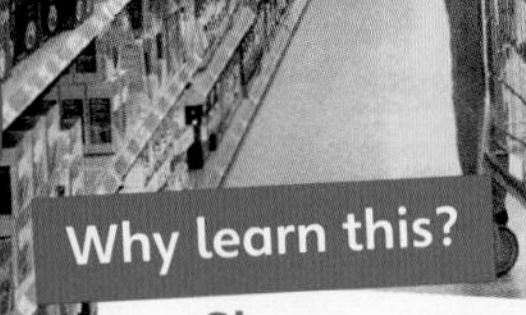

Why learn this?

Shops use simple functions to calculate prices, profits and special offers.

What's the BIG idea?

→ A **function** links two variables together. **Level 5**

→ If you know the **output** of a **function machine**, you can work backwards to find the **input**. **Level 5**

→ Functions can be written in symbols:

- as a function machine $x \rightarrow$ ×2 $\rightarrow$ +1 $\rightarrow y$
- as a **mapping** $x \rightarrow 2x + 1$
- as an equation $2x + 1 = y$ **Level 6**

→ You can use a **mapping diagram** to show the inputs and outputs of a function machine.

function machine for $x \rightarrow 2x + 1$

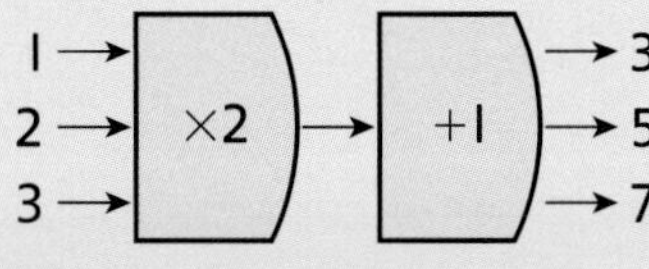

mapping diagram for $x \rightarrow 2x + 1$

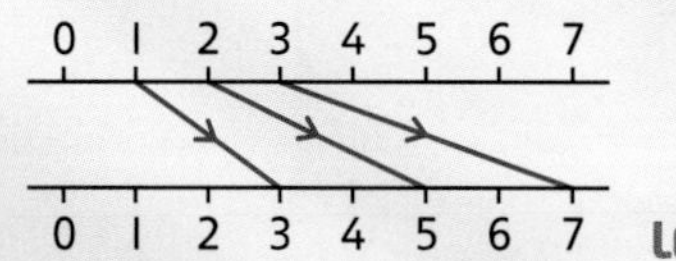

Level 6

→ You can use a function machine or **spreadsheet** to generate sets of values. **Level 6**

Practice, practice, practice!

Level 5

5c Given an output, I can find the input of a function

1 Fruit is sold at three times its wholesale price. Cheese at two and a half times its wholesale price. Work out the wholesale price of the following.

apples selling at 81p per kilogram.

$x \rightarrow$ ×3 $\rightarrow$ 81, so the wholesale price is 81p divided by 3, which is 27p.

a bananas selling at £1.20 per kg. **b** oranges selling at 96p per kg.

c cheddar selling at £5.00 per kg. **d** edam selling at £4.50 per kg.

2 Find the inputs for these function machines:

a 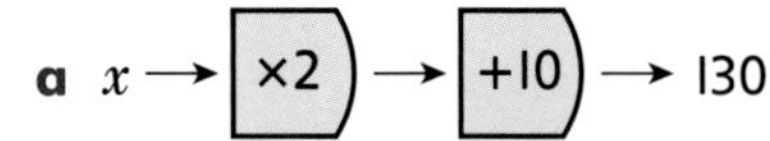

b $x \rightarrow$ ×2 $\rightarrow$ −10 $\rightarrow$ 90

c $x \rightarrow$ ×1.5 $\rightarrow$ +25 $\rightarrow$ 145

d $x \rightarrow$ ×1.5 $\rightarrow$ −25 $\rightarrow$ 175

Did you know?

The wholesale price is the price the shopkeeper pays for goods.

Level 6

6c I can express simple functions using symbols

3 Write each of these functions as a mapping.

a $x \rightarrow$ ×6 $\rightarrow$ −20 $\rightarrow y$

b $x \rightarrow$ ×19 $\rightarrow$ +8 $\rightarrow y$

function function machine input mapping

4 Alice collects stock from the cash and carry. She calculates transport cost per box as the petrol cost divided by the number of boxes, plus 18p per box. On one journey, she collects 25 boxes and spends £8 on petrol.

a Draw a function machine to work out transport costs per box.

b Complete a table of inputs and outputs for the cost per box for collecting 10 boxes, 20 boxes, 25 boxes, 40 boxes and 50 boxes.

5 Alice is thinking about buying a bigger van. It would cost more to run, but could take more boxes. The petrol cost for the same journey as in Q4 would be £10, and there would be an extra 20p per box for vehicle costs.

a Use a spreadsheet to produce a table of inputs and outputs for the total transport costs per box for 5, 10, 15, 20, 25, 30, 35 and 40 boxes.

b Using your results from Q4, decide which vehicle would be cheaper for transporting 25 boxes.

6 Sweets have either 1p, 2p or 3p added to their wholesale price to work out their selling price.

0 1 2 3 4 5 6 7 8 9 10

0 1 2 3 4 5 6 7 8 9 10

a Copy this mapping diagram.

b For sweets costing between 1p and 7p, show

i $x \longrightarrow x + 1$ in red **ii** $x \longrightarrow x + 2$ in blue **iii** $x \longrightarrow x + 3$ in black.

7 In a sale, Alice deducts 15p from the pre-sale profit of each item to work out the new profit or loss.

a Draw a mapping diagram with number lines going from −10 to 25.

b For pre-sale profits of 25p, 20p, 18p, 15p, 12p, 10p and 5p, complete the mapping diagram to show the new profit or loss in the sale.

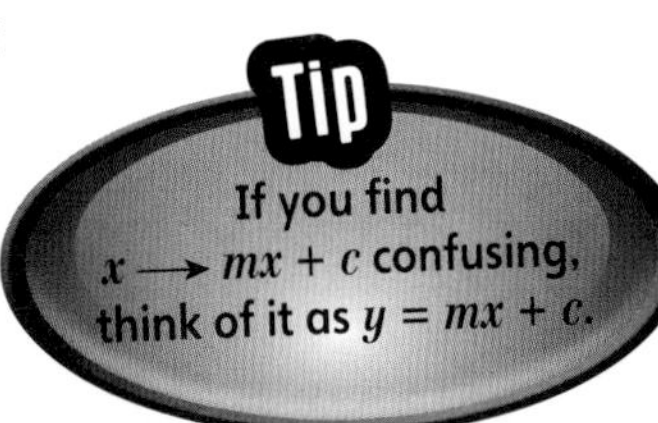

8 Alice doesn't want to make a loss on any item so instead of deducting 15p each time she decides to divide the pre-sale profit by either 2 or 3.

a Draw a mapping diagram with number lines going from 0 to 30.

b For pre-sale profits of 10p, 12p, 15p, 18p, 20p, 21p, 25p and 27p, show

i $x \longrightarrow \frac{x}{2}$ in red **ii** $x \longrightarrow \frac{x}{3}$ in blue.

Level 6

6c I can use function machines to generate sets of values

6c I can use a spreadsheet to generate sets of values for a function

6b I can draw mapping diagrams for simple functions using positive numbers

6a I can draw mapping diagrams for simple functions using negative numbers

6a I can draw mapping diagrams for simple functions using fractions

Now try this!

A How much VAT?

Work with a partner. List the selling prices of six items that may have VAT added at 17.5%. Use a function machine to work backwards to find their cost before VAT was added.

Did you know?

There is no VAT (value-added tax) on books, food or children's clothes.

B Having a map

- Draw a mapping diagram with number lines from 0 to 30.
- Add these mappings to your diagram.
  $x \longrightarrow 2x$ in red $x \longrightarrow 3x$ in blue $x \longrightarrow 4x$ in black
- Extend each set of lines so they meet at a point.
- What do you notice about the point where the lines meet?

mapping diagram **output** **spreadsheet**

5.2 More functions and mappings

- Use function machines to describe mappings
- Use algebra to describe mappings
- Understand what a linear function is and find its inverse

Why learn this?

Understanding algebra and functions helps you compare offers from different companies.

What's the BIG idea?

→ You can work out a function machine if you know its **inputs** and **outputs**. **Level 5**

→ You can use algebra to describe **mappings**.
For example, this mapping can be written as $x \rightarrow \frac{x}{2} + 1$.

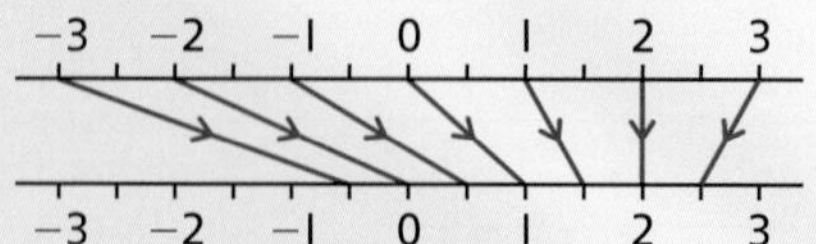

Level 6

Did you know?

A lot of computer programming is based on functions.

Watch out!

Remember that changing the order of two operations often changes the function.

→ Some functions can be written using brackets.
For example, $x \rightarrow 30x + 15$ can be written as $x \rightarrow 15(2x + 1)$. **Level 6**

→ A **linear function** has the form $x \rightarrow mx + c$.
You can find the **inverse** of a linear function by working backwards through the function machine.

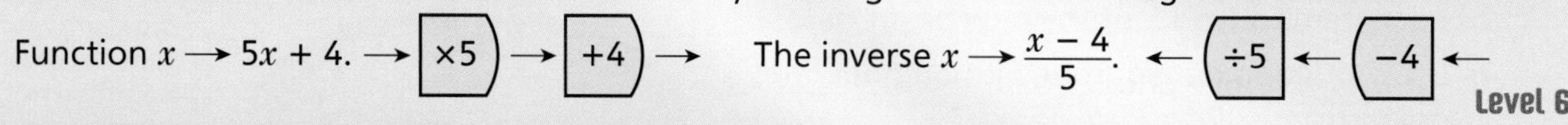

Function $x \rightarrow 5x + 4$. → ×5 → +4 → The inverse $x \rightarrow \frac{x-4}{5}$. ← ÷5 ← −4 ←

Level 6

Practice, practice, practice!

Level 5

5b I can use function machines to describe the rule that maps one set of numbers to another

1 Find the missing rules for these function machines.

a 2 → ? → 11; 7 → 16; 12 → 21

b 1 → ? → ? → 3; 3 → 7; 8 → 17

c 5 → ? → 25; 3 → 15; 7 → 35; 16 → 80; 2 → 10

d 8 → ? → ? → 36; 12 → 52; 5 → 24; 9 → 40; 4 → 20

2 Three electricity companies use different systems to calculate their bills.
All use a linear function, based on the number of units used in a month, the charge per unit and a monthly fixed charge.

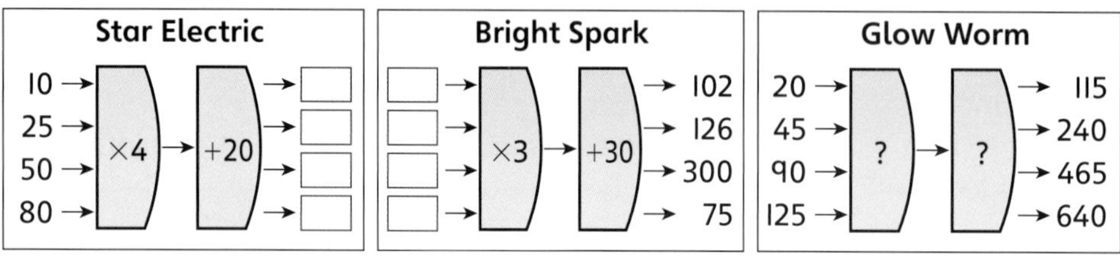

a What are Star Electric's bills for these customers?

b How many units of electricity did these customers of Bright Spark use?

c What function did Glow Worm use to calculate its customers' bills?

factorise input inverse

3 To understand her mobile phone bill, Jane draws a mapping diagram showing the length of calls in minutes and their cost in pence.

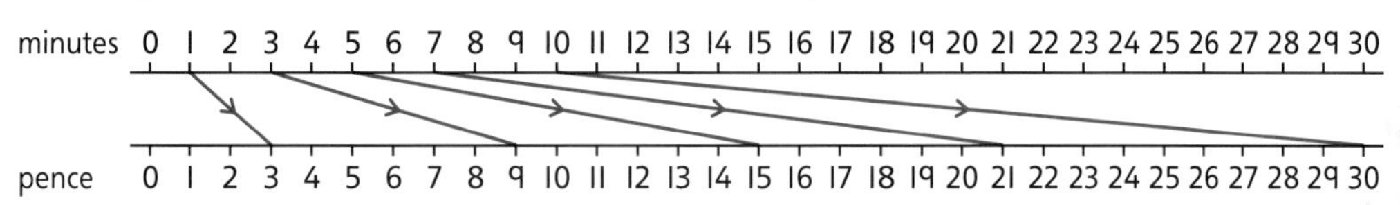

a What algebraic function describes this mapping?

b Draw a similar mapping diagram to show the costs of the same length calls if they are charged at 5p per minute.

4 A bank gives an annual bonus to students who have had an account for over a year. The mapping diagram shows the original account balance and the balance after the bonus has been paid.

pounds −50 −40 −30 −20 −10 0 10 20 30 40 50

pounds −50 −40 −30 −20 −10 0 10 20 30 40 50

a Write this mapping using algebra.

b Draw a similar mapping diagram to show a bonus of £25 for the same account balances.

Level 5

5a I can use algebra to describe mappings using positive numbers

5a I can use algebra to describe mappings using positive and negative numbers

5 The profit a mobile phone company makes on calls is a fraction of the total call charge. This mapping diagram shows the cost of the call and the profit.

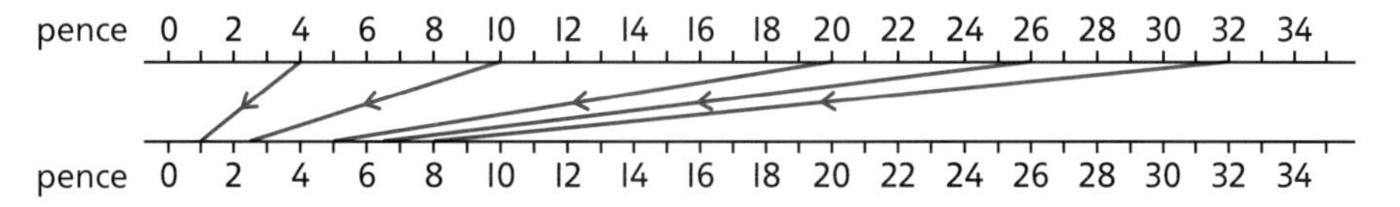

a Write this mapping using algebra.

b Using the same call costs, draw a similar mapping diagram to show a profit of one third of the total cost of the call.

6 **a** Write each of the functions in Q2 as a mapping. Use x for the number of units.

b Factorise each function.

7 Find the inverse of each function.

a $x \rightarrow 3x + 5$ **b** $x \rightarrow 5x - 9$ **c** $x \rightarrow \frac{1}{2}x - 4$

d $x \rightarrow 3(x + 2)$ **e** $x \rightarrow 4(x - 2)$ **f** $x \rightarrow \frac{1}{2}(x - 5)$

Level 6

6c I can use algebra to describe mappings using fractions

6a I can express functions in more than one way and factorise them

6a I can find the inverse of a linear function

Now try this!

A DVDs 4U

Work with a partner. Imagine you run a DVD hire shop. Decide on a basic rate of hire for one night and the charge for each additional night. Express this using algebra. Draw a mapping diagram to show hire charges for 1 to 7 nights.

B Linear functions at large

Work with a partner. List as many real-life situations as you can where linear functions are used.

Hint: Think about bills, shopping etc.

linear function mapping output

5.3 Plotting and recognising linear functions

- Generate, read and plot coordinates in all four quadrants
- Recognise straight-line graphs parallel to the x- or y-axis
- Plot graphs of simple linear functions

Why learn this?

Whether you are selling snacks or fairground rides, you can use linear functions to help you work out whether you will make a profit.

What's the BIG idea?

→ Straight-line graphs **parallel** to the x-axis have an equation of the form $y = c$.
Straight-line graphs parallel to the y-axis have an equation of the form $x = c$.
(c is a **constant** number that does not depend on x or y.) **Level 5**

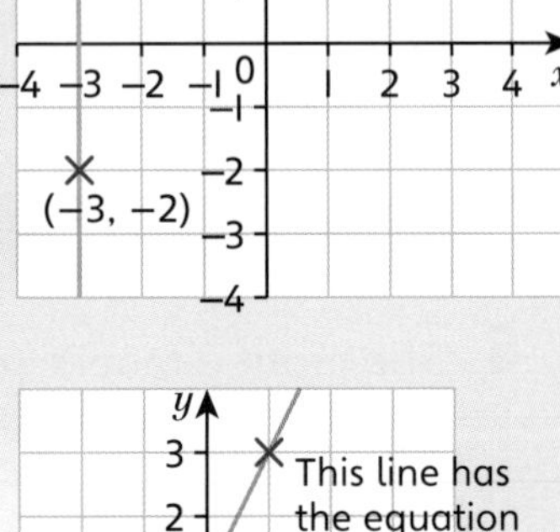

→ A function can be written as an equation: $2x + 1 = y$. You can generate sets of coordinates using a **linear function**.
This table of values gives the coordinates for the graph $y = 2x + 1$.

x	−2	−1	0	1
$y = 2x + 1$	−3	−1	1	3

Level 6

→ The graph of a linear function $y = mx + c$, where m and c are constant numbers, is a straight line.
Level 6

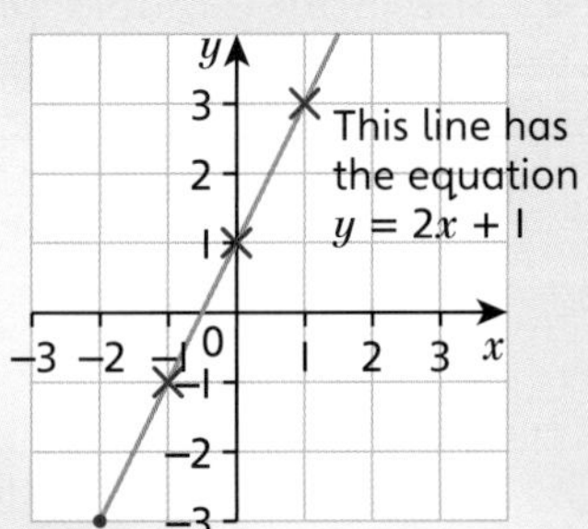

Did you know?

Graph coordinates were developed in 1637 by the French mathematician René Descartes to give a visual representation of functions.

Practice, practice, practice!

Level 5

5b I can plot coordinates in any quadrant

1 Draw a coordinate grid on squared paper with x- and y-axes from −5 to +5.

a Plot the points: (3, 0), (3, −4) and (3, 5).

b What do you notice about them?

c Plot the points: (1, −4), (−2, −1) and (−4, 1).

5b I can recognise straight-line graphs that are parallel to the x- or y-axis

2 What equation describes line P?

Find a few points on the line.
(2, 3), (2, 0), (2, 4)
Notice that x is always 2.
The equation of line P is x = 2

Write down the equations that describe lines Q to T.

constant coordinates linear function

3 It costs £3 to enter a fairground and then £2 for each ride.

a Write a linear function using algebra to calculate how much you spend. Use x for the number of rides you go on.

b Copy and complete this table of values.

Number of rides (x)	1	2	3	4
Cost in pounds (y)				

Tip You only need two values to draw a straight-line graph, but plotting a third value is a good way to check that you haven't made a mistake.

4 Draw a coordinate grid on squared paper with x-axis from 0 to 5 and y-axis from 0 to 12. Plot a graph from your table in Q3.

Level 5

5a I can generate sets of positive-value coordinates from a linear function

5a I can draw the graph of positive-value coordinates generated from a linear function

5 The dodgems cost £20 per hour to run. One ride on them costs £1.50.

a Write a linear function for the profit or loss the dodgems make per hour, where x is the number of rides sold in one hour.

b Copy and complete this table of values.

Number of rides sold in an hour (x)	6	10	12	16	20	30
Profit per hour (y)						

6 **a** Draw a suitable coordinate grid on squared paper and plot a graph from your table in Q5.

b How many dodgem rides need to be sold in an hour to make a profit?

7 **a** On squared paper, draw an x-axis from −10 to +10 and a y-axis from −35 to +35 (label your axes in steps of 5).

b Create tables of values for these functions when $x = -10, -5, 0, 5$ and 10.

$y = 3x$ $\quad$ $y = 3x + 1$ $\quad$ $y = 3x + 5$ $\quad$ $y = 3x - 4$

c Plot graphs of the functions from part **b** and label them.

d What do you notice about these lines? **Hint:** You could use a graph plotting program or calculator for this.

8 **a** What do you think this family of graphs would look like?

$y = 4x$ $\quad$ $y = 8x + 8$ $\quad$ $y = 4x - 5$

b Plot them using a spreadsheet program to check.

c Try this with other families of graphs.

Level 6

6c I can generate sets of positive and negative values from a linear function

6b I can draw the graph of coordinates generated from a linear function

6b I can plot a simple linear function

6b I can use a spreadsheet to plot linear functions

Now try this!

A Roll a function!

Draw x- and y-axes from −10 to +10. You are going to plot the function $y = ax + b$. To decide the values of a and b, roll a dice twice. The first number you roll is a and the second is b. So if you roll 2 and then 3, plot $y = 2x + 3$. Plot three functions in this way and label them. Challenge a partner to plot your three functions on their grid. Compare results.

B Candyfloss profits

Your school is lent a candyfloss machine. The ingredients for one batch of 10 candyfloss costs £1.60. Write a function to work out the profit if you sell each candyfloss for 10p. Work out your profit (or loss) if you sell 5, 10, 15 and 20 candyflosses. Plot a graph to find how many candyflosses you must sell to make a profit. How does this change if you increase the price to 20p?

parallel $\quad$ quadrant

5.4 Understanding linear functions

- Compare values of a linear function to find the coefficient of x
- Plot and compare graphs of linear functions
- Understand the meaning of m and c in linear functions in the form $y = mx + c$
- Find the gradient of a straight-line graph

Why learn this?

Slopes in computer game graphics are created by linear functions.

What's the BIG idea?

- The graph of $y = mx$ is a straight line that passes through the **origin**. Level 6
- To draw a graph of a **linear function** create a table of values.

x	0	1	2	3
$y = 2x + 1$	1	3	5	7

Level 6

- All linear functions can be written in the form $y = mx + c$, where m and c are constants.
  A graph of a linear function is a straight line. Level 6 & Level 7
- For the graph of $y = mx + c$, the value of m is the **gradient** (slope) of the line.

  $$\text{gradient } m = \frac{\text{change in } y}{\text{change in } x}$$

  The value of c tells you where the line **intercepts** (crosses) the y-axis.
  Level 6 & Level 7

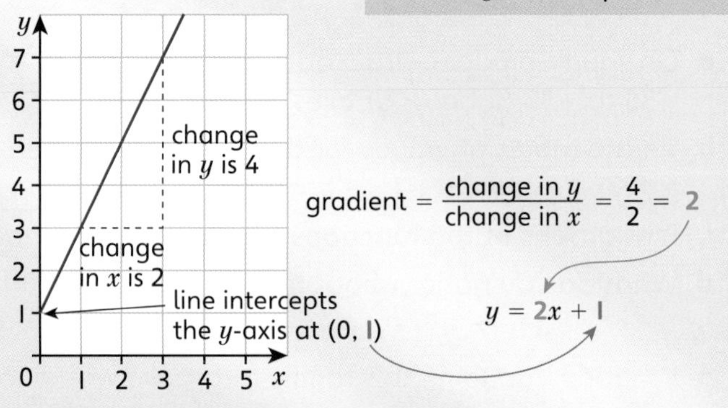

Learn this

If you plot the linear function $y = mx + c$, m is the slope or gradient and c is the y-intercept.

Practice, practice, practice!

Level 6

6b I can understand graphs of the form $y = mx$

1 **a** For each function work out the values of y for $x = 1$, 3 and 5.
  i $y = x$ **ii** $y = 2x$ **iii** $y = 3x$

b Plot the graph of each function.

c What do you notice about these lines?

d Think of an equation of another line like this and plot it to check it looks as you expected.

2 Look again at the graphs you drew for Q1.

a Which is the steepest?

b How can you tell just by looking at the equation which will be steepest?

c Which of these equations has the steepest graph?
  $y = x$ $y = 5x$ $y = \frac{1}{2}x$

coordinates gradient

3 Draw an x-axis from −3 to +3 and a y-axis from −15 to +15.

a Plot the graphs for these linear functions and label them.

i $y = 2x + 2$ **ii** $y = 3x - 4$ **iii** $y = 2x + 5$ **iv** $y = 3x - 2$

b Which lines are parallel to each other?

c Which lines are steeper: the ones generated by the equations containing $2x$ or those with $3x$?

Level 6

6a I can plot and compare the features of straight-line graphs

4 **a** What are the gradients of lines A to D?

b What do you notice about the gradients of lines C and D?

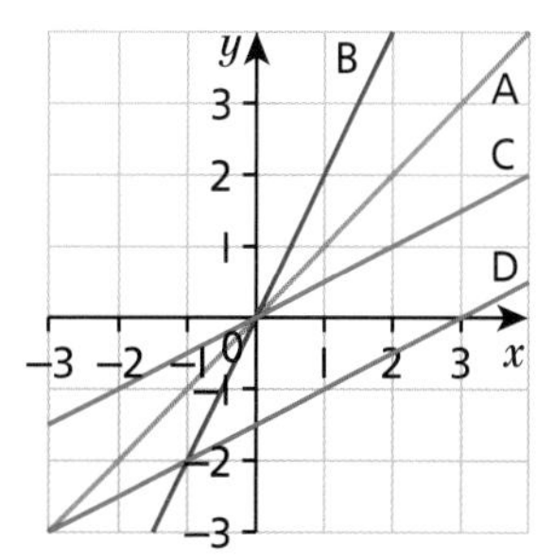

5 **a** Draw an x-axis from −4 to +4 and a y-axis from −15 to +15.

b Plot the graphs for these linear functions and label them.

i $y = -x + 6$ **ii** $y = -2x + 3$ **iii** $y = -3x - 3$ **iv** $y = x - 2$

c What do you notice about the lines of equations that contain $-x$?

6 **a** Draw x- and y-axes from −6 to +6.

b Plot the graphs for these linear functions and label them.

i $y = 2x + 1$ **ii** $y = x + 1$ **iii** $y = \frac{1}{2}x + 1$

c In a different colour, plot and label these lines.

i $y = -3x + 1$ **ii** $y = -x + 1$ **iii** $y = -\frac{1}{3}x + 1$

7 **a** Without drawing the graphs, state which of these equations give lines that have the same gradient.

A $y = -2x + 3$ B $y = \frac{1}{2}x + 3$ C $y = 2x - 3$

D $y = -2x - 3$ E $y = 2x + 3$ F $y = 0.5x - 3$

b Which of the equations in part **a** give lines that intercept the y-axis in the same place?

8 Write the equations of these lines.

a a line parallel to $y = 3x - 4$ that passes through 6 on the y-axis

b a line parallel to $y = 2x + 5$ that passes through −3 on the y-axis

Level 7

7c I can find the gradient of a line

7b I can use and understand $y = mx + c$ for any straight line

Tip

If you are trying to visualise the graph of a linear function, input a couple of simple values, for example $x = 0$ and $x = 1$, to see what happens.

Now try this!

A Obstacle course

a A computer-game designer draws an obstacle for a game. The sides are described by the linear functions $y = 2x + 8$, $y = 4$ and $y = 5 - 3x$. Draw the obstacle on a coordinate grid.

b Write four linear functions that will describe a square. Challenge a partner to work out the side length of the square.

B Look out for pitfalls!

A computer game has a rectangular pit. One side is described by the linear function $y = -\frac{1}{3}x + 1$. Work out linear functions that could describe the other three sides. Swap your chosen functions with a partner and compare the size and shape of your pits by drawing them on the same grid.

intercept linear function origin

5.5 Distance–time and other real-life graphs

- **Draw and use graphs to solve distance–time problems**
- **Plot the graph of a function derived from a real-life problem**
- **Sketch a distance–time line graph for the approximate relationship between two variables**

Why learn this?

Distance–time graphs can be used to work out journey times and help plan deliveries.

What's the BIG idea?

→ Choose suitable **scales** for both axes.
A bad choice of scale can lead to misinterpretation of data. **Level 6**

→ You can **interpret** graphs to find out more about real-life situations.
For example, the **gradient** of this **distance–time** graph shows how fast a jogger runs. **Level 6**

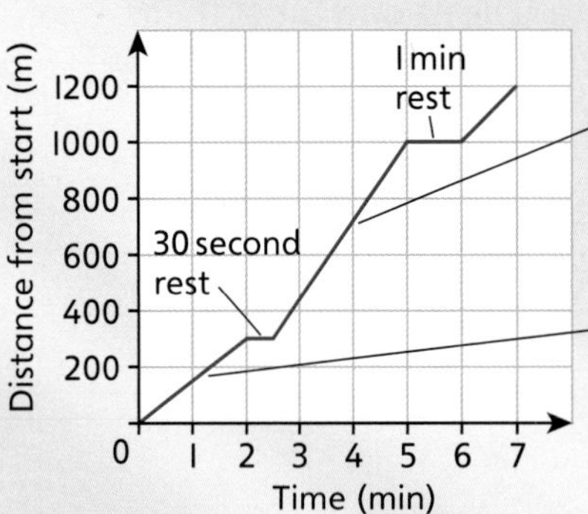

Jogger runs 700 m in $2\frac{1}{2}$ minutes

Jogger runs 300 m in 2 minutes

A steeper gradient shows a faster speed

Tip
Choosing appropriate scales for axes will help you to take accurate readings from a graph.

Practice, practice, practice!

Level 6

6c I can plot a simple distance–time graph

1 Sati drives to visit her sister who lives 200 km away.
After 2 hours she has driven 150 km. She stops for a half hour break.
Sati then drives on and reaches her sister's home 1.5 hours later.

a Draw a distance–time graph to show Sati's journey.

b Was she travelling faster before or after her break?
How can you tell?

Tip
Make a rough sketch before you draw a graph to check that you have chosen the best scales for the axes.

6c I can solve distance–time problems using graphs

2 During his lunch break, Rob leaves his office and goes to the park to read a book.
The graph shows his journey.

a How far is the park from Rob's office?

b What happens to Rob's distance from work between 12.10 and 12.40?

c How far does Rob walk in total?

Rob's journey

Distance from office (km): 0, 0.2, 0.4, 0.6, 0.8, 1

Time: 12:00, 12:10, 12:20, 12:30, 12:40, 12:50, 13:00

distance–time gradient

3 A plane takes off from Luton at 10 am, touching down in Rome at 12.30 pm. A flight from Rome to Luton also departs at 10 am. It arrives in Luton at 1 pm. The graph shows both journeys.

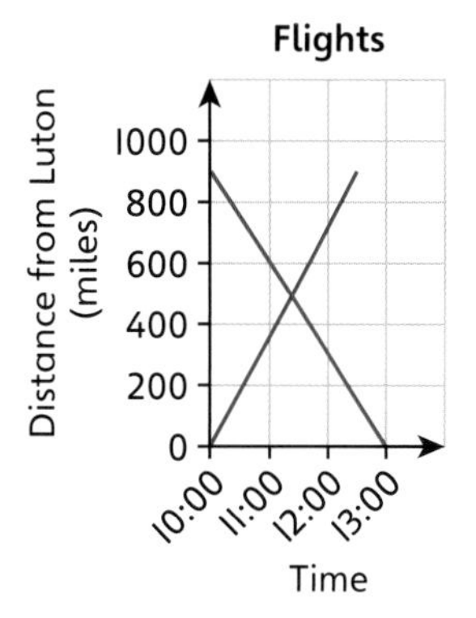

a Which line shows the Rome to Luton flight?

b Approximately how far is Rome from Luton?

c Which is the quicker flight?

Level 6

6c I can solve distance–time problems using graphs

4 Jason is a plumber. He charges a call-out fee of £25 and an hourly rate of £20.

a Draw a graph of Jason's charges for jobs lasting up to 3 hours.

b Use your graph from part **a** to work out his charge for a job lasting $1\frac{3}{4}$ hours.

c A customer gets a bill for £50. Use the graph to work out what working time this represents.

5 **a** Glass A and glass B are both filled with water at the same steady rate. The graph shows the depth of water in each glass against time. Which line is for glass A and which is for glass B?

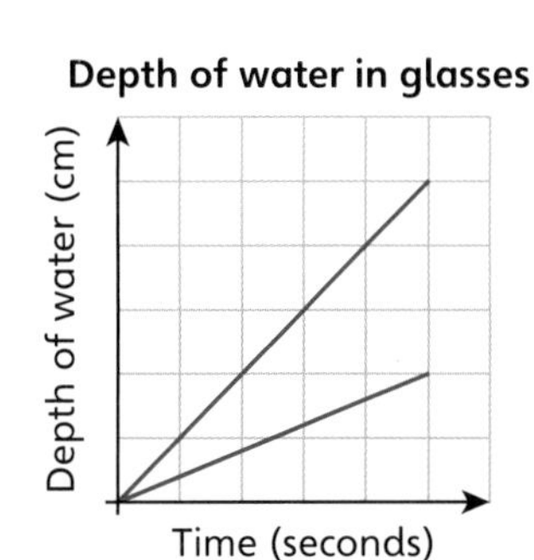

A

B

6a I can sketch a line graph to show the relationship between two variables

b Glass C is also filled with water at the same steady rate. Sketch the graph of depth of water against time for this glass.

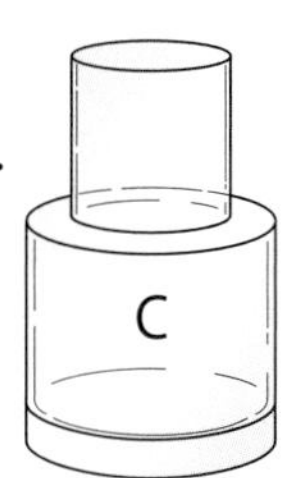

Now try this!

A Trip to town

Amy walks to the bus stop. Just before she gets there, she sees a bus and runs to catch it. Once on the bus, the road into town is clear but there is busy traffic just before the bus stops. Amy then walks around the shops with a friend. Work with a partner to sketch a distance–time graph for this trip. Label the graph to explain what is happening.

B Dream holiday

Plan a dream holiday, flying to three countries, one after the other. Which three would you choose? To minimise your carbon footprint, plan your trip to cover as few air miles as possible. Find the best order in which to visit your countries and then fly home. (Use a globe or atlas to help you.) A commercial plane flies at about 550 miles per hour. Sketch a distance–time graph to show your flights.

interpret scale

5.6 Interpreting real-life graphs

- Construct linear functions from real-life situations, plot a graph and interpret it
- Discuss and interpret distance–time graphs and other graphs, including ones which are not continuous straight lines

What's the BIG idea?

- You can **interpret** graphs from real-life situations by reading values, predicting **trends** and making generalisations. A trend is the general direction in which something is developing. **Level 5 & Level 6**
- Drawing graphs of real-life situations helps you to solve problems and understand data. **Level 6**

Why learn this?

Knowing how to work with graphs helps you to understand and use information

Practice, practice, practice!

Level 5

5a I can read values and discuss trends from a real-life graph

1 This is the graph of the amount of boiling water in a pan over a period of time.

a Construct a table of values that could have been used to produce the graph.

b Describe what happens over the 16 minutes. Suggest reasons why this happened.

c If the pan had continued to boil at the same rate as in the first 12 minutes, how long would it have taken to boil dry?

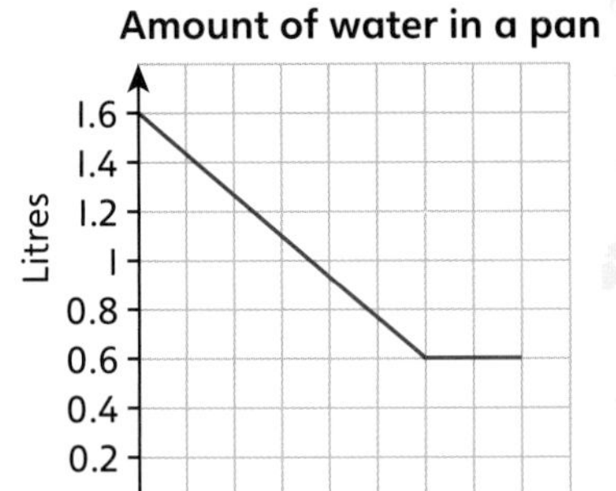

Level 6

6c I can interpret line graphs and graphs of functions that are not continuous straight lines

2 Jennifer eats an orange one segment at a time. The graph shows how much orange is left over time. How many segments did the orange have?

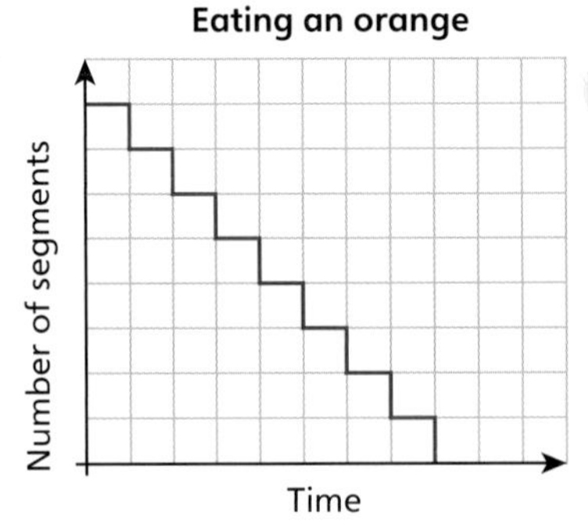

3

A
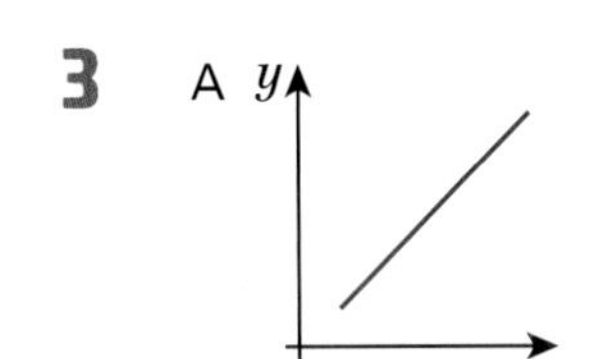

B
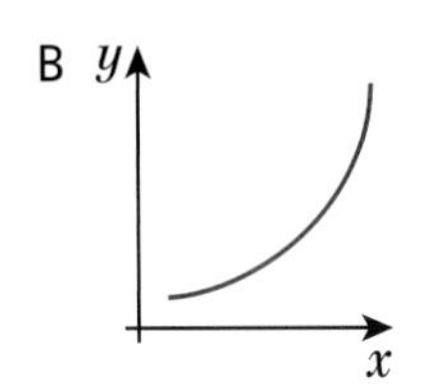

C
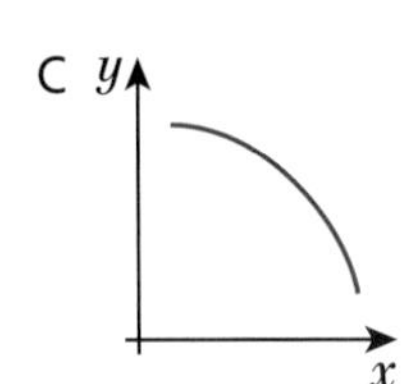

D
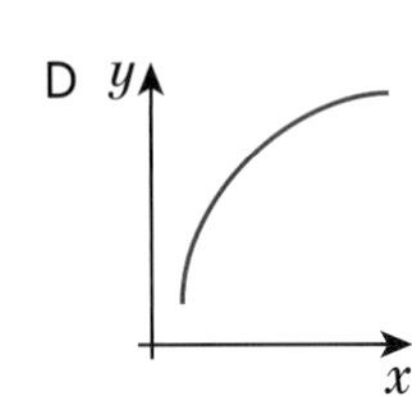

Which of these graphs is most likely to show

a the distance travelled (y) by an accelerating car over time (x)?

b the distance travelled (y) by a car as it brakes gradually over time (x)?

Super fact!

Casio produced the fx-7000G in 1985. It was the world's first calculator that could plot graphs.

deduce interpret

4 The graph shows the amount of water in a water dispenser during an 8 hour period. It starts at 8 am.

- **a** How much water was taken in the day?
- **b** Why does the amount of water drop by different amounts?
- **c** What do you think happened at 1430?
- **d** What else can you **deduce** from the graph?

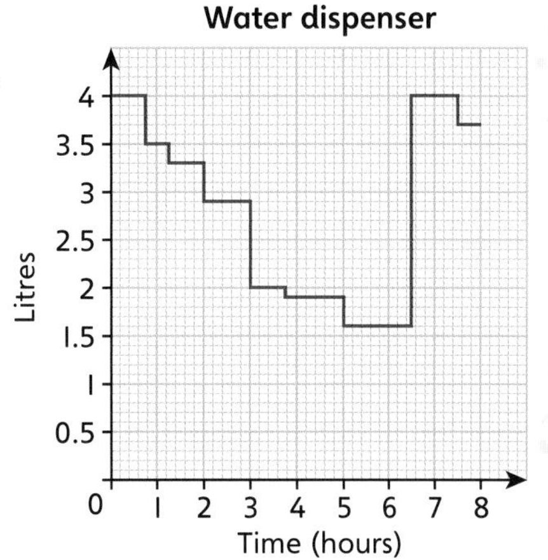

5 A shop has 50 DVDs in stock. It buys another 200 and starts to sell them on Monday. It sells 10 on Monday, 25 on Tuesday, is closed on Wednesday, sells 35 on Thursday, 60 on Friday, and another 75 on Saturday. On Sunday it is closed but gets in stock another 120 DVDs.

- **a** Draw a line graph of the number of DVDs in stock during the week.
- **b** Which days sold the most?
- **c** Do you think the shop bought enough stock at the end of the week? Why?

6 This is the graph of the height of a shuttlecock over a 12 second period. The net is 1.55 m high.

- **a** When is the shuttlecock at its highest point?
- **b** How many times does the shuttlecock clear the net?
- **c** Who wins the point, the person who serves or the opponent?
- **d** What do you think happens at around 11 seconds?

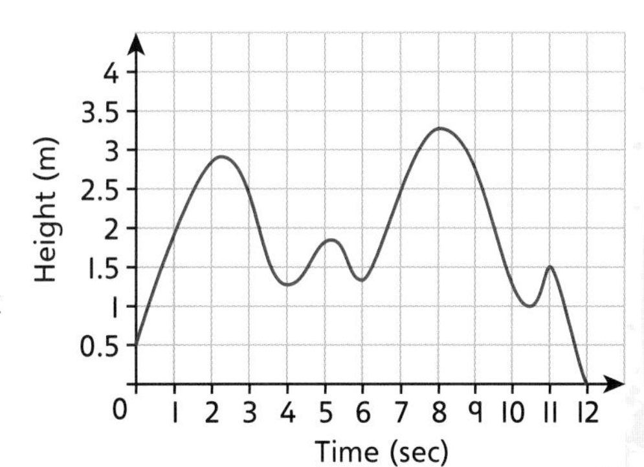

Level 6

6c I can interpret line graphs and graphs of functions that are not continuous straight lines

6b I can solve real-life problems by drawing and using graphs

6a I can interpret and discuss graphs in a range of contexts

Now try this!

A Formula 1

Draw a map of an imaginary Formula 1 circuit. The drivers slow down for the corners and speed up along the straights. Look at how far the drivers will be from the starting line during one lap of the circuit. Sketch a distance–time graph for one lap of your circuit.

B Cup of tea

Sketch a temperature–time graph to show the temperature of a cup of tea when it's left to cool at room temperature. If you leave a cold drink in the same room what trend will be shown this time? With a partner, discuss other trends that you might expect to see in science, sport and business. Sketch some graphs to show your ideas.

Did you know?

If boiling water is left to stand, the temperature of the water decreases quickly at first but gradually cools more slowly as it approaches room temperature.

linear function trend

maths!

Track side

Here is a map of the Famous Grans-Thatch race course. It is famous for its simple design.

START

It's race day and the competition is fierce. The first two cars have had their distance around the track graphed so an analysis of their performance can be made.

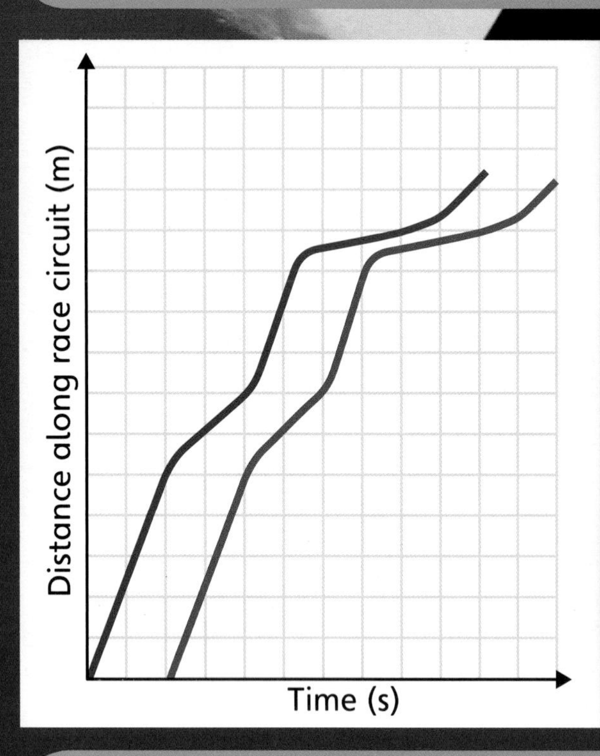

Which section of the course do you think this graph shows? Try to explain why.

At a couple of times during the race the red team were worried that the blue team was gaining on them. Why did they not need to worry?

What do you notice about the time difference between the two cars?

The graph displayed uses the distance along the track on the y-axis. Draw a graph using the distance from the start on the y-axis instead.

Distance–time graphs can tell us a lot of information about a situation.
By looking closely at details we can complete a story or explain exactly what happened.

During the race the red team monitors their car's performance and plots the distance along the course against the time.

Match the descriptions to the graphs.

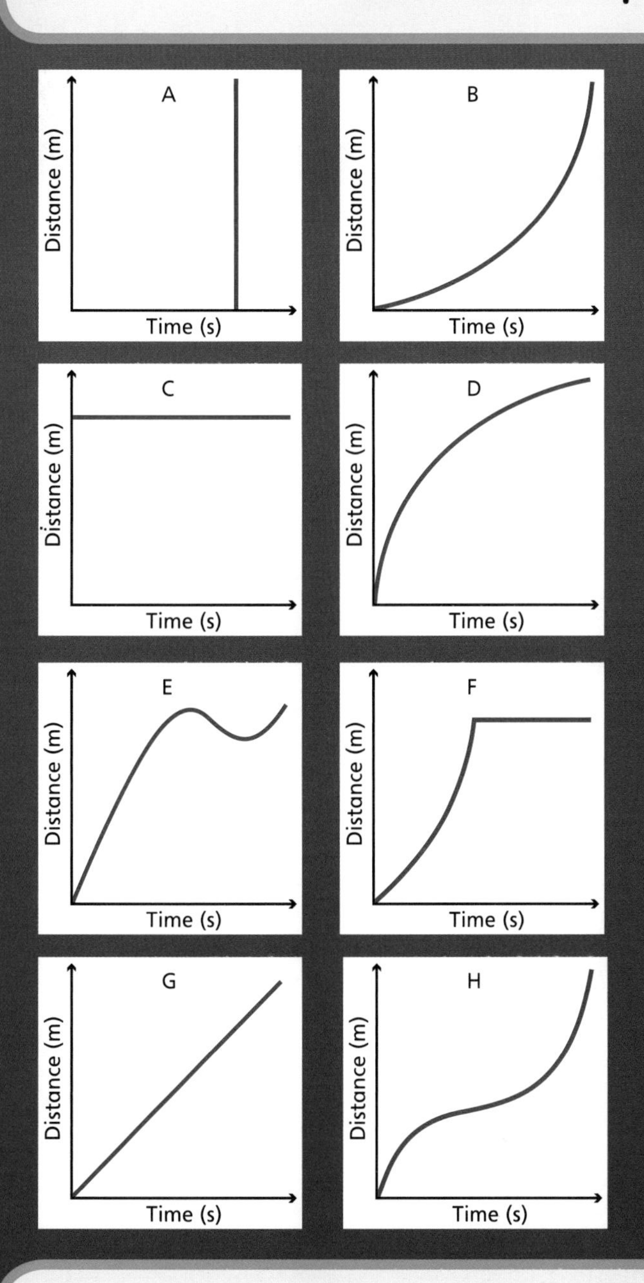

Slowing down for a corner, then speeding up after the bend

Changing the tyres

Starting the race

Slowing down near the pit lane

Error on the graphing machine

Continuing at a constant speed

There are two graphs that don't have a description with them.

What do you think is happening here? Write a description for each graph.

Where have all the fish gone?

In 2004 it was reported that the total stock of fish in the North Sea had dropped from 26 million tonnes to 10 million tonnes in just over a century. Some species have disappeared altogether, and others, such as cod, haddock and mackerel, have declined considerably. Can you think of reasons for this decline in fish stocks? In some areas around the country, and the world, fishing is now banned or limited to total catch size. Why? What environmental damage can fishing create?

This graph shows North Sea fish stocks. The vertical axis represents spawning stock biomass (the total weight of fish that are old enough to spawn).

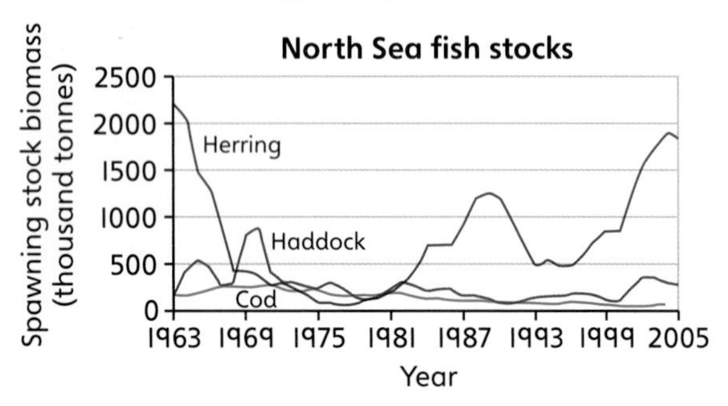

1. What does the 500 division on the vertical axis represent? **Level 5**
2. When was the stock of haddock at its highest? **Level 6**
3. Have any of the levels of the fish stock shown increased over the period 1969–1993? **Level 6**
4. Which fish stock has maintained a fairly constant level over the period shown? **Level 6**
5. Describe and explain the trend for herring over the complete period shown. **Level 6**
6. The graph below shows international fish landings for cod from the North Sea. When was the greatest amount of cod landed? **Level 6**
7. Describe the trend for the period 1963–1973. **Level 6**
8. Around which time did the amount of cod landed begin to decrease? **Level 6**
9. What explanation could there be for the low levels of cod landed in recent times? Do you think there has been a decline in the demand for cod? **Level 6**
10. What effects would the decline in cod landings have on the price of cod? **Level 6**
11. Compare this graph with the graph of the spawning stock biomass. Is there a correlation between the graphs for cod? Explain your answer fully. **Level 6**

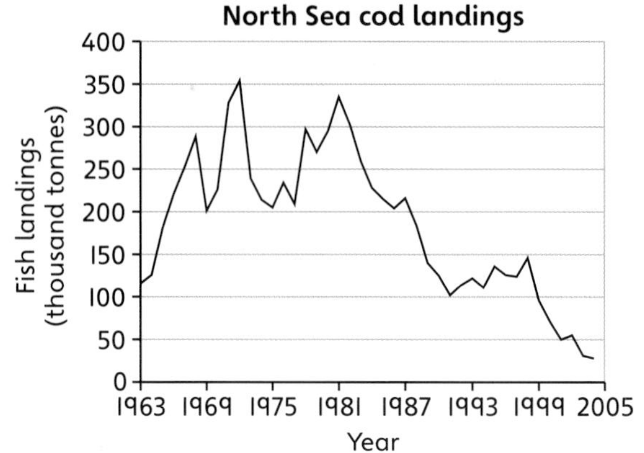

12 The table shows the spawning stock biomass of cod (thousand tonnes) in the West of Scotland and in the Irish Sea.

a Draw a graph of this data, with time (year) on the x-axis and spawning stock biomass (thousand tonnes) on the y-axis. Plot both sets of data on the same graph but use different colours to differentiate them.

b Compare the graphs and discuss the trends for both areas.

c Is there a correlation between the trends for the West of Scotland, Irish Sea and the North Sea? Give a full answer.

Year	West of Scotland	Irish Sea
1996	12.0	5.6
1997	7.5	5.6
1998	5.9	5.2
1999	5.0	5.5
2000	3.3	2.0
2001	2.9	2.9
2002	2.6	4.5
2003	2.5	3.4
2004	2.5	5.2

The BIG ideas

- → Choose suitable **scales** for both axes. **Level 6**
- → You can **interpret** graphs from real-life situations by reading values, predicting **trends** and making **generalisations**. **Level 6**
- → Drawing graphs of real-life situations helps you to solve problems and understand data. **Level 6**

Practice SATs-style questions

Level 5

Q1 Copy and complete the function machine.

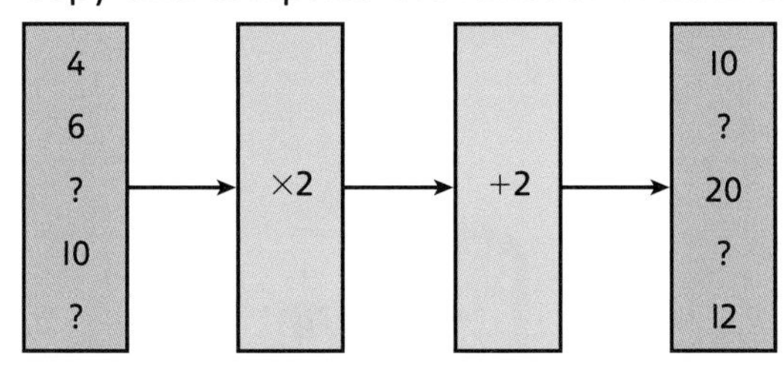

Q2 Draw x and y-axes from 0 to 10.
Plot these points:
A(0, 0), B(5, 5), C(2, 1), D(6, 2), E(10, 0)

Level 6

Q3 **a** Complete the table of values for the equation $y = 4x - 2$.

x	0	2	4
y			

b Draw the graph of $y = 4x - 2$.

c Draw the graph of $y = 4x + 1$ on the same set of axes as part **b**.

d What do you notice about the graphs?

Q4 Nia and Nathan are taking part in a sponsored walk. They set off at 10.00 am and are so excited that they run for the first 15 minutes and cover 4 km. They walk for the next hour and cover 6 km. They rest at the water station for 15 minutes before starting their return journey. They arrive at the finish line at 1.15 pm.

a Draw a distance–time graph for their journey.

b How long did they take on the return leg?

Level 7

Q5 Find the gradient of the lines through the points

a (−3, 0) and (0, 3)

b (4, 0) and (5, 2)

Q6 The graph shows a straight line with gradient 2.

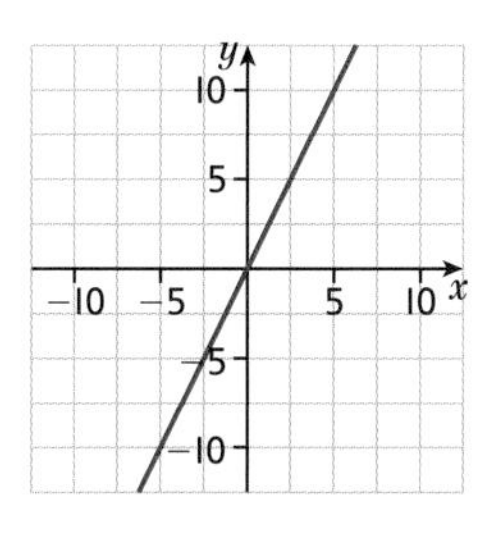

a Copy the graph and draw two other lines that also have a gradient of 2.

b The equation of a straight line is $y = 4x + 3$. At what point does the line cross the y-axis?

c A straight line parallel to $y = 4x + 3$ passes through the point (0, 8). What is the equation of this straight line?

Q7 A line parallel to $y = 3x + 2$ passes through the point (0, −2). What is the equation of this line?

6 Measure up

This unit is about units and measurements of perimeter, area and volume.

At the National Sea Life Centre in Birmingham, visitors can see fish and sea creatures from around the UK coast, as well as from tropical oceans. Different marine habitats are carefully created in large aquaria, so that the creatures feel at home. The lighting, plant life and movement of water are as similar as possible to conditions in the wild. The aquarium workers have to take regular measurements of water quality, temperature, salinity and oxygen, to check that they are all within the required levels. The amounts of food, vitamins and supplements for the creatures also have to be carefully calculated and measured.

Activities

A The Sea Life Centre has otters in its fresh water habitat. Read these scales to find the amounts of meat and carrots needed for a meal for five otters.

The five otters are also fed 20 chicks per meal.

Work out the amounts of chicks, meat and carrots needed for one otter's meal.

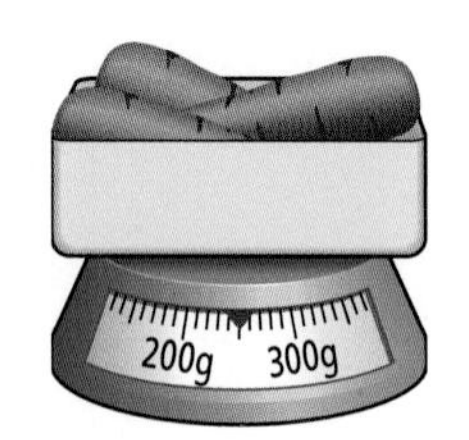

Did you know?
A grown otter's fur can contain up to one billion hairs!

B The largest tank at the Sea Life Centre holds 850 000 litres of water. One day antibiotics have to be added to the water. The dose is 100 milligrams (100 mg) for every 100 litres of water.

- **a** How many milligrams of antibiotic are needed for 1 litre of water?
- **b** How many milligrams of antibiotic are needed for 850 000 litres
- **c** Given that 1000 mg = 1 gram, work out how many grams of antibiotic are needed for the tank.

Did you know?
An octopus can change colour and grow spikes in the blink of an eye. And it has three hearts to pump its blue blood around its body.

Before you start this unit...

1 Write down the metric units of

a length **b** mass **c** capacity

Level Up Maths 4-6 page 48

2 This rectangle has a perimeter of 48 m.

15 m

What is its width?

Level Up Maths 4-6 page 40

3 Find the area of a 7 cm by 11 cm rectangle.

Level Up Maths 4-6 page 42

4 Work out the area of this right-angled triangle.

12 cm
5 cm

Level Up Maths 4-6 page 44

5 **a** Copy the diagram and choose the correct word for each arrow: edge, vertex, face.

Level Up Maths 4-6 page 296

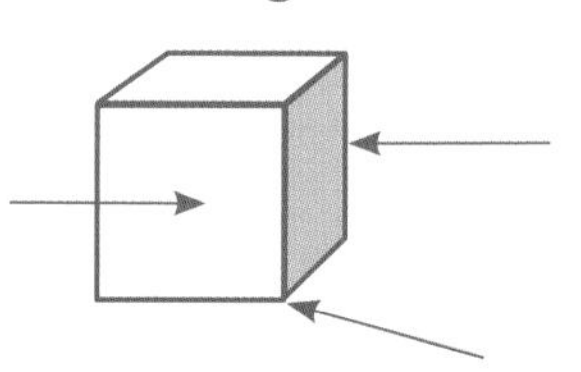

b The edges of the cube measure 2 cm. What is the area of one face?

c What is the surface area of the whole cube?

Level Up Maths 4-6 page 304

6.1 Units

- Convert between metric units
- Convert between metric and imperial units
- Convert between compound metric units

Why learn this?

Customers in a butcher's shop might ask for their meat in either kilograms or pounds. A butcher needs to know the equivalence of these units when setting prices.

What's the BIG idea?

→ You can convert between different **metric** units of capacity, length and mass.
1000 m*l* = 1 litre (*l*)   100 c*l* = 1 litre (*l*)   10 m*l* = 1 c*l*
10 mm = 1 cm   100 cm = 1 m   1000 m = 1 km
1000 g = 1 kg   **Level 5**

→ You can convert between different **imperial** units of capacity and mass.
8 **pints** = 1 **gallon**   16 **ounces** = 1 **pound** **Level 5**

→ You can convert between imperial units and metric units.
1 **mile** ≈ 1.6 km   1 **foot** (ft) ≈ 30 cm   1 pound (lb) ≈ 0.5 kg
1 ounce (oz) ≈ 30 g   1 pint ≈ 0.5 litres   1 gallon ≈ 4.5 litres   **Level 5**

→ You can convert between different metric units of area.
100 mm^2 = 1 cm^2 10 000 cm^2 = 1 m^2 **Level 6**

→ You can convert between different metric units of volume.
1000 mm^3 = 1 cm^3 1 000 000 cm^3 = 1 m^3 **Level 6**

→ You can convert between different compound measures, for example from metres per second (m/s) to kilometres per hour (km/h). **Level 7**

Did you know?

A rod (or a pole or a perch) is an old unit of measurement commonly used by medieval farmers when ploughing.
1 rod equals $16\frac{1}{2}$ feet.

Practice, practice, practice!

Level 5

5c I can convert one metric unit to another

1 **a** Copy and complete the table.

Millilitres	Centilitres	Litres
		1.1
	1250	
1 000 000		

b Rewrite these masses in order from largest to smallest.
450 g   0.4 kg   0.44 kg   444 g

c Put these lengths in order from shortest to longest.
0.65 m   69 cm   630 mm   0.0006 km

5a I can convert between imperial and metric units

2 Write all the distances shown on the map in both metric and imperial units.

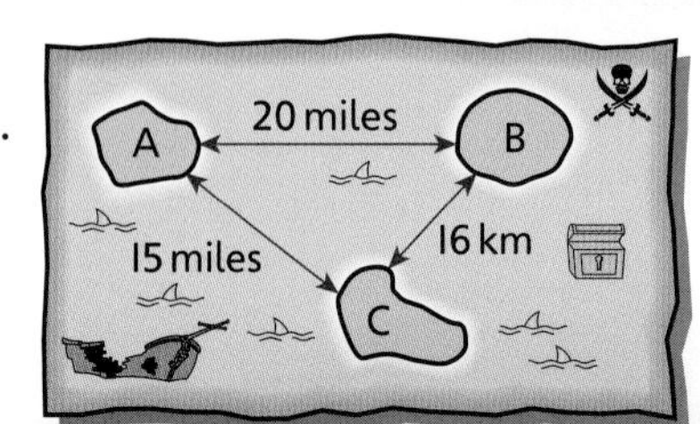

centilitre   foot   gallon   imperial   litre

3 Convert these amounts to the units shown.

a 0.5 kg (pounds) **b** 2 gallons (litres) **c** 10 pints (litres)
d 440 pounds (kilograms) **e** 10 litres (pints) **f** 7 miles (km)

Level 5
5a I can convert between imperial and metric units

4 Look at this floor plan of a house.

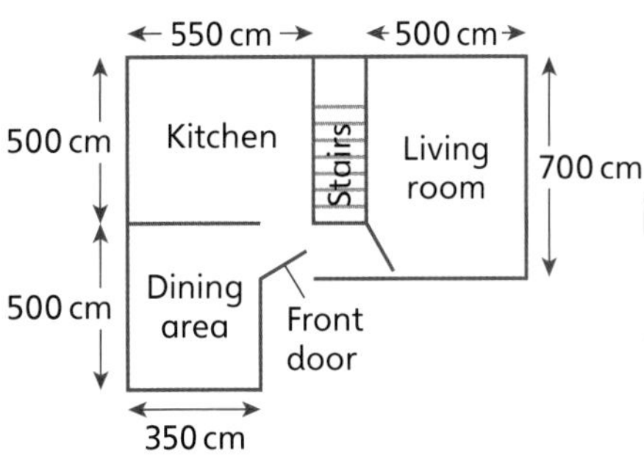

a Find the area of each room in square centimetres (cm^2).

b Convert each area to square metres (m^2).

c Check your answers to part **b** by first changing the lengths on the floor plan to metres and then finding each area.

Level 6
6b I can convert metric units of area

5 A rectangular piece of paper is 20 cm long and 7 cm wide.

a Find the area of the piece of paper in square centimetres (cm^2).

b Convert the area to square millimetres (mm^2).

c Check your answer to part **b** by first converting the lengths to millimetres and then finding the area.

d Another rectangular piece of paper is 250 mm long and 100 mm wide. What is its area in square centimetres (cm^2)?

6 **a** Copy and complete the table.

b Label each arrow with the number that you multiply or divide by to convert from one unit to the other.

6a I can convert metric units of volume

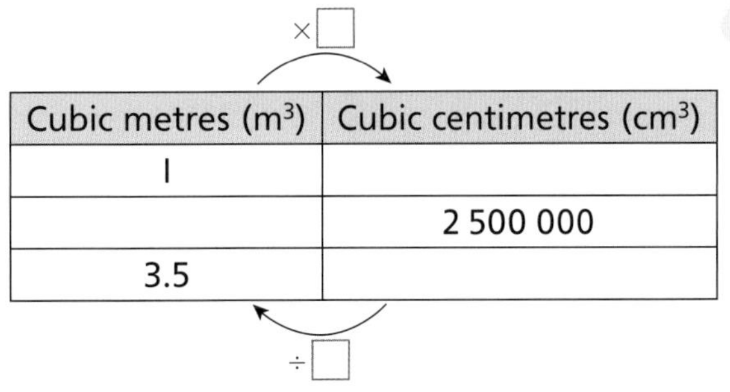

Cubic metres (m^3)	Cubic centimetres (cm^3)
1	
	2 500 000
3.5	

7 The volumes of some containers are 1000 mm^3, 1.5 cm^3, 160 mm^3 and 0.1 cm^3. Put them in order from largest to smallest.

8 Convert each animal's speed to kilometres per hour (km/h).

a cheetah 25 m/s **b** racehorse 20 m/s
c antelope 15 m/s **d** sea lion 10 m/s

Level 7
7a I can convert simple units of compound measures

Now try this!

A Units word search

Draw a 20 by 20 box on squared paper. Using one square for each letter, write the names of as many different units as you can in the box, vertically, horizontally or diagonally. Fill the remaining squares with other letters. Write the words to find underneath and challenge a partner to find them.

B Classifying units

Write as many different units of mass, length and capacity as you can on separate pieces of card and mix them up. Challenge your partner to sort them into units of mass, length and capacity and then into imperial and metric units. Time how quickly they can complete the challenge.

metric mile millilitre ounce pint pound

6.2 Area and perimeter

- Calculate the area and perimeter of rectangles and shapes made from rectangles
- Deduce and use the formulae for the areas of triangles, parallelograms and trapeziums
- Calculate the areas of composite shapes made from triangles and rectangles

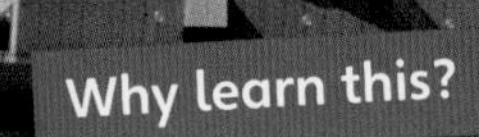

Why learn this?

Finding the areas of different shapes is essential in architecture, from houses and flats to the most spectacular buildings in the world!

What's the BIG idea?

- **Area** of a rectangle = **base** × **height**. **Level 5**
- Area of a parallelogram = base × height **Level 6**
- Area of a triangle = $\frac{1}{2}$ × base × height. **Level 6**
- Area of a trapezium = $\frac{1}{2} \times (a + b) \times h$. **Level 6**

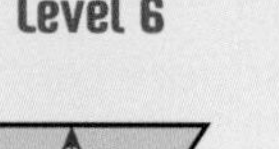

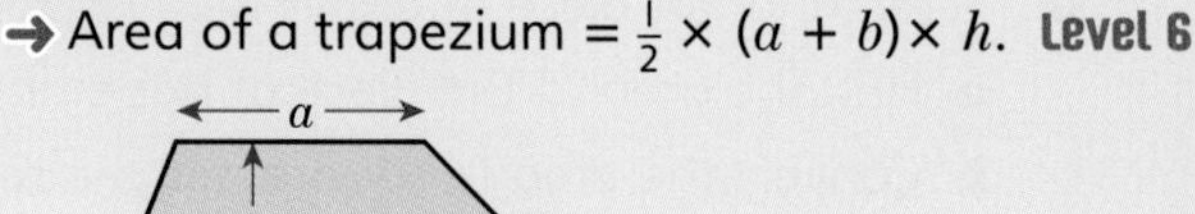

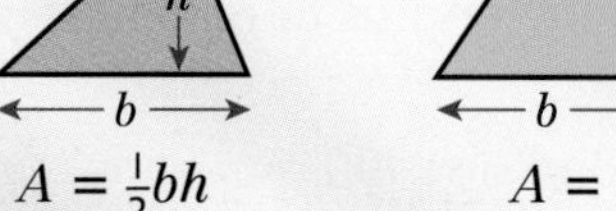

$A = bh$ $A = \frac{1}{2}bh$ $A = bh$ $A = \frac{1}{2}(a + b)h$

- A **compound** shape is a shape made up of other shapes. To find its area, find the area of each individual shape and then add all of the areas together. **Level 6**

Practice, practice, practice!

Level 5

5b I can find the area of shapes made from rectangles

1 Find the area of each shape made from rectangles.

a (15 cm, 3 cm, 9 cm, 10 cm)

b

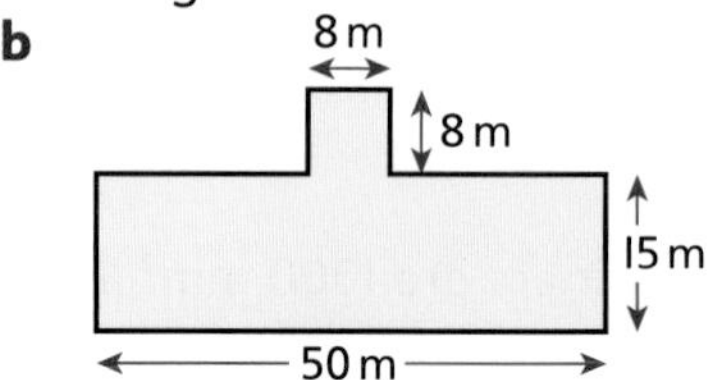

5a I can find the area and perimeter of more complex shapes made from rectangles

2 Find the area and perimeter of each shape made from rectangles.

a (12 m, 2 m, 5 m, 15 m, 2 m, 19 m)

b

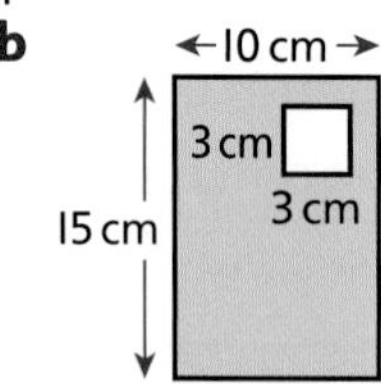

Level 6

6c I can deduce and use the formula for the area of a triangle

3 **a** Find the area of each triangle by drawing an appropriate rectangle.

i

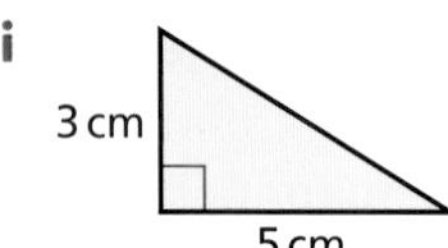

ii

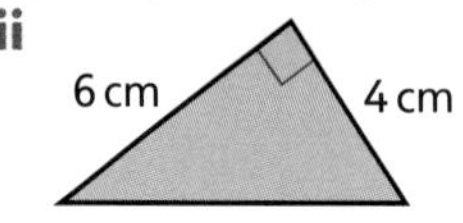

iii

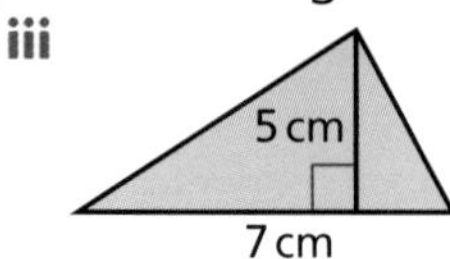

b Explain in words how to find the area of a triangle.

c Write a formula connecting the area of a triangle, its base and its height.

d Use your formula to check the area of each triangle.

area   base   compound   height

4 **a** Find the total area of the house shape.

b The blue shape is the net of a square-based pyramid.
Find the surface area of the pyramid by finding the area of the net.

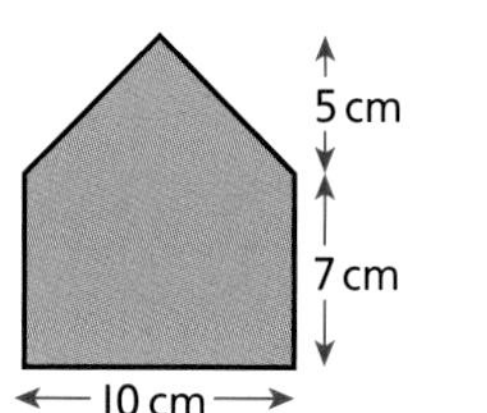

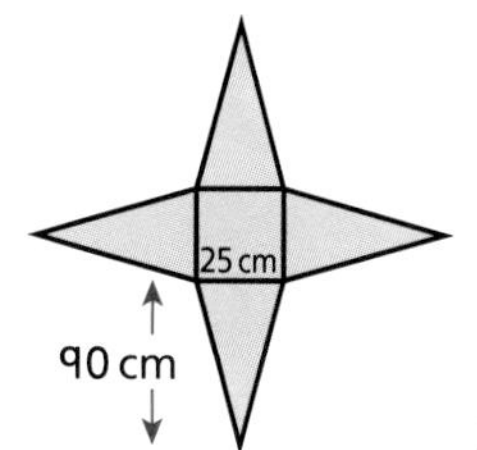

5 **a** Copy this parallelogram accurately on squared paper.

b Cut off the triangles marked by the dashed lines.

c Rearrange your shape into a rectangle and find the area of the shape.

d Describe in words how you found the area of the parallelogram.

e Write a formula connecting the area (A), perpendicular height (h) and length (l) of a parallelogram.

f Use your formula to check the area you found in part **c**.

6 **a** Match each shape to its area.

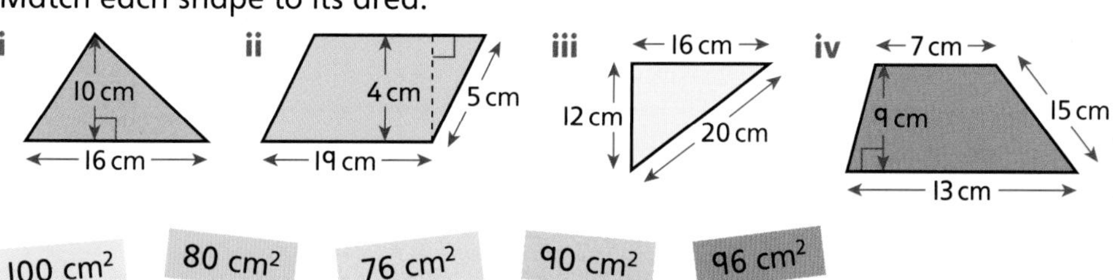

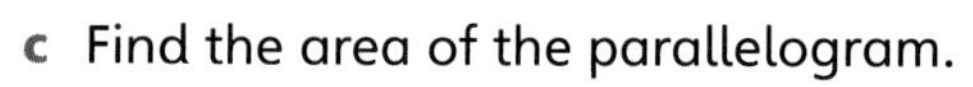

b Draw a shape to match to the area that is left over.

7 **a** Make two accurate copies of this trapezium on squared paper.

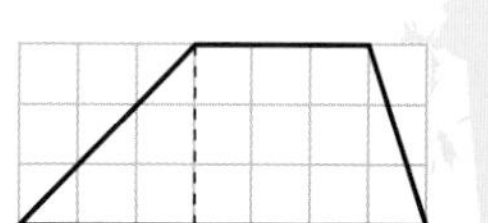

b Cut out both shapes and put them together to make a parallelogram.

c Find the area of the parallelogram.

d Halve it to find the area of the trapezium.

e Write a formula connecting the area (A), the height (h) and the lengths of the parallel sides (a and b).

f Use your formula to check the area you found in part **d**.

Tip
Write an expression for the area of the parallelogram and then multiply by a half.

Level 6

6c I can calculate the areas of compound shapes made from rectangles and triangles

6b I can deduce a formula for the area of a parallelogram

6b I can use a formula to find the area of a parallelogram, trapezium and triangle

6a I can deduce a formula for the area of a trapezium

Now try this!

A Perimeters and areas

Use squared or dotted paper to draw a variety of shapes that all have the same area. Work out the perimeter of each shape by measuring the sides. Think about which shapes have longer or shorter perimeters.

B Area poster

Make a poster explaining how to deduce the formulae for the areas of triangles, parallelograms and trapeziums. Show how each shape can be made from a rectangle by cutting it and rearranging the parts.

parallel perimeter perpendicular width

6.3 Circles

- Find the area and perimeter of circles using circle formulae
- Find the diameter or radius of a circle given its circumference or area
- Find the area and perimeter of compound shapes involving circles

Why learn this?

The distance travelled on a bicycle is calculated by multiplying the number of wheel rotations by the wheel circumference.

What's the BIG idea?

- The **area** of a **circle** can be found using the **formula** $A = \pi r^2$, where r is the **radius**. **Level 6**
- The **circumference** is the perimeter of a circle. It is found using the formula $C = 2\pi r$. This can also be written $C = \pi d$, where d is the **diameter** of the circle. **Level 6**
- You can use the formulae to calculate the radius or diameter of a circle when you know the area or circumference. **Level 7**

radius
centre of circle
diameter
circumference

Learn this

$\pi = 3.141\,59...$
You can use the π key on a calculator, or the rounded value $\pi = 3.14$ in calculations.

Practice, practice, practice!

Level 6

6b I can recognise the formulae for the circumference and area of a circle

1 Look at these expressions. πr^2 $2\pi r$ πd πd^2

- **a** Write the meaning of each letter and symbol.
- **b** Which expression gives the circumference of a circle?
- **c** Which expression gives the area of a circle?

6b I can find the circumference of a circle using a formula

2 Calculate the circumference of each circle to 1 d.p.

a

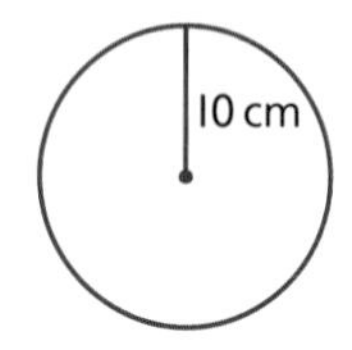

b

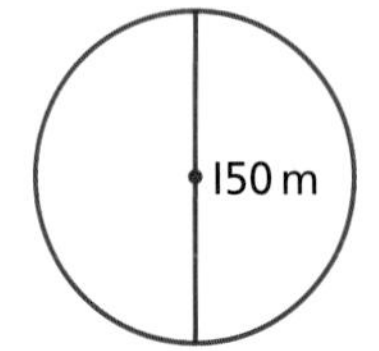

c

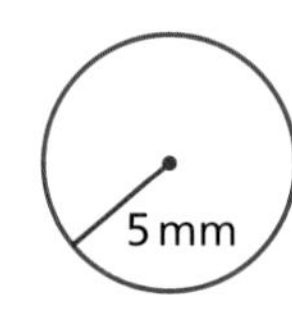

Hint: Use $\pi = 3.14$ or the π key on your calculator.

3 The London Eye has a radius of 60 m. Calculate to the nearest metre the distance each pod travels during one turn of the wheel.

6a I can use a formula to find the area of a circle

4 Find the area of each of the circles shown in Q2 to 1 d.p.

5 Pizza Planet's pizza bases come in three different sizes.
A small pizza base has diameter 20 cm, a medium base has diameter 25 cm, and a large one has diameter 30 cm.
Calculate the area of each pizza to 1 d.p.

Level 7

7c I can use circle formulae to find the radius of a circle given the circumference

6 Use a circle formula to find the radius of a circle with a circumference of

- **a** 31.4 cm
- **b** 1256 cm
- **c** 0.94 cm
- **d** 87.9 cm

Hint: Rearrange the formula so that you end up with $r = C \div 2\pi$.

area circle circumference compound

7 A bicycle moves 1.57 m during one turn of its wheels.
Calculate the diameter of the wheels.

8 Pizza Plaza's pizza bases also come in three different sizes.
The area of a small pizza is 1662 cm², the medium is 2463 cm² and the large is 3421 cm².
Calculate the diameter of each.

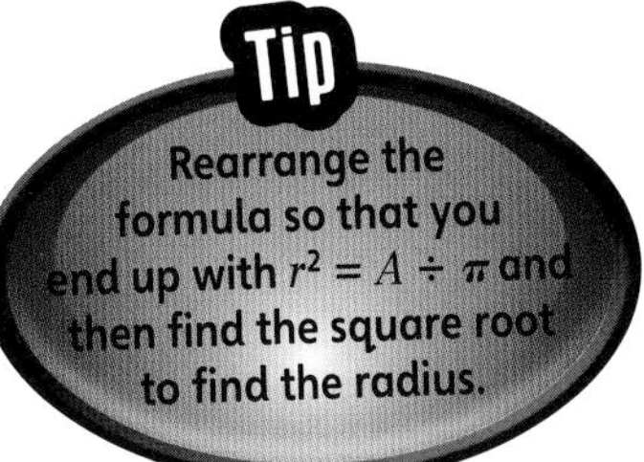

9 The circular area of this lolly is 1256 mm².
The end of the stick is in the centre of the lolly.
Find the total length of the stick in cm.

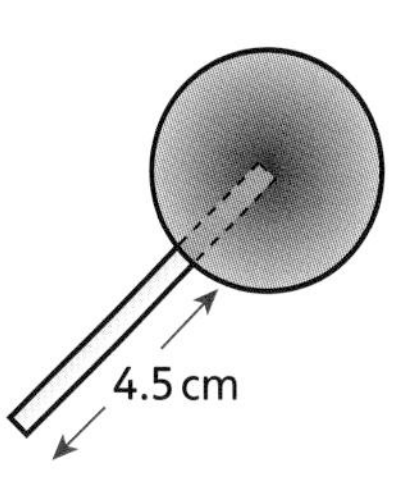

10 Find the shaded area of each shape by splitting it into smaller shapes.

a

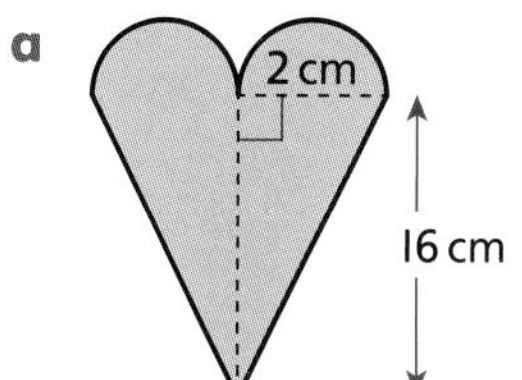

b

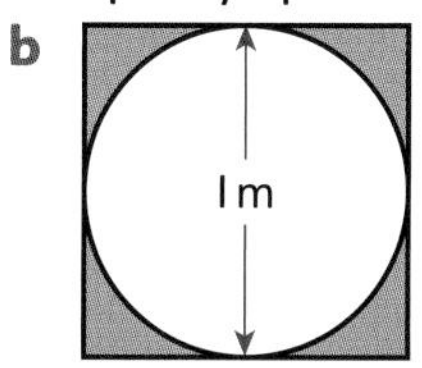

c

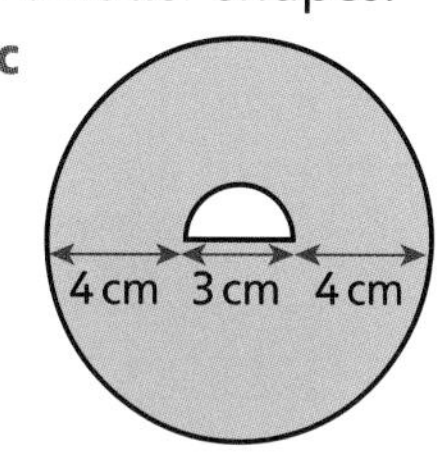

11 Calculate the total area of this track and field.
Use the length of the javelin run-up as the radius of the semicircles.

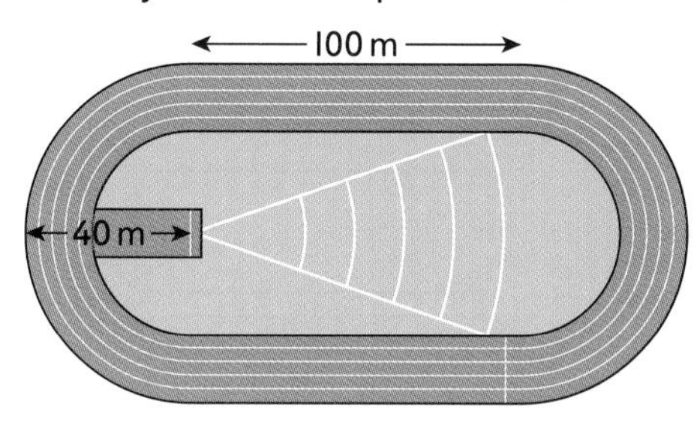

Level 7

7c I can use circle formulae to find the diameter of a circle given the circumference

7c I can use the formula for the area of a circle to calculate the radius or diameter of a circle, given its area

7b I can find the area of compound shapes involving circles

Now try this!

A Design your own pizza menu

a Design a menu with three different sizes of pizza base. Find the area of each pizza to help you decide on the prices and on the price of extra toppings, given that they will be spread over different areas.

b Find the circumference of each pizza to help you decide on the price of a stuffed crust.

c Work out what size box you will need for each pizza.

B Circle patterns

Use a pair of compasses and a pencil to draw some compound shapes that include circles or semicircles. Swap drawings with a partner and try to find the area and perimeter of each other's shapes.

Did you know?

Around 200 BC, a Greek mathematician called Archimedes wrote a book called *The Measurement of a Circle*. In the book he states that pi is a number between $3\frac{10}{71}$ and $3\frac{1}{7}$. He worked this out by taking a polygon with 96 sides and accurately fitting a circle inside it.

diameter formula pi(π) radius

6.4 Surface area

➪ **Calculate the surface area of cubes, cuboids and other prisms**

What's the BIG idea?

- → The **surface area** is the total area of all the faces of a 3-D shape. **Level 5**
- → It can sometimes be useful to draw a **net** when finding the surface area of a shape. **Level 5**
- → You can find the surface area of a shape by finding the area of each of its faces and adding them together. **Level 5, Level 6 & Level 7**

Why learn this?

The surface area of a solid in a chemical reaction affects the speed at which the chemical reaction occurs.

Practice, practice, practice!

Level 5

5b I can calculate the surface area of simple cuboids using nets

1 The diagrams show the nets of three different cuboids. Calculate the surface area of each.

a

3 cm
3 cm

b

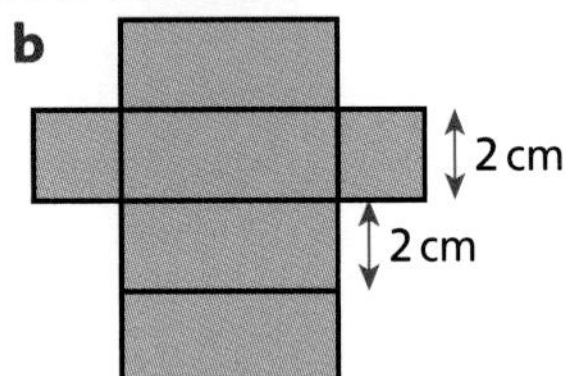

c

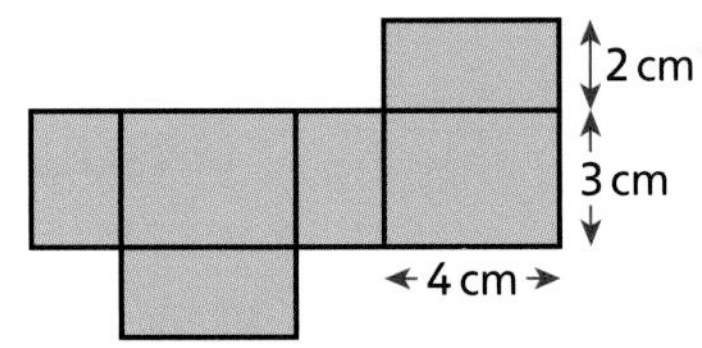

5a I can calculate the surface area of simple cuboids

2 Calculate the surface area of each cuboid.

a

5 m
8 m
10 m

b

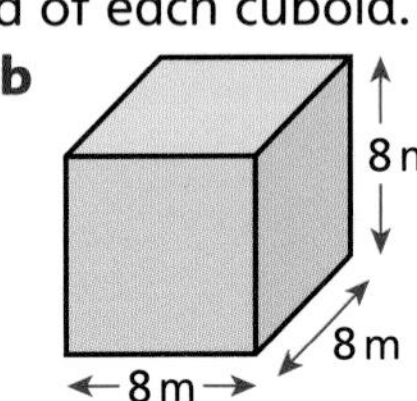

c

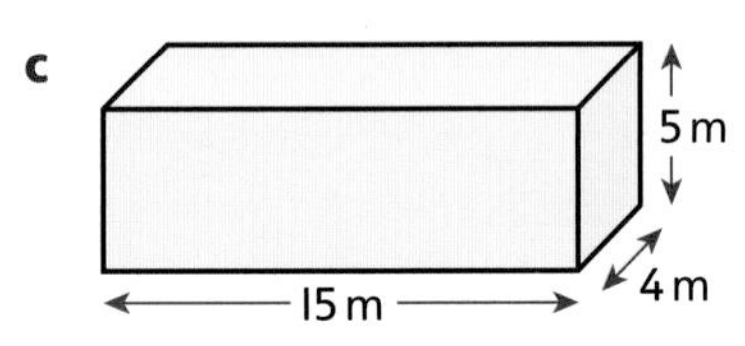

Level 6

6b I can calculate the surface area of more complicated cuboids

3 A manufacturing company is deciding which of two boxes to use for its product. Both boxes have the same volume. One has dimensions of 12.4 cm, 2.5 cm and 6 cm and the other has dimensions of 3.1 cm, 5 cm and 12 cm.

- **a** Sketch each cuboid and label three of the sides with their lengths.
- **b** Calculate the surface area of each box.
- **c** The company wants to minimise the amount of cardboard used. Which box should it use?

6a I can calculate the surface area of shapes made from cuboids

4 Calculate the surface area of each 3-D shape.

a

3 cm
6 cm
2 cm
3 cm
8 cm

b

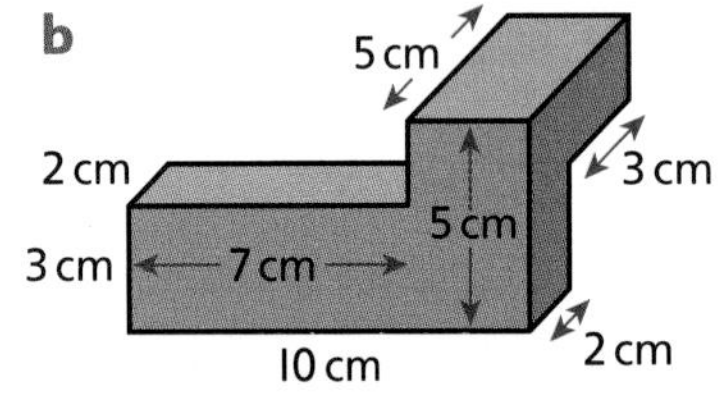

c

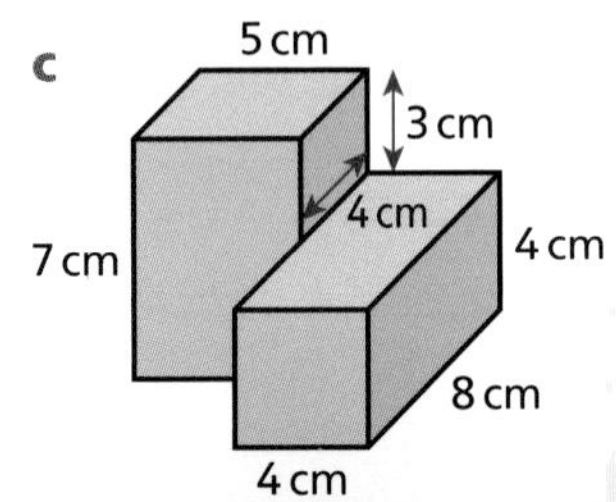

cross-section cuboid dimension length

Level 7

7b I can calculate the surface area of prisms

5 A chocolate producer uses two types of prism-shaped boxes to package their bars. Calculate the amount of cardboard used for each box shown.
Hint: Assume there are no overlaps.

a

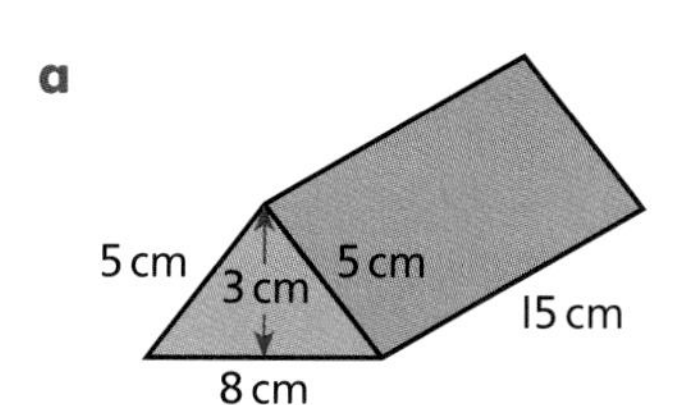

b

3 cm, 4 cm, 3 cm, 4 cm, 12 cm, 7 cm

6 Find the surface area of these shapes.

a

4 cm, 6 cm, 3 cm, 4 cm, 10 cm, 4 cm

b

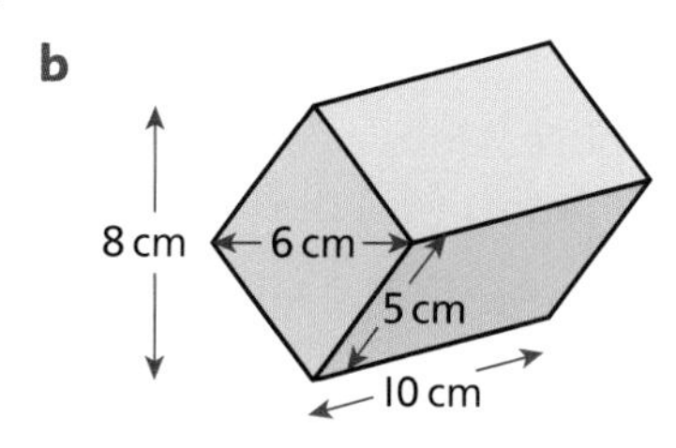

c

4 cm, 8 cm, 6 cm, 10 cm, 7 cm

d

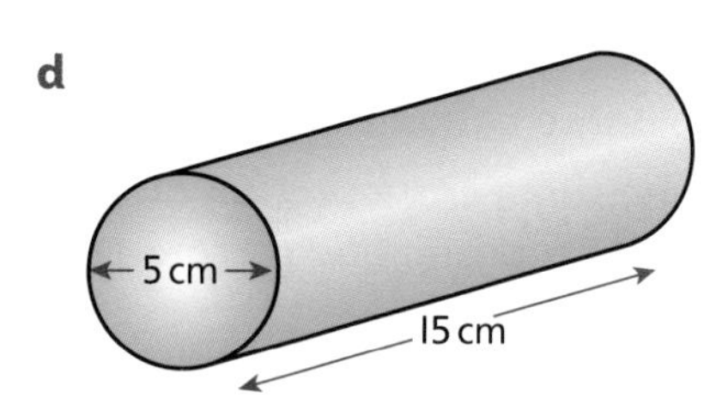

7 Draw a shape with a surface of
- **a** between 100 and 200 cm^2
- **b** between 1000 and 1500 cm^2.

Clearly label the lengths on your drawing.

8 A right-angled triangle has side lengths of 5 cm, 12 cm and 13 cm. This is the cross-section of a prism 15 cm long.
- **a** Sketch the prism.
- **b** Calculate the surface area.

Learn this

A 3-D shape which has the same cross-section along its length is called a prism.

Now try this!

A Estimation game 1

Work with a partner. Find a cuboid in the classroom, for example a book or cupboard.
Each write down your own estimate of the surface area of the cuboid.
Now measure the cuboid and calculate its actual surface area. The person who made the best estimate wins 1 point. Repeat for at least five different cuboids. The winner is the player with most points.

B Estimation game 2

Repeat Activity A but look for prisms and cylinders instead of cuboids. For example, you could use board markers or pencil cases.

Did you know?

The area of the hole in the ozone layer was observed as being 26 million km^2 in September 2006. This is the largest that it has ever been and bigger than the area of North America.

net   prism   surface area

6.5 Volume

- Know and use the formula for the volume of a cuboid
- Calculate the volumes of shapes made from cuboids
- Calculate the volume of prisms

Why learn this?

You can use volume calculations to find out how much water is needed to fill a swimming pool.

What's the BIG idea?

→ **Volume** is a measure of 3-D space. Units of volume include cubic centimetres (cm³), cubic metres (m³) and cubic kilometres (km³). **Level 5**

→ Multiply the length, width and height of a **cuboid** to find its volume.

$V = l \times w \times h$

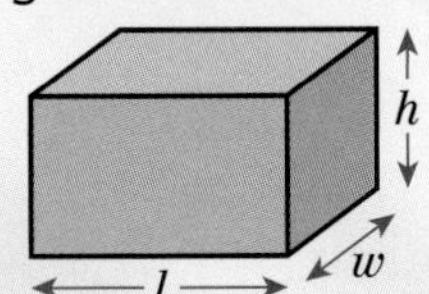

Level 6

→ You can split some shapes into cuboids to calculate their volume. **Level 6**

→ A 3-D shape which has the same **cross-section** along its length is called a **prism**. To find the volume of a prism, find the area of its cross-section and then multiply by its length.

V = area of cross-section × length **Level 7**

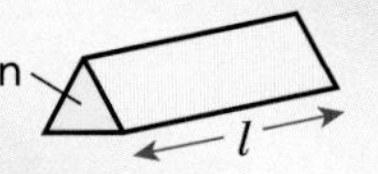

Practice, practice, practice!

Level 5

5a I can find the volume of a cuboid by counting cubes

1 **a** Find the volume of these cuboids made from centimetre cubes.

i 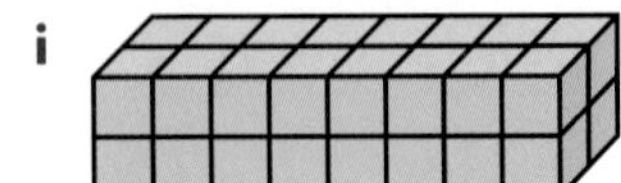

ii 

iii 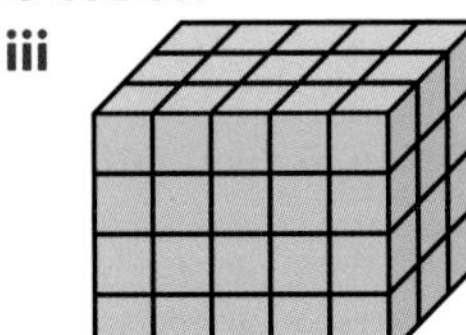

b Copy cuboid **i** and label the dimensions length, l, height, h, and width, w.

Level 6

6c I can calculate the volumes of cubes and cuboids

2 **a** Explain how to find the volume of a cuboid by using the formula.

b Check your answers to Q1 by using the formula.

3 Find the volume of these cuboids.

a

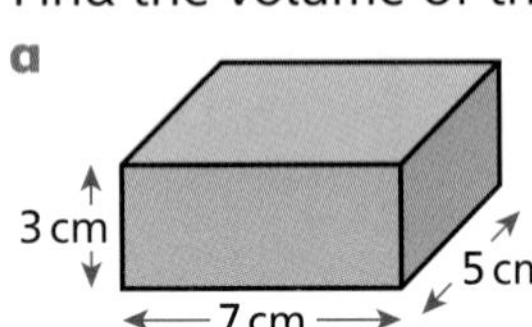

b

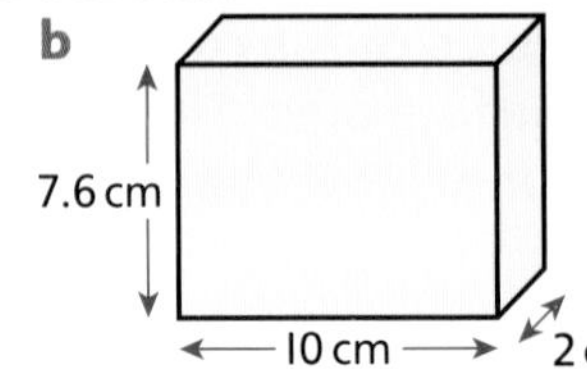

c

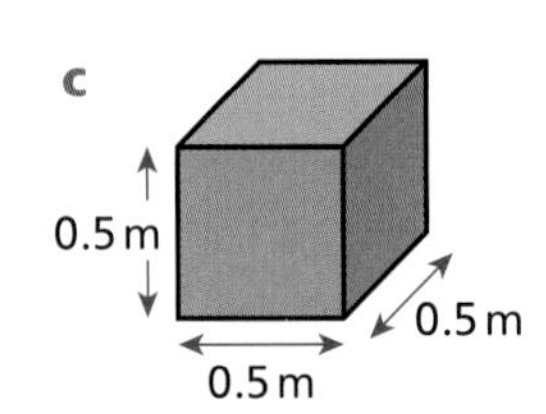

4 An Olympic sized swimming pool is 50 m long, 25 m wide and 2 m deep. Calculate the volume of water needed to fill the pool.

composite cross-section cuboid

5 a Find the volume of cuboids A and B.

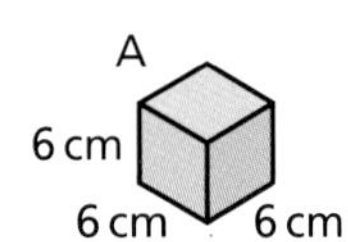

B
6 cm
6 cm
10 cm

The composite shapes are both made using cuboids A and B.

b Find the volume of each composite shape.

c Combine the original cuboids in two other ways and find the volume of the new composite shapes.

i
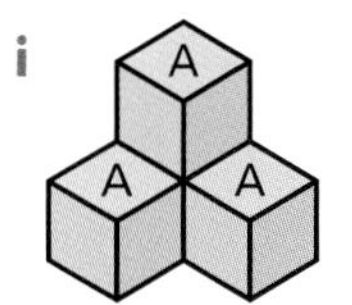

ii
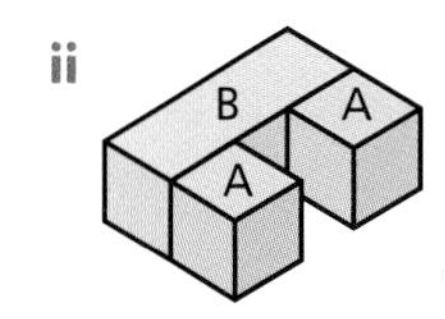

6 Find the volume of this shape.

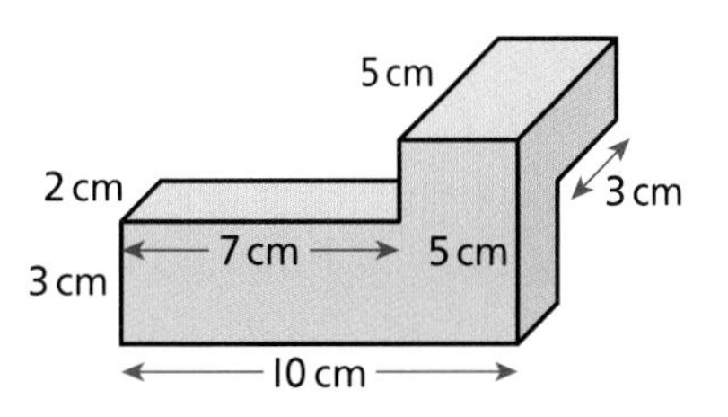

Level 6

6b I can calculate the volume of shapes made from cuboids

Learn this

To find the volume of a shape made of cuboids, find the volume of each cuboid and add the volumes together.

7 a Match each shape to the correct volume.

i
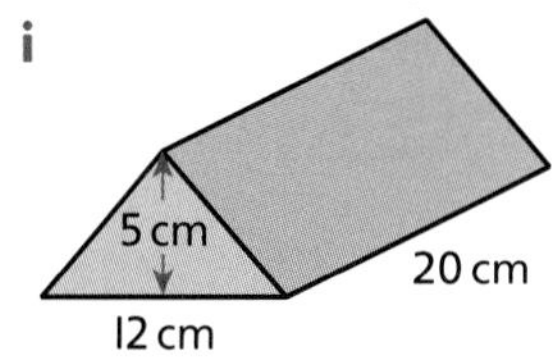

ii
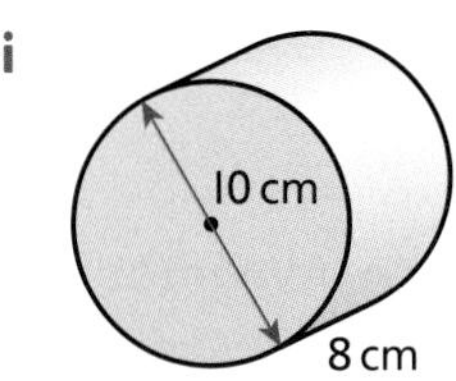

iii
2 cm
9 cm
15 cm
5 cm

630 cm^3 640 cm^3 600 cm^3 628 cm^3

b Sketch a cuboid to match the volume that is left over.

Level 7

7c I can find the volume of a prism

Now try this!

A Volume and displacement

You need a measuring cylinder or jug marked in millilitres, some centicubes and some water.

a Half-fill the jug with water and record the volume of water in the jug.

b Make three different cuboids from centicubes and write their volumes in a table like this.

Volume of cuboid (cm^3)	New reading on jug (m*l*)	Difference (m*l*)

c Put a cuboid into the water and record the new reading on the jug. Repeat with a different cuboid.

d Work out the difference between the two readings and write this in the final column.

e What do you notice about the difference between the readings and the volume of the cuboid?

B Make your own cereal box

You need to make a cereal box with a volume of 3500 cm^3. Experiment with different cuboids to find a cereal box that uses the least amount of cardboard.

Try making your box out of cardboard.

Think of a name for your cereal and design the box.

Did you know?

The volume of water stored in ice caps and glaciers is about 24 000 000 km^3. If all of this were to melt, sea levels would rise by 70 metres.

prism volume

6.6 Solving problems 1

➩ Solve problems about length, area, volume and circles
➩ Solve problems involving metric and imperial units

Why learn this?

Problem solving could help you find out how fast the Earth is spinning!

What's the BIG idea?

→ Problem solving is about using maths to help you in real-life situations. **Level 5, Level 6 & Level 7**

→ When looking at a problem for the first time, write down the key points and numbers and think about what kind of maths might help. **Level 5, Level 6 & Level 7**

→ You may need to try one or two different methods before reaching a solution. **Level 5, Level 6 & Level 7**

Practice, practice, practice!

Level 5

5a I can solve problems involving length and area

1 Rachel has twenty 1 m lengths of fencing for her vegetable garden. She wants as much space as possible inside the fenced area.

a Experiment with different rectangular-shaped gardens and record their width, length and area in a table.

b Plot a graph of width against area.

c Which sized rectangle would you recommend for Rachel's garden?

d Repeat parts **a** to **c** for fence lengths of 12 m and 24 m.

Level 6

6b I can solve problems involving length, area and volume

2 A manufacturer makes cube-shaped toys with side length 2 cm and is deciding on the dimensions of the box for them.
Each box must hold 100 toys and use the least amount of packaging possible.
Investigate different sized boxes and make a recommendation for the dimensions to use.

3 A cold water tank with a square base of side 1.20 m contains 3600 litres of water.
What is the depth of the water in centimetres?

4 A widescreen TV has a height of 45.5 cm and a width of 76.2 cm including a border of 3 cm around the edge.
Work out the screen area to the nearest square centimetre.

6a I can solve problems involving circles and measures

5 The distance from London to Leicester is about 160 km.
A bicycle wheel has a radius of 30 cm.
Calculate how many times the wheel would turn in a straight journey from Leicester to London.

circumference diameter measures

6 The diagram shows the plan of a tray carrying four large cups.
The tray is a square with side length 24 cm.

Hint: The diameter of each cup is half the length of the tray.

a How much of the tray is covered by cups? Give your answer as a percentage.

b Sketch a similar tray with the same dimensions. This time the tray has nine smaller cups – three down and three across. How much of the tray is covered?

c Investigate further using different numbers of cups.

7 The Earth takes 24 hours to make one rotation on its axis.

a The radius of the Earth at the equator is 6378 km. Find the speed that the Earth is turning at the equator in metres per second.

b Why is the speed of rotation at the Earth's equator bigger than the speed of rotation if you are in the UK?

Level 6

6a I can solve problems involving circles and measures

Did you know?

The speed at which the Earth spins at the North Pole is almost zero.

8 The wheels of a lorry have a circumference of 219.8 cm. Use this information to find the length of the lorry.
Give your answer to an appropriate degree of accuracy.

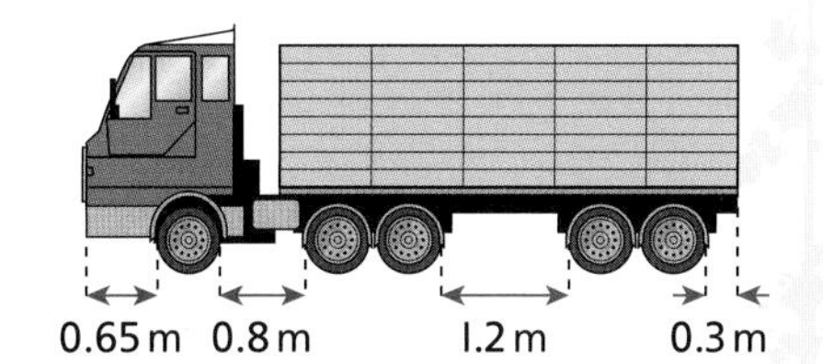

9 This table shows the dimensions of various coins.

Coin	Diameter	Thickness
1p	20.32 mm	1.65 mm
5p	18 mm	1.7 mm
10p	24.5 mm	1.85 mm
£1	22.5 mm	3.15 mm

a Nadia has £1.26. Suggest three different selections of coin she could have and calculate the total volume of coins for each selection.

Hint: Volume of a cylinder: $V = \pi r^2 h$ where r is the radius and h is the height.

b Angie has 93p. Suggest two different selections of coin she could have and calculate the total volume of coins for each selection.

Level 7

7b I can solve problems that involve finding the radius or diameter of a circle given the circumference

7a I can solve problems that involve the volume of cylinders

Now try this!

A Surface area

- Make as many different shapes as you can from six multilink cubes. Find the surface area of each shape.
- What is the largest surface area you can find? ...the smallest surface area?
- Investigate for different numbers of cubes.

B Circles, spheres and string

- Draw a circle on paper and cut a piece of string the same length as the radius.
- How many pieces of string do you need to fit around the circumference of the circle?
- Investigate for different sized circles.
- How does this relate to the circle formulae you know?

radius strategy volume

maths!

Saving space

Mathematics can help to explain the shapes that nature creates – and help us choose our own.

Hexagons in nature

The hexagon is a shape that appears throughout nature. In 1999, Professor Thomas Hales proved that by tiling regular hexagons together in a honeycomb, bees are enclosing areas using the shortest possible perimeter length.

The Giant's Causeway in Northern Ireland is an area of about 40 000 basalt columns that were formed from a time of volcanic activity 65 million years ago. As the lava cooled to form basalt it contracted and cracked. The cracks formed mainly hexagonal patterns. Can you use Professor Hales' result to explain why this might have happened?

Boxed in

Many mathematicians work on problems involving packing and stacking – finding results that improve efficiency in manufacturing. This problem involves stacking an unusual three-dimensional shape. Part **b** of this problem is currently unsolved…

a Find a way to stack copies of this four-cube shape into a $2 \times 2 \times 6$ cuboid so that there are no gaps. How many copies of the shape will fit into the cuboid?

b What different sizes of box can you stack copies of this shape into so that there are no gaps?

Packing and stacking

There will always be gaps between tubes of sweets when they are packed in a box, but can they be packed so the minimum amount of space is wasted? Consider packing 16 circular tubes with a diameter of 2.5 cm.

First pack the tubes of sweets like this:

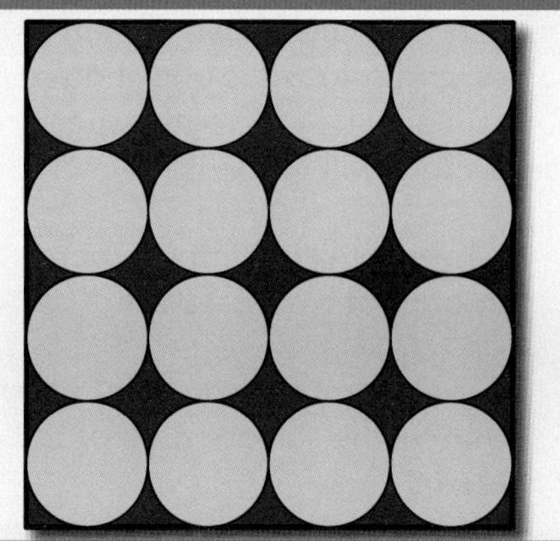

- How long is each side of the square?
- What is the area of the square?
- What is the area of each circle?
- What is the area of all 16 circles?
- What percentage of the space is used up?

Now pack them like this: (Draw it out to measure the rectangle.)

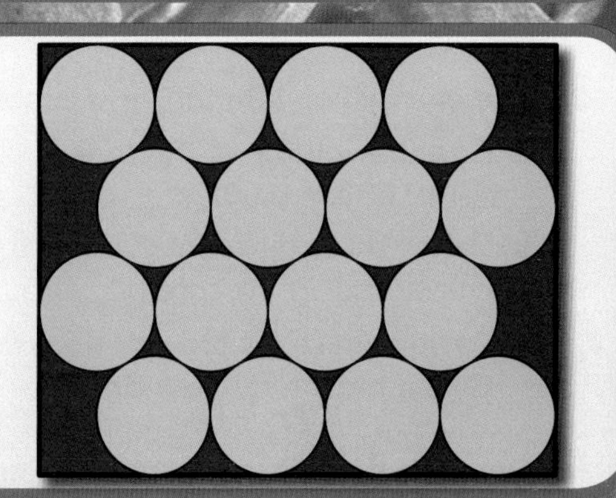

- How long is each side of the rectangle?
- What is the area of the rectangle?
- What is the area of each circle?
- What is the area of all 16 circles?
- What percentage of the space have you used up?

Now try the experiment again with 64 circles.

Which packing method is more efficient?

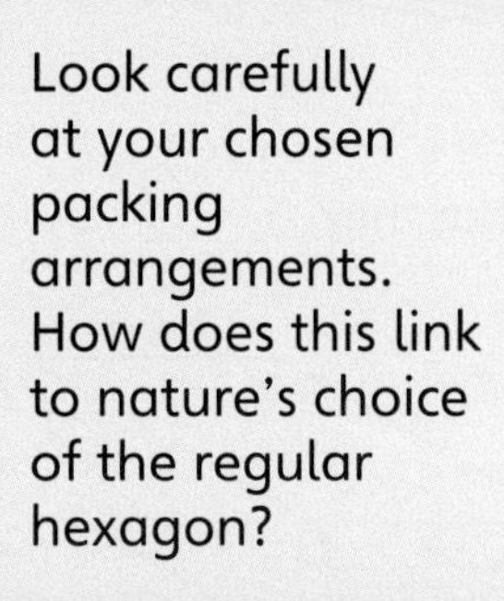

Look carefully at your chosen packing arrangements. How does this link to nature's choice of the regular hexagon?

Tank dimensions

The National Sea Life Centre in Birmingham has an enormous one million litre ocean tank housing giant green sea turtles, black tip reef sharks and tropical reef fish. They also have numerous other tanks for sea horses, crabs, lobsters and sting rays, amongst many others! Each tank is created specifically for the particular species that will live in it.

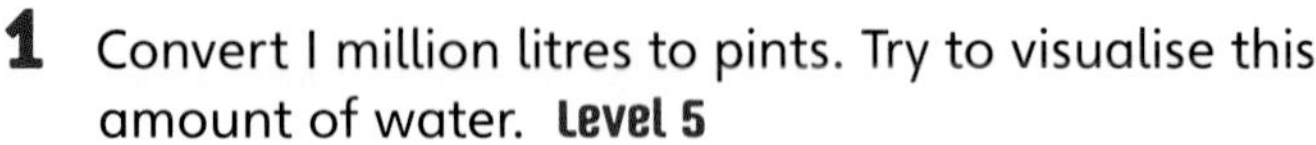

1 Convert 1 million litres to pints. Try to visualise this amount of water. **Level 5**

2 Tanks are made from reinforced glass. What is the surface area of the shark tank? **Level 5**

Hint: The tank is an open cuboid.

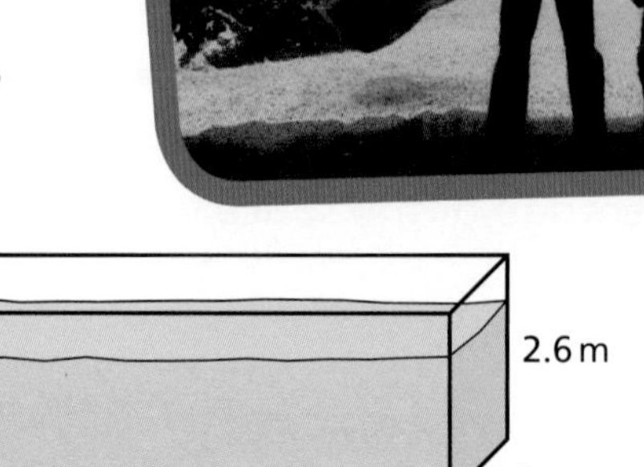

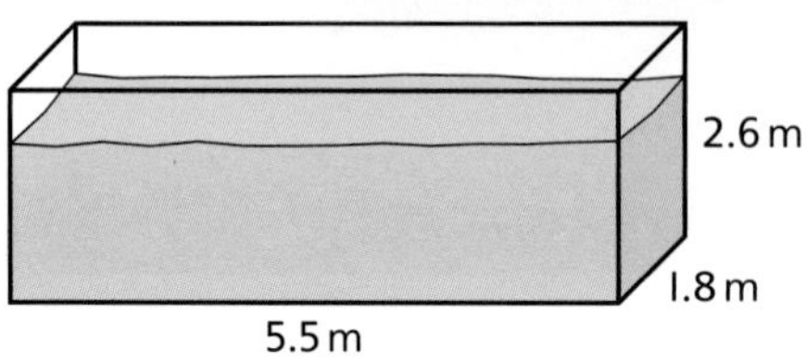

3 The one million litre tank is a cuboid.

a Find the volume of the tank in cubic metres. **Level 6**
Hint: 1 litre = 0.001 m^3

b Sketch three different cuboids that would hold the volume of water that you have calculated. Think carefully about your dimensions. **Level 6**

c Decide which cuboid you think would best suit the purpose. Give a reason for your answer. **Level 6**

4 One of the tanks in the sea life centre is a prism. Its cross-section is shown. Find the area of this cross-section in square metres. **Level 6**

200 cm
200 cm
300 cm

5 The tank in Q4 holds sea horses and is 7 m long.

a Sketch the tank and show all dimensions clearly.

b What is the volume of this tank? **Level 7**

MAKE MATHS FUNCTIONAL!

6 There is a semi-circular tunnel running through the centre of one of the larger tanks so that people can walk through the exhibit. The tunnel is a prism with a semi-circular cross-section of radius 2.4 m.

a Calculate the volume of the tunnel when the length is:
i 10 m **ii** 25 m **iii** 50 m

b How much water would each of these tunnels take away from the tank that they run through? **Level 7**
Hint: Convert the values in part **a** from m^3 to litres.

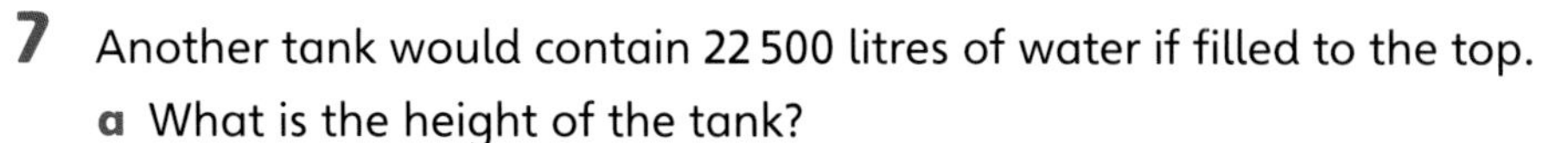

7 Another tank would contain 22 500 litres of water if filled to the top.

a What is the height of the tank?

b What is the depth of the water if it is filled to $\frac{3}{4}$ of its height? **Level 7**

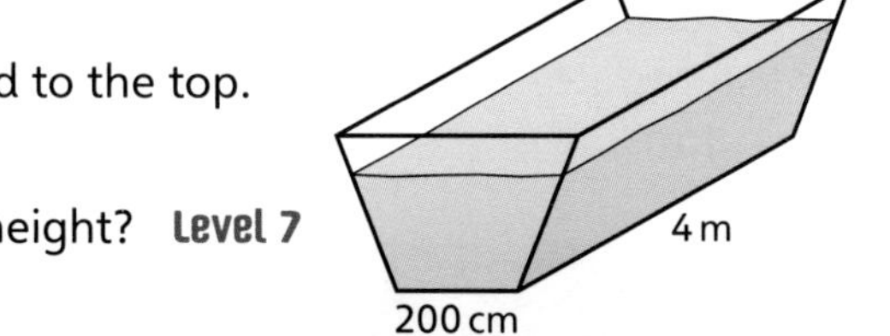

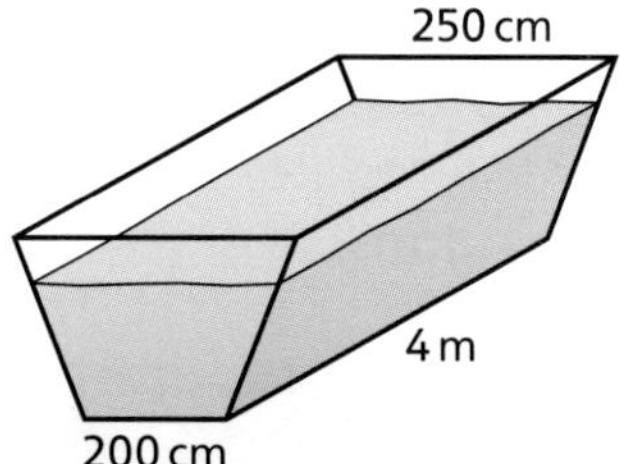

The BIG ideas

- You can convert between **imperial units** and **metric units**. 1 litre is approximately 1.75 pints. **Level 5**
- **Surface area** is the total area of the **faces** of a 3-D shape.
  You can find the surface area of a shape by finding the area of each of its faces and adding them together. **Level 5 & Level 6**
- The area of a **trapezium** is $\frac{1}{2} \times h \times (a + b)$. **Level 6**

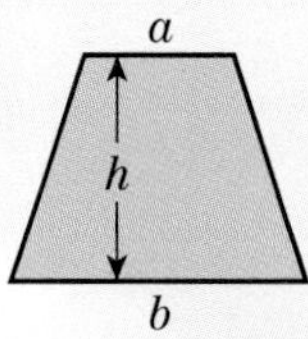

- The area of a **circle** can be found using the formula $A = \pi r^2$, where r is the **radius**. **Level 6**
- **Volume** is a measure of 3-D space. Units of volume include **cubic centimetre (cm³)** and **cubic metre (m³)**. **Level 6**
- Multiply the height, width and length of a cuboid to find its volume: $V = l \times h \times w$. **Level 6**
- To find the volume of a **prism**, find the area of its cross section and then multiply by its length. V = area of cross section × length. **Level 7**

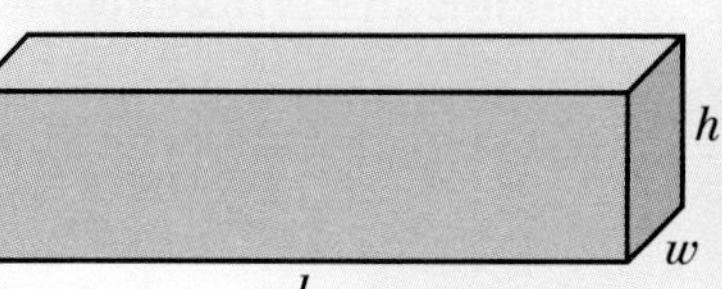

Practice SATs-style questions

Level 5

Q1 Copy and complete.

a 20 mm = ___ cm

b __ cm = 2 m

c 2000 g = __ kg

Q2 This is the net of a cube.
One face has an area of 4 cm².
What is the total surface area of the cube?

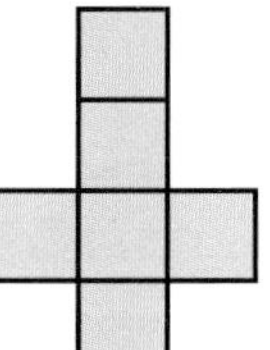

Level 6

Q3

4 cm
A
5 cm
3 cm

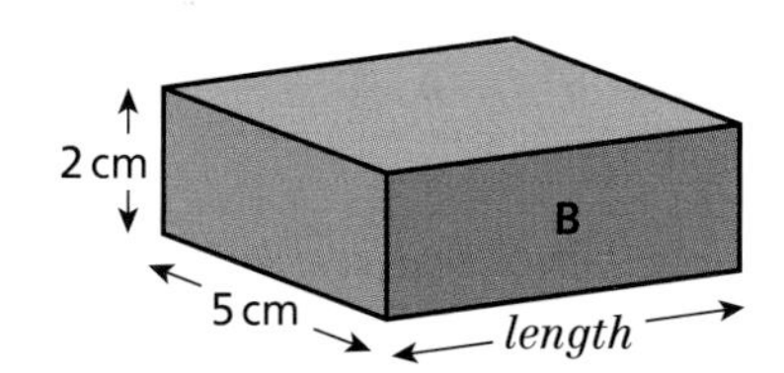

a What is the volume of cuboid A?

b Cuboid B has the same volume as cuboid A.
What is its length?

Q4 A manhole cover is circular with a radius of 65 cm.
What is the area of the cover?

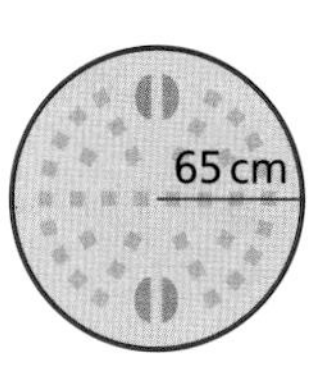

Level 7

Q5 A bicycle wheel has a circumference of 125.6 cm.
What is the radius of the wheel?

Q6 A water trough is to be filled to the top.
What volume of water will be required?

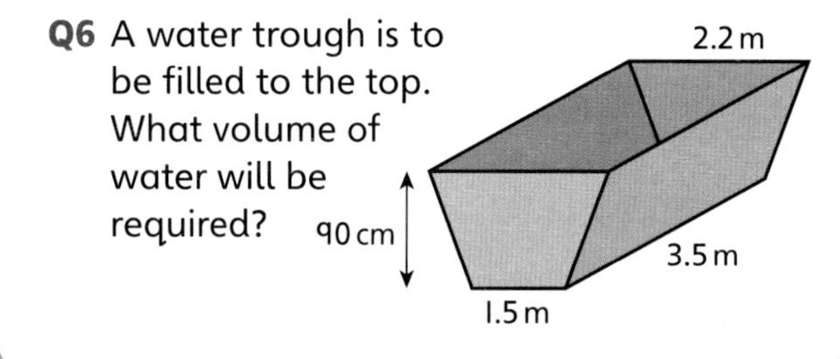

Revision 1

Quick Quiz

Q1 Work out
- **a** $-3 - 6$
- **b** $-4 + 9$
- **c** $6 - 10$

→ *See 1.1*

Q2 The probability that a school canteen serves chips on a Monday is 0.3.
What is the probability that the canteen does not serve chips on a Monday?

→ *See 3.3*

Q3 Complete these sentences.
- **a** ___ out of 10 is the same as 30%.
- **b** 4 out of 20 is the same as ___%.

→ *See 4.5*

Q4 What are the missing numbers?
- **a** 700 mm is the same as ___ cm.
- **b** 360 cm is the same as ___ m.
- **c** 4500 m is the same as ___ km.

→ *See 6.1*

Q5 Write these in order of size, smallest first.
2^5 3^3 5^2

→ *See 1.2*

Q6 Work out
- **a** $2\frac{1}{3} + 1\frac{1}{2}$
- **b** $3\frac{3}{4} - 1\frac{1}{5}$

→ *See 4.2*

Q7 Find the input (x) for this function machine.

x → ×3 → −4 → 32

→ *See 5.1*

Q8 Which two of these lines are parallel?
$y = 3x - 4$ $y = x - 4$ $y = 3x + 7$

→ *See 5.4*

Q9 The exterior angle of a regular polygon is 20°.
How many sides does the polygon have?

→ *See 2.6*

Q10 Work out the following.
Write the answers in their simplest form.
- **a** $\frac{3}{4} \times \frac{6}{11}$
- **b** $\frac{4}{5} \div \frac{2}{7}$

→ *See 4.3*

Q11 Work out the shaded area in this diagram.

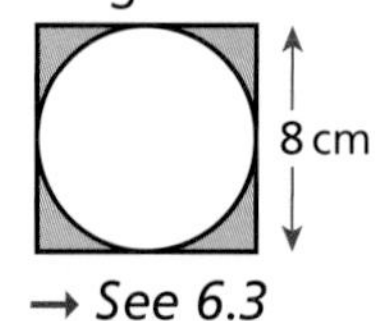

→ *See 6.3*

Activity

A company is planning to produce a new chocolate bar in the shape of a triangular prism. They are looking at two different designs.
Here are the dimensions of the two possible designs for the boxes.

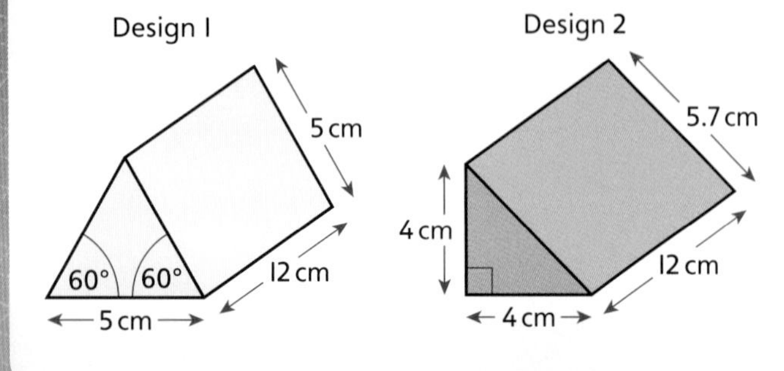

LEVEL 5

Q1 Make an accurate drawing of the triangular ends of the two box designs.

Q2 The rectangular side panel of Design 1 has an area of 60 cm^2. If the company can use a maximum of 40 per cent of this area for the company logo, what is the maximum area they can use?

LEVEL 6

Q3 Two surveys are carried out to find which design people prefer. Here are the results.

	Number of people who prefer Design 1	Number of people who prefer Design 2
Survey A	72	48
Survey B	230	270

a Calculate the percentage of people in Survey A who preferred Design 1.
b Calculate the percentage of people in Survey B who preferred Design 2.
c Which survey do you think gives the most reliable results?
d Which design would you advise the company to choose based on the results of these surveys?

Q4 Work out the area of cardboard needed to make the triangular end of Design 2.

LEVEL 7

Q5 Work out the area of cardboard needed to make the complete box for Design 2.

Q6 The company decides to use Design 2. They work out that 80 per cent of the box will be filled with chocolate. What volume of chocolate will be used in each box?

Practice SATs-style questions

LEVEL 5

Q1 a Complete the sentences.
i ___ out of 10 is the same as 20%.
ii 7 out of 25 is the same as ___%.
b Complete the sentence.
___ out of ___ is the same as 25%.
c Now complete the sentence in part **b** using different numbers.
___ out of ___ is the same as 25%.

Q2 Write the missing numbers in the boxes.
a 3500 *ml* is the same as ☐ litres.
b 600 *cl* is the same as ☐ litres.

LEVEL 6

Q3 a Write these values in order of size, smallest first.

4^3 3^4 2^3 5^2

___ ___ ___ ___
smallest largest

b Look at this information.
3^7 is 2187
What is 3^9?

Q4 Complete these fraction sums.

a $\frac{1}{5} + \frac{\square}{10} = 1$

b $\frac{1}{4} + \frac{9}{\square} = 1$

Q5 The graph shows the straight line with equation $y = 2x - 1$.

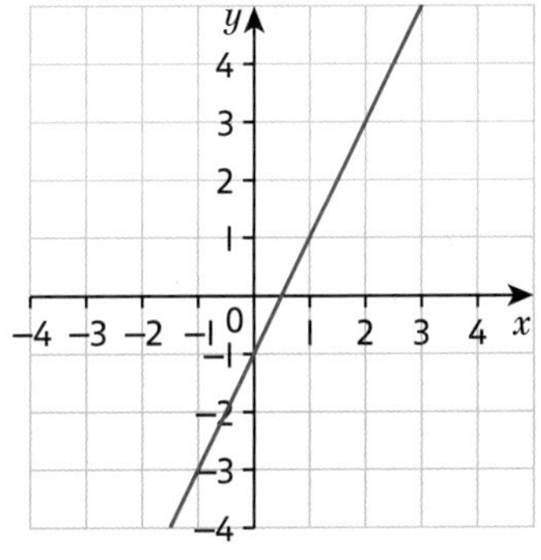

a A point on the line has an x-coordinate of 20.
What is its y-coordinate?
b A point on the line has a y-coordinate of 15.
What is its x-coordinate?

LEVEL 7

Q6 This shape is made of four congruent kites.
Calculate the size of angle x.

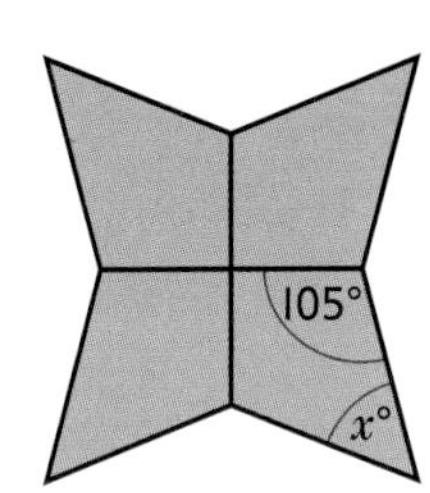

Q7 The diagram shows a circle and a square.
A is the centre of the circle.
The radius of the circle is 6 cm.
Calculate the area of the shaded part of the square.

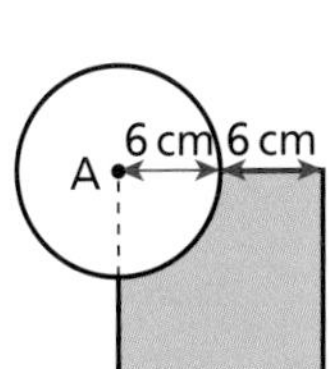

7 Into the unknown

This unit is about using letters to describe relationships in a variety of mathematical situations.

In ancient times, the cycles of the Moon and the journey of the stars across the sky were used to form relationships between divisions of time.

Early observations of the Moon showed that there were about 12 cycles in a year. Observation of a star against a landmark showed that it returned to the same landmark about 360 days later. This gave rise to 12 months in a year of 360 days, and clock faces divided up into 12.

Activities

A Hold out your hands. Your small finger on your left hand represents 2, your next finger 4, then 8, then 16 and so on.

Keep doubling until you get to your tenth finger.
Write the number that goes with each finger and thumb.

Hint: Think of powers

B In ancient times, the Sun, Moon and the five visible planets were each ranked according to how long they took to return to their starting position, as observed from the Earth. Starting with the longest, the list was Saturn, Jupiter, Mars, Sun, Venus, Mercury and Moon.

The hours were named after the planets, beginning with Saturday whose first hour was Saturn, second hour was Jupiter, and so on. The seventh hour was the Moon and (by returning to the start of the list) the eighth hour was Saturn, and so on for the 24 hours in a day. On the second day, the process continued. Each day was named after the planet of its first hour.

Work out which planet each day was named after.
Can you develop a quick way of working this out?

Use of base 60 comes from the early approximation of a year as 360 days. We still use base 60 for time and angles, but numbers and metric measurements use base 10, linked to our 10 fingers.

Before you start this unit...

1 Work out each of these:

a $3 + 4 \times 5$

b $(3 + 4) \times 5$

2 Simplify each expression.

a $2y - y + 4y$

b $5x + 7 - 2x + 4$

3 Tom has m cakes. If he gives away two, how many cakes does he have left?

4 The ABC Minibus Company work out the cost of journeys using the formula:
Cost (£) = 5 × number of miles + 8

What is the cost of each of these journeys?

a 5 miles

b 8 miles

c 20 miles

Did you know?

Between the 8th and 11th centuries, Arab and Persian astronomers in Baghdad made many amazing discoveries in astronomy, all without the aid of telescopes (which weren't invented until hundreds of years later in Europe). These medieval scientists drew up accurate 'star charts' that relied on the development of whole new fields of mathematics like algebra and geometry. They knew that the Earth was round and even predicted that it was the Earth that revolved around the Sun and not the other way around, as the ancient Greeks thought.

Plus digital resources

7.1 Using letters to communicate mathematically

- Use the equals sign correctly
- Write expressions from diagrams or word descriptions
- Explain what each letter means in a function or formula
- Recognise equations, expressions and identities

What's the BIG idea?

- **Equations** are true for particular values of x.
  For example, $2x + 4 = 12$ is only true for $x = 4$. **Level 5**
- An **expression** has no equals sign.
  In the expression $3x + 5$, $3x$ and $+5$ are **terms**. **Level 5**
- You can write expressions using algebra from word decriptions.
  For example,
  double p can be written $2p$
  p more than q can be written $p + q$
  p less than q can be written $q - p$ **Level 5 & Level 6**
- A **function** links two **variables** together.
  For example, time played (p) + time remaining (r) = length of game
  A football game is 90 minutes so you could write $p + r = 90$,
  $p = 90 - r$ or $r = 90 - p$. **Level 5 & Level 6**
- A **formula** links two or more variables together in a situation.
  It is often used to find a value for one variable given values for the others. **Level 5 & Level 6**
- **Identities** are true for every value of x. Both sides of the identity sign are equivalent, but they are written in different ways.
  For example, $3x + 2x \equiv 5x$ and $3a + a \equiv 2a + 2a$. **Level 6**
- Identities which do not have letters in them are called **arithmetic identities**.
  For example, $2 \times 17 \equiv 17 + 17$.
  Sometimes the equals sign (=) is used instead of the identity sign ($\equiv$). **Level 6**

Why learn this?

Algebra is the language of mathematics. We need to understand how to read and use it correctly to express what we mean.

Learn this

$\equiv$ is the identity sign.

Did you know?

A function is often shown as a graph.

Watch out!

Be careful how you use the equals sign.
✗ $3 \times 4 = 12 + 1 = 13$ is wrong.
✓ Write $3 \times 4 = 12$, $12 + 1 = 13$ or $3 \times 4 + 1 = 13$

Practice, practice, practice!

Level 5

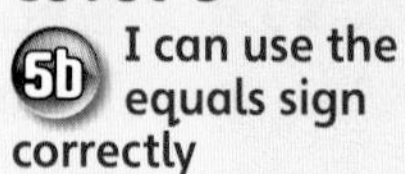
I can use the equals sign correctly

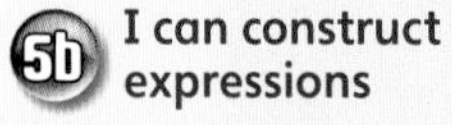
I can construct expressions

1 Copy these statements. Put = or ≠ in each empty box.

a $(7 + 3)^2$ ☐ $2^2 \times 5^2$ **b** $39 - 2$ ☐ $35 + 2$

c $3 \times 5 + 1$ ☐ 4^2 **d** $3 \times 5 + 1$ ☐ $4^2 + 1$ ☐ 17

2 Write an expression for the perimeter of each shape.

a rectangle with sides x and y **b** triangle with sides p, p, p **c** trapezium with sides 2, q, q, q

arithmetic identity   equation   expression   formula

3 Write an expression for the length of each red line.

a
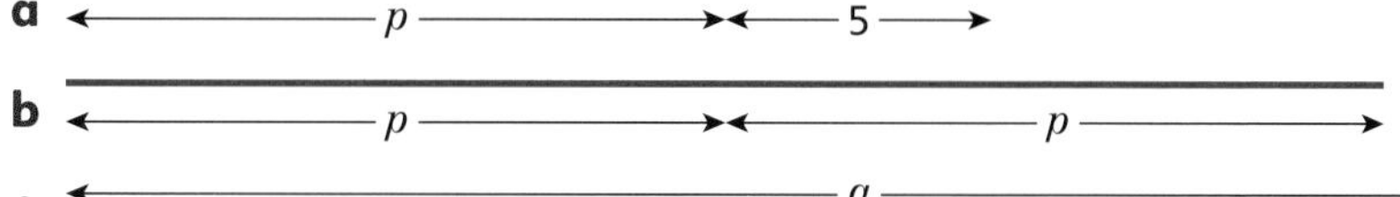

b
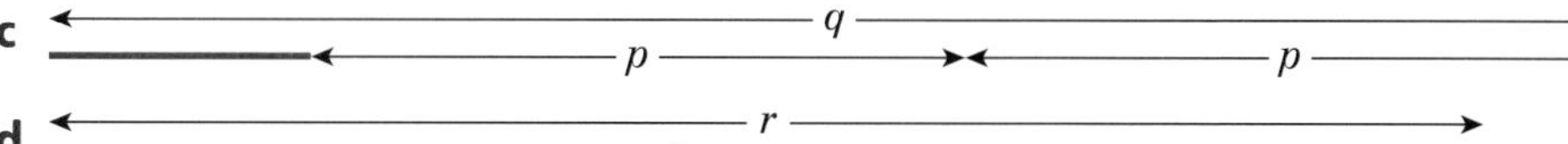

c
q
p
p

d
r
6
p

4 Write an expression for the area of each shape.

a
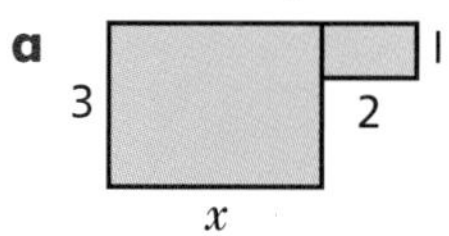

b
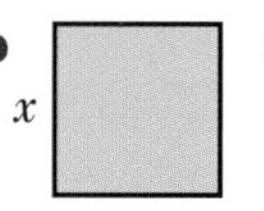

c
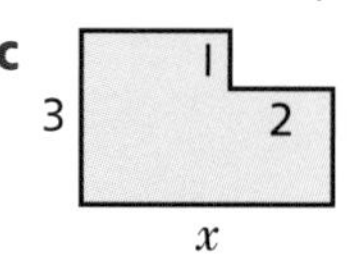

d
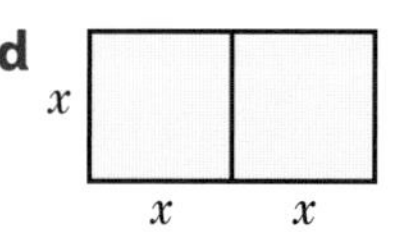

e
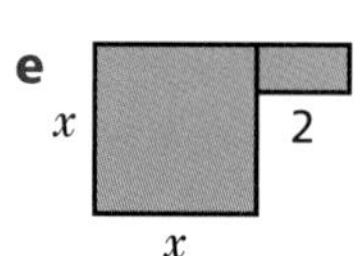

5 Write an expression for

a 3 less than n **b** n less than 3 **c** 3 more than n

d m more than n **e** m less than n **f** n less than m

g double m **h** half n

i 4 more than the square of n

j m less than the square of n

k add 4 to m and then multiply the result by 5

l subtract 3 from m and then halve the result

m multiply m by 5 and then divide by 3

Level 5

5b I can construct expressions

5a I can construct more complex expressions

6 Explain what each letter means in these formulae and functions.

a This function converts between hours and minutes: $y = 60x$

b This function converts between pounds and dollars and k is the number of dollars to one pound: $y = kx$

c This formula finds the perimeter of a regular hexagon: $y = 6x$

d This formula finds the perimeter of an isosceles triangle: $p = 2x + y$

e This formula finds the width of a rectangle: $w = \dfrac{p - 2l}{2}$

7 Copy these statements. Put = or ≡ in each empty box.

a $x + 3$ ☐ 7 **b** $x + x$ ☐ $2 \times x$

c $3 \times x + 3$ ☐ $2 + 4x - x + 1$ **d** $3 \times x + 1$ ☐ 4^2

8 Decide whether each of these is an expression, an equation or an identity.

a $3x + 4 \equiv x + 1 + 2x + 3$ **b** $3x + 4$

c $3x + 4 = 2x + 9$ **d** $3x + 4 + 2x + 9$

Level 6

6c I can explain what each letter means in a formula or function

6a I can use the identity sign correctly

6a I can distinguish between equations, expressions and identities

Now try this!

A Expressions of 23

Write some expressions which have the value 23 when $x = 5$. For example, $4x + 3$ or $x^2 - 2$.

B Hidden expressions

A game for two players. Player 1 secretly writes down an expression and then describes it in words to Player 2. Player 2 tries to write down the expression.
Player 1 scores 1 point for a correct description, Player 2 scores 1 point for a correct expression. Swap roles and repeat.

function identity term variable

7.2 From arithmetic to algebraic operations

- Use the equals sign correctly
- Understand and use the distributive law
- Work out expressions in arithmetic or algebra using the correct order of operations

Why learn this?

The order in which calculations are done makes a big difference. For example, when calculating tax on earnings, pension contributions are deducted before the tax is worked out.

What's the BIG idea?

- **Substitution** means replacing letters with numbers to work out a result. For example, substituting $a = 5$ and $b = 7$ in $c = 3a + 4b$ gives $c = 43$. **Level 5**
- You can use the **distributive law** to break up a multiplication or to combine two multiplications of the same number or letter.
  For example, $23 \times 12 = 20 \times 12 + 3 \times 12$
  $18 \times 12 = 20 \times 12 - 2 \times 12$
  $6 \times a + 4 \times a = 10 \times a$ (means the same as $6a + 4a = 10a$)
  To simplify an expression, collect **like terms**.
  Like terms have the same letter. **Level 5**
- The correct **order of operations** is
  Brackets → **I**ndices (**powers**) → **D**ivision and **M**ultiplication → **A**ddition and **S**ubtraction
  For example, $2 + 4 \times (6 + 4)^2 = 2 + 4 \times 10^2$ brackets
  $= 2 + 4 \times 100$ then powers
  $= 2 + 400$ then multiplication
  $= 402$ then addition **Level 5**
- The order of operations in **algebra** is the same as in **arithmetic**. **Level 5 & Level 6**

Watch out!

$(3 + 7) \div 5$ and $\frac{3 + 7}{5}$ are the same.
The fraction line works like a bracket. It shows that everything is divided by 5.

Practice, practice, practice!

Level 5

5c I can use the distributive law in arithmetic

1 Copy and complete these calculations.

a $27 \times 12 + 13 \times 12 = \square \times 12 = \square$

b $6.4 \times 14.7 + 3.6 \times 14.7 = \square \times 14.7 = \square$

c $27 \times 0.78 + 73 \times 0.78 = \square \times 0.78 = \square$

5c I can use the distributive law in algebra

2 Copy and complete these identities.

a $3 \times a + 5 \times a \equiv \square \times a$

b $9 \times a + \square \times a \equiv 12a$

c $2 \times a + \square \times a + 3 \times b + \square \times b \equiv 9a + 15b$

5c I can simplify expressions by collecting like terms

3 Simplify these expressions by collecting like terms.

a $13a + 10b + 8a + 3b$ **b** $12a + 18b + 4a - 8b$ **c** $12a + 18b - 4a + 8b$

algebra arithmetic distributive law expression indices

4 Work out each of these expressions.

a $3 + 4 \times 5$ **b** $80 - 3 \times 7$

c $8 - 4 \times 5$ **d** $20 + 18 \div 3$

Watch out!
$3 + 4 \times 5$ is the same as $4 \times 5 + 3$.

5 Work out each of these expressions when $a = 3$ and $b = 5$.

a $3 + 5b$ **b** $7 - 8b$ **c** $3b + a \div 2$

d $a(5 + b)$ **e** $7(2a + b)$ **f** $2a(3 - 2b)$

Level 5

5c I can use the order of operations

5a I can use the order of operations with algebra

6 Write each missing value.

a

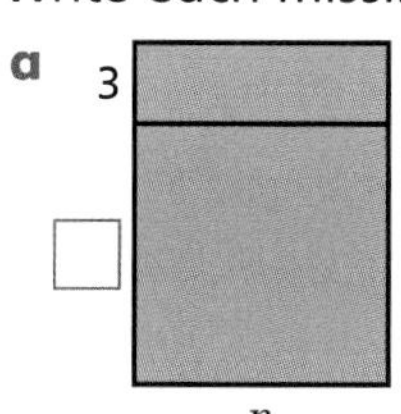

area = $3n + \square n = 7n$

b

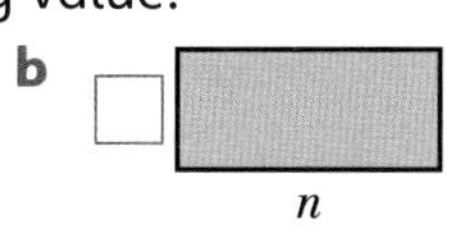

area = $2n$

c

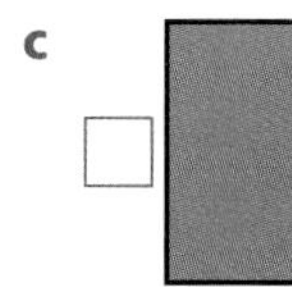

area = n^2

d

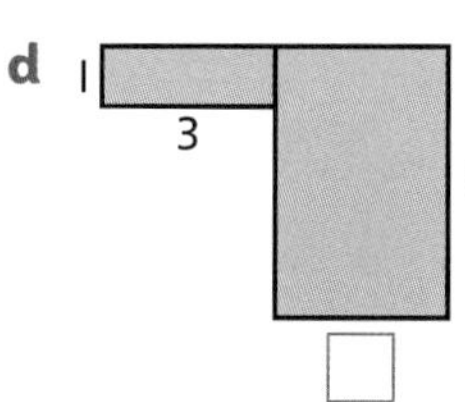

area = $3 + 4n$

7 Work out the area of each shape in Q6 when $n = 9$.

8 Copy and complete this table.

n	1	3	4		9			
$2n$							24	60
n^2				49		121		

Watch out!
$2n$ means double n; that's n multiplied by 2. n^2 means n multiplied by itself.

9 Work out these expressions.

a $3 + 4(3 + 7)^2$

b $3a^2b$, when $a = 3$ and $b = 4$

c $5 + (b^3 - a)$, when $a = 2$ and $b = 3$

d $(a + b)^2 - c$, when $a = 5$, $b = 2$ and $c = 1$

e $\frac{ab + cd}{b + c}$, when $a = 6$, $b = 3$, $c = 1$ and $d = 4$

Tip
Make sure you follow the order of operations when working out an expression. So, for example, if you're working out $5n^2$, remember to square n before multiplying by 5.

Level 6

6c I can work with diagrammatic representations of expressions

6c I can apply the order of operations to substitution in simple cases.

6b I can correctly calculate $2n$ and n^2

6a I can use the correct order of operations when substituting whole numbers into algebraic expressions

Now try this!

A Find the better deal!

A shop has a sale on. For all items originally priced above £40, the customer can choose between a £3 discount and then $\frac{1}{5}$ off, or $\frac{1}{5}$ off and then a £3 discount. Which option should they choose? Try a few examples with different prices to help you describe which is better and why.

B Special deals

Another shop has a sale where customers pay $\frac{3}{5}$ of the original price.
On Tuesdays there is an extra 10% off the sale price. Does the order in which the discounts are applied matter? Try a few different prices and explain your answer.

like terms order of operations powers substitution

7.3 Understanding powers

- Understand powers with positive whole numbers
- Understand basic rules of powers (index laws)
- Simplify expressions that include powers

What's the BIG idea?

- Positive whole-number **powers** (or **indices**) represent repeated multiplication.
  For example, $2^5 = 2 \times 2 \times 2 \times 2 \times 2$ **Level 6**
- The **index law** for multiplication is $x^a \times x^b = x^{a+b}$
  For example, $2^5 \times 2^3 = 2 \times 2 \times 2 \times 2 \times 2 \times 2 \times 2 \times 2 = 2^{5+3} = 2^8$
- The index law for division is $x^a \div x^b = x^{a-b}$
  For example, $2^5 \div 2^3 = \dfrac{2 \times 2 \times 2 \times 2 \times 2}{2 \times 2 \times 2} = 2^{5-3} = 2^2$ **Level 6 & Level 7**
- You can simplify **expressions** with powers:
  - Collect like terms.
    $3x^2 + 5x^3 - 9x^2 + 2x^3 = -6x^2 + 7x^3$
    You can only collect terms which have the same power of the same letters.
  - To multiply terms with letters and numbers, multiply the numbers then the letters.
    $6x^7 \times 3y^5 = 6 \times x^7 \times 3 \times y^5 = 6 \times 3 \times x^7 \times y^5 = 18 \times x^7 \times y^5 = 18x^7y^5$
    $6x^7 \times 3x^5 = 6 \times x^7 \times 3 \times x^5 = 6 \times 3 \times x^7 \times x^5 = 18 \times x^7 \times x^5 = 18x^{12}$
  - To divide terms with letters and numbers, divide the numbers, then the letters.
    For example, $6x^7 \div 3x^5 = 6 \div 3 \times x^7 \div x^5 = 2 \times x^7 \div x^5 = 2x^2$ or $\dfrac{6x^7}{3x^5} = 2x^{7-5} = 2x^2$ **Level 7**

Why learn this?

You have $2^5 = 32$ great great great grandparents. Using powers helps make some calculations easier.

Super fact!

You can transmit bacterial infections through touch. Some bacteria divide every 20 minutes, so even if you start off with only one bacterium, after 10×20 minutes (3 hours 20 minutes) you could have 2^{10}; that's over 1000!

Practice, practice, practice!

1 Copy and complete.

$2^5 = 2 \times 2 \times 2 \times 2 \times 2$

a $2^3 =$ ____ **b** $2^2 =$ ____ **c** $2^1 =$ ____ **d** $2^4 =$ ____

2 Simplify these expressions by using powers.

$2 \times 2 \times 2 \times 3 \times 3 \times 3 \times 3 \times 3 \times 3 = 2^3 \times 3^6$

a $2 \times 5 \times 2 \times 5 \times 5 \times 2 \times 2 \times 5 \times 5$ **b** $2 \times 3 \times 2 \times 3 \times 3 \times 2 \times 3 \times 3 \times 3$

c $y \times y \times y \times z \times z \times z \times z \times z$ **d** $y \times 3 \times y \times z \times 3 \times z \times z \times z \times z$

e $y \times 3 \times y \times z \times 3 \times z \times y \times z \times y$ **f** $x \times x \times y \times 3 \times 4 \times x \times 3 \times x \times y$

3 Simplify these expressions by collecting like terms.

$x^5 + x^5 + y^2 + x^5 + y^2 + x^5 = x^5 + x^5 + x^5 + x^5 + y^2 + y^2 = 4x^5 + 2y^2$

a $7x^5 + 2y^2 - 2x^5 + 3y^2 + x^5$ **b** $2x^5 + 2y^2 + 7x^5 - 3y^2 - x^2$

c $3x^5 + 4y^2 + 8x^5 + 3y^2 + 2x^2$ **d** $3x^5 + 4y^2 - 8x^5 - 3y^2 + 2x^2$

Level 6

6c I can use powers to describe repeated multiplication

6b I can use powers in algebra to describe repeated multiplication

6b I can simplify algebraic expressions involving powers by collecting like terms

base evaluate expression index (indices)

4 Work out the value of these expressions when $c = 3$ and $d = 2$.

a $4d + c^2$ **b** $4c^2$ **c** $3d^3$ **d** $5c^3 + 2d^3$

e $10d^3 - 6c$ **f** $2c^3 - 9$ **g** $-5c + 2d^2$ **h** $8d$

Level 6

6a I can substitute integers into simple expressions involving small powers

5 Simplify these expressions.

a $\frac{2 \times 5 \times 2 \times 5 \times 5 \times 2 \times 2 \times 5 \times 5}{2 \times 5 \times 2 \times 2 \times 5}$ **b** $\frac{y \times z \times 12 \times y \times y}{y \times z \times 3 \times z \times y}$

6 Simplify these expressions.

$3x^2 \times 4x^3 = 3 \times 4 \times x^{2+3} = 12x^5$

a $5x^4 \times 6x^2$ **b** $3x^2 \times 4y^2 \times 2x^3$ **c** $5x^4 \times y \times 8y^3$

d $7x^6 \times 4y^2 \times 5x$ **e** $3y^6 \times 5x \times 4y^2 \times 5x$ **f** $x^7 \times 2 \times 4y^4 \times 8y^8$

7 Simplify these expressions.

a $c^3 \div c$ **b** $8c^3 \div c^2$ **c** $8c^3 \div 2c$ **d** $20c^5 \div 5c^2$

8 Write each of these expressions in the form $p^x \times q^y$.

a $pq \times pq$ **b** $pq \times pq \times pq$ **c** $pq \times pq \times p$

9 **a** Work out the total area of each 2-D shape.

i

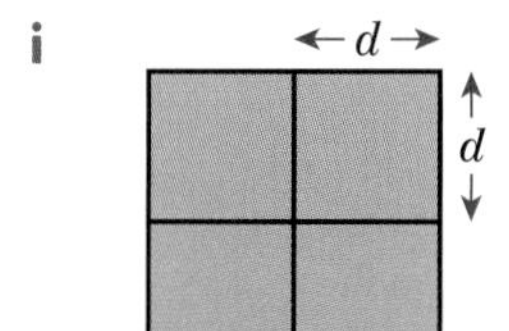

ii

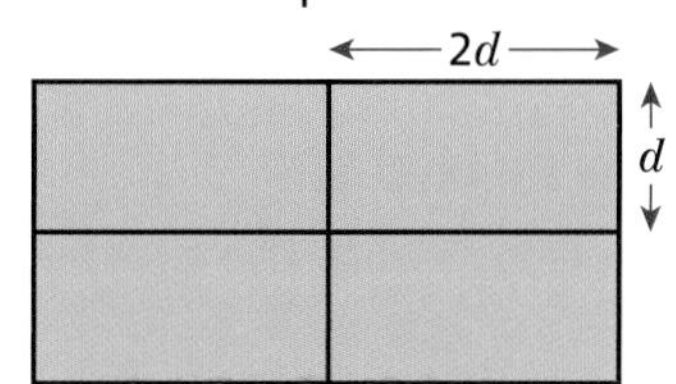

iii

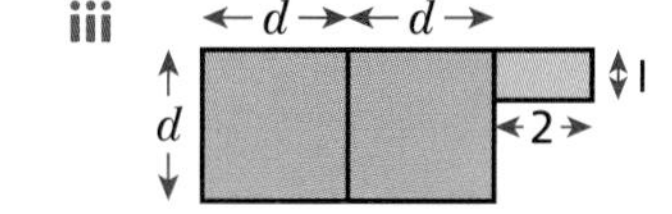

iv

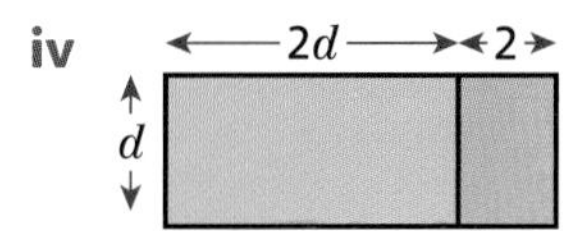

v

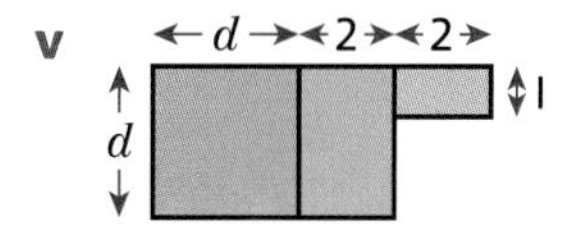

b Work out the volume of each 3-D shape.

i

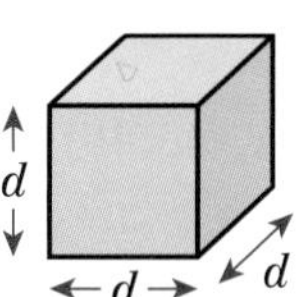

ii

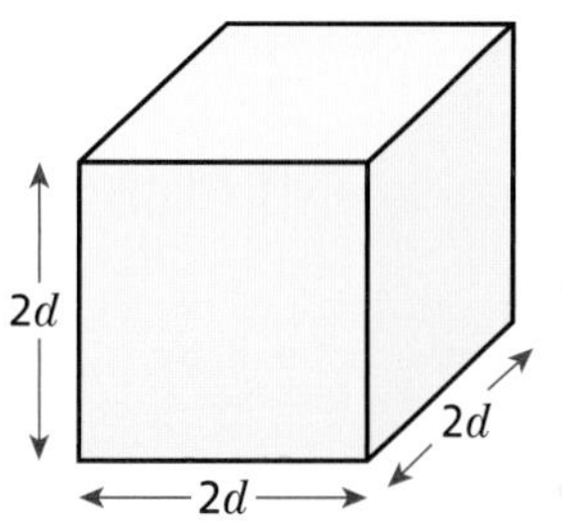

c Calculate the area of the shapes in part **a** and the volume of the shapes in part **b** when $d = 7$.

Level 7

7c I can simplify algebraic fractions by cancelling common factors

7b I can use the index laws for small positive powers of letters

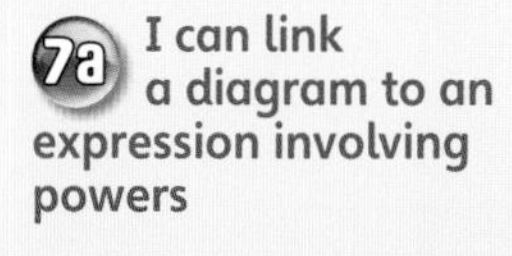

7a I can link a diagram to an expression involving powers

Tip

Volume of cube = length × width × height

Now try this!

A Powerful expressions

A game for a small group. Each player has three minutes to write $20p^8$ as the sum or product of two terms in as many ways as possible. Two examples are $12p^8 + 8p^8$ and $4p^5 \times 5p^3$. At the end, each player scores 10 points for any expression that no one else has written down.

B Find an equivalent

A game for two players. Player 1 writes an expression involving powers. Player 2 must write an equivalent expression.
For example, if Player 1 writes $2f^3$, Player 2 could write $f^3 + f^3$.
Swap roles and repeat.

index law power substitute

7.4 Understanding brackets

- Multiply out a bracket
- Simplify an expression by multiplying out brackets and collecting like terms

Why learn this?

Brackets appear in many expressions in both arithmetic and algebra. For every expression written with brackets there is an equivalent expression without brackets.

What's the BIG idea?

→ When using the **order of operations**, **brackets** are always done first.
So $3 + 4 \times 5 = 3 + 20 = 23$, but $(3 + 4) \times 5 = 7 \times 5 = 35$.
For example, if three boys each want a chocolate bar and a can of cola, they can each buy one chocolate bar and one can of cola. You can write this:

brackets mean $b + c$ *all* multiplied by 3

total cost $= 3(b + c)$

cost of chocolate bar — cost of can of cola

It will cost the same if one boy buys three chocolate bars and another buys three cans of cola. You can write this:

total cost $= 3b + 3c$

So $3(b + c) = 3b + 3c$. **Level 5 & Level 6**

→ To multiply out a bracket, multiply each term inside the bracket by the term outside. For example, $3(b + c) = 3 \times b + 3 \times c = 3b + 3c$.
This example shows why it works.
You can work out the total area of this rectangle in two ways.

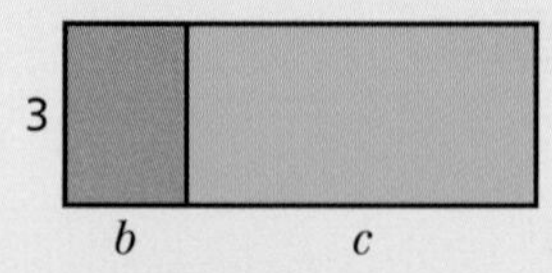

area $= 3(b + c)$

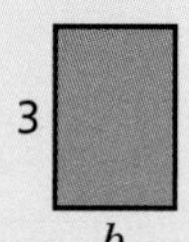

3 c

area $= 3b + 3c$ **Level 6**

→ To simplify an expression with brackets, multiply out the brackets, then collect **like terms**.
For example, $2(e + f + 3g) - 4(f + g) = 2e + 2f + 6g - 4f - 4g$
$= 2e + 2f - 4f + 6g - 4g$
$= 2e - 2f + 2g$ **Level 6**

Did you know?

'Multiplying out' a bracket is sometimes called 'expanding' the bracket.

Watch out!

Remember to multiply every term in the bracket by the term outside.

Practice, practice, practice!

Level 5

5b I can multiply out a simple bracket

1 Copy and complete.

a **i** $4(5 + 2) = 4 \times 5 + 4 \times \square = \square + \square = \square$

ii $4(5 + 2) = 4 \times \square = \square$

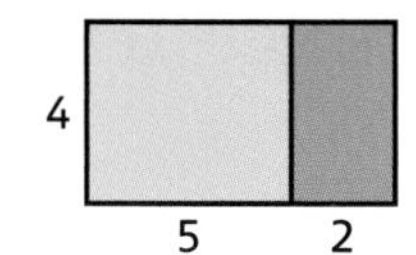

b $5(7 + a) = 5 \times 7 + \square \times \square = \square + \square$

c $6(a + b) = \square \times a + \square \times \square = \square + \square$

bracket constant expand expression

2 Copy and complete the table to show the two equivalent ways of working out the area of each diagram.

	Working out area of outer rectangle	Working out area of separate rectangles
a 3; 2, 4		$3 \times 2 + 3 \times 4 = 6 + 12$ $= 18$
b 3; a, 4		
c 3; a, b		

3 Multiply out these brackets.

a $3(x + 2)$ **b** $4(6 + y)$ **c** $2(x - 3)$ **d** $5(2m + 3)$

e $4(3n - 2)$ **f** $7(3 - 2p)$ **g** $9(5q + 7)$ **h** $6(8 - 3r)$

4 **a** Draw an area diagram for each expression.

i $3(x + 2)$ **ii** $4(3 + y)$ **iii** $x(y + 5)$ **iv** $2(x + y + 1)$

b Work out the value of each expression when $x = 5$ and $y = 4$.

Level 5

5b I can multiply out brackets involving algebra

5a I can evaluate expressions involving brackets

5 Multiply out each bracket and simplify the expression.

a $6(3x + 5) + 5$ **b** $7(3x - 5) - 8x$

c $9(7x - 2) + 8x(3 + x + 2y)$ **d** $6(3x - 7) + 2(5 - x)$

e $x(5 + 7) + y(6 - 2)$ **f** $x(8 - 3) - 2(x + 1)$

g $-3(2 + y)$ **h** $-3(2 - y + z)$

i $6(2 + 5x - z) - 3(2 + y)$ **j** $5(2 - 3x) - 4(x - 2)$

6 Find the values of a and b such that

a $3(x + 2y) + 4y \equiv ax + by$ **b** $7(x - 2y) - 3(2x + y) \equiv ax + by$

c $2(3x - 4y) + 6(2y - 5x) \equiv ax + by$ **d** $-5(x - 3y) - 4(y + x) \equiv ax + by$

Level 6

6a I can simplify expressions involving brackets

6a I can simplify expressions to find constants in an identity

Now try this!

A Looking for solutions

Use positive whole numbers to complete this equation in as many ways as you can.

□(□ + △) = 24

The numbers in both squares must be the same. The triangle can have the same number or a different one.

B Makes 24

Find all the integer values, both positive and negative, for which

a $x(x + y) = 24$

b $p(2p + q) = 24$

Make up a similar problem with a partner. Swap with another pair. Do you agree on the solutions?

identity integer like terms order of operations

7.5 More brackets

- Factorise by taking out a number as a factor
- Factorise by taking out an algebraic factor
- Substitute a positive or negative whole number into an expression with one or more brackets, involving small powers

Why learn this?

It is good to know how to write expressions in equivalent ways. Buying two cups and two saucers, $2c + 2s$, is the same as buying two cup and saucer sets, $2(c + s)$.

What's the BIG idea?

- You can find factors of an **algebraic** term.
  $18x$ has factors 1, 2, 3, (6), 9, 18, x
  6 has factors 1, 2, 3, (6) — 6 is the HCF of 6 and $18x$ **Level 6**
- To **factorise** an expression, take out a common factor of each term and put it outside the **bracket**.
  For example,
  $6(3x + 1)$ —expanding→ $18x + 6$
  $18x + 6$ —factorising→ $6(3x + 1)$
  Factorising and **expanding** brackets are **inverse** (opposite) processes. **Level 6**
- To **fully factorise** an expression, take out the **highest common factor**.
  For example, $8p + 4 = 2(4p + 2) = 4(2p + 1)$
  partly factorised — fully factorised **Level 6**
- You can find factors of algebraic terms involving **powers**.
  To fully factorise $c^3 + c^7$:
  The highest common factor is the highest power that occurs in both terms.
  So the highest common factor of $c^3 + c^7$ is c^3. $c^3 + c^7 = c^3(1 + c^4)$
  For expressions with numbers and letters, factorise the numbers, then the letters.
  For example: $2c^3y^5 + 6c^7y^2z = 2(c^3y^5 + 3c^7y^2z)$
  $= 2c^3(y^5 + 3c^4y^2z)$
  $= 2c^3y^2(y^3 + 3c^4z)$ **Level 7**

Tip
When factorising, consider the numbers first and then work through each letter at a time.

Practice, practice, practice!

Level 5
5a I can multiply out brackets involving algebra

1 Expand the brackets.

a $3(2x - 4)$ **b** $6(x - 2)$ **c** $6(3x + 6)$ **d** $18(x + 2)$

Level 6
6b I can begin to factorise an expression by taking out the common number factor

2 Copy and complete these equations.

a $3x + 15 = 3(x + \square)$
b $6x + 15 = 3(\square + \square)$
c $40 - 15x = \square(\square - \square)$
d $49x - 28 = \square(\square - \square)$
e $32 - 40x = \square(\square - \square)$
f $-6x - 12 = \square(\square + \square)$

algebraic bracket (highest) common factor expand

3 Copy and complete the tables.

a

Unfactorised	Factorised
$8x + 12$	$4(2x + 3)$
	$7(2x - 5)$
$15x + 20$	
$35x - 45$	

b

Unfactorised	Factorised
	$12(5 - 3x)$
$33x + 77$	
$75 - 45x$	
	$8(2x + 7)$

Level 6

6a I can factorise an expression by taking out the common number factor

4 Fully factorise

a $4x + 8$ **b** $4x^2 + 8x$ **c** $4x^3 + 8x^2$ **d** $6x - 2x^3$

e $y^2 + 5y^3$ **f** $9y^5 - 3y^3$ **g** $10y^4 - 5y^2$ **h** $12y^7 + 9y^5$

5 Fully factorise

a $3x + 6y + 9z$ **b** $xy + 5y + yz$ **c** $x^2 + 6xy + 9xz$

d $5x^2 + 10xy + 15xz$ **e** $3x^2 + 6xy - 9xyz$ **f** $2xy + 2y^2 + 6xyz$

g $x^3 + 2x^2y + 5x^2z$ **h** $12xy - 4x^2y^2 + 8yz$ **i** $2x^2y^2 - 4xy + 2xy^2$

6 In this identity c, d and e are positive integers.

$c(dx + ey) \equiv 36x + 54y$

a Find the maximum value of c.

b What are the values of d and e for this value of c?

7 Find the value of each expression when $x = 3$, $y = -2$ and $z = 5$.

a $3(x^3 + y)$ **b** $3x(x + z)$ **c** $y^2(x + z^3)$

d $4x(3 - z) + y$ **e** $5(x^2 + y) + x(3x + 2)$ **f** $5y(x + y^3 + z) + 3y^2(x + 3z)$

Level 7

7c I can factorise an expression by taking out an algebraic common factor

7c I can find the values of constants in an identity by factorising

7c I can substitute positive and negative numbers into expressions involving small powers and brackets

Now try this!

A Polygon factors

Draw as many regular polygons as possible with a perimeter of $24x + 36$.
Write an expression for the side of each polygon. Your expression must contain only whole numbers.
For example, a regular hexagon with sides of length $4x + 6$ has a perimeter of $6(4x + 6) = 24x + 36$.
Now write down the side length and number of sides of each regular polygon with a perimeter of $60x + 90$.

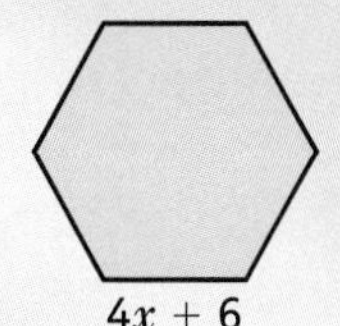

B Maximise!

A game for two players. Roll a dice twice. Use the numbers on the dice to fill in the boxes in this expression from left to right.

$x(\square x + \square y)$

Both players have one minute to find values of x and y that maximise the value of the expression, and where $x + y = 10$. The player with the largest value for the expression scores 1 point. If both players achieve the same value, both score 1 point.

Did you know?

You get exactly the same answer, whether you substitute the value for x before you factorise an expression or afterwards.

factorise fully factorise inverse power

maths!

Mathemagicians

A lot of 'magic' tricks can be explained with mathematics – how many of these can you unravel?

Card Luck

These cards are part of a magic trick. Ask a friend to pick a number between 1 and 15 and tell them to point to all of the cards on which their number appears. If you add up the numbers in the top left corners of these cards you will get their number!

1	3	5	7
9	11	13	15

2	3	6	7
10	11	14	15

4	5	6	7
12	13	14	15

8	9	10	11
12	13	14	15

Here's how it works:

- Describe the sequence of numbers in the top left hand corners of the cards.
- Any number can be written as the sum of different powers of 2 (1, 2, 4, 8…). Check this by writing 10 and 15 as the sum of powers of 2.
- Now look at the cards – which cards do 10 and 15 appear on?
- Try and explain in your own words how this trick works.
- Draw a fifth card with the next power of 2 in the top left hand corner. Fill in the numbers 16 to 31 on the correct cards so that the trick will now work with any number from 1 to 31.

*

And the Answer is...

Think of a number. Triple it, and then add 9. Multiply this by 2. Divide this by 6. Take away the number you first thought of. The number you are thinking of is 3.

Call the original number you thought of 'n' and use algebra to show why this trick always works.

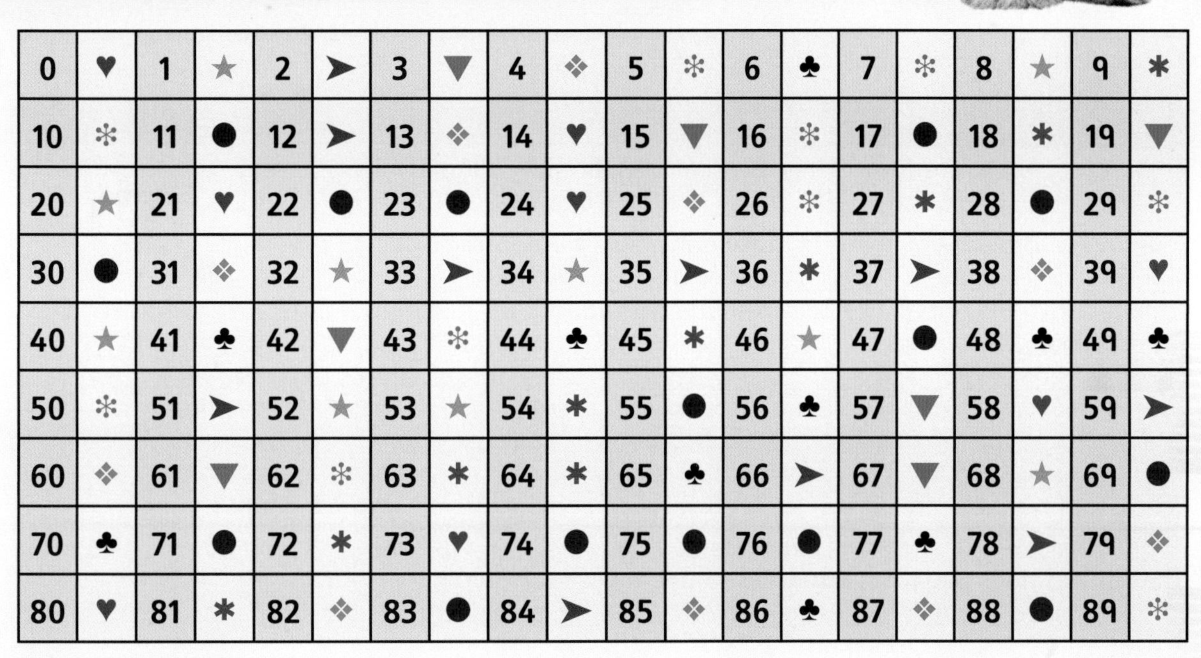

0	♥	1	★	2	➤	3	▼	4	❖	5	❇	6	♣	7	❇	8	★	9	✱
10	❇	11	●	12	➤	13	❖	14	♥	15	▼	16	❇	17	●	18	✱	19	▼
20	★	21	♥	22	●	23	●	24	♥	25	❖	26	❇	27	✱	28	●	29	❇
30	●	31	❖	32	★	33	➤	34	★	35	➤	36	✱	37	➤	38	❖	39	♥
40	★	41	♣	42	▼	43	❇	44	♣	45	✱	46	★	47	●	48	♣	49	♣
50	❇	51	➤	52	★	53	★	54	✱	55	●	56	♣	57	▼	58	♥	59	➤
60	❖	61	▼	62	❇	63	✱	64	✱	65	♣	66	➤	67	▼	68	★	69	●
70	♣	71	●	72	✱	73	♥	74	●	75	●	76	●	77	♣	78	➤	79	❖
80	♥	81	✱	82	❖	83	●	84	➤	85	❖	86	♣	87	❖	88	●	89	❇

Mind Reader

This trick is guaranteed to read your mind – or so it seems!

Choose a two digit number, for example 78. Now subtract the two digits that make up that number (so subtract 7 and subtract 8) and look in the table for the symbol to the right of your answer. Think hard about that symbol... and it will appear at the bottom of the page opposite!

Here's how it works:

- Let's call the two digit number "AB". Write down an expression in algebra for how much this number is worth.
(Hint: it's not just A + B – think about which column A is in.)
- Now take away the two digits A and B. Simplify your algebra.
- Go through the values of A to work out what your final answer could be worth. Now look at the grid carefully and explain in your own words why this trick works.

7.6 Developing and using formulae

- Substitute numbers into formulae
- Write formulae

Why learn this?

Formulae can help describe situations that work in the same way for different numbers. The cost of hiring a vehicle depends on its type, how long you have it and how far you travel.

What's the BIG idea?

- A formula links two or more variables together.
- When **substituting** into **formulae**, remember to apply the correct **order of operations**.
  Brackets → **I**ndices (powers) → **D**ivision and **M**ultiplication → **A**ddition and **S**ubtraction **Level 5 & Level 6**
- To derive a formula you need to make **generalisations**. Start by using different numbers to see what can change and what stays the same.
  Look for patterns but do not complete the calculation.
  For example

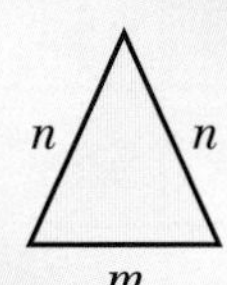

Perimeter (in cm) $3 + 2 \times 5$ $4 + 2 \times 6$ $m + 2 \times n$ **Level 5 & Level 6**

- 'Write a formula for P' means 'Write $P =$ ____'.
  '**In terms of**' tells you what **variables** to use in your formula.
  For example, a formula for the perimeter, P, of a square in terms of the side length, x, is $P = 4x$. **Level 5 & Level 6**

Tip

When evaluating expressions such as ab^2, remember that powers come before multiplication, so square b before multiplying by a.

Practice, practice, practice!

Level 5

5c I can write and use simple algebraic formulae

5b I can substitute positive numbers into algebraic formulae

1 l is the original length of a piece of ribbon. A smaller piece, c, is cut from it.

- **a** Write a formula for the length of ribbon which remains, r.
- **b** If $r = 2$ m and $l = 2.6$ m, find c.

2 This design is made with wire.
The formula for the length of the wire is $L = 3(m + 2n)$

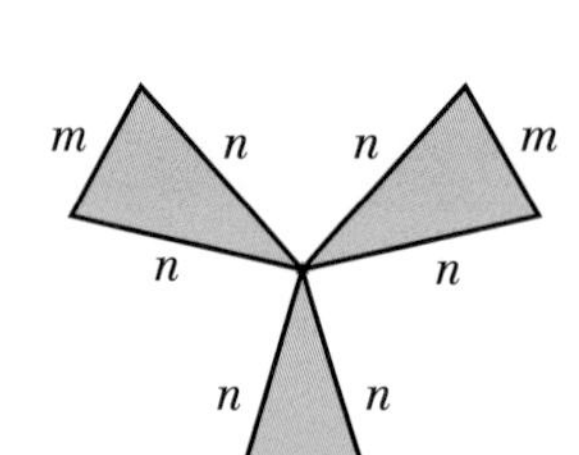

Find L when $m = 5$ cm and $n = 8$ cm.

$L = 3(5 + 2 \times 8)$
$= 3(5 + 16)$
$= 3 \times 21 = 63$ cm

- **a** Find L when $m = 10$ cm and $n = 15$ cm.
- **b** Find L when $m = 0.4$ m and $n = 0.7$ m.
- **c** Find L when $m = 0.1$ m and $n = 20$ cm.

Learn this

Learn the order of operations because you will always need it.
Brackets
Indices (power)
Division and Multiplication
Addition and Subtraction

formula (formulae) generalisation in terms of

3 **a** A cube skeleton is made with lengths of wire, p.
Write a formula for the total length of wire needed, L.

b Write a formula for the total length of wire needed, M, to make the half-cube skeleton.

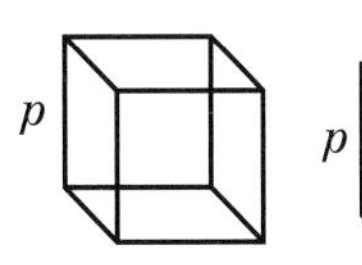

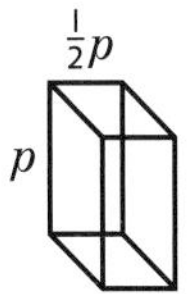

Level 5

5a I can derive a one-step formula by solving a problem

4 Find the area of each trapezium using this formula.

a

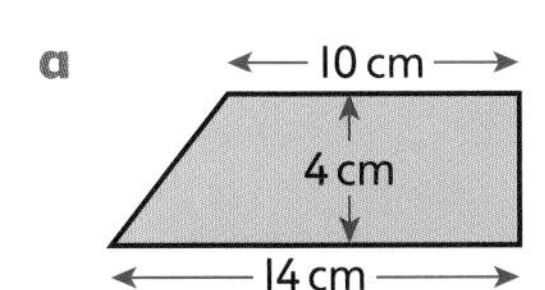

b

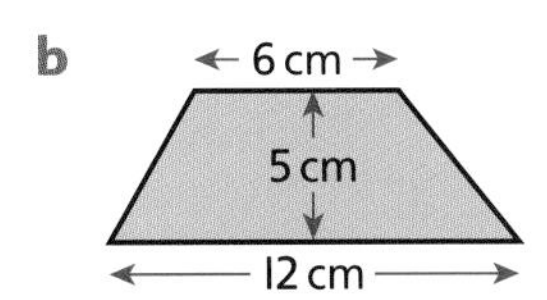

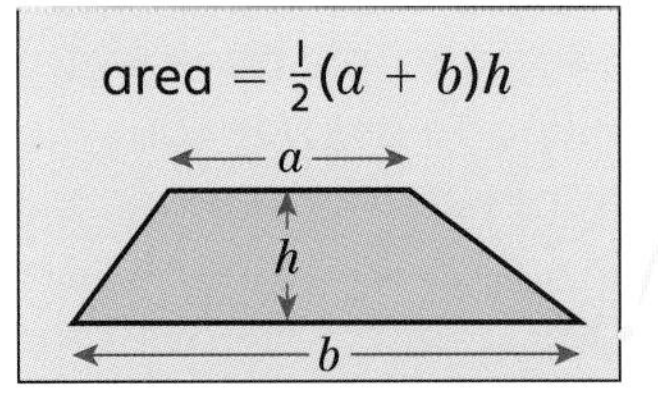

Level 6

6c I can substitute positive numbers into more difficult algebraic formulae

5 A dance studio has several rehearsal rooms, each in the shape of a regular hexagon. Each room has a door along one of the walls.
A skirting board goes around the walls but not across the door.

a Calculate the amount of skirting board needed for a room with sides of length 4 m and a door 1.2 m wide.

b Write a formula for the length of skirting board, B, needed for a room with sides of length w and a door of width d.

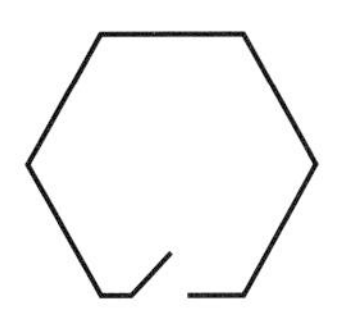

6c I can derive a two-step formula by solving a problem

6 Write a formula to find the area, A, of each shape in terms of the letters marked on the diagrams.

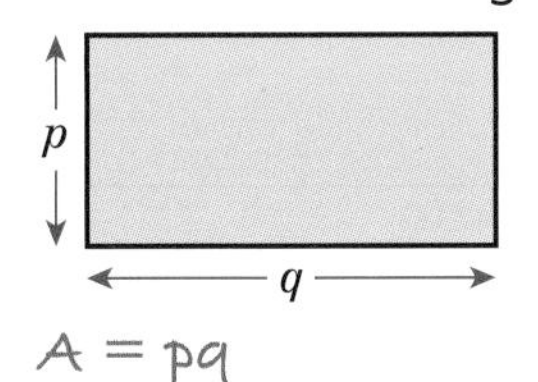

a

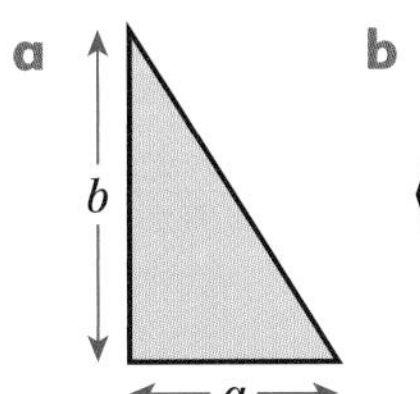

b

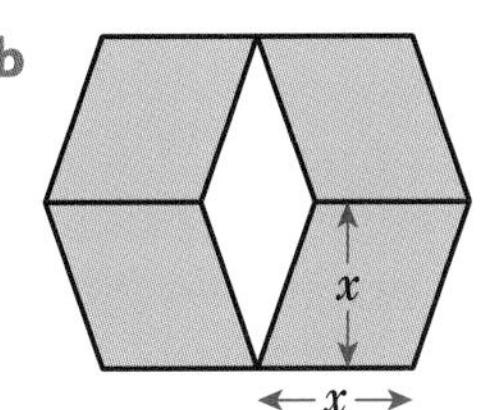

6c I can derive a formula based on the area of a shape

7 The cost of laying a wooden floor is £35 per square metre.
The floor is then edged with a narrow wooden strip which costs £4 per metre.

a How much does it cost to floor a 6 m by 4 m room, including the edging?

b Write a formula for the cost, C, of laying and edging a wooden floor in a rectangular room of width w and length l.

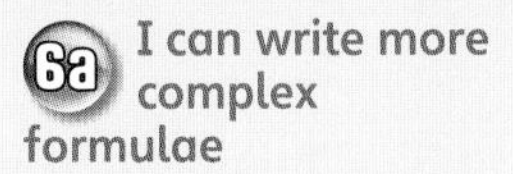

6a I can write more complex formulae

8 The formula for a worker's daily pay, P, depends on the number of hours worked, h, the hourly rate of pay, r, and a travel allowance, t, which does not depend on the hours worked or the hourly rate.

a Work out how much a worker is paid for working a 7-hour day if the hourly rate is £7.50 and the travel allowance is £8.

b Write a formula for the daily pay, P, in terms of h, r and t.

Now try this!

A Pond perimeters

A quadrilateral-shaped pond has a perimeter of 10 m and integer side lengths x m and y m. The formula for its perimeter is $P = 2x + 2y$. Sketch as many possible pond shapes as you can, writing down the values of x and y for each one.

B Going round the edges

Construct a formula to find one of the side lengths, x, of a rectangle given its perimeter P and its other side length y.
Compare this with the formula $P = 2x + 2y$. How can you tell that these formulae are equivalent?

order of operations substitution variables

New planets!

You are an astronaut. After two months in space you have discovered a new planet – the Planet Ziply. The inhabitants of Planet Ziply have welcomed you warmly and are willing to answer your questions. The only trouble is they do not answer questions fully – they give you information so that you can work out the answer yourself! Oh, ... and they love algebra!

1 *We have 8 months, each of z days.*
Write an expression for the total number of days in a Ziply year. **Level 5**

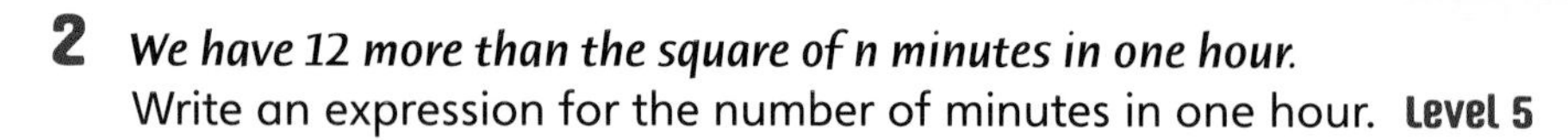

2 *We have 12 more than the square of n minutes in one hour.*
Write an expression for the number of minutes in one hour. **Level 5**

3 *Our population numbers* $17a + 4b + 12b - 6a + 9b - 2b$.
Simplify this expression. **Level 5**

4 *The Queen of Ziply has a palace with perimeter* $8(2x + 7y)$ *ziplees.*
If $x = 9$ and $y = 7$, what is the perimeter of the Queen's palace? **Level 5**

5 *We are* $4 \times 6 \times 6 \times 6 \times 6 \times 4 \times 4 \times 6 \times 4 \times 6 \times 4 \times 4$ *ziplees away from Earth.*
Use powers to simplify this expression. **Level 6**

6 *We sell our goods to the Planet Youg. In 2007, we made* $8(5x - 4) + 7(3 - 3x)$ *Ziply punds.*
Simplify this expression. **Level 6**

7 *We are* $\frac{2}{3}$ *of an Earth hour minus* $\frac{1}{2}$ *an Earth minute ahead of Earth time.*
Write a formula for the time on Planet Ziply, T_z, in terms of the time on Earth in Earth hours, E_h, and Earth minutes, E_m. **Level 6**

8 *One Ziply pund is made up of* $9f + 12g + 21h$ *coins.*
Factorise this expression. **Level 7**

9 $£1 = f^2(2g + h^2)$.
- **a** If $f = 8$, $g = -7$ and $h = 4$, how many Ziply punds is one Earth pound worth?
- **b** How many Ziply coins would you get for one Earth pound? **Level 7**

The BIG ideas

- An **expression** has no equals sign. For example, $3x + 5$. **Level 5**
- **Substitution** means replacing letters with numbers to work out a result. For example, substituting $a = 5$ and $b = 7$ in $c = 3a + 4b$ gives $c = 43$. **Level 5**
- The **order of operations** is **brackets, powers (indices)**, multiplication and division, addition and subtraction. **Level 5**
- The order of operations in algebra is the same as in arithmetic. **Level 5 & Level 6**
- When using the order of operations, brackets are always done first. So, for example, $3 + 4 \times 5 = 3 + 20 = 23$, but $(3 + 4) \times 5 = 7 \times 5 = 35$. **Level 5 & Level 6**
- You can write expressions using algebra from sentences. For example, double p can be written $2p$; p more than q can be written $p + q$; and p less than q can be written $q - p$. **Level 5 & Level 6**
- 'Write a **formula** for P' means write '$P =$ ___'. '**In terms of**' tells you what **variables** to use in your formula. For example, a formula for the perimeter, P, of a square in terms of the side length, x, is $P = 4x$. **Level 5 & Level 6**
- Positive whole-number powers (or indices) represent repeated multiplication. For example, $2^5 = 2 \times 2 \times 2 \times 2 \times 2$. **Level 6**
- To **factorise** an expression, take out a **common factor** and put it outside the bracket. For example, $18x + 6 = 6(3x + 1)$. **Level 6**
- Factorising and **expanding** brackets are opposite processes. **Level 6**
- To **fully factorise** an expression, take out the **highest common factor** and put it outside the bracket. If an expression is fully factorised, the terms inside the bracket will have no common factor other than one. For example, $8p + 4 = 4(2p + 1)$. **Level 6**
- To **simplify** an expression with brackets, multiply out the brackets, then collect **like terms**. For example, $2(e + f + 3g) - 4(f + g) = 2e + 2f + 6g - 4f - 4g = 2e + 2f - 4f + 6g - 4g = 2e - 2f + 2g$. **Level 7**
- To find **algebraic factors**, take out the letter to the highest power that appears within every term. For example, $c^3 + c^7 = c^3(1 + c^4)$. **Level 7**

Practice SATs-style questions

Level 5

Q1 An envelope costs e pence. A stamp costs s pence.
Choose an expression from the box that matches each statement:

a The total cost of 3 envelopes and 3 stamps.

b The total cost of 3 envelopes and a stamp.

$3e$ $\quad 3 + 3s \quad 3(e + s) \quad 3e + s$

Q2 a If $k = 5$, what is the value of $3k + 8$?

b If $k = 2$ and $m = 5$, what is the value of $2k + m$?

Level 6

Q3 Ana writes $4(3a + 2) = 12a + 6$.
Is Ana correct? Explain your answer.

Q4 Multiply out the expression. Write your answer as simply as possible.
$3(x + 4) + 3(4 + x)$

Q5 Look at the expressions on the cards

Card A	Card B	Card C	Card D
$3(x + 4)$	$4(x + 3) - x$	$3x + 4$	15

a Which card has the same value as card A for only one value of x?

b Which card has the same value as card A for every value of x?

c Which card does not have the same value as card A for any value of x?

Level 7

Q6 Work out the values of x and y.

$a^8 \times a^3 = a^x$

$\frac{a^8}{a^3} = a^y$

Q7 Look at these expressions:

$2a(b + c^2 + a)$ $\qquad b^2(3a + b)$

$4(c^2 + b) + a(2a + 4)$

If $a = -4$, $b = 5$ and $c = 5$, arrange the expressions in descending order of size.

8 Clever calculations

This unit is all about number and calculations.

One mathematician who found numbers fascinating from a young age was Srinivasa Ramanujan (1887–1920), from Tamil Nadu in India. As a teenager, he taught himself advanced mathematics from a textbook and worked out his own proofs for some famous theorems (mathematical rules), as well as working out some theorems of his own. Because he neglected his other subjects, he failed his exams and was unable to get into Madras University.

After a few more years studying on his own, he wrote to a famous English mathematician, G H Hardy, at Cambridge University. Hardy was so excited by some of Ramanujan's ideas, he persuaded him to come to Cambridge and work with him.

Between 1914 and 1917, Ramanujan published 21 mathematical papers.

Activities

After a taxi ride to visit Ramanujan, Hardy commented that the taxi number, 1729, was very dull. Ramanujan replied that it was not dull at all – it was the smallest number that could be made in two different ways, by adding two cube numbers.

A 1729 has another special property.

a Add all the digits together to get a two-digit number.
b Swap the two digits to get another two-digit number.
c Multiply your answers from **a** and **b** together. What do you get?
d One of the numbers in this box has this property.

39, 276, 1458

Which is it?

B Find the two pairs of cube numbers that add to make 1729.

$\square^3 + \square^3 = 1729 = \square^3 + \square^3$

Did you know?
Cashpoint machines sort out the notes to give you using partition theory – which was one of Ramanujan's ideas.

Before you start this unit...

1 Find each missing number.

a $32 \times 100 = \square$

b $\square \div 10 = 15$

c $47\,000 \div \square = 470$

Level Up Maths 4-6 page 22

2 Round these numbers to (i) the nearest whole number and (ii) one decimal place.

a 2.47 **b** 3.85 **c** 0.96

Level Up Maths 4-6 page 134

3 Put these numbers in order, smallest first.

$-4, -2, -8, -1, 0, -6$

Level Up Maths 4-6 page 24

4 Use a written method to work out these.

a 284×7 **b** $378 \div 9$

Level Up Maths 4-6 pages 30, 34

5 Work out these.

a $-12 + 8 - 5$

b $-18 + -6$

c $9 - -17$

Level Up Maths 4-6 page 4

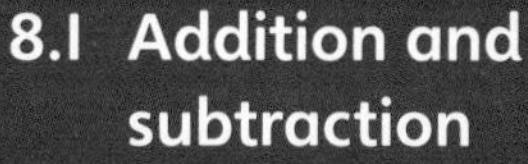

Plus digital resources

8.1 Addition and subtraction

- Add and subtract mentally
- Use standard column procedures to add and subtract integers and decimals

Why learn this?

To check a bill or receipt you may need to add several numbers to two decimal places.

What's the BIG idea?

- **Adding** a negative number is the same as **subtracting** a positive number. For example, $-4 + -9 = -4 - 9 = -13$. **Level 5**
- Subtracting a negative number is the same as adding a positive number. For example, $-4 - -9 = -4 + 9 = 5$. **Level 5**
- To add or subtract **integers** using the standard column method, you line up the units, tens, hundreds and so on, then add or subtract. **Level 5**
- To add or subtract **decimals**, you line up the decimal points, put the decimal point in the answer, then add or subtract. **Level 5**
- When adding or subtracting decimals with different numbers of **digits**, you can use a **zero place holder**. For example, $23.4 - 58.67$ is equivalent to $23.40 - 58.67$. **Level 5 & Level 6**

Did you know?

The Dewey decimal system is a method of classifying books in libraries using decimal numbers.

Practice, practice, practice!

Level 5

5c I can add and subtract positive integers to/from negative integers

5c I can add integers and decimals (up to two decimal places) with varying numbers of digits

5b I can subtract integers and decimals (up to two decimal places) with varying numbers of digits

1 Use a mental method to work out

a $-12 + 14$ **b** $-8 - 8$ **c** $-200 - 199$ **d** $11 - 25 + 4$

2 Use the standard column method to do these additions.

$4.56 + 9 + 22.1$

```
   4.56
   9.00    use zero place holders to make sure
+ 22.10    you line up the digits correctly
  35.66
  1
```

Tip

Use an estimate to check your answer.

a $5.21 + 20.78 + 31.9$ **b** $13 + 7.74 + 14.9$

c $19.9 + 0.12 + 99.99$ **d** $9.09 + 2.8 + 8 + 0.49$

Watch out!

When adding or subtracting, start from the column on the right.

3 Work out these subtractions.

a $49.46 - 7.3$ **b** $17.39 - 9$ **c** $219 - 69.29$ **d** $110.1 - 10.27$

4 Copy and complete these difference pyramids. The number in each brick is the difference (bigger – smaller) between the two numbers directly below it.

a

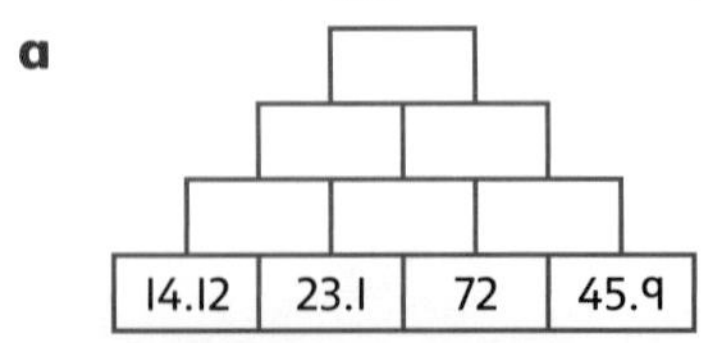

b

5.07	9	8.5	3.46

add addition decimal number difference digit

5 Use a mental method to work out

a $-13 + -12$ **b** $26 - -20$ **c** $-6 + 5 - -7$ **d** $15 - 32 + -8$

6 Find two pairs of integers whose difference is -14.
The second integer of each pair must be negative.

7 Work out

a $3.9 + 2.56 - 7.31$ **b** $37.9 + 9.34 - 26.89$

c $212.17 - 67.2 + 19$ **d** $60.89 - 20.9 + 1.5 - 8.99$

8 Zara has these items in her shopping basket.

jacket £49.99
shirt £9.49
two ties @ £5.45 each
trousers £17

a At the checkout, the price of the shirt is reduced by £1.90.
What is the total cost of Zara's items?

b Zara receives a further £3.75 discount on the total cost.
If she pays with five £20 notes, what change should she receive?

9 Use the digits 1, 2, 3, 4, 7 and 8 to complete these subtractions.

a

```
  □.□□
- □.□□
  1.79
```

b

```
  □.□□
- □.□□
  4.97
```

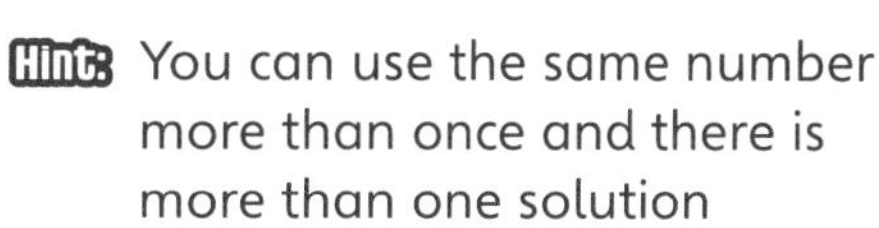

Hint: You can use the same number more than once and there is more than one solution

Level 5

5a I can add and subtract negative integers to/from positive and negative integers

5a I can add and subtract more than two integers and decimals (up to two decimal places) with varying numbers of digits

10 Work out

a $6342 + 210.013 + 0.1672$ **b** $300.2 - 54.61 - 0.71$

c $1009.02 - 99.3 + 13.6007$ **d** $2375 + 245.1 + 0.023 - 1.23$

11 During a science experiment, Mia collects samples from a material for further testing. The masses of the collected samples are

A	B	C	D
1.024 g	0.0045 g	2.705 g	0.3081 g

a The mass of material was 29.45 g after samples A and B were removed.
What was the original mass of the material?

b What is the final mass of material left after all the samples have been removed?

Level 6

6a I can add and subtract integers and decimals of any size

Now try this!

A Digit reversal

- Take any two-digit decimal number with one decimal place. Reverse the digits to make another two-digit decimal. Find the difference between these numbers.
- Do the same for the answer, and again, …
- Try this for other two-digit decimal numbers. Do you always get the same answers?

B Digit difference

Work with a partner.
Use the digits 2–7 to make two three-digit numbers (each with two decimal places).
Investigate pairs of numbers where the difference is close to 2 and 3.

integer subtract subtraction zero place holder

8.2 Powers of 10

- Multiply and divide decimals by 10, 100, 1000
- Read and write positive integer powers of 10
- Multiply and divide integers and decimals by 0.1 and 0.01
- Understand the effect of multiplying and dividing by numbers less than 1

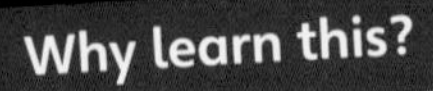

The Sun's minimum distance from the Earth is 91 000 000 miles. This can be written as 9.1×10^6 miles using powers of 10.

- To multiply a decimal by 10, 100 or 1000, move the digits one, two or three places, respectively, to the left. **Level 5**
- To divide a decimal by 10, 100 or 1000, move the digits one, two or three places, respectively, to the right. **Level 5**
- You can write **place value** headings to the left of the units column as **powers** of 10.
  $10 = 10^1$, $100 = 10 \times 10 = 10^2$, $1000 = 10 \times 10 \times 10 = 10^3$, and so on.
  The raised number (e.g. ^{1}, ^{2} or ^{3}) is called the power or **index**. **Level 6**
- 0.1 is **equivalent** to $\frac{1}{10}$.
  Multiplying by 0.1 is the same as multiplying by $\frac{1}{10}$ or dividing by 10.
  Dividing by 0.1 is the same as dividing by $\frac{1}{10}$ or multiplying by 10. **Level 6**
- 0.01 is equivalent to $\frac{1}{100}$.
  Multiplying by 0.01 is the same as multiplying by $\frac{1}{100}$ or dividing by 100.
  Dividing by 0.01 is the same as dividing by $\frac{1}{100}$ or multiplying by 100. **Level 6**
- To multiply a number by any positive integer power of 10, move the digits left by the same number of places as the integer power. **Level 7**
- To divide a number by any positive integer power of 10, move the digits right by the same number of places as the integer power. **Level 7**

Learn this

1 million
$= 10 \times 10 \times 10 \times 10 \times 10 \times 10$
$= 10^6$
1 billion $= 10 \times 10 \times 10 \times 10 \times 10 \times 10 \times 10 \times 10 \times 10$
$= 10^9$

Practice, practice, practice!

Level 5

5c I can multiply and divide decimals by 10, 100 and 1000

1 Use 10, 100, 1000, ×, ÷ and = to form five correct calculations, using the numbers given in the cloud.

2.6 0.044 11.8 821 0.821 1180 23.409 2.3409 4.4 26

2.6 × 10 = 26 multiplying by 10, digits move one place to the left

2 Copy and complete these statements.

a 5.3 × 10 = ☐ **b** 8.65 × ☐ = 865 **c** 3.9 ÷ 10 = ☐

d 12.8 ÷ ☐ = 0.0128 **e** ☐ ÷ 100 = 0.2586 **f** ☐ × 1000 = 80

billion equivalent index

3 Write these as powers of 10.

a 10 000 b 100 000 c 100 000 000 d 10

Hint: To work out the power of 10, count the zeros.

4 Use equivalent calculations to work out these.

22.5 × 0.01 $= 22.5 \times \frac{1}{100} = 22.5 \div 100 = 0.225$

a 23 × 0.1 b 78 × 0.01 c 7.12 × 0.1

d 4258 × 0.01 e 800 × 0.01 f 30.9 × 0.01

5 Use equivalent calculations to work out these.

a 7 ÷ 0.1 b 0.16 ÷ 0.01 c 103.2 ÷ 0.1

d 1.2 ÷ 0.01 e 15.15 ÷ 0.01 f 0.99 ÷ 0.01

6 Copy and complete these statements.

a 2.3 × 0.1 = ☐ b 56 × ☐ = 5.6 c ☐ × 0.01 = 4.36

d 0.3 × ☐ = 0.003 e ☐ ÷ 0.1 = 124 f 0.13 ÷ ☐ = 0.013

g ☐ ÷ 0.01 = 348 h ☐ ÷ 0.01 = 0.23 i ☐ ÷ 0.1 = 79

Level 6

6c I can write integers as powers of 10

6c I can multiply by 0.1 and 0.01

6b I can divide by 0.1 and 0.01

6b I can use the equivalents of 0.1 and 0.01 to solve problems

7 Work out

a 27.72×10^3 b 0.173×10^2 c 2.0202×10^3

d 0.045×10^4 e 0.36×0.01 f $52 \times \frac{1}{100}$

8 Work out

a $8.3 \div 10^2$ b $2.56 \div 10^2$ c $0.1 \div 10^3$

d $70.28 \div 10^3$ e $4589 \div 10^4$ f $0.13 \div \frac{1}{10}$

g $2.003 \div \frac{1}{100}$ h $394.76 \div 10^5$ i $5.324 \div \frac{1}{1000}$

9 Use the fact that $1\text{ m}^2 = 10\,000\text{ cm}^2$ to convert these areas to square metres.

a $56\,000\text{ cm}^2$ b $183\,550\text{ cm}^2$ c 4500 cm^2

d 975 cm^2 e 305 cm^2 f $900\,080\text{ cm}^2$

Level 7

7c I can multiply any number by an integer power of 10

7b I can divide any number by an integer power of 10

Now try this!

A Multiplying by a number less than 1

A	B	C
Multiplying a positive number by a number greater than 1 always increases the number.	Multiplying a positive number by a number between 0 and 1 always increases the number.	Multiplying a negative number by a positive number always increases the first number.

For each statement decide whether it is 'always true', 'always false' or 'sometimes true and sometimes false'.

Tip

Choose suitable numbers to test the statements.

B Dividing by a number less than 1

Investigate and discuss the effects of dividing by a number less than 1. Give examples and show the multiplication which has the same effect.

Did you know?

The prefix for 10^3 is 'kilo', so 1 kilometre = 1000 metres. The prefix 'mega' means 10^6 and 'giga' means 10^9.

place value power

8.3 Rounding and ordering

- Round positive whole numbers to any given power of 10
- Round decimals to one or two decimal places
- Compare and order decimals
- Recognise integer powers of 10

Why learn this?

The capacity of the Nou Camp football stadium in Barcelona is 98 772. This is rounded to 99 000 for simplicity.

What's the BIG idea?

- To **round** a number to the **nearest** 10 000, look at the digit in the thousands column. If the digit is **less than** 5, round down. If the digit is 5 or more, round up. **Level 5**
- You can round larger numbers to the nearest 100 000, 1 000 000, and so on. **Level 5**
- To round a decimal to two **decimal places**, look at the digit in the third decimal place. If the digit is less than 5, round down. If the digit is 5 or more, round up. **Level 5**
- You can write place value headings to the right of the units column as powers of 10.
  $0.1 = \frac{1}{10} = 10^{-1}$, $0.01 = \frac{1}{100} = 10^{-2}$, $0.001 = \frac{1}{1000} = 10^{-3}$, and so on. **Level 6**
- To order decimals, first **compare** the whole numbers, next compare the tenths, then the hundredths, and so on. **Level 6**

Learn this

Prefixes for negative powers of 10:

10^{-2} centi-
10^{-3} milli-
10^{-6} micro-
10^{-9} nano-
10^{-12} pico-

Practice, practice, practice!

Level 5

5a I can round whole numbers to any given power of 10

1 Round these numbers to the nearest 1000.

a 4167 **b** 1905 **c** 38 249 **d** 34 259

2 **a** Round the population figures for New Zealand and Poland to the nearest 100 000.

b Round the population figures for China, Brazil and the UK to the nearest million.

Country	Population (2007)
China	1 321 851 888
Brazil	190 010 647
UK	60 776 238
Poland	38 518 241
New Zealand	4 115 771

5a I can round decimals to two decimal places

3 Round these numbers to two decimal places.

a 4.156 **b** 19.024 **c** 76.097 **d** 27.995

Level 6

6c I can order positive decimals (to four or five significant figures) in ascending order

4 Put these decimal numbers in order, smallest first.

a 1.081, 0.087 65, 1.378, 0.210 05, 0.1763

b 3.297, 3.151, 3.294, 3.781, 2.2978

c 0.6217, 0.063 19, 6.237, 0.6429, 6.5132

ascending compare decimal place descending greater than (>)

5 Copy and complete.

46 800 = *46.8 thousand*

a 5 120 000 = ____ million　　b 9 723 100 = ____ million

c ____ = 3.9 thousand　　d ____ = 0.5 million

6 Rearrange these in descending order (highest first).

71.459, 74.945, 71.023, 73.917, 74.912

7 Rearrange these numbers in ascending order (lowest first).

a −4.12, −0.17, −3.26, −2.01, −1.17

b −0.0246, −0.0237, −0.0251, −0.0216, −0.0238

8 Write these as powers of 10.

a $\frac{1}{10\,000}$　　b $\frac{1}{100\,000}$　　c 0.000 000 01　　d 0.000 001

9 Which prefix is associated with each of these?

a 10^{-3}　　b 10^{6}　　c 10^{9}

d 10^{-9}　　e 10^{-12}　　f 10^{3}

milli–　nano–　kilo–　giga–　mega–　micro–　pico–　cent–

10 Rearrange these in descending order.

−0.058, −0.0508, −0.0505, −0.085, −0.0855

11 Put the correct sign, < or >, between each pair of numbers.

a 1.032 ☐ 1.012　　b 7.139 ☐ 7.193

c 4.156 ☐ 4.159　　d 0.043 77 ☐ 0.043 07

12 Put the correct sign, < or >, between each pair of numbers.

a −12.9 ☐ −9.12　　b −3.51 ☐ −3.05　　c −0.86 ☐ −0.865

d −4.932 ☐ −4.923　　e −1.008 ☐ −1.012　　f −5.1 ☐ −5.09

Level 6

6b I can write numbers as decimal multiples of millions or thousands

6b I can order positive decimals (to four or five significant figures) in descending order

6b I can order negative decimals (to two or three significant figures) in ascending order

6b I can write decimals as powers of ten

6a I know the prefixes associated with powers of 10

6a I can order negative decimals (to two or three significant figures) in descending order

6a I can use < and > to compare positive decimals (to four or five significant figures)

Level 7

7c I can use < and > to compare negative decimals (to two or three significant figures)

Now try this!

A Rounded groups

a Use the digits 2, 3, 5, and 9 to make different four-digit numbers with **i** one decimal place **ii** two decimal places and **iii** three decimal places.

b Where possible round these numbers to **i** the nearest whole number **ii** 1 d.p. **iii** 2 d.p.

c How many numbers are now the same in each group?

B Ordered decimals

a Use the digits 2, 3, 5, 7 and 9 to make five different numbers with three decimal places. Put them in order, smallest first.

b Using the same five decimal numbers again, put a minus sign in front of each. Put these in order, smallest first.

c What do you notice about the two lists of numbers?

less than (<)　nearest　round　to one decimal place (1 d.p.)

8.4 Mental methods 2

- Mentally multiply integers and decimals
- Use doubling and halving for mental calculations involving negative numbers
- Multiply and divide integers and decimals by 0.1 and 0.01

Why learn this?

Mental maths skills are used in a range of jobs and everyday activities.

What's the BIG idea?

→ You can use **partitioning** to turn one hard **multiplication** into two easier ones.
For example, $5.9 \times 23 = (5.9 \times 20) + (5.9 \times 3) = 118 + 17.7 = 135.7$ **Level 5**

→ You can use **factors** to make mental multiplication easier.
For example, $8.3 \times 20 = 8.3 \times 10 \times 2 = 83 \times 2 = 166$ **Level 5**

→ You can also use **doubling** and **halving** strategies.
For example, $6 \times 3.5 = 3 \times 7 = 21$ **Level 5 & Level 6**

Practice, practice, practice!

Level 5

1 Use partitioning to multiply these.

a 12×1.5 **b** 19×2.3 **c** 6.3×21 **d** 9.4×37
e 8.5×25 **f** 47×3.8 **g** 12.1×39 **h** 44×10.4

5a I can use partitioning to multiply numbers mentally

2 Use factors to work out these.

360×1.5

Factors of 1.5: 5 and 0.3 ($5 \times 0.3 = 1.5$) or 3 and 0.5 ($3 \times 0.5 = 1.5$)
So $360 \times 1.5 = 360 \times 5 \times 0.3 = 1800 \times 0.3 = 540$
or $360 \times 1.5 = 360 \times 3 \times 0.3 = 1080 \times 0.5 = 540$

a 15×1.6 **b** 96×0.08 **c** 56×2.4 **d** 3.2×85

5a I can use factors to multiply mentally

3 Use doubling and halving to multiply these.

a 7.5×16 **b** 6.8×2.5 **c** 3.5×6.4 **d** 8.6×4.5
e 5.5×8 **f** 6.5×3.2 **g** 9.8×1.5 **h** 5.6×2.5

5a I can multiply mentally using doubling and halving

4 Use any mental method to work out these.

a A bedroom wall measures 8.4 m × 1.5 m.
What is its area?

b One ounce is about 28 grams.
How many grams are there in 8.8 ounces?

c A bank offers 2.2 Australian dollars for every £1.
How many Australian dollars will you get for £43?

d There are about 1.8 pints to a litre. How many pints are there in
i 12 litres **ii** 15 litres **iii** 30 litres **iv** 48 litres?

5a I can multiply mentally

divide division double factor halve multiplication

5 Four lemons cost 98p. Work out the cost of

a 12 lemons b 20 lemons c 18 lemons

6 Use doubling and halving to work out these.

a -15×1.5 b -7.5×6
c -25×1.2 d -16.4×-1.25
e -12×7.5 f -7.6×-20

Watch out!
A negative multiplied by a positive gives a negative answer. A negative multiplied by a negative gives a positive answer.

7 Use a mental method to work out

a 5.2×0.1 b -76.3×0.1 c -45.9×0.01
d 0.81×0.01 e 791.4×0.01 f 302.99×0.1
g 0.79×0.1 h 412.1×0.01 i -1.23×0.1

8 At the beginning of June, Jared put £44.75 in a bank account offering 1% interest on savings per month.

a How much interest will Jared receive at the end of June?

b The bank charges a 10% fee on all overdrawn amounts.
In September, Jared's account balance is −£82.75.
How much will the bank charge him for being overdrawn?

9 Work out

a $-3.2 \div 0.1$ b $-49.7 \div 0.01$ c $0.47 \div 0.01$
d $-1.39 \div 0.1$ e $-91.001 \div 0.1$ f $-1.64 \div 0.01$
g $50.1 \div 0.01$ h $456.2 \div 0.1$ i $0.231 \div 0.001$

10 Copy and complete.

a $26.8 \times 0.01 =$ ____ $\div 0.1 =$ ____
b ____ $\times 0.1 = -0.485 \div 0.01 =$ ____
c ____ $\div 0.1 =$ ____ $\times 0.01 = -0.079$
d ____ $\div 0.01 =$ ____ $\times 0.1 = -3.08 \times 0.01 =$ ____

11 $A \div B = 560$
When A is multiplied by 0.01, the answer is 0.056.
What are the values of A and B?

Learn this

$0.1 = \frac{1}{10}$ Multiplying by 0.1 is the same as dividing by 10.
Dividing by 0.1 is the same as multiplying by 10.

$0.01 = \frac{1}{100}$ Multiplying by 0.01 is the same as dividing by 100.
Dividing by 0.01 is the same as multiplying by 100.

Level 6

6c I can solve problems mentally

6c I can use doubling and halving to multiply negative numbers

6b I can multiply any number by 0.1 and 0.01

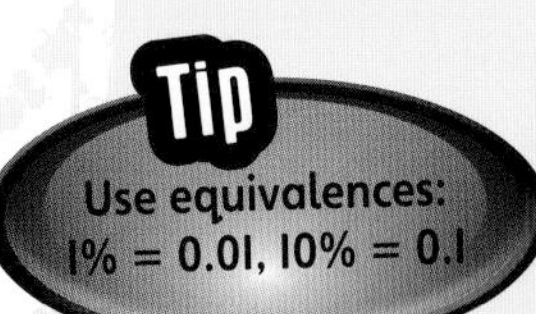

6a I can divide any number by 0.1 and 0.01

6a I can multiply and divide any number by 0.1 and 0.01

Now try this!

A Make 10

Use brackets, the four operations + − × ÷ and the digits 4 6 6 8.
Try to make the number 10.

B Who are we?

a Find two numbers whose sum is 0.2 and whose product is −0.48.
b Find two numbers whose sum is −11.5 and whose product is 28.
c Make up your own 'Who are we?' puzzles and test them out on a partner.
Make sure you know the answers first!

multiply partition product sum

maths!

Check digits

Look for the barcode on the back cover of this book. The last number of a barcode is called a check digit. The barcode scanner uses this digit to make sure that it has scanned the item code correctly.

ISBN 10

Every book in the world has an International Standard Book Number (ISBN), which is the same number as on the barcode. Look for the ISBN number on the back of this book. In older books the ISBN is 10 digits long, in new books it is 13 digits long. The ISBN contains information about the language of the book and who published it. The last number is a check digit.

To find the check digit, multiply each of the first nine numbers in the ISBN by its position and add up these results. Divide this number by 11, and the remainder is the check digit.

Example: **ISBN 0-14-021300-?**

$1\times0 + 2\times1 + 3\times4 + 4\times0 + 5\times2 + 6\times1 + 7\times3 + 8\times0 + 9\times0 = 51$

$51 \div 11 = 4$ remainder 7, so the check digit is 7.

- Calculate the check digit for each of the following ISBNs:

0-14-026149-?

0-590-11260-?

- Matt works for a publishing company, but he can't remember whether an ISBN starts with 047 or 074. Which of these is the correct ISBN: **0-477-40413-5** or **0-747-40413-5**?

- The check digit can also help fill in missing digits if an item doesn't scan properly.
  Work out what the missing digit is in this ISBN:

0-00-?34347-6

ISBN 13

The ISBN for this book is:

978-0-435537-32-6

The check digit for 13 digit ISBNs works in a slightly different way. To find the check digit, add up the six digits in the odd numbered positions (1st, 3rd, 5th...) and write this down. Now add up the six digits in even numbered positions, but multiply this total by 3 before writing it down. Add up the two totals that you have written down, and divide it by 10. If the remainder is 0, the check digit is 0; otherwise, subtract the remainder from 10 to get the check digit.

Example: **ISBN 978-0-435537-32-6**

Odd numbered total: 9 + 8 + 4 + 5 + 3 + 3 = 32
Even numbered total: 7 + 0 + 3 + 5 + 7 + 2 = 24
Multiply by 3 to get 72.
32 + 72 = 104. This leaves a remainder of 4 when divided by 10.
10 − 4 = 6, so the check digit is 6.

Calculate the check digit for each of the following ISBN:

978-0-563-48654-?

978-1-846-07204-?

Using check digits

Check digits aren't just useful for barcodes and ISBNs – you can use them for checking your maths too.
Explain in your own words why the last digit in the answer to 42 × 23 must be 6.
(Hint: Think about what would happen in the units column of your workings.)
What digit must the answer to 5226 × 23 853 end in?

8.5 Powers and roots

- Estimate square roots
- Mentally calculate the squares of numbers that are multiples of a power of 10
- Find square roots by factorising
- Use known cube roots to work out others mentally
- Solve word problems, involving squares, square roots, cubes and cube roots, using a mental method

Why learn this?

Some square roots are special. The dimensions of the King's Chamber in the Great Pyramid in Egypt are all multiples of $\sqrt{5}$.

What's the BIG idea?

- 6^2 is 'six **squared**' and equals $6 \times 6 = 36$. 36 is a **square number**. **Level 5**
- The inverse of squaring is finding the **square root**. $\sqrt{36} = 6$ because $6^2 = 36$. 6 is called the square root of 36. **Level 5**
- 2^3 is 'two **cubed**' which means $2 \times 2 \times 2 = 8$. 8 is called a **cube number**. **Level 6**
- The inverse of cubing is finding the **cube root**. $\sqrt[3]{8} = 2$ because $2^3 = 8$. 2 is called the cube root of 8. **Level 6**
- You can find a square root by **factorising**, that is by breaking a whole number up into two (or more) numbers which can be multiplied together to make the original number. For example, $324 = 4 \times 81$ so $\sqrt{324} = \sqrt{4} \times \sqrt{81} = 2 \times 9 = 18$ **Level 6**

Learn this

A positive integer has two square roots, one positive and one negative. The square roots of 16 are 4 and −4. When you use the $\sqrt{\ }$ notation, it always means the positive square root, so $\sqrt{16} = 4$.

Practice, practice, practice!

Level 5

5a I can identify the two whole numbers that the square root of a non-square number lies between

5a I can calculate mentally with squares and square roots

1 Which two whole numbers do these square roots lie between?

$\sqrt{6}$ $2^2 = 4$ and $3^2 = 9$, so $\sqrt{6}$ lies between 2 and 3. $2 < \sqrt{6} < 3$

a $\sqrt{11}$ **b** $\sqrt{87}$ **c** $\sqrt{3}$ **d** $\sqrt{53}$

e $\sqrt{29}$ **f** $\sqrt{65}$ **g** $\sqrt{91}$ **h** $\sqrt{72.5}$

2 Use a mental method to work out

a $\sqrt{16} + 9$ **b** $13 + \sqrt{36}$ **c** $8^2 + 9$ **d** $\sqrt{81} - 4$

Level 6

6c I can find squares of multiples of 10

6c I can recall the cubes of 1 to 5 and 10, and their roots

3 Find these squares by factorising.

300^2 $= 3^2 \times 100^2 = 9 \times 10\,000 = 90\,000$

a 20^2 **b** 60^2 **c** 200^2

d 500^2 **e** 0.2^2 **f** 0.03^2

Hint: $0.2^2 = 2^2 \div 10^2$

4 Write the value of

a 2^3 **b** 4^3 **c** $\sqrt[3]{1000}$

d 5^3 **e** 3^3 **f** $\sqrt[3]{125}$

cube | cubed (e.g. 3^3) | cube number | cube root (e.g. $\sqrt[3]{27}$) | factorise

5 Mentally calculate

a $(15 - 8 + 12 - 4)^3$

b $\sqrt[3]{48 + 16}$

c $2^3 + 19$

d $38 - \sqrt[3]{27}$

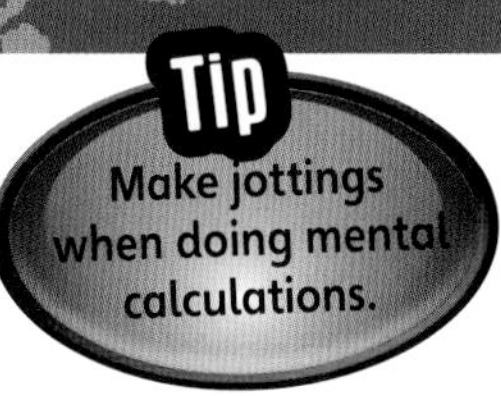

Level 6

6c I can do mental calculations with cubes and cube roots

6 Use the items in the box to construct true relationships.

$\sqrt{25}$	6	5	−5	9	$\sqrt{144}$	30	−9	$\sqrt{900}$	−6
square roots of 36	12	square roots of 81							

The square roots of 36 = 6 and −6

6c I can identify that $\sqrt{\ }$ denotes the positive square root

7 Use a mental method to work out

a $(85 - 13 - 8)^3$

b $(4^2 + 3^2) \div 5$

c $\frac{120}{2^3 + 12}$

d $(27 - 18)^2 \div 3^2 \times 4^3$

6b I can do mental calculations with brackets, squares and cubes

8 Heather thinks of a number. The cube root of it is −4.
What number is Heather thinking of?

6b I can solve mental problems involving cubes

9 Use the factors to find these square roots.

1600 *= 16 × 100, so $\sqrt{1600} = \sqrt{16} \times \sqrt{100} = 4 \times 10 = 40$*

a $324 = 9 \times 36$, so $\sqrt{324}$ = _____

b $256 = 16 \times 16$, so $\sqrt{256}$ = _____

c $400 = 4 \times 100$, so $\sqrt{400}$ = _____

d $576 = 16 \times 36$, so $\sqrt{576}$ = _____

e $2025 = 81 \times 25$, so $\sqrt{2025}$ = _____

f $3136 = 64 \times 49$, so $\sqrt{3136}$ = _____

6b I can find square roots by factorising

10 Use a mental method to work out

a $\sqrt[3]{84 + 41} - 45$

b $\sqrt[3]{4^2 + 48}$

c $\frac{\sqrt[3]{1000}}{\sqrt{32 - 7}}$

6a I can do mental calculations with brackets, cube roots and square roots

11 Use the factors to find the cube roots.

a $512 = 64 \times 8$. What is $\sqrt[3]{512}$?

b $5832 = 216 \times 27$. What is $\sqrt[3]{5832}$?

c $13\,824 = 8 \times 64 \times 27$. What is $\sqrt[3]{13\,824}$?

6a I can find cube roots by factorising

12 Cube A has sides of length 4 cm.
Cube B has a volume of 216 cm^3.
Cube C has a surface area of 486 cm^2.

a Which cube has the greatest surface area?

b Which cube has the smallest volume?

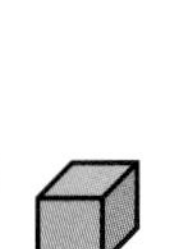
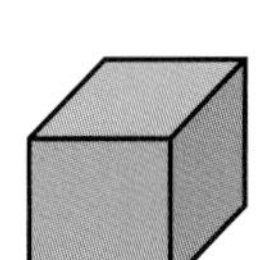
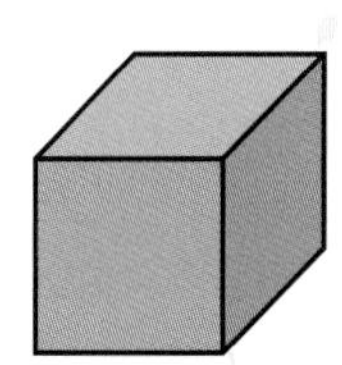

6a I can use mental strategies to solve word problems using square roots and cube roots

Now try this!

A Sum of square numbers

You can write 13 as the sum of two square numbers $9 + 4 = 13$

Which other numbers from 1 to 20 can be written as either the sum or the difference of two square numbers?

B Power pattern

Investigate these number patterns.

1	1^3
1 + 2	$1^3 + 2^3$
1 + 2 + 3	$1^3 + 2^3 + 3^3$
1 + 2 + 3 + 4	$1^3 + 2^3 + 3^3 + 4^3$

index power squared square number square root

8.6 Written multiplication

- Multiply integers and decimals using written methods
- Check answers by using approximate calculations

Why learn this?

Caterers use multiplication to calculate the total cost of party food when the quoted price is 'per head'.

What's the BIG idea?

- You can use the **grid method** or the **standard method** for **multiplication**. Level 5
- You can use **estimation** to check the answer to a calculation. For example, 126 × 18 is about 130 × 20 = 2600. Level 5 & Level 6
- To **multiply** a **decimal number** by a whole number using the standard method ignore the decimal point and multiply the whole numbers. Then work out where to put the decimal point. For example, 8.36 × 9 = (836 × 9) ÷ 100. Level 5 & Level 6
- You can use an **equivalent** calculation to multiply a decimal by a decimal. For example, 5.8 × 7.6 = (58 ÷ 10) × (76 ÷ 10) = 58 × 76 ÷ 100. Level 5 & Level 6

Practice, practice, practice!

Level 5

5c I can use the grid method for TU × TU

1 Use the grid method to work out these multiplications.

86 × 27 *Estimate: 86 × 27 is about 90 × 30 = 2700*

×	80	6
20	1600	120
7	560	42

86 × 27 = 1600 + 120 + 560 + 42
= 2322
Check: 2322 is close to 2700 ✓

a 23 × 39 **b** 56 × 79 **c** 47 × 95 **d** 77 × 55
e 83 × 95 **f** 38 × 89 **g** 62 × 19 **h** 35 × 43

5b I can use the standard method for HTU × TU

2 Use the standard method to work out these multiplications.

376 × 42 *Estimate: 376 × 42 is about 400 × 40 = 16 000.*

```
    3 7 6
×     4 2
  1 5 0 4 0   (376 × 40)
+     7 5 2   (376 × 2)
  1 5 7 9 2
```

Check: 15 792 is close to 16 000 ✓

a 259 × 29 **b** 518 × 37 **c** 456 × 87 **d** 919 × 88

3 The food for a birthday party will cost £28 per head.
133 people attend the party. What is the total cost of the food?

decimal number decimal place equivalent estimate grid metho

4 Use the grid method to work out these multiplications. Estimate your answer first.

4.35 × 6   *Estimate: 4 × 6 = 24*

×	4	0.3	0.05
6	24	1.8	0.30

4.35 × 6 = 24 + 1.8 + 0.30
= 26.1
Check: 26.1 is close to 24 ✓

a 5.6 × 8   b 9.03 × 7   c 4.53 × 9   d 28.19 × 6
e 7 × 4.2   f 33.33 × 8   g 0.57 × 6   h 1.07 × 9

5 A bread roll weighs 102.59 g. What do eight rolls weigh?

6 Use the fact that 29 × 0.09 = 2.61 to work out

a 0.9 × 29   b 290 × 0.09   c 0.29 × 0.9   d 90 × 0.0029
e 2.61 ÷ 0.09   f 2.61 ÷ 29   g 2.61 ÷ 290   h 0.261 ÷ 9

Level 5

5b I can use the grid method to multiply a decimal (up to 2 d.p.) by a single digit

5b I can multiply a decimal with two decimal places by a single digit

5a I can position the decimal point by considering a given calculation

7 Use a mental or written method to work out

a 0.9 × 0.4   b 0.5 × 0.6   c 0.08 × 0.8   d 0.07 × 0.04
e 0.17 × 0.05   f 1.2 × 1.9   g 3.12 × 0.17   h 0.71 × 0.23

8 Use the standard method to work out

a 2.7 × 3.2   b 4.5 × 2.7
c 8.91 × 5.6   d 7.26 × 9.8
e 6.93 × 0.42   f 3.24 × 7.2

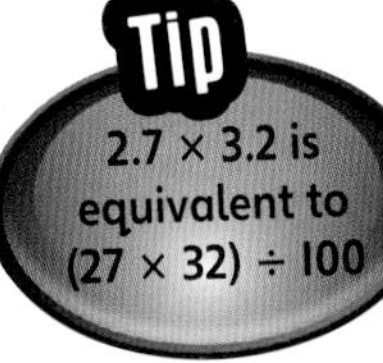

9 A car can travel 23.6 miles on 1 gallon of petrol.
How far can it travel on 5.2 gallons of petrol?

10 A rectangular field is measured to be 2.35 km by 3.5 km.

a Work out the area.

b Work out the perimeter.

11 One day the exchange rate is £1 for €1.23.
How many euros would you receive in exchange for

a £57   b £98   c £250?

Level 6

6c I can multiply decimals with up to two decimal places

Now try this!

A Napier's Bones

Research Napier's Bones on the internet.
Find out how they are used to multiply two numbers together.
Give two examples.

B Puzzling

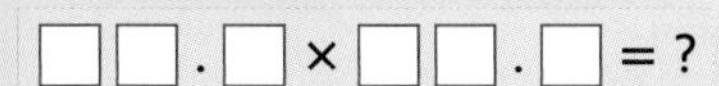

a Use the digits 1 2 5 6 7 8 to make the product 4739.28

b Use the digits 0 2 3 4 5 7 to make the product 728.28

Did you know?

John Napier, a Scottish mathematician, invented Napier's Bones which were multiplication tables written on strips of wood or bone.

multiplication   multiply   product   standard method

8.7 Written division

➪ Divide integers and decimals using written methods
➪ Check answers by using approximate calculations

Why learn this?

When marking up parking spaces, it is necessary to divide the length and width of the whole area by the length and width of each individual parking space.

What's the BIG idea?

→ You can use repeated subtraction for **division**. The number you **divide by** is called the **divisor**. Keep subtracting multiples of the divisor until you can't subtract any more, then see how many lots of the divisor you subtracted altogether. **Level 5 & Level 6**

→ Sometimes you will not be able to get to zero by subtracting multiples. The number you have left is called the **remainder**.
For example, the answer to 247 ÷ 17 can be written as '14 remainder 9', $14\frac{9}{17}$, 14.5 **to 1 d.p.** or 14.53 to 2 d.p. **Level 5 & Level 6**

→ You can use an equivalent calculation to divide a decimal by a decimal. For example, 3.86 ÷ 0.09 = 386 ÷ 9 (both sides have been multiplied by 100). **Level 6**

Practice, practice, practice!

Level 5

5b I can divide a three-digit number by a two-digit number

1 Work out these divisions. Some have remainders.

485 ÷ 14 *Estimate: 450 ÷ 15 = 30*

```
14)4 8 5
  -4 2 0   (14 × 30)
     6 5
  -  5 6   (14 × 4)
       9
```

485 ÷ 14 = 34 remainder 9
Check: 34 remainder 9 is close to 30 ✓

a 297 ÷ 11 **b** 570 ÷ 15 **c** 758 ÷ 18 **d** 460 ÷ 26

2 An allotment of area 895 m^2 is to be divided into 14 equal plots. What is the area of each plot?

5a I can divide decimals by a single-digit whole number

3 Work out these exact divisions. Estimate the answer first.

125.6 ÷ 8 *Estimate: 130 ÷ 10 = 13*

```
8)1 2 5 . 6
 -  8 0 . 0   (8 × 10)
    4 5 . 6
 -  4 0 . 0   (8 × 5)
        5 . 6
 -      5 . 6   (8 × 0.7)
            0
```

125.6 ÷ 8 = 10 + 5 + 0.7 = 15.7 Check: 15.7 is close to 13 ✓

a 131.5 ÷ 5 **b** 229.6 ÷ 7 **c** 195.39 ÷ 9 **d** 114.66 ÷ 6

divide division divisor estimate

4 Marcos has £39.20 pocket money every four weeks.
How much is that per day?

5 Harry buys 12 of the same chocolate bars and spends a total of £5.76.
How much does each chocolate bar cost?

6 Fifteen children have £261.30 to share equally between themselves.
How much does each child get?

7 Nia's yearly car insurance totals £285.60.
She decides to pay by monthly direct debit.
How much will she pay each month?

8 Work out these exact divisions.

a 37.6 ÷ 16 **b** 683.8 ÷ 13 **c** 535.5 ÷ 12 **d** 626.4 ÷ 18

e 68.4 ÷ 15 **f** 1225.7 ÷ 17 **g** 775.6 ÷ 14 **h** 1637.8 ÷ 19

Level 5

5a I can divide £.p by a two-digit number

5a I can divide decimals by a two-digit whole number

9 Use a mental or written method to work out

a 0.8 ÷ 0.2 **b** 0.9 ÷ 0.03 **c** 0.05 ÷ 0.2 **d** 0.04 ÷ 0.05

10 Work these out using a written method.
Give your answers to one decimal place where appropriate.

a 3.6 ÷ 0.6 **b** 8.4 ÷ 0.06 **c** 367 ÷ 2.4 **d** 18.9 ÷ 0.09

e 0.556 ÷ 3.6 **f** 3.9 ÷ 0.75 **g** 131.72 ÷ 0.37 **h** 3.48 ÷ 5.8

11 A factory makes 6.5 wooden chopsticks every second.

a If each chopstick uses 25.8 cm of wood, how many metres of wood are used every minute?

b Each chopstick has a 1.85 cm length of silver insert. If the factory has 0.37 m of silver bar left, how many silver inserts can it make?

12 George earns £9.86 per hour. He works 38.5 hours each week.

a How much does George earn in a week?

b How much does George earn in a year?

Level 6

6b I can divide a decimal by a decimal

6b I can divide by a decimal

6a I can multiply and divide with decimals to solve problems

Now try this!

A Four-card division

A game for 2 players. Use cards marked 1 to 9.
Deal out four cards each. Use your cards to make a division calculation that gives you the biggest possible answer.
The winner is the player with the bigger answer.

B Six-card division

A game for two players. Use cards marked 1 to 9 and three cards marked with 0.
Deal out six cards each. Use your cards to make a division calculation with the smallest possible answer. The winner is the person with the smaller answer.

quotient remainder to one decimal place (1 d.p.)

8.8 Estimates and checking

- Use approximate calculations to check answers
- Check a result by working the problem backwards
- Recognise what makes a good approximation
- Use rounding to make estimates

What's the BIG idea?

Why learn this?
When shopping, you can use estimation to make sure you don't blow your budget!

- → You can use **estimation** to check the answer to a calculation.
  For example, $447 \div 9 \approx 450 \div 10 = 45$. **Level 5**
- → You can also check a result by working it backwards.
  For example, you can check $4.29 \times 3.8 = 16.302$ by calculating $16.302 \div 3.8$. **Level 5**
- → When using an **estimate** for a multiplication or an addition it is often a good idea to round one number up and round the other number down. **Level 6 & Level 7**
- → When using an estimate for a division or subtraction it is usually best to either round both numbers up or round both numbers down. **Level 6 & Level 7**

Practice, practice, practice!

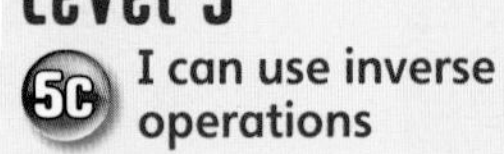

Level 5

5c I can use inverse operations

1 Use inverse operations to check these calculations.

a $34.2 \times 56.1 = 19\,862$ **b** $569 \div 8 = 71.12$

c $56 \times 58 = 3428$ **d** $7232.4 \div 12.6 = 574$

5b I can identify different ways of finding an approximate answer

2 Identify two different approximate calculations for these.

$302 - 137$ $\approx 300 - 100 = 200$ or $300 - 140 = 160$

a $441 - 179$ **b** $892 - 537$

c $847 + 192$ **d** $435 - 106 + 271$

e 624×38 **f** $341 \div 38$

g 6.89×1.23 **h** $34.9 - 12.5$

Tip
When estimating the answer, look for numbers that are easy to work with.

3 a Estimate the answers to these in two different ways.

i 8.8×3.5 **ii** 4.3×8.7 **iii** $20.8 \div 6.5$ **iv** $506 \div 10.4$

b Which of your two estimates do you think is the better?
Use your calculator to check.

5b I can round numbers to the nearest 10, or to a 'nice' number, to check calculations mentally

4 Use rounding to the nearest 10, or to a 'nice' number, to mentally check these calculations.

$61 \div 9$ $\approx 63 \div 9 = 7$

a $73 \div 8 = 9.125$ **b** $46 \div 9 = 6$ **c** $3.41 \times 9 = 32$ **d** $569 \div 8 = 71.125$

5a I can estimate the position of a pointer on an unmarked scale

5 Estimate the number each arrow is pointing to.

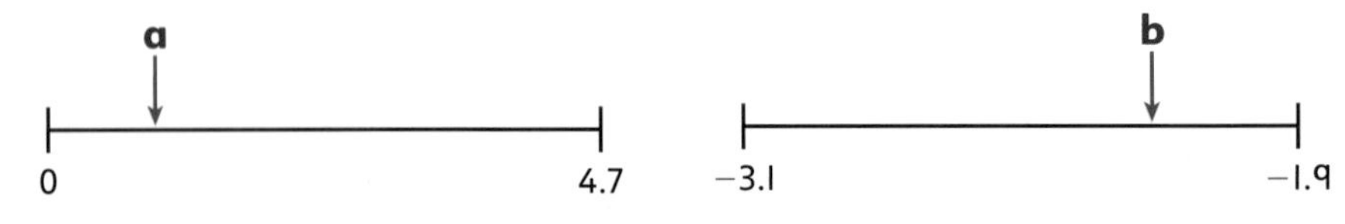

approximate approximately approximately equal to (≈)

6 Use inverse operations and a calculator to check these calculations.

a $\sqrt{11} = 3.317$ to 3 d.p. **b** $8.43^2 = 70.0649$

c $15.4 \div \sqrt{12} = 5.4$ **d** $11.3^2 \div 8^2 = 1.995$ to 3 d.p.

Level 5

5a I can use inverses to check calculations involving squares and square roots

7 Choose the best approximation for

a $51.2 - 28.7$

$51 - 30$ | $50 - 30$ | $512 - 287$ | $5.1 - 2.8$

b 6.81×4.15

10×4 | 7×5 | 7×4 | 10×3

8 **a** Which is the better approximation for $8.69 \div 3.37$?

$8 \div 3$ | $9 \div 3$

b Explain your choice in part **a**.

c Use a calculator to check the exact answer.
Was your approximation the better choice?

9 A supermarket sells dishwasher tablets in these packets.

20 tablets for £2.99 | 32 tablets for £3.99 | 72 tablets for £7.99

Use estimation to work out which packet is the best value for money.
Use a calculator to check your answer.

Tip
When working with money calculations, round the answers to 2 d.p.

Level 6

6b I can recognise what makes a good approximation

6b I can use an appropriate rounding to make estimates

10 **a** Estimate the answers to these. Explain your choice of estimate.

i $(429 - 17.3) \div (15.1 + 6.7)$ **ii** $(9.3 \times 4.2) \div (0.36 \times 1.9)$

iii $4.84 \times (8.96 - 0.89)$ **iv** $\dfrac{82.36 - 63.25}{\sqrt{9.4}}$

v $(14.8 - \sqrt{25}) \times 2.199^2$ **vi** $(24.49 + \sqrt{13}) \div 0.09$

b Use a calculator to work out each answer.

11 Carpet is sold in widths of 4 m and costs £8.98 per square metre.
You can buy any length of carpet.

a Estimate the cost of carpet required for rooms of the following sizes.
Explain your choice of estimate.

i 3.6 m by 1.2 m **ii** 4.65 m by 3.71 m **iii** 8.15 m by 6.35 m

b Use a calculator to work out each answer.

Level 7

7c I can make and justify estimates and approximations of calculations

Now try this!

A Total tiles

How many tiles are there in your school?
How might you make this estimate?
What would you need to define?

B Water usage

How much water do you use at home?
Explain how you might make this estimate.

estimate estimation inverse operation

8.9 Using a calculator

- Use brackets and the memory on a calculator
- Use a calculator to find squares, square roots, cubes and cube roots
- Carry out calculations with more than one step
- Do calculations involving fractions and mixed numbers on a calculator

Why learn this?

Calculators are used to compile budgets, prepare accounts and calculate profit and loss.

What's the BIG idea?

- You use the **sign change key** [+/−] to **enter** negative numbers. **Level 5**
- You use the [√] key to find the square root of a number. **Level 5**
- You use the [∛] function to find the cube root of a number. **Level 6**
- A **recurring decimal** is a decimal fraction which goes on repeating itself without end.
  For example, $\frac{1}{3} = 0.333...$. When your **calculator displays** 0.333..., you should write the answer as $\frac{1}{3}$. **Level 6**
- Most calculators have a function key for entering fractions: [$a\frac{b}{c}$].
  For example, to enter $\frac{5}{6}$, press [5] [$a\frac{b}{c}$] [6], and to enter $3\frac{4}{7}$, press [3] [$a\frac{b}{c}$] [4] [$a\frac{b}{c}$] [7]. **Level 6**
- Try to avoid rounding during an intermediate step of a **calculation**. **Level 7**

Tip

Different calculators have different keys. Get to know the [√] and [∛] functions on your calculator.

Practice, practice, practice!

Level 5

5c I can use the square root key on a calculator

5c I can use the sign change key

1 Use a calculator to work out these.
Give your answers to 1 d.p. where appropriate.

a $\sqrt{529}$ **b** $\sqrt{0.0676}$ **c** $\sqrt{295.84}$
d $\sqrt{12\,544}$ **e** $\sqrt{456}$ **f** $\sqrt{5.49}$

2 Use the sign change key to help with these calculations.
Give your answers to 1 d.p. where appropriate.

a $48 \div (3.2 \times -4.9)$ **b** $9.82 - -7.12$ **c** $\sqrt{5808.81} \div -4.4$
d -6.1^2 **e** $-5.7^2 - -34.1$ **f** $-\sqrt{55} \times -2.5$

Level 6

6c I can interpret rounded-off recurring decimals displayed on a calculator as fractions

3 Write the numbers shown on the calculator displays as fractions.

a 0.333333333 **b** 0.833333333
c 0.777777778 **d** 2.166666667

Watch out!

Some calculators round recurring decimals. $\frac{5}{9}$ as a recurring decimal could be shown as 0.555 555 556.

brackets calculate calculation calculator clear display

4 Use the brackets or memory keys on your calculator to work out these calculations.
Give your answers to 2 d.p. where appropriate.

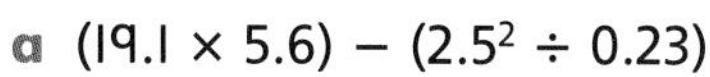

a $(19.1 \times 5.6) - (2.5^2 \div 0.23)$
b $15.4^2 - 9.1^2 + 2.6 - (1.7 - 1.1^2)$
c $36.1 \div 9.2 + (9.7 - 3.2 \div 1.9)^2$
d $24 \div 3.6 + 2.9^2 - \sqrt{30.8 \times 2.2}$

Tip Remember the correct order of operations.

Watch out! Don't forget to clear the memory between calculations.

Level 6

6c I can carry out complex calculations on a calculator using the memory and brackets

5 Work out these on your calculator.

a $\frac{3}{5} + \frac{1}{3}$ b $\frac{9}{11} - \frac{2}{3}$ c $\left(\frac{7}{12} - \frac{1}{8}\right) \times 2$ d $\frac{1}{3} \times \frac{2}{5}$

6b I can use the function key to enter a fraction

6 Use your calculator to work out

a $1\frac{3}{8} + 2\frac{1}{3}$ b $2\frac{1}{3} \times 3\frac{2}{5}$ c $1\frac{1}{3} \times 2\frac{2}{5}$ d $\left(1\frac{1}{2} + 2\frac{1}{6}\right) - \left(\frac{3}{5}\right)^2$
e $\left(1\frac{1}{2} \times 2\frac{1}{4}\right) + \left(1\frac{3}{4} - 1\frac{4}{5}\right)$ f $\left(\frac{9}{10} \times 1\frac{2}{3}\right) \div \left(2\frac{1}{2} + 3\frac{1}{3}\right)$

6a I can use the function key to enter a mixed number

7 Use your calculator to work out these.
Give your answers to 2 d.p. where appropriate.

a $\sqrt[3]{2197}$ b $\sqrt[3]{74.088}$ c $\sqrt[3]{9^2} - 4^2$ d $\dfrac{11^3 + 17^3}{\sqrt[3]{2744}}$
e $\dfrac{\sqrt{1.2} + 4.2^2}{(4.1 + 2.3)^3}$ f $\dfrac{5.7^2 + 6.3^3}{1 - \sqrt[3]{96.1}}$ g $\dfrac{17.5 \times 301.45}{0.81^2}$

6a I can use the function keys for cubes and cube roots

8 The volume of a cone is given by the formula $\frac{1}{3}\pi r^2 h$.
The volume is 256 cm³ and the height is 4.5 cm.
Calculate the radius.
Give your answer to 2 d.p.

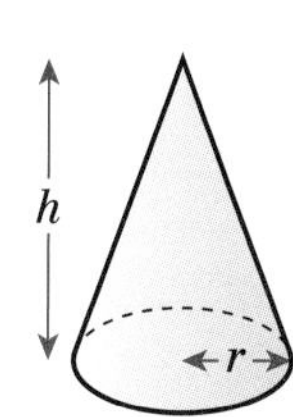

6a I can use the function keys on a calculator to solve problems

9 Use your calculator to find the value of x in each case.
Give your answers to 2 d.p.

a $x^2 = 13.26 \div 2.82$ b $3x^3 - 14.8 = 2.62$ c $2\pi - 5.85 = 3x^2$
d $\dfrac{14.86}{9.37 - 7.72} = x^2$ e $\sqrt{x} = \dfrac{7.23^2 - 1.19}{\sqrt{9.3^2 - 2.1}}$ f $\sqrt{x} = \dfrac{\pi + 2.9^2}{3.76 - \pi}$

Level 7

7c I know not to round during the intermediate steps of a calculation

Now try this!

A £1 million target

If you invest £5 in a bank at 4% simple interest per year, how many years will it take to reach £1 million?

Tip Simple interest is interest worked out only on the principal – the amount of money invested to start with.

B Chessboard squares

How many squares are there on a chessboard?
Use your calculator to help you.

Tip There are more than 8^2!

enter key memory recurring decimal sign change key

Unit 8 plenary

Number puzzles

Creators of puzzles often look for numbers with special properties. For example, the square number 81 is special because

- the sum of its digits is also a square number ($8 + 1 = 9$)
- it is equal to the square of the sum of its digits ($81 = 9 \times 9$).

In the unit opener, you discovered that 1458 and 1729 share a special property.
Can you remember what it is?
In the following activities, you will use 81, 1458 and 1729 to provide you with answers to number puzzles.

1 When rounded to the nearest 1000, the answer is 1000.
Which number has been rounded? **Level 5**

2 The square root of this number is 41.58 (to 2 decimal places).
Which number is this? **Level 5**

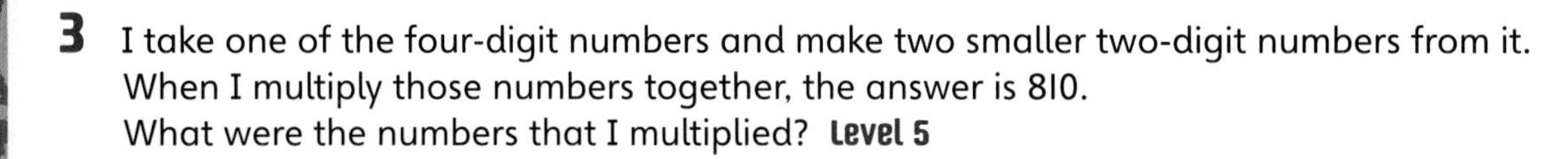

3 I take one of the four-digit numbers and make two smaller two-digit numbers from it.
When I multiply those numbers together, the answer is 810.
What were the numbers that I multiplied? **Level 5**

4 I take one of the numbers and remove one of its digits. I am left with a three-digit number. When I divide the three-digit number by 18, the answer is 40.5.
What is the three-digit number? **Level 5**

5 I took two of the numbers and placed a decimal point in each one. The total of these decimal numbers is 16.309.
Which numbers did I add together? **Level 6**

Hint: I did not place the decimal point in the same position in each number.

6 I took two of the numbers and placed a decimal point in each one.
The product of these decimal numbers is 118.098.
Which numbers did I multiply? **Level 6**

Hint: I did not place the decimal point in the same position in each number.

7 I took two of the numbers and placed a decimal point in one only. When I divide the bigger number by the smaller, the answer is 1800.
Which numbers did I divide? **Level 6**

8 The cube root of this number is 11.34 (to 2 decimal places).
Which number is this? **Level 6**

9 Complete these calculations:

a ____ $\times 10^4 = 81$

b ____ $\div 10^3 = 1458$

c ____ $\div \frac{1}{10} = 1729$ **Level 7**

The BIG ideas

- The inverse of **squaring** is finding the **square root**. $\sqrt{36} = 6$ because $6^2 = 36$. 6 is called the square root of 36. **Level 5**
- Use the $\sqrt{\ }$ key to find the square root of a number using a calculator. **Level 5**
- To **add** or **subtract decimals**: line up the decimal points, put the decimal point in the answer, then add or subtract. **Level 5**
- You can use the grid method or the standard column procedure for multiplication. **Level 5**
- You can use an **equivalent** calculation to multiply a decimal by a decimal. For example, $5.8 \times 7.6 = (58 \div 10) \times (76 \div 10) = 58 \times 76 \div 100$. **Level 5 & Level 6**
- You can use repeated subtraction for division. The number you divide by is called the **divisor**. Keep subtracting **multiples of the divisor** until you can't subtract any more, then see how many lots of the divisor you subtracted altogether. **Level 5 & Level 6**
- When adding or subtracting decimals with different numbers of digits you can use a **zero place holder**. For example, 23.4 – 58.67 is equivalent to 23.40 – 58.67. **Level 5 & Level 6**
- 0.1 is **equivalent** to $\frac{1}{10}$. Dividing by 0.1 is the same as dividing by $\frac{1}{10}$ or multiplying by 10. **Level 6**
- To multiply a number by any positive integer power of ten, move the digits the index value number of places to the left. **Level 6**
- To divide a number by any positive integer power of ten, move the digits the index value number of places to the right. **Level 6**
- The inverse of **cubing** is finding the **cube root**. $\sqrt[3]{8} = 2$ because $2^3 = 8$. So the cube root of 8 is 2. **Level 6**
- You use the $\sqrt[3]{\ }$ function to find the cube root of a number using a calculator. **Level 6**

Practice SATs-style questions

Level 5

Q1 **a** Show that 6×24 is 144.
b Use part **a** to work out 18×24.

Q2 Complete the grid.

×		4
40	800	
	80	

Q3 Find the missing numbers to make the calculations correct.
a $\square + 8 = -4$ **b** $\square - -8 = 4$

Level 6

Q4 Pack A: 12 ink cartridges costs £14.40.
Pack B: 18 ink cartridges costs £18.90.
Which pack gives you better value for money? Show all your workings.

Q5 Ravi is decorating his house and has bought five items at the Do-it-now store. The total bill was £312. The drill was twice as expensive as the lampshade.
What was the cost of the drill?
Show all your workings.

Do-it-now Store

	£	p
Wallpaper	80	
Lampshade		
Wood flooring	149	93
Tape		77

Level 7

Q6 $1\ m^2 = 10^4\ cm^2$
Convert these areas to the units given.
a $28750\ cm^2 =$ _____ m^2
b $35.5\ m^2 =$ _____ cm^2
c $980\ cm^2 =$ _____ m^2

Q7 Estimate the answer to this calculation.
$84.2 \times 38.9 \div 15.44 \times \sqrt{19}$

9 Tons of transformations

This unit is about transformations.

Crop circles are patterns made in fields by flattening crops such as wheat. Although many people have admitted creating them, others still believe that there is an alien explanation for the sudden appearance of these circles. What do you think?

The crop circle design in the large photo contains a lot of mathematics. It is made up of circles and parts of circles. The design has one line of symmetry – can you work out where?

The design in this small photo is also made from circles. All the circle patterns in the outer ring are different sized copies of the same basic design. This unit will show you how to accurately describe shapes that are copies or enlargements of each other.

Activities

A Design a crop circle of your own with four lines of symmetry. Use compasses to draw the circles accurately.

B This shape has order of rotational symmetry 4.

Design a crop circle which has no lines of symmetry but rotational symmetry of order 3.

Did you know?
A crop circle discovered at Longwood Warren in England was thought to represent the solar system. The only problem was that the Earth was missing!

Before you start this unit...

1 How many lines of symmetry do these shapes have?

a Square
b Rectangle
c Isosceles triangle
d Parallelogram

2 Copy the diagram and reflect the shape in the dotted line.

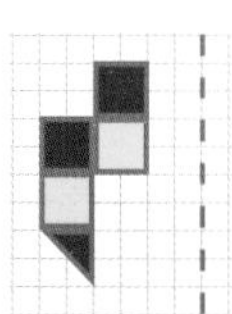

Level Up Maths 4-6 page 214

3 Copy the above shape onto squared paper and translate it three squares to the right and two squares down.

4

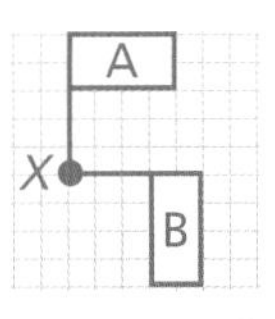

a Describe the rotation of flag A onto flag B.
b Draw flag A and rotate it 180° anticlockwise about point X.

Did you know?
The crop circle formed on 12 August 2001 on Milk Hill, Wiltshire had over 400 circles as part of its design.

Plus digital resources

9.1 Symmetry and congruence

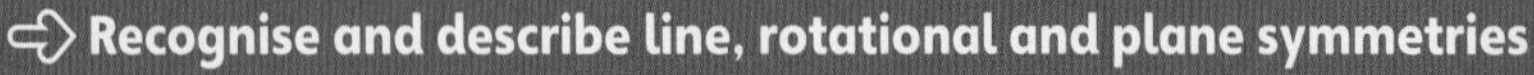

- Recognise and describe line, rotational and plane symmetries
- Know what 'congruent' means and identify congruent shapes

Why learn this?

Snowflakes have almost perfect symmetry – although each flake is different, they usually have six lines of symmetry and rotational symmetry of order 6.

What's the BIG idea?

- The **order** of **rotational symmetry** of a shape is the number of times it would fit onto itself in a whole turn. **Level 5**
- Shapes are **congruent** if they are exactly the same shape and size. **Level 5**
- You can use congruency to help you solve problems. **Level 6**
- When a 2-D shape is **translated**, **rotated** or **reflected**, the shape and its image are congruent. **Level 6**
- Some 3-D shapes have **plane symmetry**. **Level 6 & Level 7**

Did you know?

'Congruent' comes from the Latin word 'congruere' which means 'to agree with or correspond with'.

Practice, practice, practice!

Level 5

5c I can identify the order of rotational symmetry of 2-D shapes

1 Name each of these shapes and state their order of rotational symmetry.

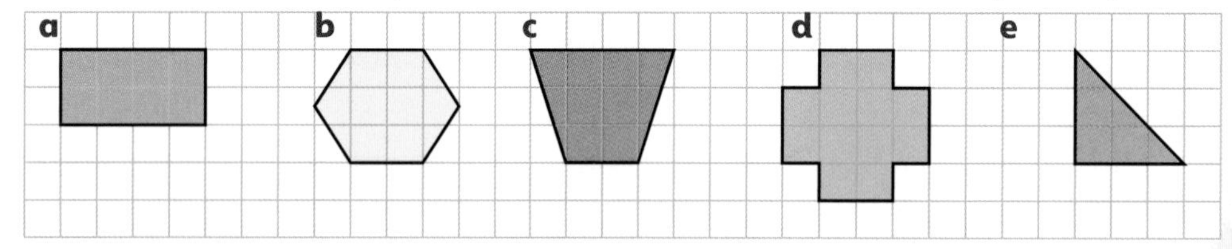

5c I can identify congruent shapes

2 Look at the grid below.
Write the letters of as many sets of congruent shapes as you can find.

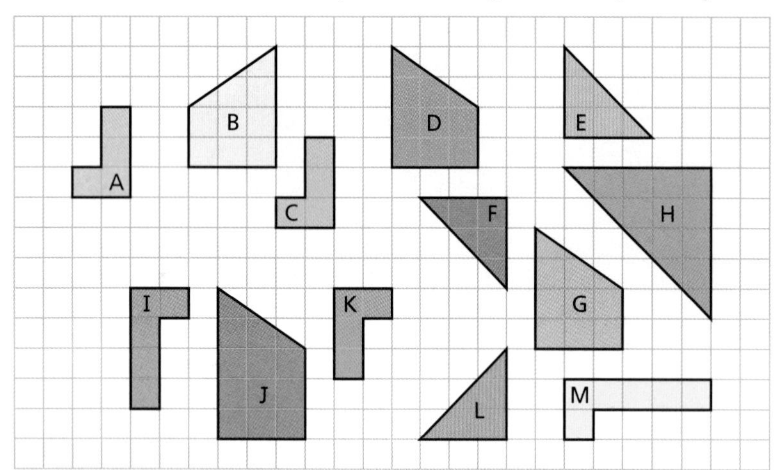

5b I can explain the rules about congruent shapes

3 Explain how you decided whether shapes were congruent in Q2.

congruent line symmetry order plane symmetry

4 Find two examples of each of these types of transformation in the grid in Q2.
Write the letters of the shapes you have chosen.
Describe each transformation fully.

a translations **b** reflections **c** rotations

Shape A to shape C. Translated 7 squares right and 1 square down.

Tip
Never use the word 'across' when describing a translation as it doesn't tell you the direction. Always specify 'up' or 'down', 'left' or 'right'.

5 Name each of these shapes and write down its number of lines of symmetry and its order of rotational symmetry.

a  **b**  **c** 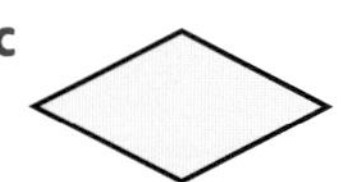 **d** **e** 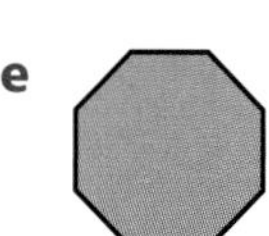

Level 5

5b I can visualise and describe transformations of 2-D shapes

5a I can describe all of the symmetries of a 2-D shape

6 Which quadrilaterals could you make by putting these shapes together?

a two congruent isosceles triangles

b two congruent right-angled triangles

7 Use the words below to copy and complete these sentences.
Congruent shapes have exactly the same ________ and ________. If I reflect, ________ or ________ a 2-D shape, the ________ is congruent to the object. This means that all of the ________ are the same and all of the angles are ________.

shape | image | the same | enlarge | rotate | size | stretch | sides | different | translate

Level 6

6b I can use congruency to solve simple problems

6a I can understand how translations, reflections and rotations map 2-D objects onto congruent images

8 Which of these shapes have planes of symmetry?

A 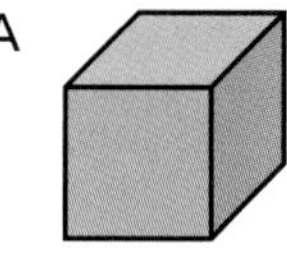 B 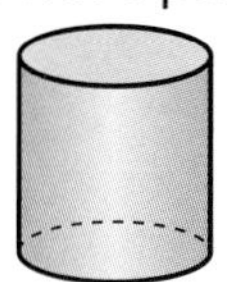 C 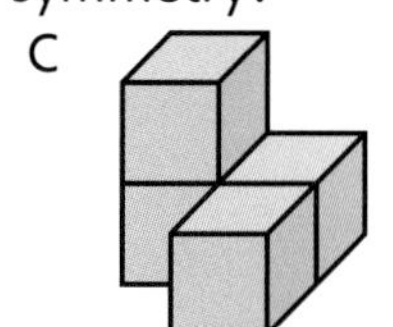 D 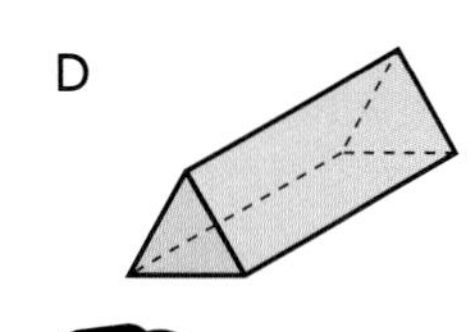

9 Draw two copies of each 3-D shape in Q8 that has reflection symmetry. Draw in two different planes of symmetry.

Tip
When a 3-D shape has reflection symmetry, the mirror is described as a 'plane of symmetry'.

Level 7

7c I can identify planes of symmetry in 3-D shapes

Now try this!

A Logos

Sketch some company logos in your book. How many lines of symmetry do they have? What order of rotational symmetry do they have?

B Enough information?

Imagine you are talking to a friend on the phone, and you are both drawing a triangle. Which of these sets of information would be enough to make sure that your triangles are congruent? Explain your decisions.

- The lengths of the three sides (SSS).
- The sizes of the three angles (AAA).
- The lengths of two sides and the size of the angle between them (SAS).

reflection | rotation | rotational symmetry | translation

9.2 Combining transformations

- Transform 2-D shapes by combining reflections, rotations and translations
- Understand that these transformations map objects onto congruent images

Why learn this?

Combining reflections, rotations and translations helps us to describe real-world movement accurately.

What's the BIG idea?

- You can perform more than one transformation on the same shape. This is a combination of transformations. **Level 5 & Level 6**
- The **object** and the **image** of a **reflection**, **rotation** or **translation** always have the same lengths and angles. This means they are **congruent**. **Level 6**

Practice, practice, practice!

Level 5

5a I can use and describe simple combinations of transformations

1 Look at the crazy transformation golf course.

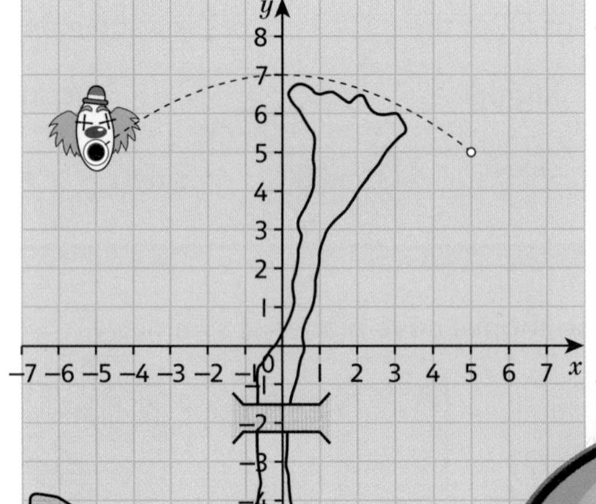

a Describe fully a single reflection that would move the golf ball into the clown's mouth.

b Alice doesn't want to hit her ball over the water and chooses to use the bridge. Describe the ball's journey by using a translation followed by a reflection and finally another translation.

c Find a single transformation that would get the ball round the top of the water and into the clown's mouth.

For Q2–4, use the shapes from this grid.

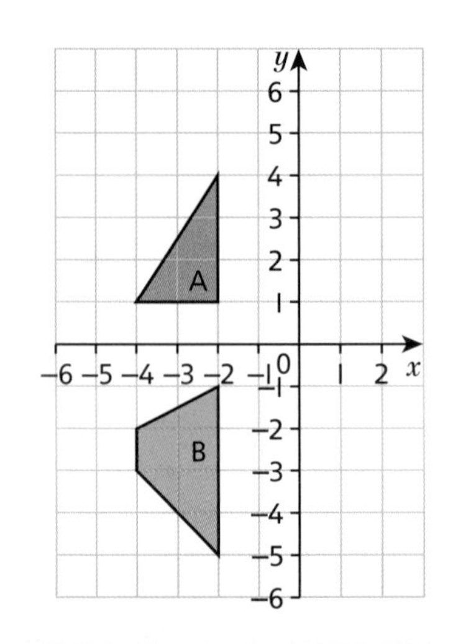

2 **a** Draw x- and y-axes from −6 to 6. Copy shape A onto them.

b Reflect shape A in the x-axis. Label the image A_2.

c Reflect shape A_2 in the y-axis. Label the image A_3.

d Write the coordinates of the vertices of shape A_3.

e What single transformation would map shape A directly onto shape A_3?

Watch out!

To describe a rotation fully you need to write down three things – the size of the rotation in degrees, the coordinates of the centre of rotation and whether it is clockwise or anticlockwise.

anticlockwise centre of rotation clockwise congruent image

3 a Draw x- and y-axes from −6 to 6. Copy shape B onto them.
b Rotate shape B 180° about the point (−2, −1). Label the image B_2.
c Translate shape B_2 down 4. Label the image B_3.
d Write the coordinates of the vertices of shape B_3.
e What single transformation would map shape B directly onto shape B_3?

4 Look again at the transformations you have drawn in **Q3** and **Q4**.
a When you reflect, rotate or translate a shape, do
i the lengths of the sides change ii the angles inside the shape change?
b If they do, describe the change.

For Q5–8, use the shapes from this grid.

5 Describe a way of mapping shape E onto shape H using
a just one transformation
b a combination of two transformations.

6 Describe a way of mapping shape F onto shape G using
a just one transformation
b a combination of two transformations.

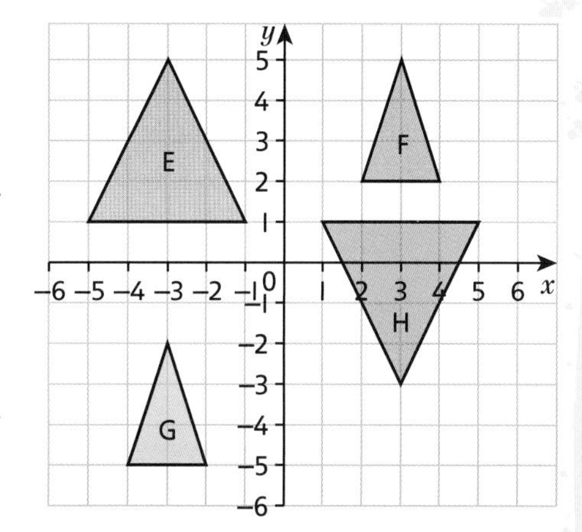

Level 6

6C I can use and describe more complex combinations of transformations

6C I can explain what effect translations, rotations and reflections have on lengths and angles

6C I can use and describe more complex combinations of transformations

7 Explain why no combination of reflections, rotations or translations will map shape E onto shape F.

8 Decide whether these statements are true or false.
a A combination of two translations can always be written as one translation.
b Reflecting in the x-axis then the y-axis is the same as rotating 180° about (0, 0).
c A combination of two reflections can always be written as one rotation.

Hint: Try some examples if necessary.

Level 7

7C I can understand how reflections, rotations and translations map objects onto congruent images

Learn this

Shapes are congruent if they are exactly the same shape and size.

Now try this!

A Over the line

On a set of axes from −5 to 5, draw a triangle with vertices at (2, 1), (3, 3) and (4, 0). Reflect this shape in the x-axis and write the coordinates of the image vertices. What has happened to the coordinates? What would the coordinates of the image of point (a, b) be if it was reflected like this?

B Combining combinations

Look again at the grid for Q2–4. Shape D has been made up of shapes A, B and C after they have been transformed. Find the transformation or combination of transformations that would move each shape to become part of shape D.

line of symmetry object reflection rotation translation

maths!

Ambigrams

An ambigram is a word designed so that it can be read in more than one direction or orientation.

An ambigram is a word designed so that it can be read in more than one direction or orientation.

Ambigrams have either reflection symmetry or rotational symmetry. Look at these ambigrams. Which type of symmetry does each have?

Mathematics

fantasy

dollop

Some letters are easier to use in ambigrams than others. A letter d and a letter p would work well in a rotational ambigram.

Which other letters pair up? Which letters are a reflection of another letter? If words are allowed to have a line of symmetry, what other letters could be used?

CHOICE

Complete each of these ambigrams. You will need to decide whether they will have reflection or rotational symmetry.

Have a go at creating your own ambigrams. Try using your own name or a name of a family member.

Calculator Ambigrams

Numbers on a calculator often look the same when turned upside down. The number 2 on a calculator is an ambigram.

What's the biggest four digit number you can make on a calculator using two numbers that also is an ambigram? What about a five digit number with 3 numbers? Find a square number (bigger than 1) that is an ambigram.

9.3 Ratios

- Write and simplify ratios in ratio notation
- Use ratios and fractions to solve problems involving proportion

Why learn this?

Ratios help us to compare two or more amounts. Betting odds tell people how much they might win from a given bet.

What's the BIG idea?

- You can write **ratios** using a colon (:). For example, in a class there are three girls for every two boys. As a ratio this is 3 : 2. **Level 5**
- You can sometimes **simplify** ratios to make them easier to understand. Dive both parts by a **common factor**. 6 : 4 = 3 : 2 **Level 5**
- Ratios and **fractions** can both be used to solve problems involving **proportions**, and you can swap between them. For example, if the ratio of girls to boys in a class is 3 : 2, then $\frac{3}{5}$ of the class are girls and $\frac{2}{5}$ of the class are boys. **Level 5**

Did you know?

The ratio of the volumes of the Moon and the Earth is about 1 : 50 – so 50 Moons could fit inside the Earth!

Practice, practice, practice!

Level 5

5c I can solve problems using direct proportion

1 5 miles is approximately equal to 8 km.

a Roughly how many kilometres are 30 miles?

b Roughly how many miles are 88 km?

2 Here are the ingredients for a recipe for 20 muffins.

a What quantities would you need to make four muffins?

b How much milk would a recipe for 12 muffins need?

c Wilma made the recipe using four eggs. How many muffins did she make?

Choc muffins (makes 20)
250 g butter
200 g sugar
5 eggs
250 g plain flour
20 g baking powder
60 ml milk
100 g chocolate chips
150 g drinking chocolate

5b I can reduce a ratio to its simplest form

3 Write each ratio in its simplest form.

2 : 8 = 1 : 4

a 2 : 10	**b** 3 : 9	**c** 12 : 3	**d** 15 : 25
e 6 : 24	**f** 120 : 150	**g** 15 : 35	**h** 56 : 42

5b I can divide a quantity into parts in a given ratio

4 James is running a raffle and has £300 to give away in prizes. Work out how much the first prize would be if he has

two prizes in the ratio 7 : 3   Total number of parts = 10

1 part = £300 ÷ 10 = £30, so first prize = £30 × 7 = £210

a two prizes in the ratio 5 : 1

b two prizes in the ratio 3 : 2

c three prizes in the ratio 5 : 3 : 2

fraction proportion

5 On an average weekday, Abi sleeps for 8 hours, goes to school for 6 hours and has free time for the rest of the day.

a Write down the ratio of the times Abi spends sleeping : at school : free time.

b Simplify this ratio as much as possible.

c Compare this with your own average weekday. Do you think this is a realistic ratio?

Level 5

5a I can simplify a three-part ratio

6 Write these ratios in their simplest form.

50p : £2 = 50p : 200p = 1 : 4

a 600 m : 3 km **b** 2 kg : 700 g

c 20 minutes : 1 hour **d** 2 months : 1 year

e 12 minutes : $\frac{1}{4}$ of an hour **f** £2.80 : 40p : £1.20

g 250 g : 750 g : 3 kg **h** 2 *l* : 75 *cl* : 200 m*l*

Watch out!

Make sure both quantities are in the same units before you simplify a ratio, and check that the answer makes sense.

5a I can reduce a ratio in mixed units to its simplest form

7 A sculpture contains 144 bricks.
The bricks are coloured white, purple and orange in the ratio 3 : 2 : 1.

a How many purple bricks are there?

b What fraction of the bricks are purple?

c How many more white bricks than orange bricks are there?

5a I can understand the relationship between ratio and proportion

8 Ian has 60 DVDs in his collection. The ratio of comedy : drama : horror is 1 : 6 : 3.

a What fraction of the DVDs are comedies?

b What fraction of the DVDs are dramas?

c Ian buys six more comedy DVDs. What fraction of the DVDs are comedies now?

9 You can make orange paint by mixing red and yellow paint .
You get a darker orange if you use a greater proportion of red paint.
Jo creates three different orange colours using these amounts of paint.

Paint 1	400 m*l* of red, 2 *l* of yellow
Paint 2	3 *l* of red, 12 *l* of yellow
Paint 3	150 ml of red, 900 ml of yellow

a Simplify the ratio of red : yellow paint in each orange colour.

b Write the amount of red in each orange colour as a fraction.

c Which of Jo's paints is the darkest orange?

Now try this!

A Hair proportions

- How many people in your class have black hair?
- How many people in your class have brown hair?
- How many people in your class have blonde hair?
- How many people in your class have another colour of hair, or no hair?
- Write these four numbers down as a ratio.
- Can you simplify it?

B Stuck in the middle

Which of these middle values represents the largest fraction?

- '2' in 1 : 2 : 3
- '3' in 1 : 2 : 3 : 4 : 5
- '4' in 1 : 2 : 3 : 4 : 5 : 6 : 7

Explain your answer. By looking at your answers, work out what the fraction of the middle value in this ratio is. 1 : 2 : 3 : 4 : ... : 97 : 98 : 99.

ratio simplify

9.4 Solving problems with proportion

- Use proportional reasoning to solve problems
- Use ratios to solve problems

Why learn this?

You can use ratio and proportion to help you decide which products are best value for money.

What's the BIG idea?

- You can use **proportion** to compare the relative sizes of two or more things. **Level 5**
- You can use **ratio** and proportion to help solve problems and make comparisons in many different situations. **Level 5, Level 6 & Level 7**

Practice, practice, practice!

Level 5

5a I can solve problems involving ratio and proportion

1 In the first three months of the football season, Linfield Rovers won three matches out of eight. Wyechester United won four matches out of 10. Which team won the greater proportion of matches?

2 Westco Supermarkets sell Morning Flakes in three different sizes of box. Which box is the best value for money? Show your working.

3 A manufacturing plant makes 10 000 components a day. The quality control manager will stop the machines if more than one component in 20 is found to be faulty.

a On Tuesday, a sample of 300 components is taken. Thirteen of them are faulty. Do the machines need to be stopped?

b On Wednesday, a sample of 150 components is taken. Eight of them are faulty. Do the machines need to be stopped?

c On Thursday, a sample of 170 components is taken. What is the largest number of faulty components that could be found in the sample without having to stop the machines?

4 Environmental scientists are trying out a new pesticide. The table shows the numbers of three species before the pesticide was used, and three days after the pesticide was used.

Species	Before	After
Fly species A	870	32
Fly species B	415	15
Spider	38	40

Comment on the general effect the pesticide has had on

a the numbers of each species **b** the proportions of the species?

fraction proportion

5 The ratio of the ages of Helen and her older brother is 3 : 4.

a Helen is 18 years old. How old is her brother?

b What will the ratio of their ages be in three years' time?

6 Four hundred and fifty people took part in a taste test. The ratio of people who chose Brand A to people who chose Brand B is 2 : 7.

a What fraction chose Brand B?

b How many more people chose Brand B rather than Brand A?

Level 6

6C I can interpret and use ratio in different contexts

7 The radius of the small circle is 1 cm, and the radius of the large circle is 3 cm. Find the ratio of the area of the small circle to that of the large circle.

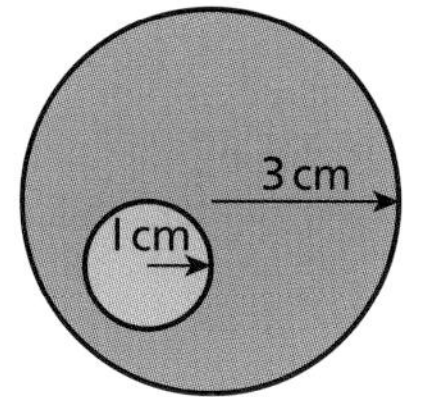

Tip

You might find it easier to leave π as a symbol when working out the areas of the circles – it might cancel out at a later stage.

8 The sides of A4 paper measure 210 mm by 297 mm.

a What proportion of the smaller side is the larger side? Use a calculator. Your answer should be a decimal number.

b Square your answer to part **a**. What do you notice?

c The length of the longer side of A4 paper is the same as length of the shorter side of A3 paper. Use your answer from part **a** to find the length of the longer side of a A3 paper.

d The length the longer side of A5 paper is the same length as the shorter side of A4 paper. Use your answer from part **a** to find the length of the shorter side of A5 paper.

e What is the ratio of the longer side of A5 paper to the longer side of A3 paper?

Did you know?

The ratio of the side lengths is the same for all paper in the 'A' series.

9 Here are two cubes. The length of a side of the smaller cube is 2 cm. The ratio of the surface areas of the cubes is 1 : 16. Find the volume of the larger cube.

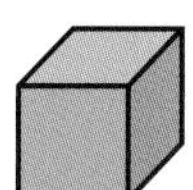

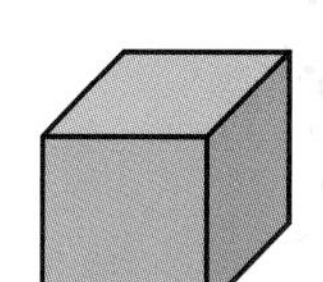

Level 7

7C I can use ratio in more complicated contexts

Now try this!

A Proportional representation

Market research companies often try to choose samples of people in the same proportions as the whole population. What proportion of your class is male, and what proportion is female? If you take a representative sample of ten people from your class, how many should be male and how many should be female?

B Paper sizes

The next largest size of paper after A3 is A2, and then A1. Check that the ratio of side lengths you worked out in Q8 is correct, and use it to work out the size of a piece of A1 paper.

ratio simplify

9.5 Enlargement

- Enlarge 2-D shapes using a positive integer scale factor
- Enlarge 2-D shapes given a positive integer scale factor and a centre of enlargement inside or on the shape

Why learn this?

Enlargements are often used in advertising to attract people's attention.

What's the BIG idea?

- A copy of a shape that keeps the same proportions but changes the lengths is called an **enlargement**. **Level 5 & Level 6**
- The **scale factor** tells you how many times bigger each length is. For example, a scale factor of 2 tells you to double every length. **Level 5 & Level 6**
- The **centre of enlargement** tells you where to place the enlarged shape on a grid. You use the centre of enlargement to draw the **image**. You can then check it using **rays** drawn from the centre. **Level 6 & Level 7**

Did you know?

The UK's tallest billboard is 64 feet high. The first poster on it enlarged a model's legs so that they were 23 feet long – what scale factor do you think was used?

Practice, practice, practice!

Level 6

6c I can understand and use the language of enlargement

1 The scale on a map is 1 : 50 000.

a Write down the scale factor.

b A walk is 4 cm long on the map. How many kilometres is it in real life?

6c I can enlarge a shape using a positive integer scale factor

2 Draw an enlarged copy of each of these shapes using the scale factors given.

a

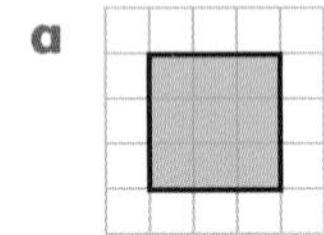

Scale factor 3

b

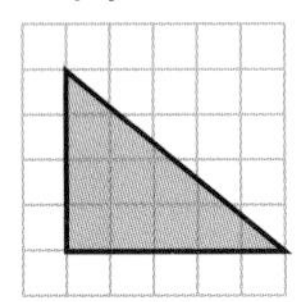

Scale factor 4

c

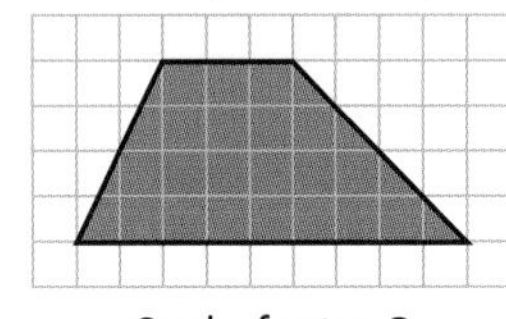

Scale factor 2

d

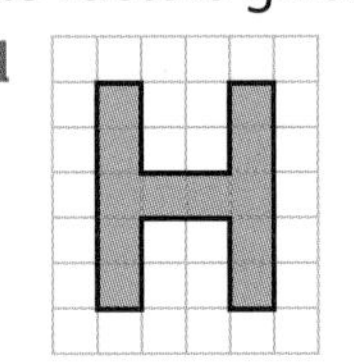

Scale factor 5

6c I can work out and use scale factors

3 A model car is 10 cm wide. The real car is 2 m wide.

a Write down the scale factor of the enlargement that maps the model car to the real car.

b Another model car with the same scale factor is 15 cm long. How long is the real car?

c The real rear-view mirror is 20 cm wide. How wide is the model mirror?

6a I can enlarge a shape given the centre of enlargement and the scale factor

4 Copy these shapes onto squared paper, and then enlarge them using the marked centres of enlargement and scale factors.

a

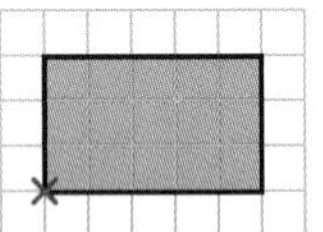

Scale factor 2

b

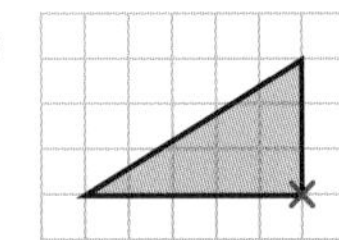

Scale factor 3

c

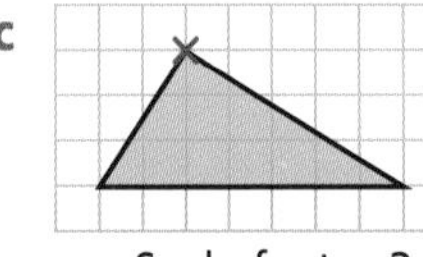

Scale factor 3

Watch out!

Remember that the centre of enlargement is the point from which everything spreads out.

centre of enlargement | enlargement | image

5 Copy these shapes onto squared paper, and then enlarge them using the marked centres of enlargement and scale factors.

a

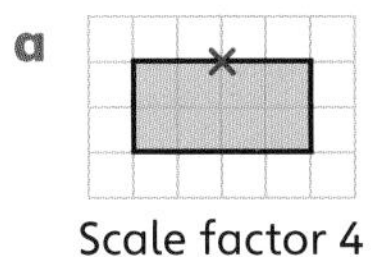

Scale factor 4

b

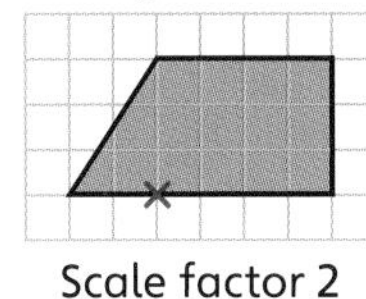

Scale factor 2

c

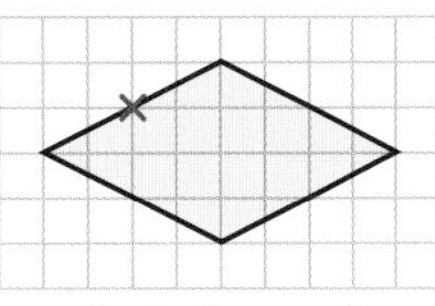

Scale factor 2

6 Copy these shapes onto squared paper, and then enlarge them using the marked centres of enlargement and scale factors.

a

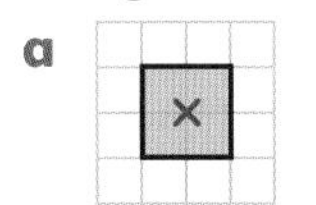

Scale factor 5

b

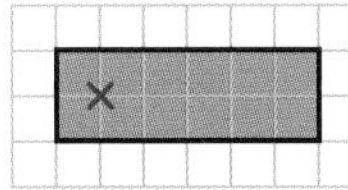

Scale factor 2

c

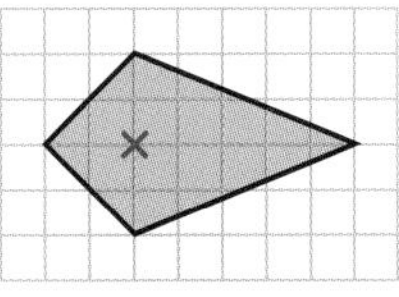

Scale factor 3

Tip

If you have enlarged a shape correctly, the rays that connect each corner of the original shape to the same corner of the image should all meet at the centre of enlargement.

7 Draw a pair of axes from 0 to 10.
Draw the triangle with vertices (2, 3), (4, 3) and (4, 6).
Draw an enlargement of the triangle with scale factor 2 and centre of enlargement (3, 4).

8 Using dynamic geometry software, draw a quadrilateral and enlarge it. Move the centre of enlargement and see what happens to the image. Make sure you try moving it inside and outside of the shape.

a Does the image change size?

b Explain in your own words what you know if you are given the centre of enlargement.

Level 6

6a I can enlarge a shape given the centre of enlargement and the scale factor

6a I can explore enlargement using ICT

9 An object has vertices at (3, 2), (6, 2), (4, 4) and (7, 4).
The image given by an enlargement has vertices at (2, 1), (8, 1), (4, 5) and (10, 5).

a Draw the shape on suitable axes.

b Identify the shape.

c Work out the scale factor.

d Find the centre of enlargement.

10 An object has vertices at (1, 1), (1, 3), (4, 1) and (4, 3). The image given by an enlargement has vertices at (–3, –3), (–3, 3), (6, –3) and (6, 3).

a Draw the shape on suitable axes.

b Identify the shape.

c Work out the scale factor.

d Find the centre of enlargement.

Level 7

7c I can work out the centre of enlargement and scale factor of an enlargement by comparing shapes

Now try this!

A An initial problem

Draw your initials in capital letters on squared paper and enlarge them exactly using a scale factor of 2. Try placing the centre of enlargement at different points on your initials, and using different scale factors.

B Bigger box

Imagine a cube with side length 1 m. What is its volume? Enlarge the cube using a scale factor of 2. What has happened to the volume? Find a scale factor so that the volume doubles when the cube is enlarged.

object ray scale factor

9.6 More enlargement

- Enlarge 2-D shapes given a scale factor and a centre of enlargement
- Understand the effect of enlargements on lengths, angles and perimeters of shapes

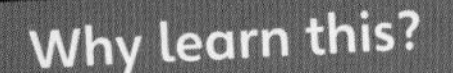

Scientists use enlargements with very large scale factors to study the microscopic world around us.

What's the BIG idea?

- An **enlargement** can be described by a **scale factor** and a **centre of enlargement**. Level 6 & Level 7
- A negative scale factor takes the shape back through the centre of enlargement and changes its orientation. Level 7
- **Similar** shapes have matching angles and corresponding sides that are in the same proportion. Enlargements change lengths but keep angles the same – so **images** and **objects** are similar but not **congruent**. Level 7

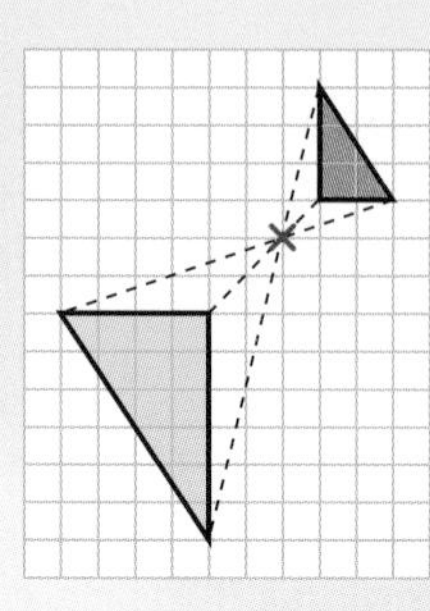

Learn this

A negative scale factor works the same way as a positive scale factor, except that it takes the image through to the other side of the centre of enlargement.

Practice, practice, practice!

Level 6

6a I can enlarge shapes using a centre of enlargement outside the object

1 Copy these shapes onto squared paper, and then enlarge them using the marked centres of enlargement and scale factors.

a 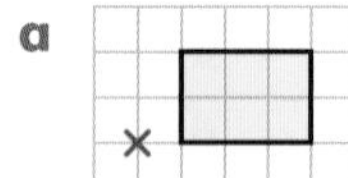
Scale factor 2

b 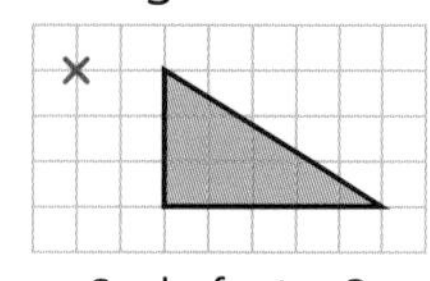
Scale factor 2

c 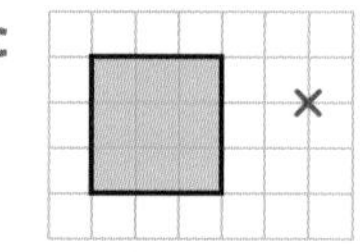
Scale factor 3

Tip
Remember to enlarge the distance from the centre of enlargement to the shape as well as enlarging the shape itself.

2 Copy these shapes onto squared paper, and then enlarge them using the marked centres of enlargement and scale factors.

a 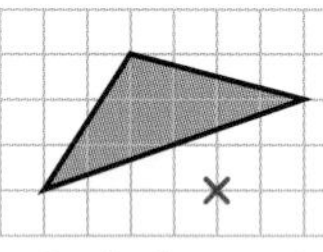
Scale factor 3

b 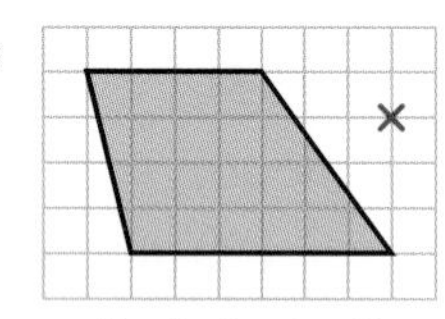
Scale factor 2

c 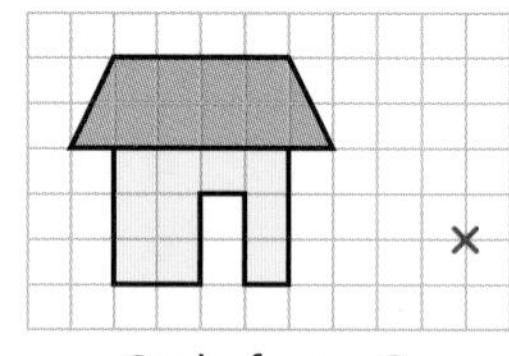
Scale factor 2

Level 7

7c I can describe how enlargements affect lengths and angles

3 **a** Copy this triangle onto squared paper and measure and label all of the sides and angles.

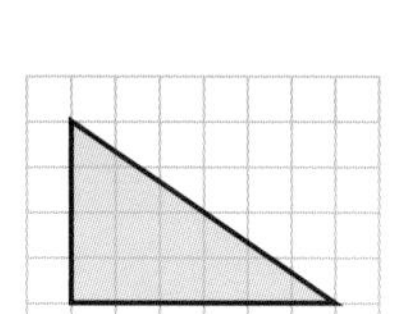

b Enlarge the triangle using a scale factor of 3. Measure and label all of the sides and angles of your image.

c What has happened to the lengths of the sides?

d What has happened to the size of the angles?

centre of enlargement | congruent | enlargement | image

4 Copy these shapes onto squared paper, and then enlarge them using the marked centres of enlargement and negative scale factors.

a

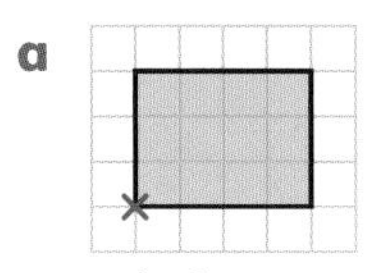

Scale factor −3

b

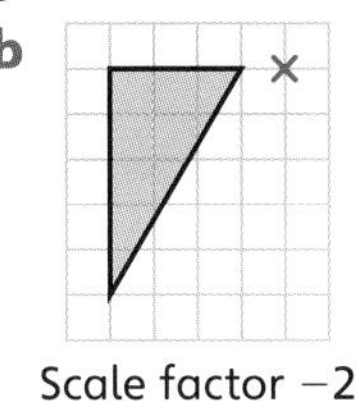

Scale factor −2

c

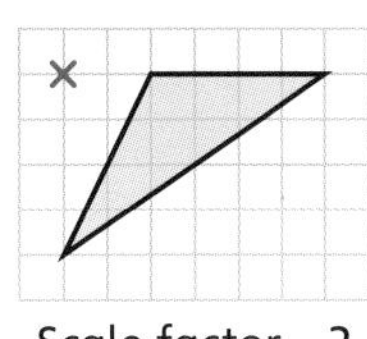

Scale factor −2

Level 7

7b I can enlarge shapes with a negative integer scale factor

5 An object has vertices at (−1, −1), (−1, −4) and (−5, −1). The image given by an enlargement has vertices at (2, 5), (10, 5) and (2, 11).

a Draw the object and image on suitable axes.

b Name the shape and give the scale factor and centre of the enlargement.

Tip

You can still use rays to find the centre of enlargement when it lies outside the shape.

6 Brian draws a triangle on a set of axes and enlarges it with scale factor −1 and with a centre of enlargement (0, 0). Find and describe another transformation that would have exactly the same effect.

7 **a** Draw the green rectangle from Q4 on squared paper. State its perimeter.

b Enlarge the rectangle with a scale factor of 2.
What is the perimeter of the image?

c Enlarge the original rectangle with a scale factor of 5.
What is the perimeter of the image?

d Use your answers to parts **a**, **b** and **c** to find the perimeter of the rectangle after it is enlarged by a scale factor of k.

7b I can explain how enlargement affects perimeter

8 The large rectangle is an enlargement of the smaller rectangle.

a What is the scale factor of this enlargement?

b Work out the value of x.

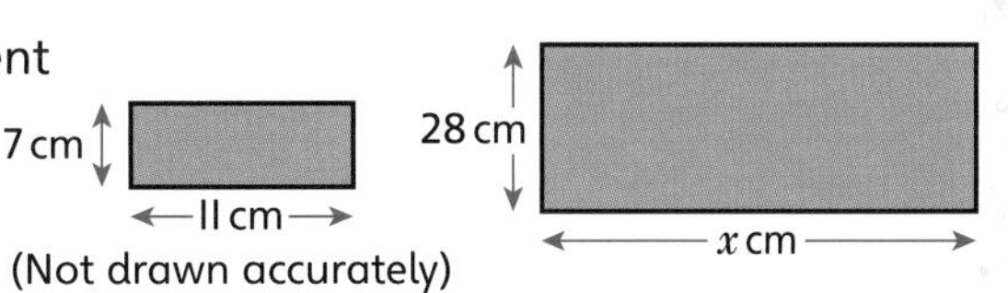

(Not drawn accurately)

7a I can work out the scale factor of an enlargement by using ratios of corresponding line segments

9 The two triangles are similar.

a What is the scale factor of this enlargement?

b Work out the lengths of sides x and y.

c Work out the sizes of angles a and b.

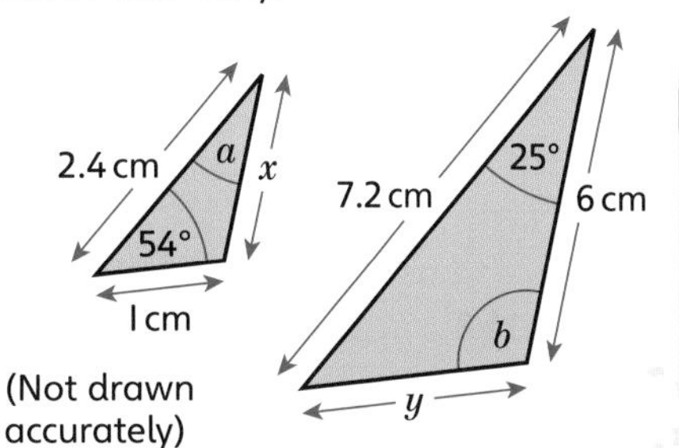

(Not drawn accurately)

Learn this

Similar shapes have sides in the same proportions, and angles that are the same.

Now try this!

A Somewhere in-between

Copy the right-angled triangle from Q3 onto squared paper and label it 'scale factor 1'. Now enlarge it using a scale factor of 2 and label it 'scale factor 2'.

- What would a scale factor of $1\frac{1}{2}$ look like.
- Draw an enlargement with scale factor $2\frac{1}{2}$.
- Draw an enlargement with scale factor $\frac{1}{2}$.

Hint: It would lie somewhere between these two shapes.

B Getting the point

What are the new coordinates of the point (x, y) after an enlargement by a scale factor k with centre of enlargement (0, 0)?

Try to answer this question either by experimenting with values, or by exploring enlargement with ICT.

object **ray** **scale factor** **similar**

A crop of transformations

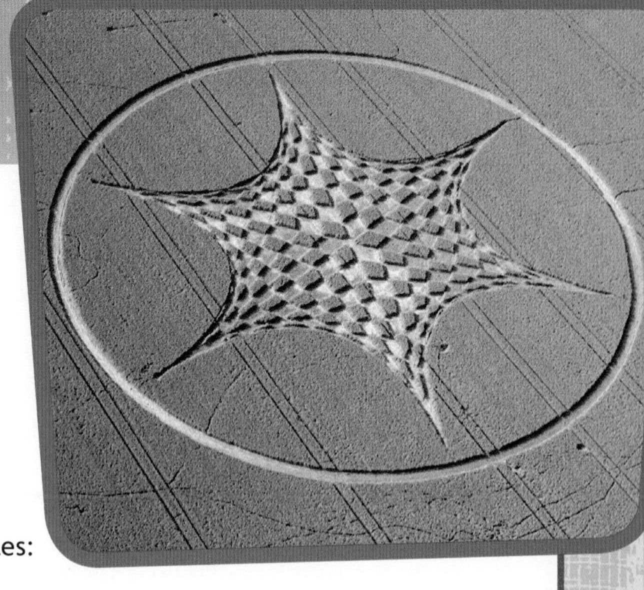

Look at this crop circle design. What symmetries and transformations have been used in the design?

1 How many lines of symmetry does the design have? What order of rotational symmetry does the design have? **Level 5**

2 Describe fully a rotation that would map the design onto itself. **Level 5**

3 Part of a similar crop circle design consists of these circles:

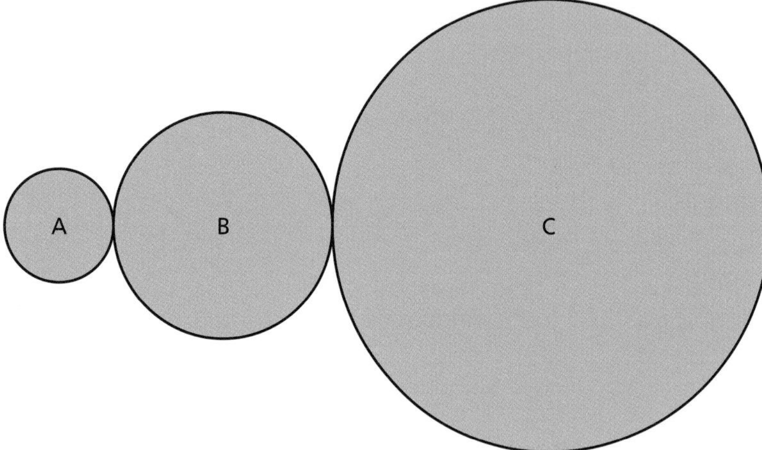

Measure the diameters of the three circles and write them as a three part ratio, A : B : C. Simplify as fully as possible.

4 Write down the scale factors of the enlargements that would take:

a circle A to circle B

b circle B to circle C

c circle A to circle C **Level 6**

5 Circle D is an enlargement of circle C by scale factor 3. What is the diameter of circle D? **Level 6**

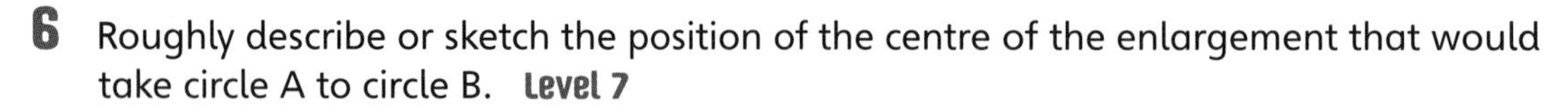

6 Roughly describe or sketch the position of the centre of the enlargement that would take circle A to circle B. **Level 7**

7 A more complex crop circle design contains similar triangles. Work out the values of lengths x and y. **Level 7**

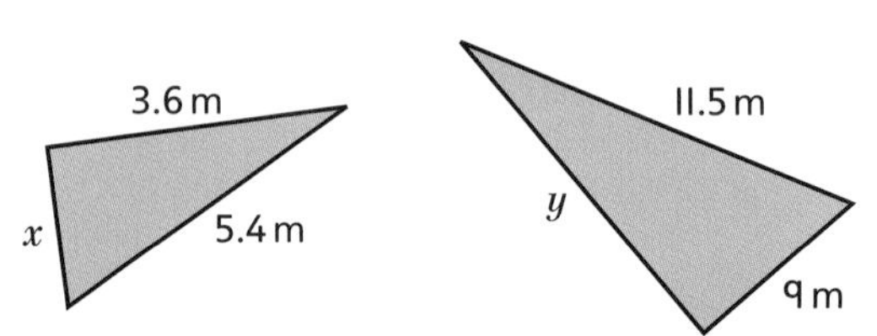

The BIG ideas

- The **order of rotational symmetry** of a shape is the number of times it would fit into itself in a whole turn. **Level 5**
- To describe a rotation you need to give the angle and direction (**clockwise** and **anticlockwise**) of rotation as well as the **centre of rotation**. **Level 5**
- You can write **ratios** using a colon (:). For example, if your class had three girls for every two boys, the ratio of girls to boys would be 3 : 2. **Level 5**
- You can sometimes **simplify** ratios to make them easier to understand. **Level 5 & Level 6**
- A copy of a shape that keeps the same proportions but increases the lengths is called an **enlargement**. **Level 5 & Level 6**
- The **scale factor** tells you how many times bigger each length is. For example, a scale factor of 2 tells you to double every length. **Level 5 & Level 6**
- The **centre of enlargement** tells you where to place the enlarged shape on a grid. You use the centre of enlargement to draw the image, and you can then check it using rays. **Level 6 & Level 7**
- An enlargement can be described by a scale factor and a centre of enlargement. **Level 6 & Level 7**
- **Similar shapes** have matching angles and corresponding sides that are in the same proportion. Enlargements change lengths but keep angles the same – so images and objects are similar but not congruent. **Level 7**

Practice SATs-style questions

Level 5

Q1 Sameed has two identical right-angled triangles.
How can Sameed place them together to create a shape with:

a 2 lines of symmetry **and** order of rotational symmetry 2?

b **no** lines of symmetry but order of rotational symmetry 2?

Q2 Copy the rectangle onto squared paper and rotate it twice, using the dot as the centre of rotation.

i Rotate 90° anticlockwise **ii** Rotate another 90° anticlockwise

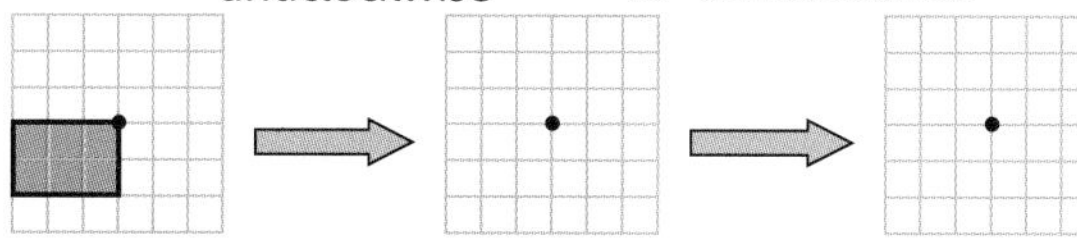

Level 6

Q3 The large triangle is an enlargement of the smaller triangle.
Write down the scale factor of the enlargement.

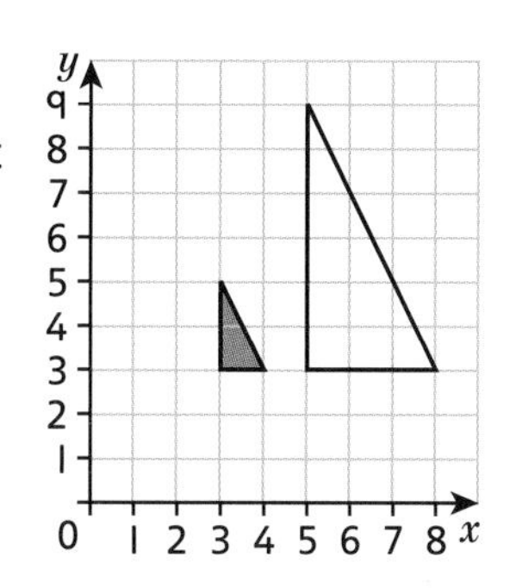

Q4 Enlarge this shape by a scale factor of 3.

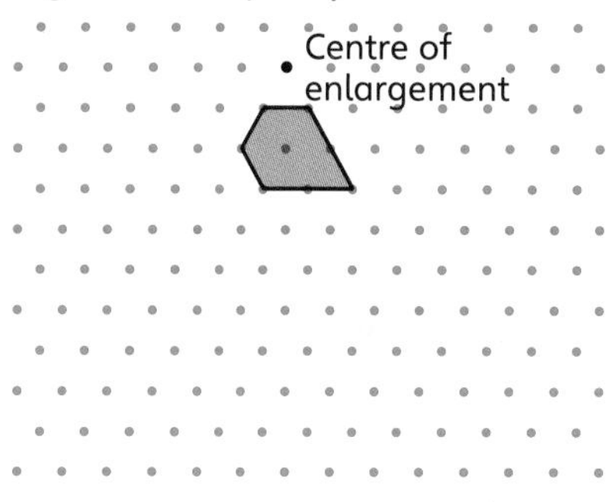

Level 7

Q5 Draw two sketches of this cuboid and add in two **different** planes of symmetry.

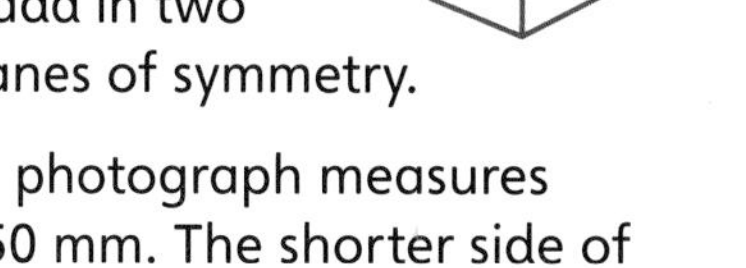

Q6 An enlarged photograph measures 270 mm × 450 mm. The shorter side of the original photograph was 180 mm long. Calculate the length of the longer side of the original photograph.

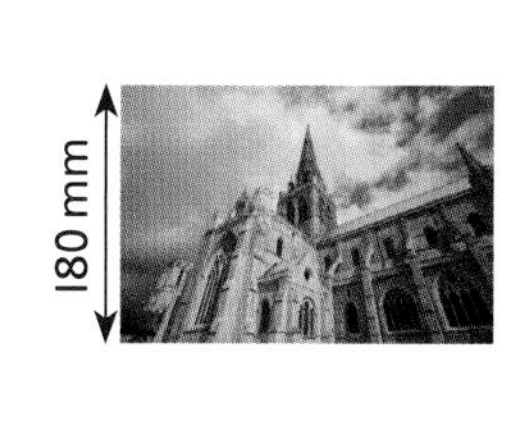

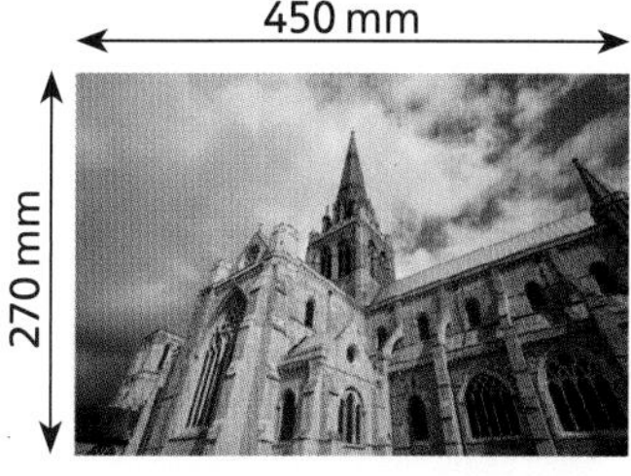

10 Under construction

This unit is about constructing and using equations and formulae.

The Ancient Egyptians were using maths and formulae to work out measurements for their buildings thousands of years ago. Two ancient documents, the Moscow Papyrus and the Rhind Papyrus, are almost 4000 years old. They set out problems with solutions and show how mathematics was used in Egypt at that time. When you have completed this unit, you can try out some of these ancient problems – turn to the plenary to see them!

It is useful to be able to identify mathematical aspects of a situation. Look at the beach huts in the photo. The front section of the huts on the left and right has been divided into smaller equal sections by a set of vertical supports. If you want to build a similar beach hut, you can write a formula to work out the widths of the smaller sections from the overall width of the hut.

Activities

A Look at the left- and right-hand beach huts again. Describe how to work out the width of the smaller front sections.

Look at the beach hut in the middle. Here the sections are not of equal width. Assume you are told the total width of the beach hut and the width of the middle section. Describe how to work out the widths of the other sections.

B Design your own beach hut. Write a set of instructions to tell someone else how to work out the widths of each front section.

Swap instructions with a partner. Choose a width for the beach hut and a width for the vertical supports and try out the instructions. Write on all the measurements.

Did you know?
The formula for the volume, V, of a truncated square-based pyramid was known to the Egyptians around 1850 BC.

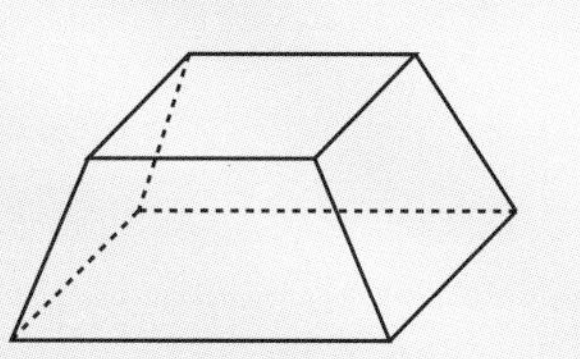

Before you start this unit...

1 What are the missing numbers?

Level Up Maths 4-6 pages 25, 30

a $12 \times \square = 48$

b $\square \div 3 = 7$

c $\square \times -4 = 24$

2 $a = 3$, $b = 5$ and $c = 7$.
Write down the value of each expression.

a $a + b + c$

b $21 - c$

c $a(4 + b)$

3 Find the area in cm² of this shape when $x = 7$.
All lengths are in cm.

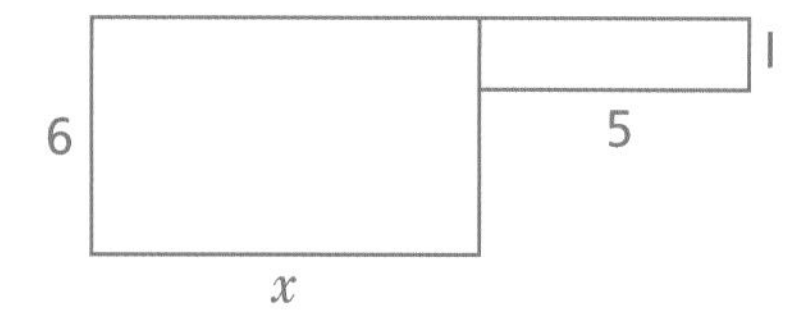

4 Multiply out each bracket.

page 113

a $2(2x + 3)$

b $8(3 - 4x)$

The areas of mathematics used and developed by the Egyptians include the Egyptian number system; measurements of land and boundaries; a standard system of weights and measures; and the mathematics involved in the construction of pyramids and temples.

10.1 Constructing equations

- Link equations to descriptions
- Write expressions and form equations
- Solve simple equations

Why learn this?

Using letters to represent numbers is useful. You can move from solving specific problems to expressing relationships, for example between ages.

What's the BIG idea?

- An **equation** has an **equals** sign. Both sides of the equals sign must have the same value. An **expression** describes something using letters and numbers, but has no equals sign. If an isosceles triangle has angles of 30°, x° and x°, an expression for the sum of the angles in degrees is $30 + 2x$. An equation for its sum would be $30 + 2x = 180$. **Level 5**
- Solving an equation means finding the value of the letter. The **solution** for the equation $30 + 2x = 180$, is $x = 75$. **Level 5 & Level 6**
- You can solve a problem by constructing an equation. The phrase '**in terms of**' tells you which letter to use. $30 + 2x = 180$ is an equation in terms of x. **Level 5 & Level 6**

Super fact!

The equals sign (=) was introduced by the Welsh mathematician Robert Recorde in 1557, to save the tedium of writing out the words 'is equal to'.

Practice, practice, practice!

Level 5

5c I can identify missing numbers in one-step equations

1 Copy and complete these equations.

a $4 + \square = 20$ **b** $\frac{20}{\square} = 4$ **c** $20 \times \square = 40$ **d** $34 - \square = 20$

5b I can match equations to worded descriptions

2 Match each description to an equation.

$2x + 4 = 30$ $2(4 + x) = 30$ $2x^2 = 30$ $x = 30$ $2x = 30$ $\frac{x^2}{2} = 30$ $x^2 = 30$

a If you double x you get 30.
b If you square x you get 30.
c If you square x and double the result you get 30.
d If you add 4 to x and then double the result you get 30.
e If you double x and then add 4 to the result you get 30.
f If you square x and then halve the result you get 30.

Hint: One of the equations does not match any of the descriptions.

5b I can identify what letters represent in an expression

3 Each of these expressions consists of a single term. For each expression, write what x represents.

a $4x$ is the cost of four bags of crisps.
b xy is the cost of y bags of crisps.
c $6x$ is the perimeter of a regular hexagon.
d xy is the perimeter of a regular polygon with sides of length y.

5a I can write a simple expression and use it to form and solve a one-step equation

4 **a** Write an expression for each of these descriptions.

11 more than x $x + 11$

i x less than 11 **ii** 11 less than x

b Write an equation for each expression from part **a**, stating that is has the value 6.

c Solve each equation from part **b** to find the value of x.

equal equate equation expression

5 Write an expression in terms of x for each of these descriptions.

a 5 more than half of x

b 5 less than one third of x

c half of the result of 3 more than x

6 p represents the cost, in pounds, of one pen. Write an expression for the amount of money I have in each of these cases.

a I have enough money for seven pens with £6 left over.

b I have £6 less than I need for twelve pens.

c I only have half the money I need for one pen.

7 a Use each of these statements to write an equation.
Your equations must use only the numbers that appear in the question.

i Three identical books cost £15.75. The cost of one book is x.

ii The area of a room is 156 m^2. The width is 12 m. The length is x.

iii The original price of a toy is £46.50. The sale price, x, is £4.65 less.

b Solve each equation from part **a** to find the value of x.

Level 5

5a I can construct more complex expressions

5a I can use letters to write expressions involving all four operations

5a I can construct and solve one-step equations

8 a For each diagram, write an expression for the sum of the angles.

b Use your expression to form an equation with 180 on the right-hand side.

i 130° 5x°

ii 94° x° x°

iii $(x + 5)°$ $(x + 5)°$ $(x + 5)°$

c Solve each equation from part **b** to find the value of x.

9 Bethany is x years old. Alexandra is two years older than Bethany.

a Write an expression for Alexandra's age.

b If the sum of their ages is 24, write an equation in terms of x.

c Solve your equation to find Bethany's age.

Level 6

6c I can use an expression to form and solve a simple two-step equation

6b I can form and solve a two-step equation

Now try this!

A In terms of age

- Make up a sentence describing the different ages of a group of people.
Example: Seth is two years older than his brother Jared, and their mother Fiona is six times Seth's age.
- Using x for the youngest person's age, write algebraic expressions for the other people's age.
If Jared's age is x, then Seth's age is $x + 2$ and Fiona's is $6(x + 2)$ or $6x + 12$.
- Challenge your partner to construct expressions from your sentence. Compare them with yours. Tell them the age of one person so that they can form an equation to solve and work out the other ages in the group.

B Marbles

- Naomi has ten marbles, Elaine has four fewer marbles than Naomi and John has twice as many marbles as Elaine. First write an equation to find how many marbles Elaine has. Once you know this, write a second equation to find how many marbles John has.
- Write your own marble problem involving three people. Tell a partner how many marbles one person has, and challenge them to construct two equations to solve the problem and find how many marbles the other two have.

in terms of operation solution

10.2 Solving equations 1

- Represent equations using area diagrams
- Solve equations which have the unknown on one side only and where the solutions might be positive or negative, or a whole number or a fraction

Why learn this?

If you can solve equations, you can work backwards to solve problems involving length and area.

What's the BIG idea?

- The letter in an equation is often called the '**unknown**'. **Level 5**
- Simple **equations** can be represented by the areas of rectangles. **Level 5 & Level 6**
- The equation $10x + 11 = 16$ can be represented by this diagram.

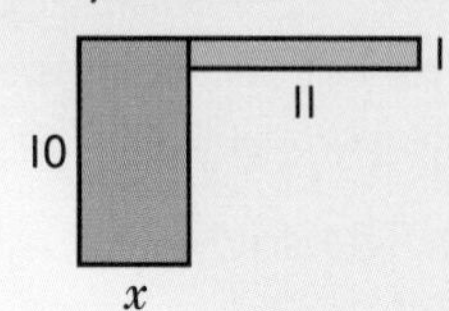

Level 5 & Level 6

- You can solve **linear equations** in two steps.
  The area of this shape is 16 square units.

Step 1 Subtract the 11×1 rectangle

$10x + 11 = 16$

$10x + 11 - 11 = 16 - 11$

$10x = 5$

Step 2 Find the length x by dividing the area by the height

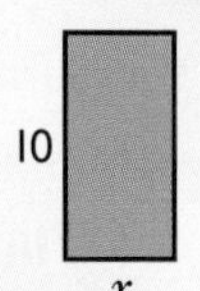

$10x = 5$ Divide both sides by 10

$x = \frac{5}{10} = \frac{1}{2}$

You can also think of this as doing the same to both sides of the equation.
Level 5 & Level 6

- Equations may involve calculations with negative numbers.

$$2x + 20 = 16$$
$$2x + 20 - 20 = 16 - 20$$
$$2x = -4$$
$$x = -2$$

Level 6

Did you know?

The idea of using areas to represent expressions and to solve equations is thousands of years old.

Watch out!

In algebra you can miss out the multiplication sign, and write $4 \times x$ as just $4x$.

1 For each rectangle, write an equation using only the numbers given. Then solve it to find x.

a area = 24 m², 4 m, x m

b area = 175 m², 5 m, x m

2 Use the diagrams to copy and complete the equations.

a

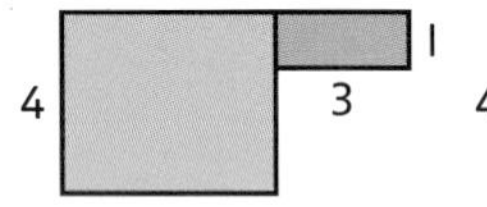

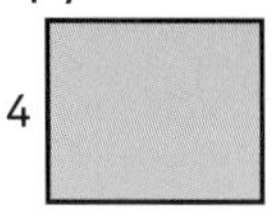

$4x + 3 = 207$

$4x = \square$

$x = \square$

b

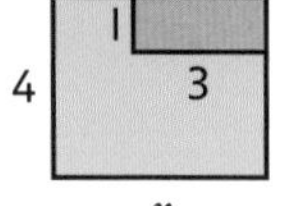

$4x - 3 = 225$

$4x = \square$

$x = \square$

Level 5

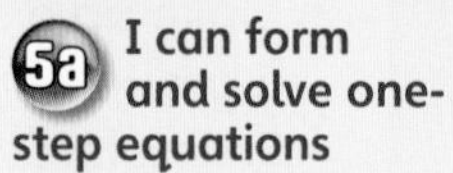

5a I can form and solve one-step equations

5a I can solve two-step equations uing diagrams

compound shape · equation · equivalent

3 Solve each equation to find the value of x.

a $x + 20 = 30$ b $x - 20 = -3$ c $x - 7 = -30$

d $40 - x = -5$ e $-8 + x = -30$ f $5x = -40$

Level 5

5a I can solve one-step equations where the solutions are either positive or negative

4 Solve each equation.

a $3 + 13x = 120$ b $9x - 7 = 47$ c $3 + 5x = 68$

d $5x - 1 = 129$ e $7x - 5 = 44$ f $3x + 9 = 111$

5 Solve these equations.

a $7x + 5 = 768$ b $6x + 33 = 741$ c $7x - 3 = 137$

d $8x - 10 = 974$ e $15x - 3x = 108$ f $3x - 4 + 2x = 41$

6 The total area of each diagram is 23 square units. Form an equation to find the length x in each case.

a

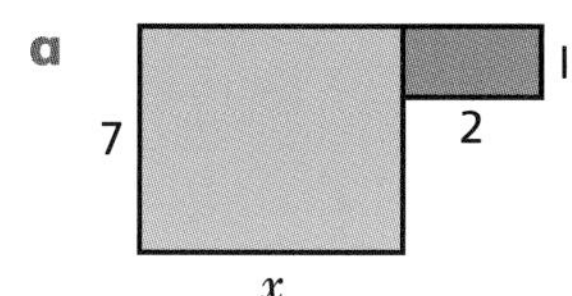

b

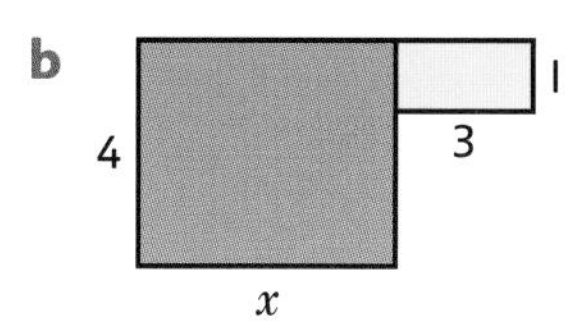

7 I buy nine identical books and get £13.28 change from £50.

a Write an equation using only the numbers given.

b Solve your equation from part **a** to find the cost of one book.

8 Solve each equation.

a $8x = 4$ b $9x + 3 = 5$ c $7x - 4 = 1$

d $9x - 7 = 100$ e $5x + 18 = 3$ f $7x - 5 = -33$

g $8x + 96 = 0$ h $2x - 3 + 4x = 45$ i $5x - 12 = -3 - 4$

9 Solve each equation.

a $21 - x = 16$ b $21 - 2x = 11$ c $40 - 4x = 29$

d $\frac{1}{2}x + 3 = 97$ e $\frac{x}{3} + 5 = 13$ f $10 - \frac{x}{2} = 7.5$

g $\frac{2x}{3} + 1 = 11$ h $\frac{3}{4}x - 2 = 28$ i $1 + \frac{x}{5} = -10$

Level 6

6c I can solve two-step equations where the solutions are positive whole numbers

6c I can construct a two-step equation to solve a problem

6b I can solve two-step equations including those with fraction and negative answers

6a I can solve two-step equations where fractions and negative signs can appear anywhere within the equation

Now try this!

A Area solutions

Draw a pair of diagrams similar to these, with different numbers for the dimensions in red.

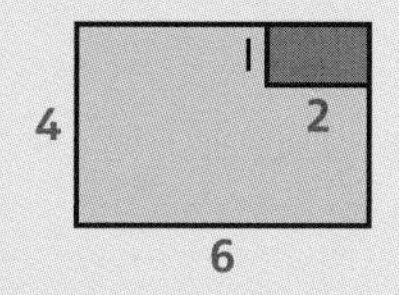

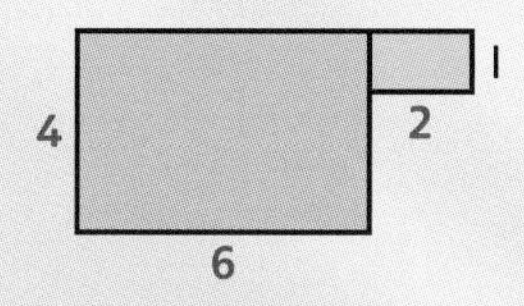

Write an equation for each new area. Use a dark shaded rectangle to indicate that an area is being subtracted. Hide the bottom length in the diagram and replace it by x in the equation. Challenge a partner to work out the missing values.

B Simplify and solve

Draw a diagram similar to this, with different numbers for the dimensions in red.

Decide on a value for x and work out the total area of the diagram.

Write the equation, for example $4x - 2 + 3x = 33$, where the chosen value of x was 5.

Challenge a partner to solve your equation.

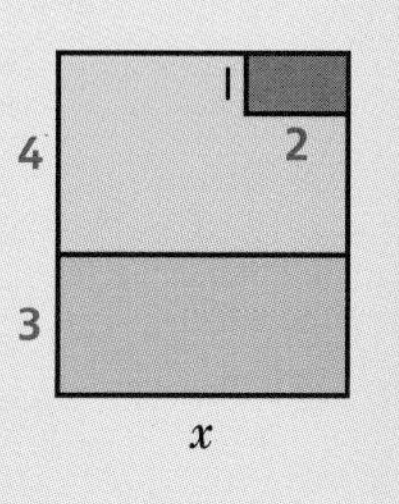

linear equation solution unknown

10.3 Solving equations 2

- Recognise equivalent equations
- Given an equation with x on both sides, generate an equivalent equation which has x on one side only
- Solve an equation with x on both sides

Why learn this?

Understanding how to rearrange equations is important for editors checking the accuracy of scientific books and journals.

What's the BIG idea?

→ To solve an **equation** with the unknown on both sides, rearrange the equation so the unknown is on one side only.

$$3x + 4 = 2x + 6$$
$$3x + 4 - 2x = 2x + 6 - 2x$$
$$x + 4 = 6$$
$$x = 2$$ **Level 6**

→ You can use the area of rectangles to show this.

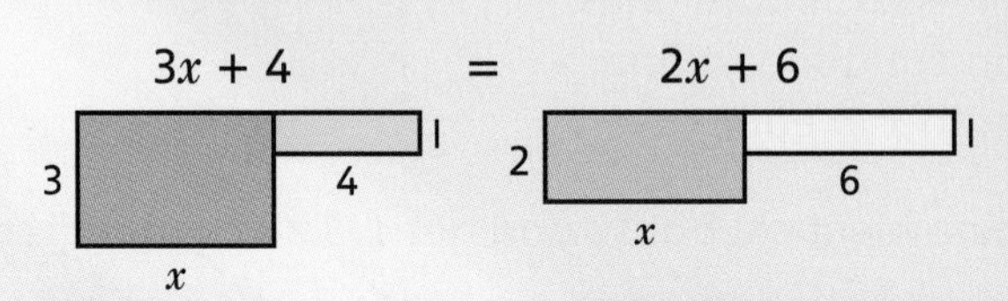

Subtract the largest possible rectangle of length x from both diagrams (shown in pink)

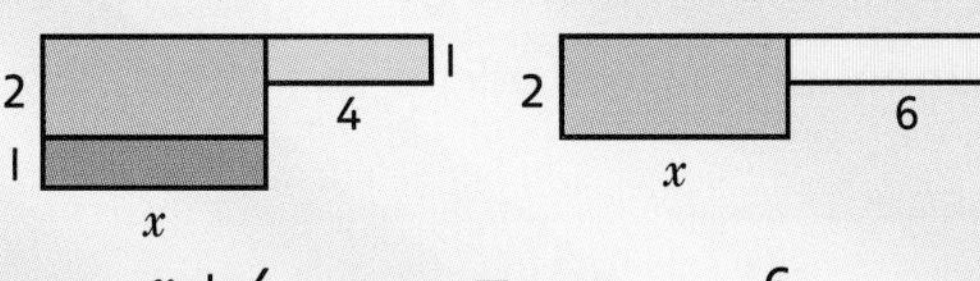

$$x + 4 = 6$$
$$x = 2$$

→ You can rearrange an equation in many ways, adding or subtracting the same amount to or from both sides. **Level 6**

→ You can check the solution to an equation by **substituting** it into the original equation.

$$3x + 4 = 2x + 6 \qquad \text{Solution } x = 2$$
$$3 \times 2 + 4 = 2 \times 2 + 6$$
$$6 + 4 = 4 + 6$$ ✓ **Level 6**

Practice, practice, practice!

Level 6

6c I can use diagrams to solve an equation with x on both sides

1 The total areas of these two diagrams are the same.

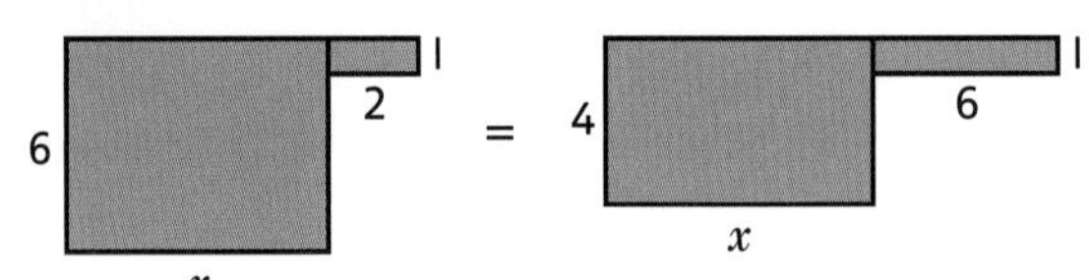
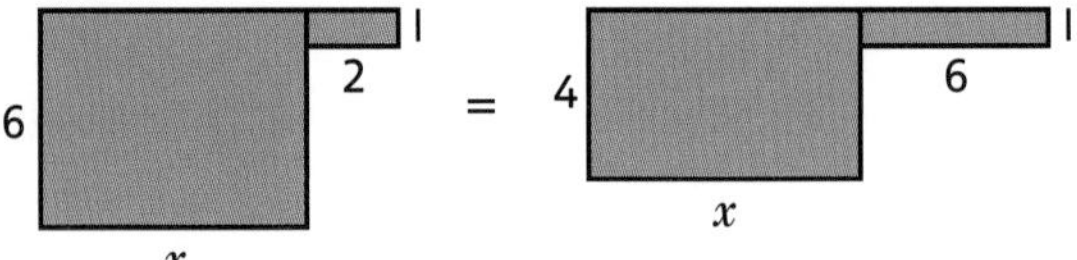

a Copy and complete this equation. $6x + 2 = \square x + \square$

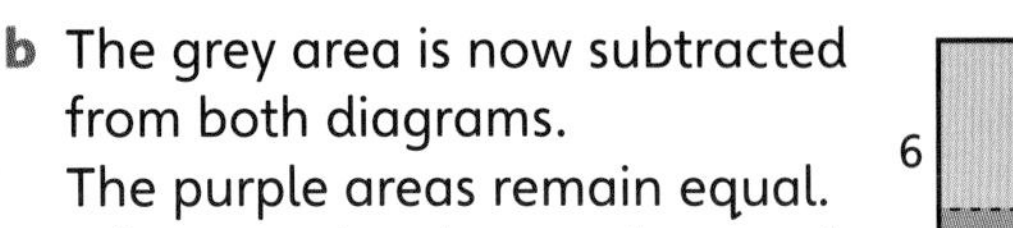
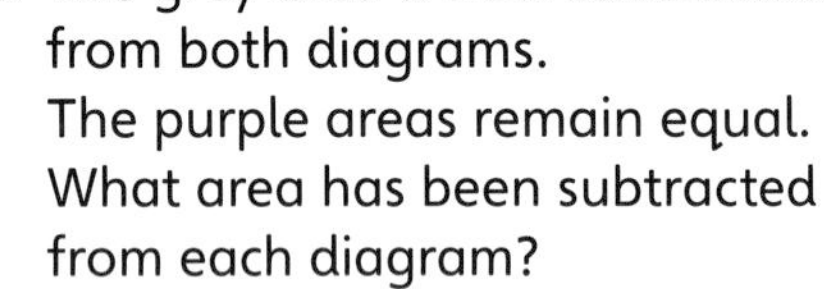

b The grey area is now subtracted from both diagrams. The purple areas remain equal. What area has been subtracted from each diagram?

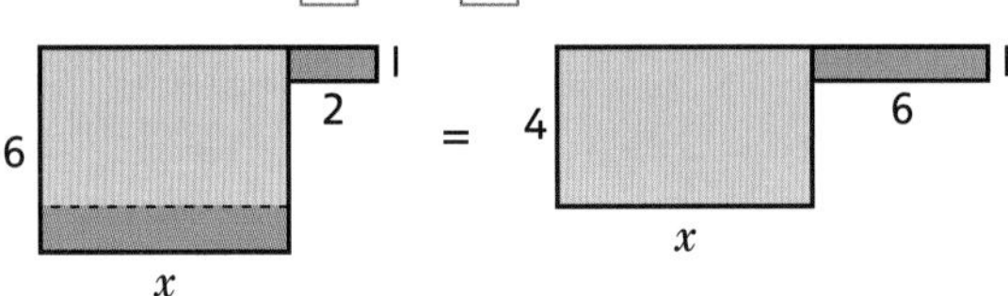

c Copy and complete this equation to show the remaining purple area.

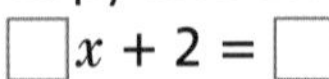

$\square x + 2 = \square$

d Solve this equation to find the value of x.

equation equivalent

2 **a** Draw diagrams to represent the equation $6x + 2 = 3x + 17$.
b Subtract the largest possible rectangle of length x from both diagrams.
c Write the equation for the remaining areas.
d Solve your equation to find the value of x.

3 Copy and complete the working to solve each equation.

a $5x + 2 = 3x + 8$
$\square x + 2 = 8$
$\square x = 6$
$x = \square$

b $7x + 2 = 4x + 14$
$\square x + 2 = 14$
$\square x = 12$
$x = \square$

Hint: Remember to check your solution by substituting it into the original equation.

4 Solve each equation.
a $4x + 6 = 2x + 10$ **b** $4x + 3 = x + 12$ **c** $7x + 4 = 3x + 24$
d $20x + 8 = 21x + 3$ **e** $3x - 10 = x + 2$ **f** $6x - 3 = 5x - 7$

5 **a** Which of these equations is equivalent to $62 - 3x = 12 + 7x$?
A $62 = 12 + 4x$ B $62 = 12 + 10x$ C $59 = 19x$ D $74 - 3x = 7x$
b Find the value of x by solving the equation.

6 In each part, two equations have the same value for x and one does not. Without finding the value of x, find the odd one out in each set.
a $3x + 4 = 11$ $5x + 4 = 11 + 2x$ $x + 4 = 11 + 2x$
b $9x = 21.4 + 4x$ $5x - 3 = 18.4$ $2x = 15.4 + 3x$
c $5x + 5 = 2x + 1$ $3x = 4$ $-3x + 5 = -6x + 1$

7 Solve each equation.
a $7x - 15 = 2x - 40$ **b** $-4x + 10 = 6x + 30$ **c** $3x + 27 = 5 - x$
d $-4x + 9 = -6x + 30$ **e** $7x + 3 = 4x + 17$ **f** $-9x + 4 = -2x + 24$

8 **a** Use each diagram to form and solve an equation to find x. The given sides are equal for each shape.

i
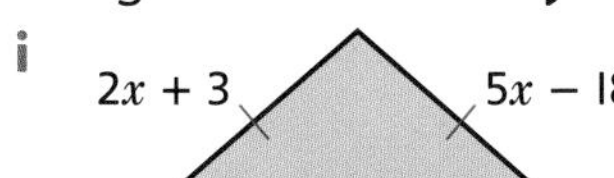

ii
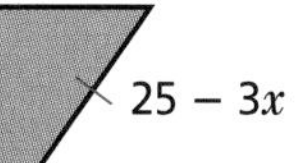

b The perimeter of each shape is 50 units. Work out the length of each side.

Level 6

6c I can use diagrams to solve an equation with x on both sides

6c I can complete lines of working to solve equations with x on both sides

6b I can solve equations with x on both sides where the solutions are positive whole numbers

6b I can recognise equivalent equations by adding or subtracting the same to/from both sides

6a I can solve equations with x on both sides where the solution is a fraction or negative

6a I can form and solve a two-step equation with x on both sides, check my solution and use it to solve a problem

Now try this!

A Equivalent areas

You need squared paper. Draw two different rectangles with the same length, but different heights. Add a rectangle to the smaller one and subtract a rectangle from the larger one so the overall areas of both diagrams are the same.

B Equal expressions

Think of a value for x. Write two different expressions which both have the same value for your chosen x. For example, $4x + 2$ and $6x - 12$ both have the value 30 when $x = 7$. Equate your two expressions to form an equation, like this: $4x + 2 = 6x - 12$. Challenge a partner to solve your equation.

expression operate substitute

10.4 Equations with brackets

- Write an equation involving brackets
- Solve an equation with brackets on one or both sides
- Solve an equation which involves multiplying a bracket by a negative number

Why learn this?

Visualising mathematical structures helps us to understand equivalence and solve problems.

What's the BIG idea?

→ Sometimes **equations** involve **brackets**. The equation $5(x + 2) = 45$ can be represented by a split rectangle of area 45. **Level 6**

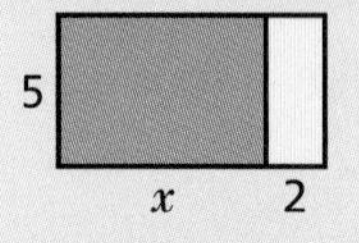

→ An equation like this can be solved by dividing the area by the height to find the total length of the rectangle.

$5(x + 2) = 45$ Both sides have a common factor

$5 \times \text{length} = 45$

$\text{length} = 9$, so $x + 2 = 9$ $x = 7$ **Level 6**

5

9

→ **Linear equations** with brackets can be solved by multiplying out the brackets.

$5(x + 2) = 3(x + 4)$

$5x + 10 = 3x + 12$

$2x + 10 = 12$

$x = 1$ **Level 6**

→ You can use **square roots** to solve equations involving squares.

$(x - 2)^2 = 81$

$x - 2 = \pm 9$

$x = 11$ or $x = -7$ **Level 7**

Did you know?

Every expression written with brackets can be written in an equivalent way without brackets.

Practice, practice, practice!

Level 6

6c I can solve simple equations with brackets with the aid of a diagram

1 Solve each equation by finding the missing length.

a

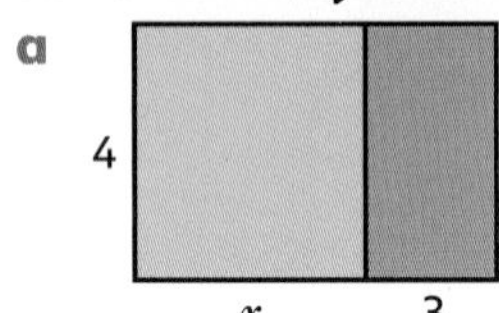

total area = 36
$4(x + 3) = 36$

b

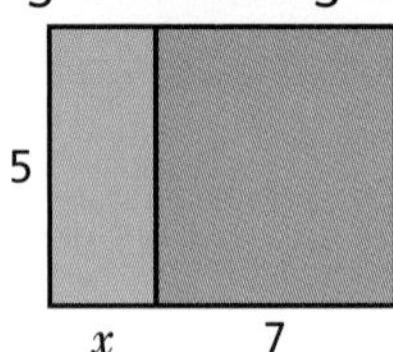

total area = 50
$5(x + 7) = 50$

c

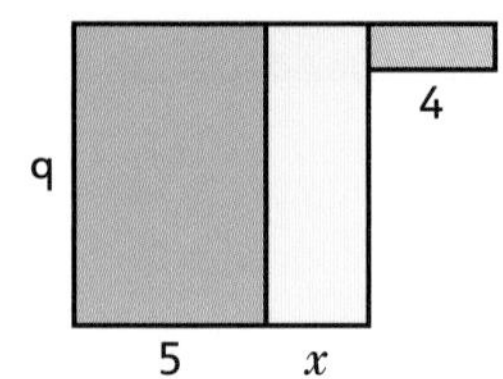

$9(5 + x) + 4 = 85$

6c I can solve equations involving brackets

2 Solve each equation.

a $6(3 + x) = 48$ **b** $5(x + 3) = 35$

c $3(x + 8) = 24$ **d** $5(2x + 3) + 2 = 37$

e $8(2x + 5) + 5x - 3 = 100$ **f** $8(3 + 5x) - 2x = 100$

bracket equation expression linear equation

3 Find length x for each diagram.

a

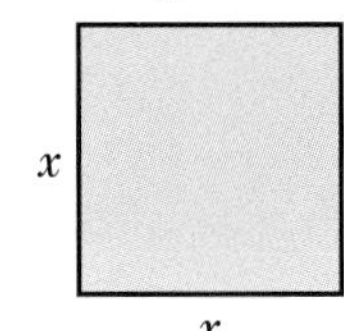

area = 225

b

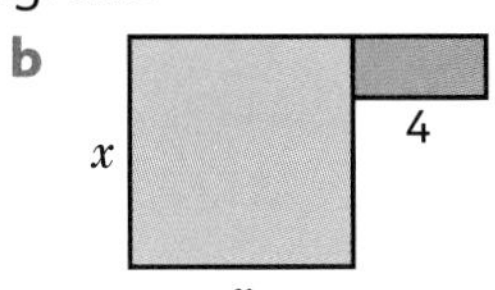

total area = 200

c

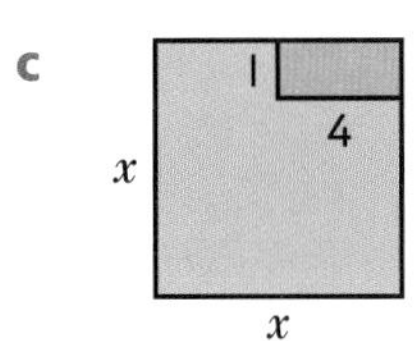

green area = 252

4 Write an equation for each diagram and solve it to find length x.

a

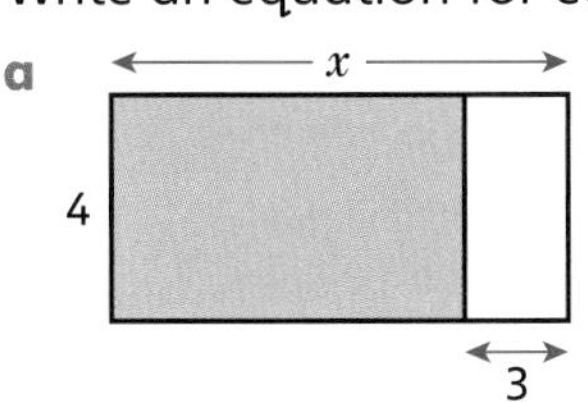

blue area = 32

b

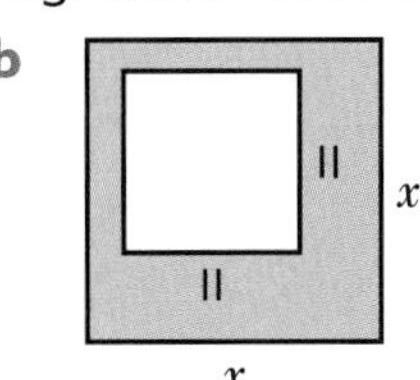

blue area = 203

c

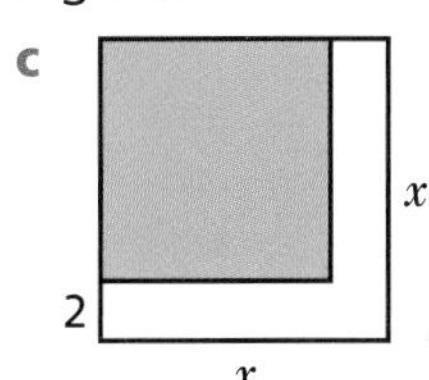

green area = 144

Level 6

6a I can find a missing side length of a square from a diagram

6a I can construct and solve an equation from a diagram

5 Solve each equation to find both the positive and negative value of x.

a $x^2 - 9 = 91$ **b** $x^2 + 10 = 131$

c $(x - 4)^2 = 121$ **d** $(x - 3)^2 + 5 = 54$

e $(x + 2)^2 - 7 = 393$ **f** $(12 - x)^2 - 5 = 59$

Learn this

It is useful to learn at least the first 15 square numbers and the corresponding square roots.

6 Solve each equation.

a $5(x - 3) = 30 + 2x$ **b** $2(10 - x) = x + 50$

c $3(x - 5) + 2 = 17 + x$ **d** $4(2x - 4) + 2x = 64 + 3x$

e $4(x + 3) = x - 2$ **f** $3(4x - 2) = x - 28$

7 Solve each equation.

a $3(2x + 4) = 4(3x - 2)$ **b** $20 + 2(x - 4) = 3(x + 4)$

c $20 - 2(x + 4) = 3(2x - 3)$ **d** $20 - 2(x - 4) = 3(1 + 4x)$

e $20 - 2(3x - 4) = 3(6 - 5x)$ **f** $3(2x + 4) = 6(x - 4) - 2(x - 1)$

Level 7

7c I can solve equations involving x^2 and give both solutions

7c I can solve equations with a bracket on one side and x on both sides with positive or negative solutions

7b I can solve equations with brackets on both sides and negative signs anywhere in the equation

Watch out!

If you multiply out a bracket, make sure you remember to multiply every term inside the bracket by the term outside.

Now try this!

A Squares within squares

Sketch one square inside another, as shown.
Think of a side length for each square. Write down the area of the small square. Work out the visible area of the large square.

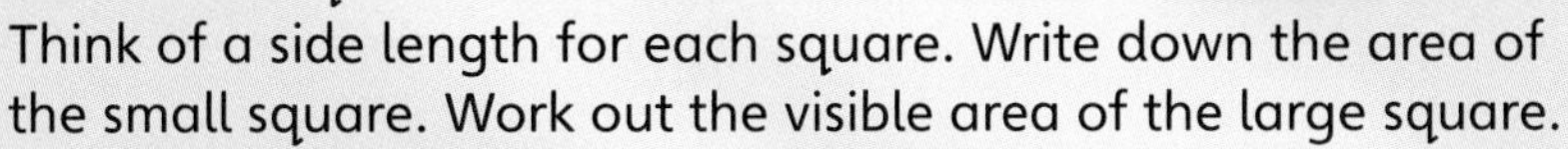

B Equate and solve

- Think of a value for x. Write two different expressions involving brackets and other terms which both have the same value for your chosen x. For example, $3(x + 2) + x$ and $8(x - 2) + 2(6 - x)$ both have the value 26 when $x = 5$.
- Equate these two expressions to form an equation. For example, $3(x + 2) + x = 8(x - 2) + 2(6 - x)$.
- Challenge a partner to solve your equation.

negative square numbers square root

10.5 Using formulae

- Substitute values into a formula and use the correct order of operations
- Use a formula written in words or algebraically using letters
- Use a formula and find the value of a letter which is not the subject of the formula

What's the BIG idea?

- A **formula** tells you how to work something out. It can be written in words.
  daily wage = £10 × hours worked **Level 5**
- Formulae can be written using letters.
  The formula for a daily wage, w pounds, for working h hours at a rate of r pounds per hour, with travel cost t pounds, is $w = rh + t$. **Level 6**
- To use a formula you need to **substitute** in the values of the letters you are given and then use the correct **order of operations**. **Level 6**
- If the letter you need to find the value of is not the **subject** of the formula, you need to substitute as before and then solve an equation to find its value. **Level 7**

Why learn this?

Formulae help us to repeat the same process over and over again. Once a formula is agreed on, such as for hiring clothes, it can be reused without having to work it all out again from scratch.

Practice, practice, practice!

Level 5

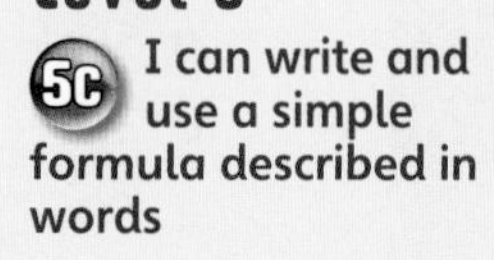
5c I can write and use a simple formula described in words

5b I can use a simple formula

1 It costs £80 per day to hire a dress, plus a final cleaning cost of £30.

a Write a word formula to calculate the cost of hiring a dress.

b Find the cost of hiring the dress for one day.

c Find the cost of hiring the dress for three days.

d The total bill is £190. How many days has the dress been hired for?

2 The cost of an advert, in pounds, is given by cost = $8 + 0.5n$, where n is the number of words.
What is the cost of an advert with

a 20 words **b** 40 words **c** 60 words?

Level 6

6c I can substitute positive integers into algebraic formulae

6a I can substitute positive and negative numbers into algebraic expressions and can work backwards to complete a table from any given value

3 Find the area A of each circle (to 2 d.p.) using the formula $A = \pi r^2$, where r is the radius in centimetres. Use $\pi = 3.14$ or the π key on your calculator.

a $r = 7$ **b** $r = 14$ **c** $r = 9.5$

4 Copy and complete the table.

a	$a + 2$	$2a$	a^2	$2a^2$	$2(a + 2)^2$
4		8			
	0				
		−20			
			64		
				50	
					800

algebraic expression formula (formulae) operation

Level 7

7c I can substitute positive integers into algebraic formulae involving algebraic terms with small powers

5 The hire cost, C, of a suit depends on its original value, v, its age in months, m, and the number of days, d, that it is hired for.
The cost in pounds is given by the formula.

$$C = 30 + \frac{dv}{5\left(1 + \frac{m}{12}\right)^2}$$

Work out the cost of these suit-hires.

a suit with original value £450, aged 6 months, for 2 days

b suit with original value £300, aged 2 years, for 1 day

Watch out!
Multiplication signs are often missed out in algebra. So ab means $a \times b$ and $2(a + b)$ means $2 \times (a + b)$. When you substitute in numbers you need to write in the multiplication signs.

7b I can substitute positive integers into a formula to form an equation and solve it

6 The formula for the area of a trapezium is $A = \frac{1}{2}(a + b)h$.

a Work out A when $a = 9$, $b = 5$ and $h = 5$.

b Work out a when $A = 24$, $b = 3$ and $h = 6$.

c Work out h when $A = 30$, $a = 3$ and $b = 7$.

7a I can substitute positive integers into a formula involving squares to form an equation and solve it

7 **a** Find the volume, V, of a cylinder using the formula $V = \pi r^2h$, when the radius, r, is 5 cm and the height, h, is 10 cm.

b Find the height of a cylinder with volume 240 cm^3 and radius 6 cm.

c Find the radius of a cylinder with volume 200 cm^3 and height 15 cm.
Use $\pi = 3.14$ or the π key on your calculator.

7a I can solve problems involving use of formulae where the required unknown is not the subject

8 A straight line has the equation $y = 4x + 3$.

a Write the coordinates of the point where the line cuts the y-axis.

b Solve an equation to find the coordinates of the point where the line cuts the x-axis.

9 The relationship between average speed, v, distance, d, and time, t, is given by the formula $v = \frac{d}{t}$. A bus travels at 50 mph and covers a distance of 65 miles. How long does the journey take?

Now try this!

A Triangle formulations

Draw a triangle. Measure its base and perpendicular height.
Work out its area using the formula area = $\frac{1}{2}$ × base × height.
Swap your values for the area and base with a partner and work out the height of each other's triangles.
Discuss and write down the steps required to find the perpendicular height of a triangle if you know its area and base length.

B Trapezium work out

Draw a trapezium. Measure lengths a, b and h.
Work out its area using the formula $A = \frac{1}{2}(a + b)h$.
Swap values for A, a and h with a partner and work out the value of b for each other's trapeziums.
Discuss the steps involved.

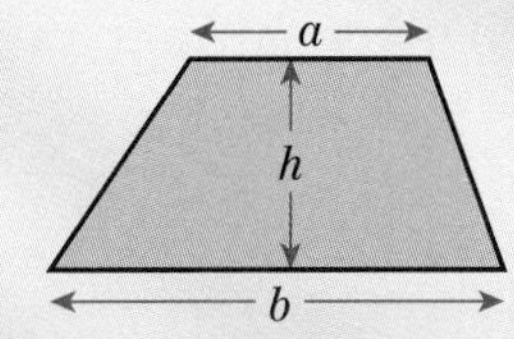

Learn this

The order of operations
1. Brackets
2. Indices (powers)
3. Multiplication and division
4. Addition and subtraction

order of operations subject substitute

10.6 Constructing formulae

- Substitute using the correct order of operations
- Work backwards, for example, from the area of a circle to its radius
- Generalise, using a letter for a value which can change
- Write formulae

Why learn this?

Formulae enable us to describe important relationships between two things in a simple way. The famous formula $E = mc^2$ states that there is an equivalence between mass and energy.

What's the BIG idea?

- To **derive** a **formula** using letters, you can first start to understand the process using numbers. For example,
  - the perimeter, in centimetres, of a 3 cm by 4 cm rectangle is 2(3 + 4)
  - the perimeter, in centimetres, of a 6 cm by 7 cm rectangle is 2(6 + 7). **Level 5**
- To derive a formula using letters, you need to **generalise** what happens.
  1. Work out which numbers always stay the same, and leave these numbers as they are.
  2. Replace each of the other numbers with a letter. Make sure you know what each letter represents.

  When calculating the perimeter of a rectangle, the 2 (outside the bracket) stays the same and the length and width change. $P = 2(w + l)$ where w = width and l = length.

  Don't use more letters than you need to.
  - If you are told the length of a rectangle is double its width then the length is $2w$, so the formula is $P = 2(w + 2w) = 2(3w) = 6w$.
  - If the length is 3 more than the width, the length is $w + 3$, so the formula is $P = 2(w + w + 3) = 2(2w + 3) = 4w + 6$. **Level 6 & Level 7**

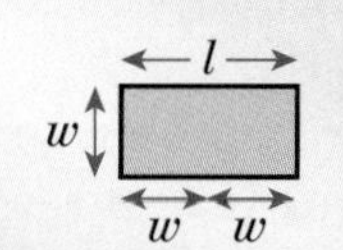

Did you know?

When you want to use a formula repeatedly, spreadsheet software and other computer programs can often do the work for you.

Practice, practice, practice!

Level 5

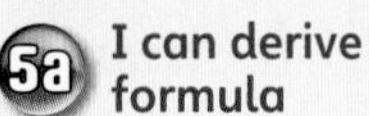
5a I can derive formula

1 On St Valentine's Day, a school newsletter raises money for charity by charging for messages published. The cost is 50p in addition to 10p per word. Write a formula for the cost, C, in pence of an advert with w words.

Level 6

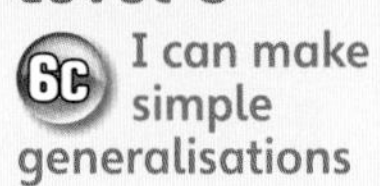
6c I can make simple generalisations

6b I can write algebraic formulae to describe two-step cases

2 A rectangle's length is double its width. Find its area if its width is

a 5 cm **b** 8 cm **c** x cm **d** $3x$ cm

3 A rectangle's length is 2 cm more than its width.

a Write a formula for its area A in terms of its width w.

b Find its area if its width were 5 cm.

c Find its area if its length were 9 cm.

calculate formula (formulae) generalise

4 Paul hires out his limousine for one evening for £100 with an extra charge of £2 per mile driven.

a Write a formula for the cost, C, in pounds of hiring the limousine for an evening and driving m miles.

b A group of g people share the cost of the limousine equally for an evening, and travel m miles. Write a formula to calculate the cost to each person.

5 Copy and complete the table.

Radius (cm)	Diameter (cm) (= 2 × radius)	Area (cm²) (= π × radius²)	Height (cm)	Volume of cylinder (cm³) (= π × radius² × height)
4			7	
	12		10	
		20	10	
			8	400
r			h	

Level 6

6b I can write algebraic formulae

6a I can substitute positive numbers into simple algebraic formulae and can work backwards to complete a table

6 A cuboid has side lengths in the ratio 1 : 3 : 5.

a Write a formula to calculate the volume of the cuboid in terms of its shortest side length, x.

b Use your formula to find the volume if the shortest length is 3 cm.

c Use your formula to find the shortest side length if the volume is 120 cm³.

7 A plumber charges a £20 call-out fee in addition to £30 per hour for labour. Write formulae for

a the cost, C, in pounds, in terms of the number of hours worked, h

b the number of hours worked, h, in terms of the cost, C.

8 Write formulae to calculate

a the surface area, A, of a cube given its side length, s

b the side length, s, given the surface area, A, of the cube.

Level 7

7b I can write a formula, use substitution and solve an equation to find an unknown which is not the subject

7a I can write a formula and rewrite it with a different subject

Tip

The area of a trapezium is its height multiplied by half the sum of lengths a and b.

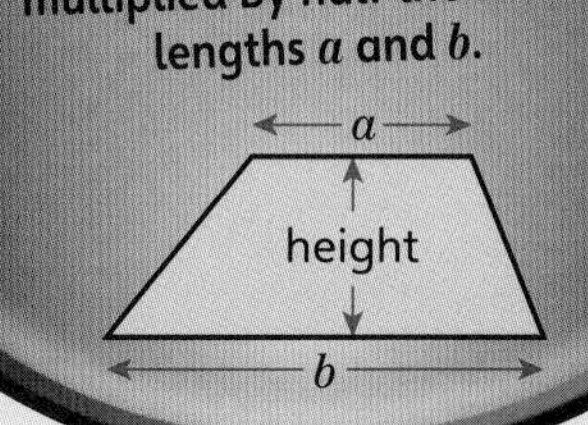

Now try this!

A Good area for a house?

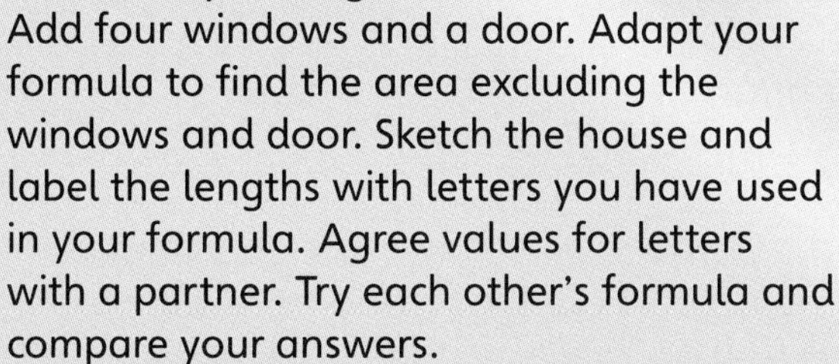

Write a formula to work out the area of this house shape.
Label the lengths, giving the same letter to equal lengths.
Add four windows and a door. Adapt your formula to find the area excluding the windows and door. Sketch the house and label the lengths with letters you have used in your formula. Agree values for letters with a partner. Try each other's formula and compare your answers.

B Terrific tariffs

Imagine you run a mobile phone company. Make up two different tariffs, one charging a high monthly rental and a low call-rate per minute, and the other charging a lower monthly rental and a higher call-rate per minute. For each tariff, write a formula to calculate a monthly bill. Tell your partner the amount of a monthly bill, and ask them to work out which of your tariffs would give the most minutes for that price.
Draw a straight-line graph for each tariff on the same grid and find the number of minutes for which both tariffs charge the same.

in terms of subject

maths!

Fairground formulae

Fairground ride designers use formulae to check that their rides are safe – and exciting!

Pendulums

Some amusement park rides are similar to pendulums. An estimation for T, the time taken for the pendulum to swing back and forth in seconds, is given by the formula:

$$T = 2\pi\sqrt{\frac{l}{g}}$$

where l is the length of the pendulum and g is the acceleration due to gravity – this is always $9.81\ \text{m/s}^2$ on Earth.

- Calculate the time taken
  - a for a 10 m pendulum ride to swing back and forth
  - b for a 14 m pendulum ride to swing back and forth.
- A pendulum ride takes 8 seconds to swing back and forth. Work out the length of the pendulum in metres.

Carousels

Have you ever noticed that the outermost horses on carousels seem to be travelling faster than the ones on the inside? Mathematics can explain why…

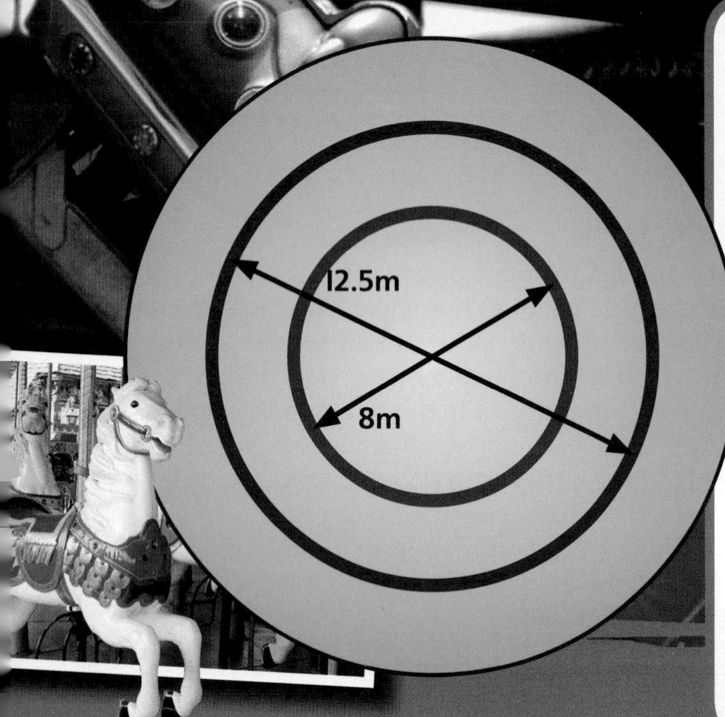

- Use the formula for the circumference of a circle to work out how far a horse on the red circle would travel in one revolution.
- Use the formula

  $$\textbf{speed} = \frac{\textbf{distance}}{\textbf{time}}$$

  to find the speed of the horse if the carousel takes 60 seconds to make one revolution.
- Work out the speed of a horse on the blue circle. Which horse is travelling faster?

Roller coasters

Many roller coasters start by pulling a carriage up a 'lift hill' to the first peak. The carriage is then released and speeds off along the track.
At the top of the peak, the carriage has potential energy, or PE, which is measured in joules. This is given by the formula:

$$\mathrm{PE} = mgh$$

where m is the mass of the carriage in kilograms, g is the acceleration due to gravity (9.81 $\mathrm{m/s^2}$) and h is the height of the peak in metres.

When the carriage is released, the potential energy is turned into kinetic energy. The kinetic energy in joules is given by the formula:

$$\mathrm{KE} = \frac{1}{2}mv^2$$

where v is the speed of the carriage at the base of the hill in metres per second.

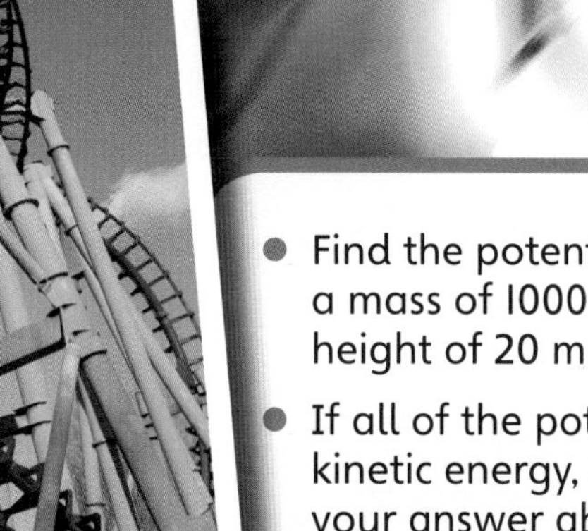

- Find the potential energy of a carriage with a mass of 1000 kg that is released from a height of 20 m.
- If all of the potential energy is turned into kinetic energy, use the formula for KE and your answer above to prove that the speed of the carriage at the bottom of the hill is 19.8 m/s to one decimal place.
- A carriage of mass 964 kg is released from a height of 18.2 m. Find its speed at the bottom of the hill.
- Does the mass of the carriage make the ride travel faster or slower at the bottom of the hill? Explain your answer.

Unit 10 plenary

Egyptian problems

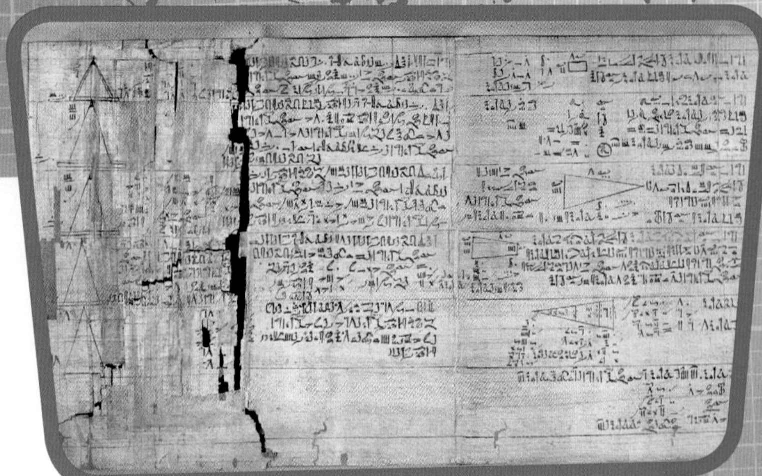

The Moscow Papyrus and Rhind Papyrus are important documents that detail the mathematics of Ancient Egypt.
In an opening paragraph of the Rhind Papyrus, we are told that the papyrus gives 'accurate reckoning for inquiring into things, and the knowledge of all things, mysteries ... all secrets'.

Rhind Papyrus activities

1 $8x = 60$. Find the value of x. **Level 5**

2 $x + \frac{1}{7}x = 19$.
Solve the equation to find the value of x.
(This is Problem 24 on the Rhind Papyrus.) **Level 6**

3 A quantity added to a quarter of that quantity becomes 15.
Form an equation and solve it to find the quantity. **Level 6**

4 The basic unit for area used in Ancient Egypt was the setat, which was based on the area of a square field of side length 1 khet.
A round field has a diameter of 9 khet. Find its area in setat. **Level 6**

Hint: Area of a circle = πr^2, where r = radius.

Did you know?

The Ancient Egyptians used different parts of the papyrus plant to make paper, pens, mats, mattresses and boats.

Moscow Papyrus activities

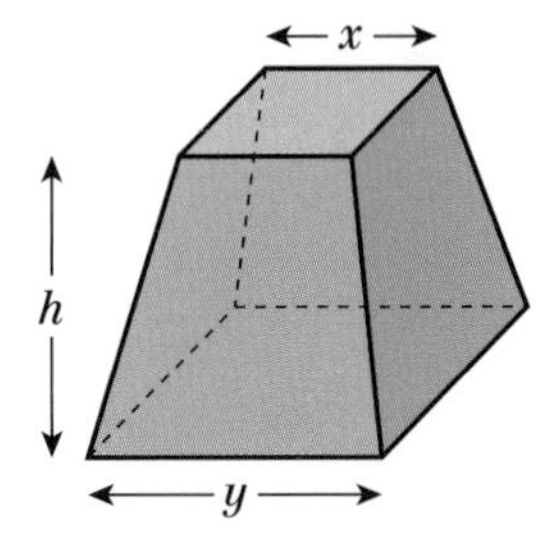

The Egyptian instructions for finding the volume of a truncated square-based pyramid were equivalent to:

$$V = \frac{1}{3}h(x^2 + xy + y^2)$$

The truncated pyramid is made from two squares, of side lengths x and y. One square is smaller than the other and is placed centrally over it. The squares are joined together by slanted sides of perpendicular height h.

1 The truncated pyramid has a top square of side length 2 units, a bottom square of side length 4 units, and a height of 6 units.
Find the volume of the pyramid.
(This is Problem 14 on the Moscow Papyrus.) **Level 6**

2 A truncated pyramid has square top and base with side lengths of 3 cm and 6 cm and a volume of 84 cm^3.
Find the height of the pyramid. **Level 7**

Hint: You will need to form an equation and solve it.

The BIG ideas

- All **equations** have an **equals** sign. Both sides of the equals sign must have the same value. **Level 5**
- A **formula** tells you how to work something out. It can be written in words.
  For example, daily wage = £10 × hours worked. **Level 5**
- Use the information in the question to help you construct an equation. For example, if an isosceles triangle has angles 30°, x° and x°, the equation would be $30 + 2x = 180$. **Level 6**
- The **solution** of an equation is the value of x for which both sides are equal.
  For example, if $30 + 2x = 180$, then $2x = 150$, which has the solution $x = 75$. **Level 6**
- Formulae can be written using letters. Generally, formulae do not include units because these are described with the letters. For example, the formula for a daily wage, w in pounds, for working h hours, at a rate of r pounds per hour, with travel costs t pounds, is $w = rh + t$. **Level 6**
- To use a formula you need to **substitute** in the values of the letters you are given and then use the correct **order of operations**. **Level 6**
- If you need to find the value of a letter that is not the **subject** of the formula, substitute as before and then solve the equation to find its value. **Level 7**

Practice SATs-style questions

Level 5

Q1 A formula to calculate the daily pay, in pounds, for the number of hours worked is:

Daily pay = 8 × number of hours worked + 5

a On Monday, Rose works 6 hours. Work out her pay for Monday.

b On Tuesday Rose works 3 hours. What is her pay for Tuesday? Explain why her pay on Tuesday is more than half of what it was on Monday.

Q2 Write a number in each box to make these equations correct.

a $\square - 5 = -11$ **b** $\frac{42}{\square} = 7$

Level 6

Q3 Solve this equation: $2t + 8 = 6t + 2$

Q4 $x = 4$. Pair up the cards to make three equations.

$3x + 5$	$= 6$
$3(x - 2)$	$= 28$
$40 - 3x$	$= 5x - 3$
	$= 148$

Q5 Solve this equation: $4(2y + 3) = 16$

Level 7

Q6 This shape is made up of two squares and a rectangle.

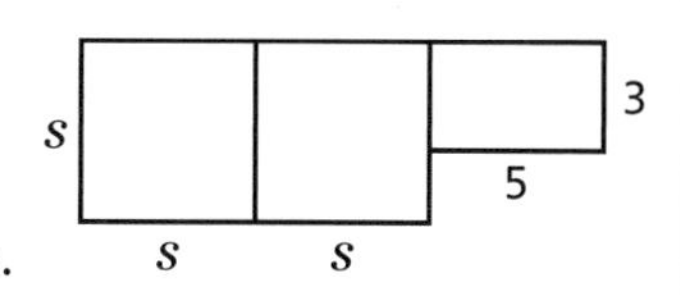

a Write a formula for the area, A, of the shape using the given side lengths.

b The area, A, equals 465 cm². Use this to find the value of s.

Q7 The formula for the volume of a trapezium is

$$A = \frac{1}{2}(a + b)h$$

Find a when $A = 36$ m², $b = 9$ m and $h = 3$ m.

11 Dealing with data

This unit is about handling data and statistics.

Mike Herbert is completing a 4-year apprenticeship to become a marine engineer with ***South Boats*** on the Isle of Wight. His job is to fit engines to small aluminium catamarans, which are used for a range of purposes, from fishing trips to ferrying supplies to offshore wind farms. The catamarans are able to carry big loads and are very stable, even in rough seas. The design for these boats is used all round the world.

Mike has found that maths, including statistics, is used in his everyday work. For example, once a boat has been launched, it undergoes sea trials in Southampton Water to test its top speed when fully loaded. To perform the trials, a nautical mile is marked out by poles on the shoreline. The boat makes four trial runs, two in each direction. To calculate the speed, Mike times the boat with a stopwatch and divides the distance (1 nautical mile) by the time taken (in hours). The results vary with the effects of wind and tide, so Mike needs to calculate the mean speed. This is usually around 26 knots (30 mph).

Activities

A Here are the results for four trial runs for Boat A:

26 knots	20 knots	30 knots	24 knots

- What is the mean speed of Boat A?

Here are the results for Boat B:

28 knots	? knots	30 knots	26 knots

Boat B has a mean speed of 28 knots.

- What was its speed on the second trial run?

B The knot is a unit of speed and is equal to I nautical mile per hour. A speed of 25 knots means the boat would travel 25 nautical miles in one hour.

Look at the speeds of Boat A in Activity A.

- How long did the fastest run take?
- How long did the slowest run take?
- What was the range of the times taken?

Did you know?
A nautical (or sea) mile is not the same as a land mile. 1 nautical mile is approximately 1.15 land miles.

Before you start this unit...

1 Put these numbers in order, starting with the smallest.

Level Up Maths 4-6 page 22

a 2, 6, 3, 7, 4, 8, 5.5

b 1.6, 2.7, 0.3, 0.35, 4.5, 0.92, 9.2

2 The most popular colours of football boots are:

Level Up Maths 4-6 pages 70, 72

black, black, white, red, black, white, red, black, gold, gold, black, red, black, gold, red, black, black, gold, red, black, black, white

a Put this data in a frequency table.

b What is the mode of the data?

c Draw a bar chart to illustrate the data.

3 The pie chart shows the favourite authors of 40 young people.

Level Up Maths 4-6 page 124

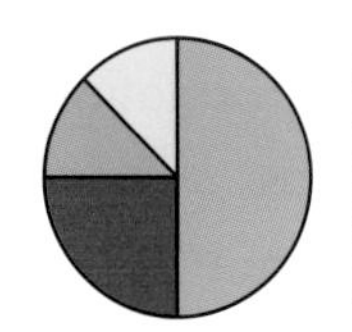

a How many prefer Rowling?
b How many prefer Pratchett?
c How many do not prefer Blackman?

World's Greatest Maths

Plus digital resources

Did you know?
The nautical mile was devised using the measurement of the circumference of the Earth at the equator. It is roughly equal to $\frac{1}{60}$ of a degree along any meridian.

11.1 Collecting data

- Identify sources from which data can be collected
- Identify factors that may affect the collection of data
- Choose a suitable sample size for an investigation
- Describe possible methods for collecting primary and secondary data
- Read data from two-way tables

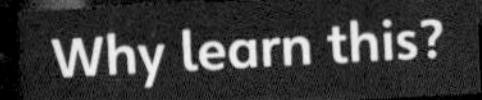

The results of a survey often depend on when and where it is carried out.

What's the BIG idea?

- **Data** you collect yourself by doing a survey or experiment is called **primary data**. Level 5
- It is important to identify which groups of people need to be included in a **survey**. Level 5
- **Sample sizes** need to be large enough to be representative but small enough to make it practical to collect the data. Level 5
- Data collected by someone else is called **secondary data**. Secondary sources include newspapers and the internet. Level 5 & Level 6

Did you know?

Viewing figures for TV programmes are worked out from a small sample of households that have dataloggers.

Practice, practice, practice!

Level 5

1 Where or how could you find information about

a house prices in different areas

b how pupils travel to your school

c what types of films are shown at the cinema

d how good pupils are at estimating one minute without a watch?

5c I can identify sources from which data can be collected

2 a Kirsty is doing a survey to see what age groups use the local library. She records people's ages as they go into the library one Saturday afternoon. Will Kirsty's data be representative?

b Sarah wants to know whether people eat the recommended five portions of fruit and vegetables a day. She asks all the people at her aerobics class. Will Sarah's data be representative?

c David wants to know what people think about the new speed bumps on Laurel Avenue. He asks, 'Do you find it annoying that the speed bumps slow you down so much?' What is wrong with David's question?

5b I can identify factors that may affect the collection of data

3 Select the most appropriate level of accuracy for each of these investigations.

a times taken to run 100 m

A nearest minute B nearest second C nearest 0.1 second

b heights of pupils.

A nearest metre B nearest centimetre C nearest millimetre

c mass of school bags.

A nearest 100 g B nearest 10 g C nearest gram

5b I can select an appropriate level of accuracy for data from limited choices

data hypothesis primary data

4 What data would you need to test each of these hypotheses?

- **a** Coffee cools down more quickly than tea.
- **b** People in London earn more than people in Cardiff.
- **c** It rains more than it used to.

Did you know?

The average wage in India is about £400 a year compared with more than £20 000 in Britain.

5
- **a** Anita is investigating whether a dice is biased. Should she roll the dice 10, 30 or 100 times?
- **b** A charity wants to know if a live band or a DJ would be more popular for a fundraising evening. Should they ask 50, 500 or 1000 people?

6 Taller people are better at throwing a ball.

Describe how you would collect primary data to test this hypothesis.

7 Think about your answer to Q6.
Suggest a sensible sample size for your investigation.

8 Jack's table shows how many pupils in his class have school dinners.

	School dinner	Packed lunch	Go home for lunch	Total
Boys	7		3	14
Girls	4	11	1	
Total	11	15		

- **a** How many boys in Jack's class have school dinners?
- **b** How many girls are there in Jack's class?
- **c** Copy and complete Jack's table.

Level 5

5b I can identify relevant data and discuss how it relates to a problem

5b I can choose a sample size from a number of options

5a I can describe a range of possible methods for collecting primary data

5a I can choose a sample size that is sensible for my investigation

5a I can read data from two-way tables

9 Fewer people can afford to buy their own house these days.

Describe what secondary data you would collect to see whether this statement is correct.

Level 6

6c I can describe a range of possible methods that could be used to collect secondary data

Now try this!

A Speedy animals

Pick two of these animals: elephant giraffe zebra grizzly bear

Ask five of your classmates which of your animals they think is the faster.
Which animal did the majority of pupils choose? Do you agree with them?
How could you find out if they are correct?

B Number plates

Asma says that some digits appear in number plates more often than others.
Describe how you would investigate whether Asma is correct.
Carry out your investigation.
Which digits appear more often? Why?

Did you know?

People doing market research in the high street often have quotas of types of people to interview.

sample size secondary data survey two-way table

11.2 Interpreting data

- Calculate the mean for a small set of discrete data
- Work out the mean from a frequency table
- Know when it is best to use the mean, median or mode
- Draw a stem-and-leaf diagram and use it to find averages and the range

Why learn this?

We're all different, but it's useful for businesses to know their 'average customer'.

What's the BIG idea?

- The **mode** is the most common value. **Level 5 & Level 6**
- The **median** is the middle value when the data are in order. **Level 5 & Level 6**
- The **mean** is the total value divided by the number of values. **Level 5 & Level 6**
- The **range** is the highest value minus the lowest value. **Level 5 & Level 6**
- A **stem-and-leaf diagram** shows numerical data that is split into a stem and a leaf. **Level 6**
- The stem often represents tens and the units are the leaves. For example, you could write 35 as 3|5. **Level 6**
- Stem-and-leaf diagrams should be ordered and have a key. **Level 6**

Did you know?

The average person will eat 10 000 bars of chocolate in their lifetime!

Practice, practice, practice!

Level 5

5c I can calculate the mean for a small set of discrete data

5c I can draw conclusions from simple statistics for a single distribution

5a I can work out the mean from a frequency table

1 Calculate the mean for each data set.

a The shoes sizes in the Patel family are 3, 12, 6, 4 and 5.

b The times that Josh had to wait for the bus each day one week were 5, 8, 2, 7 and 12 minutes.

2 Candice has made four pairs of earrings.
She sells them on the internet for £3.50, £2.80, £6.00 and £4.20.
Candice only makes a profit if the mean price is greater than £4.
Does she make a profit?

3 Work out the mean for the data in each frequency table.

a Letters delivered to the houses on Paddock Lane.

Number of letters	0	1	2	3	4	5
Frequency	5	3	7	4	0	1

b Cost of a packet of crisps at different shops.

Cost	35p	36p	37p	38p	39p	40p
Frequency	8	6	1	3	2	5

c Hourly rate of pay for employees at a supermarket.

Hourly rate	£5.90	£6.10	£6.52	£7.04	£9.71
Frequency	8	27	14	5	2

average frequency interpret mean

4 Seven friends spend these amounts buying their lunch.

£3.20 £2.79 £4.25 £3.20 £3.98 £4.19 £3.81

a Tracy wants to know the most common cost of a meal. Which average will tell her this? Find this average.

b Connor would like to know if his meal costs more than most others. Which average should he use? What is the value of this average?

c Alex suggests they all pay an equal share for the meals. Which average gives equal shares? Calculate this average.

d What would you calculate if you wanted to know the spread of the prices? Calculate this value.

5 Find the mean, median and mode for each data set. Which average best describes the data?

a Pocket money: £6, £5, £6.50, £15, £5.50, £5

b Shoe sizes: 5, 6, 4, 6, 6, 3, 6, 6, 5, 6

c Test marks: 14, 17, 16, 12, 18, 16, 15, 17, 18

6 These are the weights (in kilograms) of 20 children.

37 42 31 35 48 29 50 36 44 28

63 35 41 52 43 61 38 42 39 30

Copy and complete this stem-and-leaf diagram to show the data.

2	8
3	
4	
5	
6	

Key: 2|8 represents 28 kg

Tip Order the data first.

Watch out! You must always provide a key for a stem and leaf diagram.

7 These are the file sizes (in megabytes) of 14 songs in MP3 format.

4.1 3.8 5.6 6.0 3.4 4.9 6.5

3.7 4.3 4.1 5.2 4.1 6.3 3.6

a Draw a stem-and-leaf diagram for this data. Remember to include a key.

b What is the mode of the data?

c What is the range?

d What is the median of the data?

Level 6

6c I can recognise when to use the range, mean, median or mode

6b I can recognise which average is most appropriate

6b I can draw a stem-and-leaf diagram

6b I can find the mode and range from a stem-and-leaf diagram

6a I can find the median from a stem-and-leaf diagram

Now try this!

A Five numbers

a Find five numbers whose median, mode and range are all the same.

b Find five numbers that have a mode of 10, a median of 11 and a range of 12.

c Are there any other correct answers for parts **a** and **b**?

B Algebra averages

a Find five numbers that have a mean of 10, a range of 11, a median of 12 and a mode of 13.

b Find five numbers that have a mode of x, a median of y and a range of z. What is the mean of your five numbers?

Tip Use the letter a to represent the last number when you have found the other four.

median mode range stem-and-leaf diagram

11.3 Bar charts

- Group data in equal class intervals
- Construct compound and comparative bar charts
- Interpret compound and comparative bar charts

Why learn this?
It's often easier to quickly interpret data in a bar chart.

What's the BIG idea?

- When there are a lot of different values, it is often easier to **group data** in a frequency table. The groups are sometimes called **class intervals**. The group with the highest **frequency** is called the **modal group**. **Level 5**
- A **comparative bar chart** shows two or more bar charts on the same graph. **Level 5**
- A **compound bar chart** can be used to show fractions or proportions of the whole. **Level 5 & Level 6**

Watch out!
Compound and comparative bar charts need a key.

Practice, practice, practice!

Level 5

5b I can draw compound bar charts

1 The SuperKit Motor Company is investigating the changing demand for its cars.
Use the table to copy and complete this compound bar chart.

Year	Type of car		
	Sport	Estate	4 × 4
1998	3	4	1
2003	2	2	3
2008	1	3	4

Cars sold by the SuperKit Motor Company

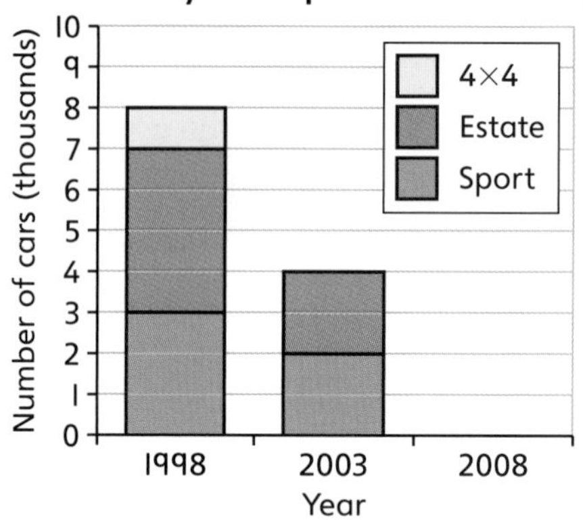

Tip
Check that the height of the bar in a compound bar chart is the same as the total frequency for that category.

2 Draw a rectangular bar 10 squares long.
Shade the bar in 4 sections to represent the percentages in the table.

Ingredients in muesli bar	Oats	Raisins	Syrup	Nuts
Percentage by weight	55	15	20	10

5b I can interpret data from simple compound and comparative bar charts

3 This comparative bar chart shows the colours of pupils' MP3 players.

a How many girls have a pink MP3 player?

b Which is the most popular colour for girls?

c How many pupils have a white MP3 player?

d How many more boys have a black MP3 player than girls?

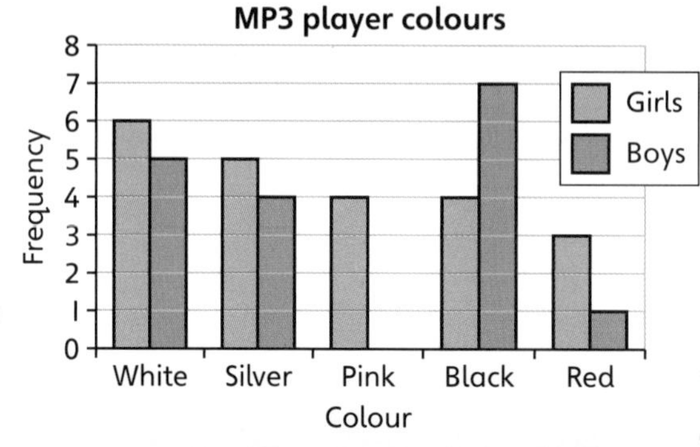

comparative bar chart · class interval · compound bar chart · continuous

4 A supermarket is investigating how much their average customer spends. These are the total amounts spent by 18 customers.

£25.60	£47.62	£4.95	£19.59	£53.42	£3.65
£28.20	£20.85	£28.32	£34.50	£57.45	£84.46
£70.72	£16.75	£98.99	£79.24	£84.10	£29.50

a Copy and complete this frequency table for the data.

Shopping bill	£0 to £19.99	£20 to £39.99
Tally		
Frequency		

b Which is the modal group?

Level 5

5a I can group data, where appropriate, in equal class intervals

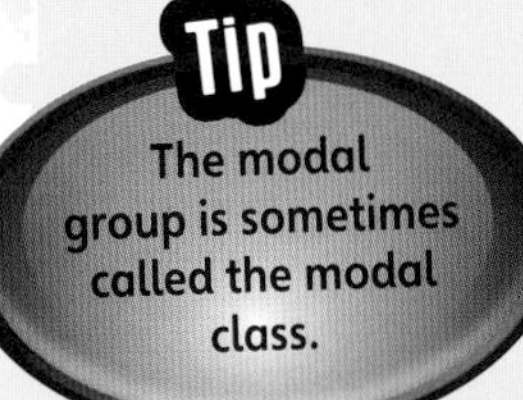

5 The bar chart shows the different types of properties offered by estate agents in two different areas.

a Approximately what percentage of properties in Area A are flats?

b Approximately what percentage of properties in Area B are not flats?

c Megan says that Area A has more houses than Area B. Why might Megan be wrong?

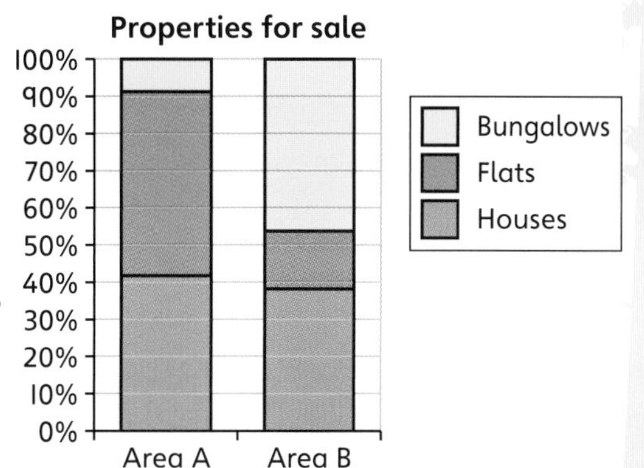

Level 6

6c I can read information from a bar chart

6 The bar charts show how many medals Great Britain and Japan won over three Olympic Games.

a Which team won more silver medals in total?

b Which team won more gold medals in 2000?

c Predict which team will win more medals in the 2008 Olympics. Use the charts to justify your prediction. Use websites to check whether you are right.

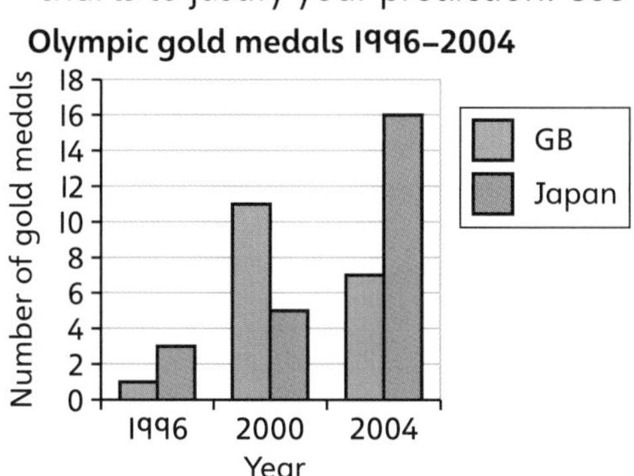

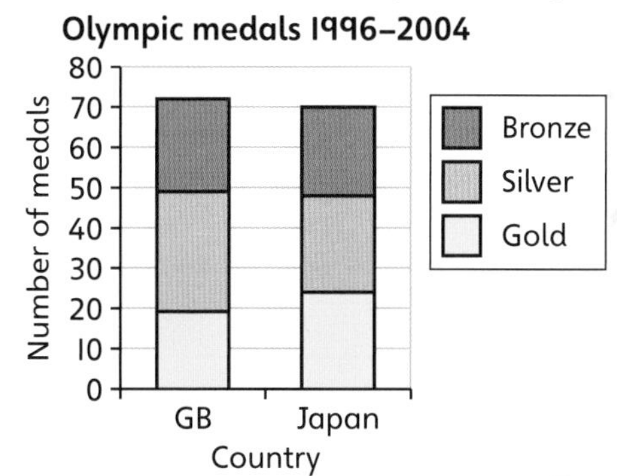

6a I can pick out information from different graphs and use these facts to answer questions

Now try this!

A Compound bars

You will need Resource sheet 11.3. Cut out the bars and fit them together so that you make four bars of value 100 (length 10 cm). Is it possible to do it a different way?

B Vowel frequency

- Choose a page of any textbook. Record the frequency of the vowels (a, e, i, o, u) in a frequency table.
- Draw a compound bar chart to show the data.
- Choose a second page in your book. Make another frequency table and then draw a comparative bar chart to compare the frequencies on the two pages.

discrete grouped data frequency modal group

11.4 Line graphs

- Draw line graphs on paper or using ICT
- Interpret line graphs

Why learn this?

Line graphs can be used to show and predict trends, such as global temperatures.

What's the BIG idea?

- A **line graph** is a series of points joined by straight lines. Level 6
- Line graphs are often used to show **trends** over periods of time. These are called **time series** graphs. Time goes on the horizontal axis. Level 6
- **Spreadsheet** packages can be used to draw line graphs. Level 6

Practice, practice, practice!

Level 6

6c I can construct simple line graphs for time series using ICT

1 The table shows the numbers of visitors to an indoor ski slope during one year.

Month	J	F	M	A	M	J	J	A	S	O	N	D
Number of visitors (thousands)	14	13	11	10	9	7	7	8	9	11	12	12

Use ICT to draw a line graph of the data.

2 Maria runs a small mail-order jewellery business.
She recorded the number of orders received each day for a week.

Day	Mon	Tues	Wed	Thurs	Fri	Sat	Sun
Number of orders	10	12	6	7	9	4	0

a Use ICT to draw a line graph of the data.

b Maria only has time to process seven orders each day.
Does she manage to process all her orders by the end of the week?

Did you know?

Spreadsheets get their name from the charts that used to be spread across two facing pages of a book.

6b I can construct and use line graphs for time series

3 **a** Draw a line graph to show the price of gold over this 30-year period.

Year	1975	1980	1985	1990	1995	2000	2005
Average price of gold ($)	160	620	320	380	380	280	440

b In which five-year period did the price of gold change the most?

c In which five-year period did the price of gold stay the same?

4 The table shows the value of a car over a period of seven years.

Age of car (years)	0	1	2	3	4	5	6	7
Value (£)	19 500	15 900	12 500	10 000	8100	6500	5200	4200

a Draw a line graph of the data.

b In which year did the car lose the most value?

c Use your graph to estimate the value of the car after $5\frac{1}{2}$ years.

line graph spreadsheet

5 Joe recorded the sales at his bicycle shop each month for one year. The data is shown in the line graph.

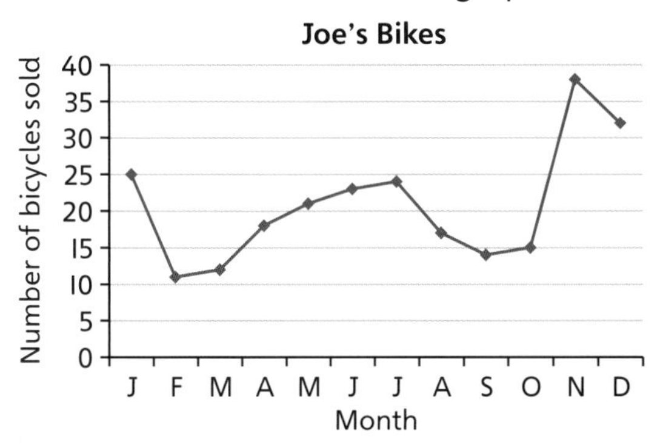

a Which month saw the most sales?

b How many bicycles were sold in January?

c Suggest a reason for the peak in sales at the end of the year.

6 David has carried out an investigation into temperatures inside and outside his garage.

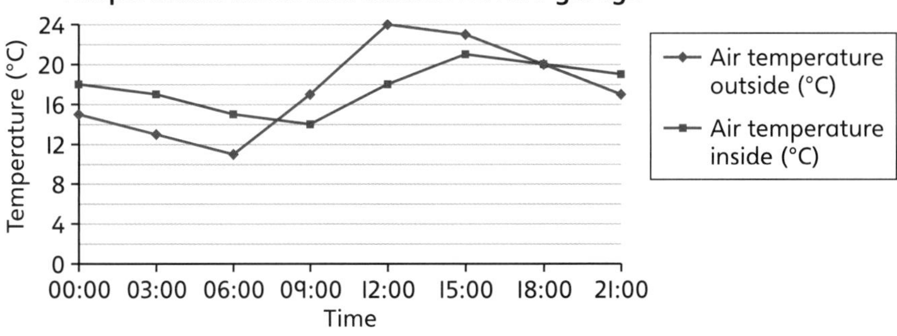

a What is the temperature outside David's garage at 3 pm?

b When was the temperature inside David's garage 15°C?

c When were the temperatures the same?

d When was the temperature difference between inside and outside the greatest?

Level 6

6b I can interpret line graphs

Tip

Use a ruler or set square to help you read points off a line graph accurately.

Now try this!

A Weather forecast

a Use the internet to find a five-day weather forecast for your area.

b Draw a line graph to show the forecast maximum temperatures for the next five days.

B Average temperature difference

a Add another line to your line graph from Activity A, to show the minimum temperatures.

b What is the average difference between the maximum and minimum temperatures?

c Find a city with **i** a larger average difference **ii** a smaller average difference.

Super fact!

The highest temperature recorded on Earth was 58°C at Al' Aziziyah, Libya in September 1922.

time series trend

11.5 Pie charts

- Draw pie charts
- Interpret pie charts

Why learn this?

Pie charts are often used to show sales data as they show proportions clearly.

What's the BIG idea?

- A **pie chart** uses **sectors** of a circle to show different categories of data. **Level 5 & Level 6**
- Each sector of the circle represents a different category. If the sector is $\frac{1}{4}$ of the circle then $\frac{1}{4}$ of the data is in this category. **Level 5 & Level 6**
- There are 360° in a circle. Use this formula to work out the angle for each category:
  angle of sector = $\frac{\textbf{frequency}}{\text{total frequency}} \times 360°$ or $\frac{360°}{\text{total frequency}} \times$ frequency **Level 6**

Practice, practice, practice!

Level 5

5c I can interpret simple pie charts

1 Jenny drew a pie chart to show the numbers of different types of pets on her street.

a Which is the most common pet? How can you tell?

b What fraction of the pets are cats?

c There are three hamsters.
How many pets are there altogether?

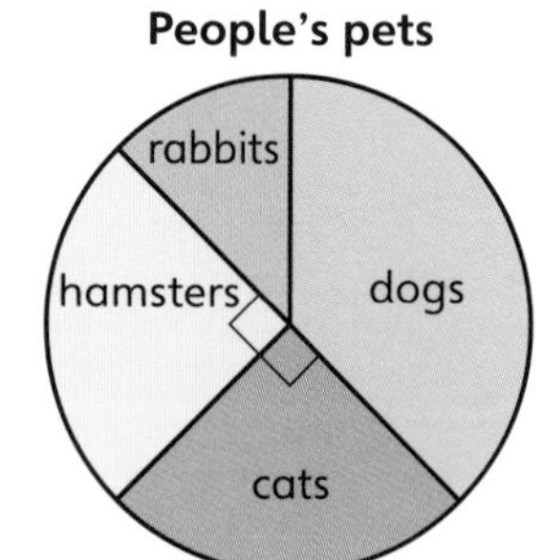

2 The Cox family spend £1600 each month. The pie chart shows what they spend their money on. Is each statement true or false?

a They spend 25% of their money on household bills.

b Their rent is £800.

c One third of their money goes on groceries and entertainment.

d Household bills cost less than £200.

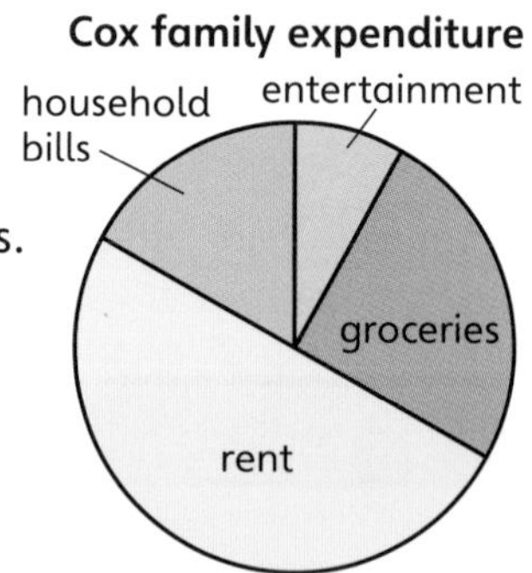

5b I can construct pie charts depicting simple proportions of data

3 50% of the members of a judo club are boys, 25% are girls and the rest are adults. Draw a pie chart to show the proportions of girls, boys and adults.

Level 6

6c I can draw pie charts using simple whole-number angles

4 This table shows the numbers of trains leaving Birmingham New Street for various destinations one day.

	Manchester	Nottingham	Reading	Bristol	Total
Number of trains	6	3	5	4	18
Angle	$\frac{6}{18} \times 360° = 120°$				

a Copy and complete the table. **b** Draw a pie chart to show the data.

frequency pie chart

5 Matt has found out the favourite football teams of 36 of his friends.

MU	L	B	AV	AV	L	B	AV	B
B	B	MU	AV	C	A	AV	MU	AV
AV	AV	B	L	AV	MU	B	AV	A
L	A	B	B	C	AV	AV	MU	AV

Key: MU = Manchester United, L = Liverpool, A = Arsenal,
C = Chelsea, AV = Aston Villa, B = Birmingham City

a Construct a frequency table for the data.

b Draw a pie chart for the data. **Hint:** Tally the data

Level 6

6c I can draw pie charts using simple whole-number angles

Tip
You do not need to draw the last angle on a pie chart, but you should still check that it is the right size.

6 This pie chart shows the results of a survey of people's favourite fruits. 60 people chose apple as their favourite fruit.

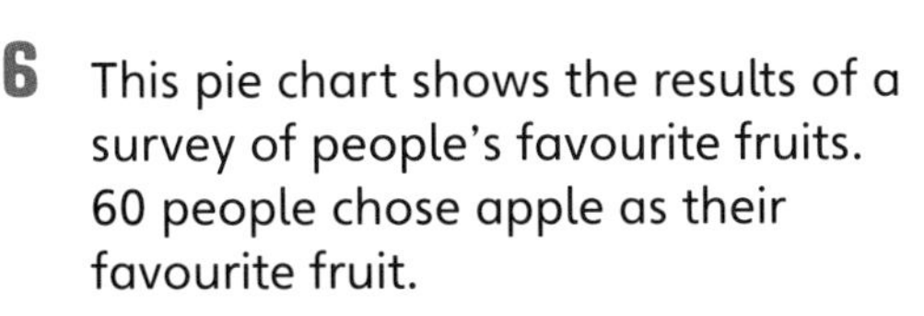

a How many people were surveyed altogether?

b How many people chose banana?

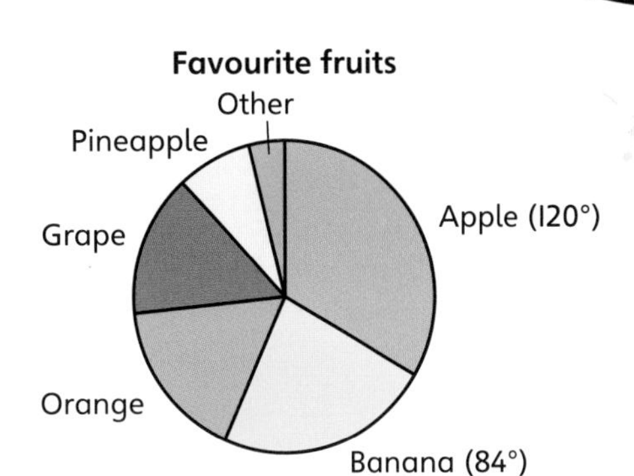

6b I can answer questions about pie charts

7 These pie charts show how much time pupils spend on sport at two schools.

Athletic High School

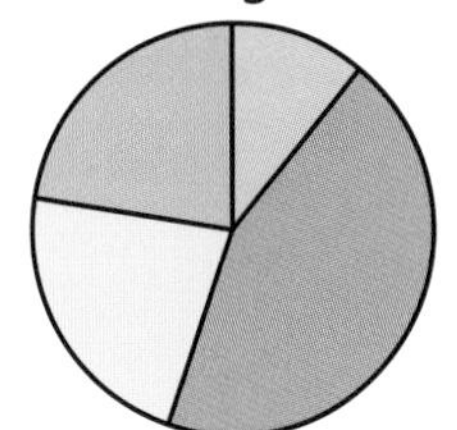

Champions' Academy

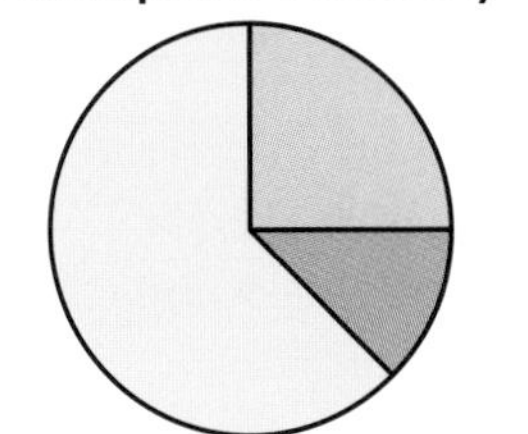

- 0–2 hours per week
- 3–4 hours per week
- 5–6 hours per week
- 7–8 hours per week

Use the pie chart to decide whether each statement is true or false, or whether there is not enough information to decide. Explain your answers.

a There are more pupils at Athletic High School.

b The pupil who plays sport for the longest goes to Athletic High School.

c The pupil who plays the least goes to Champions' Academy.

6a I can compare two pie charts

Now try this!

A Roll a dice

Roll a dice eight times and record the results in a frequency table.
Draw a pie chart to show your results. (A frequency of 1 corresponds to $\frac{1}{8}$ of the circle, a frequency of 2 corresponds to $\frac{2}{8} = \frac{1}{4}$ of the circle, and so on.)

B 24 hours

Construct a pie chart to show how much time you spend doing different things in a day. Your total time should be 24 hours. Remember to include time for sleeping and eating!

Did you know?
Florence Nightingale used pie charts to highlight the unsanitary conditions in army hospitals in the 1850s.

interpret proportion sector

GLASTONSTOCK!

You're planning this year's Glastonstock music festival. You need to use statistics from previous festivals to make it as successful as possible.

YOU'RE NICKED, SUNSHINE

You need to know how many security guards to hire for the festival. This table shows the number of people who attended the last ten Glastonstock festivals, and the number of security guards at each one.

Number of people (1000s)	7	2	22	13	16	9	28	11	10	4
Number of security guards	22	8	62	46	52	30	84	24	38	6

- Copy and complete this scatter graph.

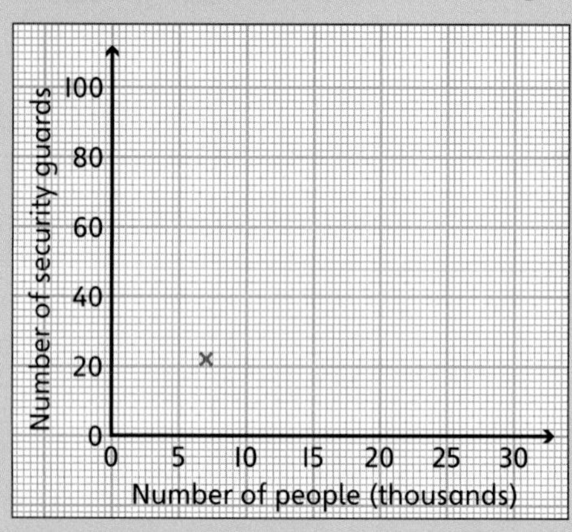

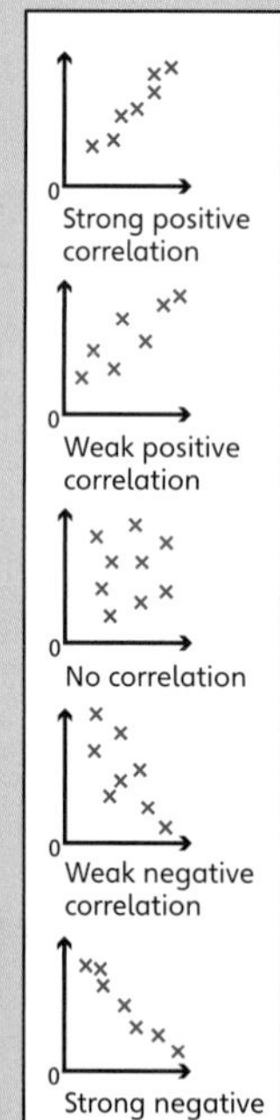

- Choose the type of correlation that best matches your scatter graph.
- There will be 20 000 people at your festival. Use your graph to estimate the number of security guards you will need to hire.

PORTALOO® PROBLEMS

You've booked six great bands. Now you need to choose which stages they're going to play on. The six stages have different numbers of Portaloos®. You need to make sure there is a strong positive correlation between the number of fans each band has and the number of Portaloos® available.

Bands

The Futons	300 fans
The Nutellis	420 fans
James Sharp	710 fans
Empty House	750 fans
Red Hot Cauliflowers	900 fans
The Tenderstems	990 fans

Stages

Diamond Stage	6 portaloos
Cone Stage	4 portaloos
Sunshine Stage	4 portaloos
Wellies Tent	1 portaloos
Plastic FM Stage	2 portaloos
Cellophane Stage	5 portaloos

- Choose a stage for each band to play on.
- Copy and complete this table showing the numbers of fans and Portaloos®.

Number of fans						
Number of Portaloos®						

- Draw a scatter graph showing the relationship between the number of fans and the number of Portaloos®.

CHECKING THE FACTS

This is a newspaper review of last year's festival.

- Decide which highlighted statement is relevant to each table of data below.
- Draw a scatter graph for that data.
- Write down whether you think the reviewer's statement is true or false based on your scatter graph. Write a sentence using the word 'correlation' to explain your answer.

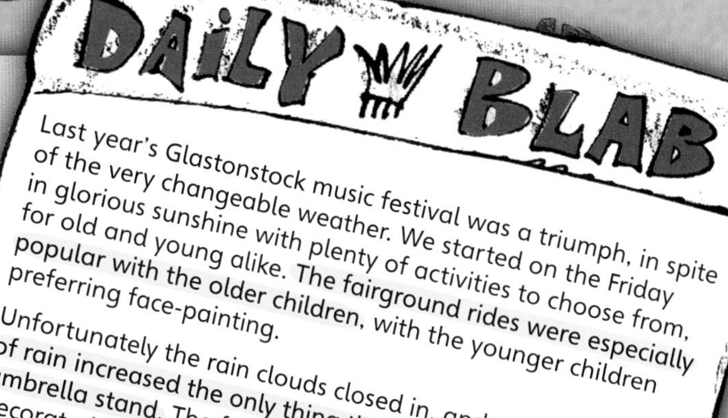

Last year's Glastonstock music festival was a triumph, in spite of the very changeable weather. We started on the Friday in glorious sunshine with plenty of activities to choose from, for old and young alike. The fairground rides were especially popular with the older children, with the younger children preferring face-painting.

Unfortunately the rain clouds closed in, and as the amount of rain increased the only thing that was selling out was the umbrella stand. The food and drink stalls were beautifully decorated in a medieval theme, but people only seemed to want to buy drinks when it was hot and sunny.

The headline act was a huge hit. From a distance you could hardly hear the band, but as I got closer to the stage the noise became deafening. Clearly there were plenty of fans who were ready to dance! There was a lot of variety on offer, and even though some of the music tents were bigger than others festival-goers chose which bands to listen to at random.

So another fantastic Glastonstock festival... more of the same next year please!

a

Age of child	14	4	10	9	6	8	3	11
Number of children on fairground	1	5	3	3	4	3	5	2

b

Number of umbrellas sold each hour	31	4	42	48	0	50	11	38
Rainfall (mm)	5.5	2.6	7.0	7.4	0.8	8.0	3.9	5.7

c

Number of drinks sold each hour	200	430	560	730	250	500	610	380
Temperature (°C)	26	24	26	24	22	30	20	20

d

Size of music tent (m^2)	500	820	910	650	410	910	540	950
Size of audience	770	1250	1500	860	580	1100	950	1330

e

Music volume (decibels)	45	86	30	59	75	38	100	70
Distance from stage (m)	240	100	500	220	150	350	110	140

QUICK QUIZ

Choose **positive**, **negative** or **no correlation** to describe the relationship between:

- the amount of rain and the number of people at the outdoor stage
- the amount of litter left behind and the number of people at the festival
- the temperature and the number of people wearing coats
- the number of people at the outdoor stage and the mobile phone signal strength
- the distance from the festival and the time taken to travel there.

The mathematical boat show

Many boat shows are held around the country each year, to advertise new boat designs and to attract new people to the world of boating.
When buying a boat, many features need to be considered. One basic requirement is that the cabin headroom is suitable for your height!

The table shows some specifications for certain types of speedboat.

	350 Sun Sport	310 Sun Sport	260 Sun Sport	400 Super Sport	370 Super Sport
Cabin headroom (m)	1.77	1.63	1.35	1.88	1.88
Fuel capacity (litres)	651	492	348	946	901
Water capacity (litres)	113	114	57	189	163
Holding tank capacity (litres)	140	136	68	189	189
Draft (m)	0.99	0.94	0.81	0.91	0.91
Approximate weight (kg)	6109	4423	2858	7303	6849
Bridge clearance (m)	2.08	1.83	1.52	?	3.05

1 What is the modal draft? **Level 5**

2 What is the mean fuel capacity? **Level 5**

3 'The British team are amongst the best performers in rowing events at the Olympic Games.'

What data would you collect to confirm that this statement is true? **Level 6**

4 a Find the mean, median and range of the speedboat weights.
b Which average best describes the data? Give a full reason for your answer. **Level 6**

5 a The range of the bridge clearance is 1.68 m.
Can you use this to work out the missing value? Give a reason for your answer.
b The median of the bridge clearance is 2.08 m.
Use this fact to work out the missing value. **Level 6**

6 a What type of diagram would you choose to show
i cabin headroom and ii the speed of the boats?
b Why are these diagrams best for this type of data? **Level 6**

7 The chart shows the bridge clearance of the speedboats.
a Identify any problems with this graph.
Explain how each could be resolved.
b Draw your own graph to show the data.
Include your suggested improvements.
c When might this chart be used?
Why is bridge clearance an important part of the boat specification? **Level 7**

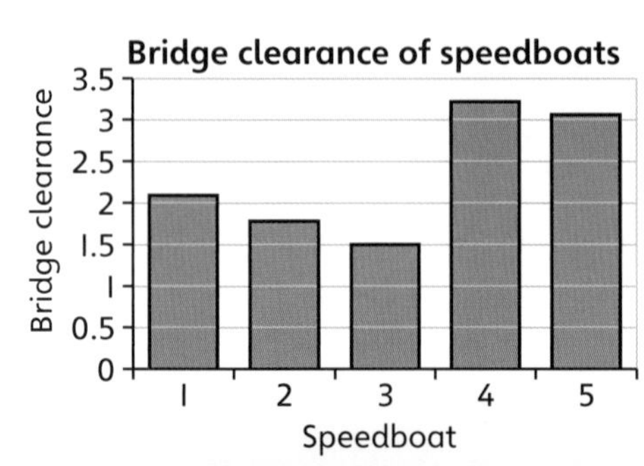

The BIG ideas

- **Data** you collect yourself by doing a survey or experiment is called **primary data**. Level 5
- The **mode** is the most common value. Level 5 & Level 6
- The **median** is the middle value when the data are in order. Level 5 & Level 6
- The **mean** is the total of the values divided by the number of values. Level 5 & Level 6
- **Range** = highest value − lowest value. Level 5 & Level 6
- A **comparative bar chart** shows two or more bars on the same graph. Level 5 & Level 6
- Data collected by someone else is called **secondary data**. Secondary sources include newspapers and the internet. Level 5 & Level 6
- You need to decide which diagram is most appropriate:
  - A **pie chart** is best for **categorical** data.
  - A **bar chart** is best for **discrete** data, which may be grouped.
  - A **frequency diagram** is best for **continuous** data, which may be grouped.
  - A **line graph** is best to show **trends** over time.
  - A **scatter graph** is best when you want to show the relationship between two sets of data. Level 6

Practice SATs-style questions

Level 5

Q1 David saw this poster at his bus stop.

> 87% of people take the bus every week.
> Why don't you?

David thinks that the percentage of people who take the bus every week is lower than 87%.
He decides to do a survey by asking 10 people if they take the bus every week.
Give two different reasons why David's method might not give very good data.

Q2 The frequency table shows the number of rooms in the houses in one street.

Number of rooms	Frequency	Number of rooms × Frequency
5	2	5 × 2 = 10
6	4	
7	2	
8	2	
TOTALS	**10**	

a Copy and complete the table.

b Work out the mean number of rooms per house.

Level 6

Q3 The comparative bar chart shows the favourite subjects of a group of pupils.

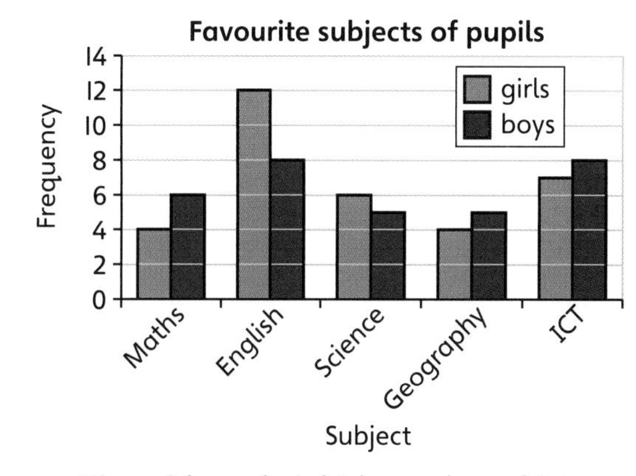

a Nine girls and eight boys chose history. Copy and complete the bar chart to show this missing data.

b How many boys chose science?

c Which is the most popular subject for girls?

d How many pupils chose ICT?

Q4 There are 80 members in a judo club. 20 of the members are left-handed, the rest are right-handed. Draw a pie chart to show this data.

Level 7

Q5 Joanne has drawn a scatter graph of the number of words per minute that pupils in her class can type against the length of time they have been learning.
She has extended the line of best fit so that she can estimate typing speeds for pupils who have been learning longer.
Why might her conclusions be misleading?

Revision 2

Quick Quiz

Q1 Multiply out and simplify this expression.
$2(4x + 3) - 5$
→ *See 7.4*

Q2 Use a written method to work out
a 13.47 + 152.9
b 367 − 43.18
→ *See 8.1*

Q3 Write the order of rotational symmetry of each shape.

a 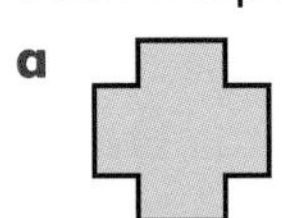 **b** 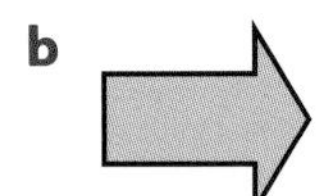 **c** 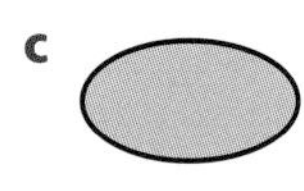

→ *See 9.1*

Q4 Put the correct sign < or > between each pair of numbers.
a 2.043 ___ 2.034
b 16.426 ___ 16.43
→ *See 8.3*

Q5 What scale factor has been used to enlarge shape A to shape B?

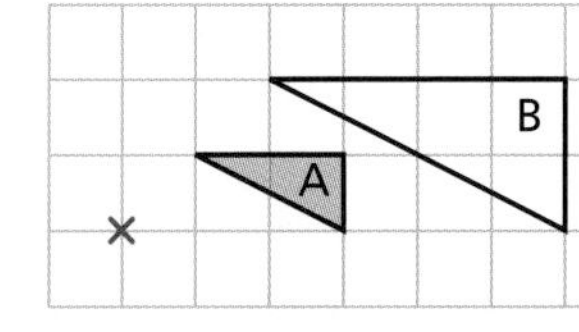

→ *See 9.6*

Q6 Solve the equation $8x - 3 = 53$.
→ *See 10.2*

Q7 A rectangle has a width of x cm. Its length is 5 cm more than its width. Write down a formula for A, the area of the rectangle, in terms of x.
→ *See 10.6*

Q8 Factorise $3x + 12$.
→ *See 7.5*

Q9 Work out
a 42.35×10^3
b 4.76×0.01
→ *See 8.2*

Q10 Solve the equation $5(x + 2) = 3x + 22$.
→ *See 10.3*

Activity

You are starting a new job in a café.

LEVEL 5

Q1 Here is a recipe for flapjacks.

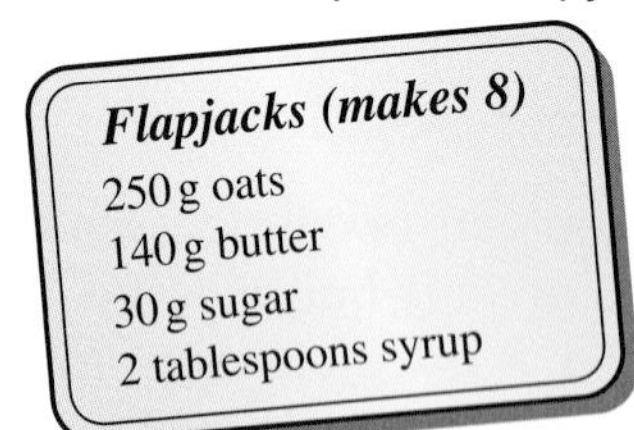

Write the amount of each ingredient you will need to make 20 flapjacks.

Q2 The owner of the café keeps a record of the amount each customer spends. Here is her list for Saturday lunchtime.

£5.65, £4.35, £8.60, £9.40, £2.75, £3.55
£6.50, £4.50, £3.25, £3.85, £4.65, £5.35

The mean amount spent by customers on Friday lunchtime was £5.80. Is the mean amount spent by customers on Saturday more than the mean amount spent by customers on Friday?

LEVEL 6

Q3 Here is the price list for the café.

Tea	£1.10	Flapjack	£1.10
Coffee	£1.15	Muffin	£1.85
Hot chocolate	£1.80	Donut	£1.20
Soup	£1.75	Cereal bar	85p
Sandwiches	£3.80	Chocolate bar	47p

A group of people order four hot chocolates, two coffees, three teas, six sandwiches, four muffins and five chocolate bars.
Use rounding to estimate the total cost for this group.

Q4 There are four different flavours of muffin on sale in the café. This table shows the number of each flavour sold in one week.

Flavour of muffin	Number sold
Chocolate	22
Choc-chip	49
Blueberry	64
Vanilla	45

Draw a pie chart to represent this information.

Q5 This graph shows the average maximum and minimum temperatures in Sabres. What is the difference between the average maximum and minimum temperatures in June?

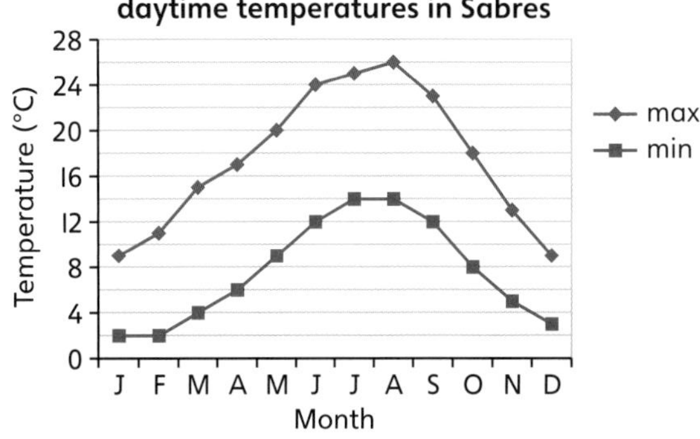

Practice SATs-style questions

LEVEL 5

Q1 Work out 582×34.

Q2 Work out the numbers of males and females in the fitness classes below.

a In the aerobics class, there are 36 people. There are twice as many females as males.

b In the judo class, there are 19 people. There are five more males than females.

c In the yoga class there are three males. The ratio of males to females is 1 : 4.

Q3 Solve these equations.

a $4x + 5 = 21$

b $27 = 6y - 3$

LEVEL 6

Q4 Donna wants to multiply out the brackets in the expression $4(3y + 2)$.
She writes $4(3y + 2) = 12y + 2$.
Show why Donna is wrong.

Q5 Solve this equation.
$34 + 6p = 64 - 4p$

Q6 In a survey, 30 people were asked what they had for breakfast that morning. Here are the results.

Breakfast	Number of people
Cereal	12
Toast	16
Porridge	2

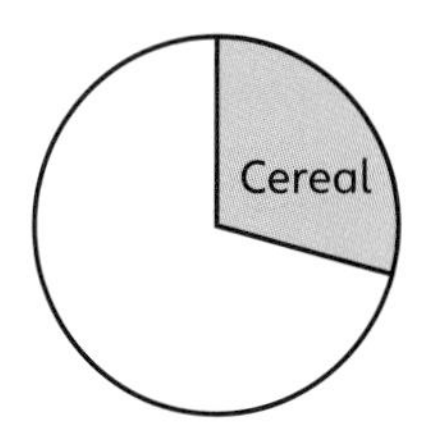

Copy and complete the pie chart to show this information.

LEVEL 7

Q7 The diagram shows a rectangle that is divided into four smaller rectangles, labelled P, Q, R and S. The ratio of area P to area S is 1 : 3. Calculate area Q.

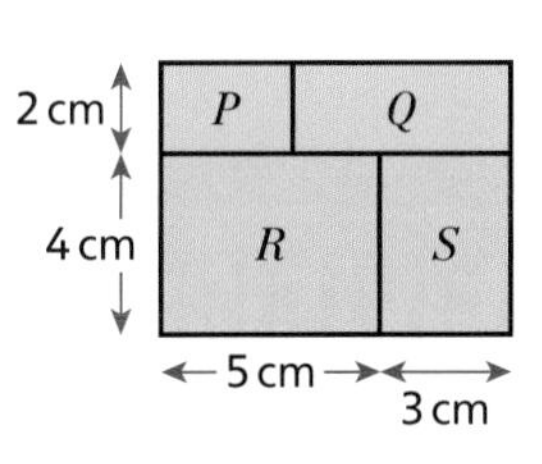

Q8 a Write the missing number.
The straight line $y = 4x + 12$ passes through (0, ___).

b A straight line parallel to the line in part **a** passes through the point (0, −5).
What is its equation?

12 Number know-how

This unit is about written and mental calculations with all forms of number.

Jen is in her final year of training to become a vet.

'I'm learning to be a vet and often have to use maths.

'When an animal is ill, it may need tablets or an injection. It is really important to get the number of tablets or the volume of liquid in a syringe correct. Too little and the treatment won't work; too much and it could make the animal's condition worse.

'Units are very important for working out the correct dose (amount of drug needed). Doses for tablets can be in milligrams (mg) or grams. A milligram is $\frac{1}{1000}$ of a gram – it is vital not to get the units confused, as the animal could get one thousand times more or less of the drug than it needs! Drug doses usually vary with the weight of the animal and can be expressed as milligrams per kilogram (mg/kg) or millilitres per kilogram (ml/kg).

'For example, consider a dog that weighs 7.5 kg. If the dog needs a drug which has a dose of 10 milligrams per kilogram of body weight (10 mg/kg) and each tablet contains 25 mg of the drug, the dog will need three tablets. (Calculation: $7.5 \times 10 \div 25 = 75 \div 25 = 3$)

'If a dose of liquid for a syringe is 0.2 ml per kg of body weight and the cat needing it weighs 3.5 kg, then the syringe must be filled to the 0.7 ml mark.' (Calculation: $3.5 \times 0.2 = 0.7$)

Activities

A The table shows the amount of drug needed for a dose of 0.2 ml per kg of body weight.

- Copy and complete the table.
- What would be the correct dose of this drug for an animal weighing 18.5 kg?

Weight of animal (kg)	Amount of drug needed (ml)
3	
3.5	0.7
4	
4.5	

B The table gives information for a drug which has a dose of 10 mg per kg of body weight. Which of the calculations are incorrect?

For the incorrect calculations, what should the number of tablets be?

	Weight of animal	Strength of 1 tablet	Number of tablets
A	0.5 kg	10 mg	5
B	15 kg	50 mg	3
C	50 kg	1 g	0.5
D	125 kg	1 g	12.5

Before you start this unit...

1 Use a written method to work out these.

a $\frac{3}{8} + \frac{2}{3}$ **b** $\frac{5}{6} - \frac{1}{4}$

c 125×25 **d** $962 \div 37$

page 56

pages 140, 142

2 Copy and complete these.

page 130

a $45.6 \div 10 = \square$

b $\square \times 1000 = 2530$

c $18.4 \div \square = 0.0184$

d $12.3 \times 0.01 = \square$

3 **a** Find 10% of 75 m.

b Find 15% of 75 m.

c Find $\frac{2}{3}$ of £27.

page 62

4 Estimate the answer for each calculation.

page 144

a 5.4×2.9

b 286×23

c $20.8 \div 6.5$

The kilogram is the SI unit of mass. It is equal to the mass of an international prototype in the form of a platinum-iridium cylinder, which is kept at Sèvres in France.

Did you know?

Rabbits and rodents have teeth that are 'open rooted', which means they never stop growing. That is why it's important that they are given the right sort of food to stop their teeth getting too long.

12.1 More fractions

- Add and subtract fractions by writing them with a common denominator
- Add and subtract mixed numbers
- Calculate fractions of quantities
- Multiply and divide an integer by a fraction
- Multiply and divide fractions

Why learn this?

Understanding fractions helps you to understand musical note lengths. A crotchet is a quarter note and four quarter notes last the same amount of time as one whole note.

What's the BIG idea?

- To find a **fraction** of a quantity, divide by the **denominator** and then multiply by the **numerator**. **Level 5**
- To add or subtract fractions with different denominators, first find **equivalent** fractions with the same denominator. Then add or subtract the numerators and write the result over the denominator. **Level 6**
- To add **mixed numbers**, you can add the whole-number parts and then add the fractions. **Level 6**
- To subtract mixed numbers, you may need to change them into **improper fractions** first. Subtract and then rewrite as a mixed number if necessary. **Level 6**
- To multiply fractions, multiply the numerators and multiply the denominators. **Level 7**
- To divide fractions, invert the dividing fraction (turn it upside down) and change the division sign to multiplication. **Level 7**

Learn this

The denominator is the bottom number, the numerator is the top number.

Practice, practice, practice!

Level 5

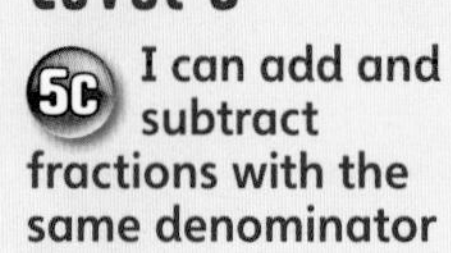

5c I can add and subtract fractions with the same denominator

5b I can find fractions of quantities (whole-number answers)

1 Work out

a $\frac{5}{8} + \frac{2}{8}$ b $\frac{7}{12} - \frac{4}{12}$ c $\frac{3}{4} + \frac{3}{4} + \frac{1}{4}$ d $\frac{3}{7} + \frac{4}{7} - \frac{5}{7}$

2 Work out

a $\frac{3}{10}$ of 350 miles b $\frac{4}{5}$ of 55 m c $\frac{3}{4}$ of 48 kg d $\frac{3}{7}$ of 91 cm

3 Fabian needs four ninths of a bag of flour.
If the bag contains 450 g, how much should he measure out?

Level 6

6c I can add fractions by writing them with a common denominator

4 Work out these additions. Write the answers in their simplest form.

a $\frac{3}{5} + \frac{3}{10}$ b $\frac{3}{5} + \frac{1}{6}$

c $\frac{2}{3} + \frac{1}{4}$ d $\frac{2}{9} + \frac{2}{3}$

e Look at your answers to parts **a–d**.
When you add positive fractions, is the answer bigger or smaller than the original fractions?

Tip

If you cannot find the LCM of the denominators, multiply the denominators together and use that number.

6c I can subtract fractions by writing them with a common denominator

5 Work out these subtractions. Write the answers in their simplest form.

a $\frac{5}{6} - \frac{2}{3}$ b $\frac{10}{12} - \frac{4}{9}$ c $\frac{8}{9} - \frac{4}{6}$ d $\frac{5}{7} - \frac{3}{14}$

e Look at your answers to parts **a–d**. When you subtract positive fractions, is the answer bigger or smaller than the first fraction?

f Is the answer bigger or smaller than the second fraction?

denominator equivalent fraction lowest terms mixed number

6 Marco wins £10 500 in a competition. He gives $\frac{1}{3}$ of his winnings to his mother, $\frac{1}{8}$ to his brother, keeps $\frac{1}{8}$ for himself and gives the rest to his sister. What fraction of his winnings does he give to his sister?

7 Martha writes $\frac{1}{3} + \frac{2}{12} + \frac{2}{9} = \frac{13}{18}$

Use inverse operations to check if she is correct.

8 Add these mixed numbers. Write the answers in their simplest form.

a $3\frac{1}{4} + 2\frac{1}{2}$ **b** $1\frac{1}{2} + 5\frac{2}{3}$ **c** $3\frac{2}{3} + 4\frac{4}{5}$ **d** $5\frac{3}{8} + 2\frac{7}{9}$

9 Work out

a $125 \times \frac{3}{5}$ **b** $56 \times \frac{1}{7}$ **c** $215 \times \frac{4}{5}$ **d** $350 \times \frac{5}{7}$

10 Work out

$2 \div \frac{1}{5}$ $1 \div \frac{1}{5} = 5$, so $2 \div \frac{1}{5} = 2 \times 5 = 10$

a $10 \div \frac{2}{5}$ **b** $27 \div \frac{3}{7}$ **c** $8 \div \frac{4}{9}$ **d** $45 \div \frac{9}{10}$

11 Work out these subtractions. Write the answers in their simplest form.

a $4\frac{3}{4} - \frac{5}{8}$ **b** $6\frac{5}{8} - 3\frac{1}{3}$ **c** $4\frac{1}{3} - 2\frac{3}{4}$ **d** $5\frac{2}{3} - 3\frac{1}{6}$

12 Sanjay has completed $15\frac{2}{3}$ miles of a $24\frac{5}{7}$ mile race. How far does he have left to run?

13 Work out these multiplications, cancelling where possible.

a $\frac{1}{2} \times \frac{4}{5}$ **b** $\frac{3}{4} \times \frac{4}{5}$ **c** $\frac{3}{7} \times \frac{21}{24}$

d $\frac{7}{8} \times \frac{32}{35}$ **e** $1\frac{4}{5} \times 2\frac{1}{3}$

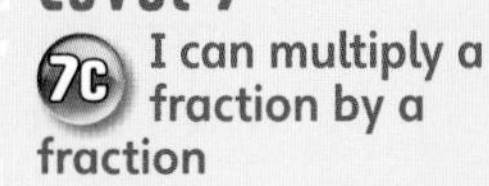

Tip

Write any mixed numbers as improper fractions first.

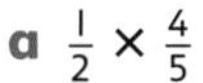

14 Work out these divisions.

a $\frac{1}{3} \div \frac{1}{5}$ **b** $\frac{3}{4} \div \frac{1}{2}$

c $\frac{2}{5} \div \frac{3}{4}$ **d** $3\frac{1}{4} \div 2\frac{1}{2}$

Watch out!

You only turn the second fraction upside down.

15 A rectangle has an area of $3\frac{1}{16}$ m^2. Its width is $1\frac{5}{8}$ m. What is its length?

Level 6

6c I can add and subtract several fractions by writing them with a common denominator

6c I can use inverse operations

6c I can add mixed numbers

6c I can multiply an integer by a fraction

6b I can divide an integer by a fraction

6a I can subtract mixed numbers

Level 7

7c I can multiply a fraction by a fraction

7b I can divide a fraction by a fraction

Now try this!

A Smallest answer

a Work with a partner. Each use the digits 1 to 6 to make a pair of proper fractions. You can only use each digit once. Subtract your fractions. Who has the smaller answer?

b How many different answers can you make with this group of digits?

B Whole-number answer

Use the digits 1 to 6 to make fraction multiplication and division calculations. How many ways can you arrange the digits to make 1, 2, 3, 4, 5 and 6?

numerator proper/improper fraction simplest form

12.2 Multiplying and dividing

- Make and justify estimates and approximations of calculations
- Multiply and divide any number by 0.1, 0.01 and multiples of them
- Multiply and divide both sides of an inequality by a negative number
- Generalise inequalities
- Understand the effects of multiplying and dividing positive numbers by fractions less than 1

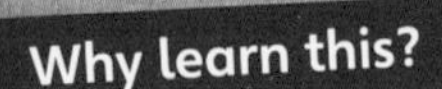

Why learn this?

Improving the aerodynamics of racing cars involves using multiplication and division to work out force and velocity.

What's the BIG idea?

- **Multiplying** by 0.1 is the same as multiplying by $\frac{1}{10}$ or **dividing** by 10. Dividing by 0.1 is the same as dividing by $\frac{1}{10}$ or multiplying by 10. **Level 6**
- Multiplying by 0.01 is the same as multiplying by $\frac{1}{100}$ or dividing by 100. Dividing by 0.01 is the same as dividing by $\frac{1}{100}$ or multiplying by 100. **Level 6**
- **Inequalities** are equations that are not equal. For example, $x > 2$ means that x is **greater than** 2. **Level 6**
- When you multiply or divide an inequality by a negative number, you must reverse the inequality sign for the statement to remain true. **Level 6**
- When **estimating** a calculation, more than one **approximation** is possible. **Level 6 & Level 7**
- When you multiply a positive number by a fraction less than 1, the result is a smaller number. **Level 7**
- When you divide a positive number by a fraction less than 1, the result is a larger number. **Level 7**

Learn this

$>$ means 'greater than'

$<$ means 'less than'

$\geqslant$ means 'greater than or equal to'

$\leqslant$ means 'less than or equal to'

Practice, practice, practice!

Level 6

6c I can estimate answers to calculations involving two or more operations

1 Use estimation to find which of these calculations are incorrect.

a $(237 \times 48) + 489 = 11\,865$

b $(14.7 + 4.2) \times (12.9 - 8.4) = 65.05$

c $\frac{32.8 \times 6.8}{2.5} = 98.216$

6b I can use the laws of arithmetic to perform mental calculations

2 Use a mental method to work out

a $(39 \times 8) \div 4$　　b $22 \times (1175 \div 25)$　　c $\frac{18.74 \times 25}{4}$

6b I can use the laws of arithmetic and inverse operations

3 Use inverse operations to check these calculations.

a $205.32 \div 23.6 = 8.7$

b $446.592 \div 12.8 = 83.48$

c $109.96 \div 9.5 = 13.68$

approximate　division　estimate　explain　explore　greater than >

4 Use equivalent calculations to work out these.

a 74×0.1 b 7×0.02 c 352×0.01 d 0.5×0.2

Hint: $0.02 = 0.01 \times 2$

5 Multiply both sides of the inequality by the number shown.

$x > 4$ $(\times -2)$ $-2 \times x < 4 \times -2$
$-2x < -8$

a $2y < 3$ $(\times -8)$ b $x \leq -2$ $(\times -6)$

c $3y \geq -4$ $(\times -5)$ d $2x + 4 > 12$ $(\times -3)$

Watch out!
When you multiply or divide an inequality by a negative number, you must reverse the inequality sign.

6 Use equivalent calculations to work out these.

a $74 \div 0.1$ b $3.6 \div 0.2$ c $0.24 \div 0.01$ d $0.48 \div 0.02$

7 Divide both sides of the inequality by the number shown.

a $-2x < 5$ $(\div -2)$ b $-4x \leq -36$ $(\div -4)$ c $6 - 3x \geq 18$ $(\div -3)$

Level 6

6b I can multiply by 0.1, 0.01 and multiples of them

6b I can multiply both sides of an inequality by a negative number

6a I can divide by 0.1, 0.01 and multiples of them

6a I can divide both sides of an inequality by a negative number

8 Generalise these inequalities.

$a > 1$ and $b > 1$ so $ab > 1$

a $a > 4$ and $b > 2$ b $a \geq 2$ and $b > 3$

c $a < -6$ and $b < 4$ d $a < -2$ and $b \leq -8$

Watch out!
Think about the direction of the inequality sign in parts c and d.

9 Estimate the answers to these.

a $9.6^3 \div 23.84 \times 2.8^2$ b $\frac{107 \times 0.22}{\sqrt{25.2}}$ c $\sqrt{37.9} \times \frac{\sqrt{23.1}}{12.36 - 9.12}$

10 a Copy and complete the table.

	÷0.1	÷0.05	÷0.01	÷0.005	÷0.001	÷0.0005
10		200				
−10				−2000		

b What do you notice?

c What happens when you divide by a very small number close to zero?

11 a Copy and complete the multiplication grid.

b Look at your starting values and the results.
What do you notice?

c Repeat parts **a** and **b** for division.

×	$\frac{1}{6}$	$\frac{2}{6}$	$\frac{3}{6}$	$\frac{4}{6}$	$\frac{5}{6}$
1	$\frac{1}{6}$				
2				$\frac{8}{6}$	
3					
4			$\frac{12}{6}$		

Level 7

7c I can generalise inequalities

7c I can estimate answers to calculations involving powers and roots

7c I can understand that division by zero has no meaning

7b I can understand the effect of multiplying or dividing a positive number by a fraction less than 1

Now try this!

A Smallest multiplication

Work with a partner. Use digit cards 1 to 9. Shuffle the cards and deal two cards each.
Each use your cards to create a calculation like this: ☐ × 0.☐ Who has the smaller answer?

B Biggest division

Repeat Activity A but use division.
Who has the bigger answer?

reater than or equal to ⩾ inequality less than < less than or equal to ⩽ multiplication

12.3 Order of operations

- Know and use the order of operations
- Do mental calculations with squares, square roots, cubes and cube roots
- Simplify expressions containing powers

Why learn this?

When making a product or component part, the order of operations is important.

What's the BIG idea?

- When you **square** a number, you multiply it by itself. The **inverse** of squaring is finding the **square root**. **Level 5 & Level 6**
- You must perform calculations in the right order. **B**rackets → **I**ndices → **D**ivision and **M**ultiplication → **A**ddition and **S**ubtraction **Level 5, Level 6 & Level 7**
- Division and multiplication, and addition and subtraction, have the same importance so these should be done in the order in which they appear in the calculation. **Level 5, Level 6 & Level 7**
- When you **cube** a number, you multiply it by itself and then multiply the result by the original number. The inverse of cubing is finding the **cube root**. **Level 6**
- Subtracting a **squared** number and squaring a negative number are different operations.
  $-3^2 = -(3 \times 3) = -9$
  $(-3)^2 = -3 \times -3 = 9$ **Level 7**
- You can use the **order of operations** to simplify expressions with **powers** and brackets.
  $\frac{(4 \times 6)^2}{4 \times 2} = \frac{4 \times 6 \times 4 \times 6}{4 \times 2} = 72$ **Level 6 & Level 7**

Learn this

$1^3 = 1$	$\sqrt[3]{1} = 1$
$2^3 = 8$	$\sqrt[3]{8} = 2$
$3^3 = 27$	$\sqrt[3]{27} = 3$
$4^3 = 64$	$\sqrt[3]{64} = 4$
$5^3 = 125$	$\sqrt[3]{125} = 5$
$10^3 = 1000$	$\sqrt[3]{1000} = 10$

Practice, practice, practice!

Level 5

1 Rewrite these calculations in a different but equivalent form by using brackets.

$2 \times 3 + 2 \times 7 = 2(3 + 7)$

Check: $2 \times 3 + 2 \times 7 = 6 + 14 = 20$ and $2(3 + 7) = 2 \times 10 = 20$

a $5 \times 8 + 3 \times 5$ **b** $11 \times 9 - 11 \times 3$ **c** $5 \times 7 + 3 \times 7$

d $6 \times 11 + 11 \times 5$ **e** $2 \times 9 - 4 \times 7$ **f** $6 \times 9 + 4 \times 4$

Hint Take the factor 2 outside the brackets.

5c I can rewrite calculations in a different but equivalent form

2 Work out

a $5 + 10^2$ **b** $12 + (8 \div 2)^2$ **c** $(12 + 5^2) - 9$

d $\frac{125}{5^2}$ **e** $32 \div 8 + (4 \times 2)^2$ **f** $36 + 6^2 \div 3$

5b I can do calculations involving squares and brackets

3 Work out

a $2^2 + 3^2$ **b** $4^2 - (1^2 + 2)$ **c** $\frac{5^2 - 3^2}{10 - 2}$

d $\frac{8^2 + 1}{3^2 - 4}$ **e** $\sqrt{121} - 3^2$ **f** $\frac{8^2 - \sqrt{4}}{2}$

5a I can do calculations involving squares, roots and brackets

brackets cube cubed (e.g. 3^3) cube number cube root (e.g. $\sqrt[3]{27}$)

4 Use a mental method to work out

a $(16 - 9 + 5 - 2)^2$ b $(23 - 13 + 4 - 8)^2$ c $(16 \div 4 \div 2)^2$

d $(9 + 6 - 7)^2$ e $24 + (19 - 12)^2$ f $\dfrac{7^2}{21 - 14}$

5 Use a calculator to work out these. Give your answers to one decimal place.

a $(3.6 + 4.5) - (5.7 + 2.1) - 1.6$ b $\dfrac{91 - 7.6}{9}$

c $\dfrac{9 + 5}{5.1 - 4}$ d $19^2 - 13^2 + (1.4 \times 3)$

e $\sqrt{4.2^2 - 1.8^2}$ f $23.4 - (42 - (4 - 9))$

6 Use a mental method to work out

a $(23 - 13 + 4 - 8)^3$ b $\dfrac{120}{2^3 + 12}$ c $2^3 \times (13 - 8 + 5)$

7 Use a mental method to work out

a $\sqrt{28 + 8}$ b $\sqrt{45 + 36}$ c $\sqrt{81} + 63$ d $\dfrac{32 - 8}{\sqrt{16}}$

8 Use a mental method to work out

a $\sqrt[3]{(89 + 36)}$ b $\sqrt[3]{319 + 524 + 157}$ c $\sqrt[3]{81 - 12 - 5}$

9 a The volume of a cube-shaped package is 125 m^3. What is its side length?

b An inflatable cube has a volume of 8 m^3 before inflation.
After inflation its volume has increased eight times.
What is the side length of the inflated cube?

10 Work out

a $36 \div (3 + 9) - 6 + 2 \times (12 \div 3)^3$ b $24 \times (3 + 2) + 2 - 5 + 36 \div (9 - 3)^2$

c $(4 \times 9) - 20 \times (8 \div 2)^3 - 1$ d $(35 \div 7)^3 - 6 \times 3 + 5$

Level 6

6c I can do mental calculations with squares and brackets

6b I can do calculations involving decimals, squares, roots and brackets

6b I can do mental calculations with cubes and brackets

6b I can do mental calculations with square roots and brackets

6a I can do mental calculations with cube roots

6a I can simplify expressions containing powers to calculate the answer

11 Work out

a $-6^2 + 3$ b $(-6)^2 + 3$

c $-9^2 + (-9)^2$ d $-5^2 + (-3)^2 - 6^2$

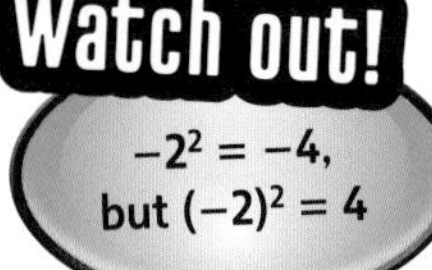

12 Work out

a $\dfrac{7 \times 8^2}{7 \times 2^2}$ b $\dfrac{(7 \times 8)^2}{7 \times 2^2}$ c $\left(\dfrac{5}{2}\right)^2$ d $\left(\dfrac{9}{7}\right)^2$

e $\dfrac{(5 \times 6)^2}{5 \times 6}$ f $\dfrac{(4 \times 3)^2}{2^3}$ g $\dfrac{(6 - 3)^3}{5^2 - 7}$ h $\dfrac{14^2 - 13^2}{6^2 - 9}$

Level 7

7c I can understand the difference between squaring a negative number and subtracting a squared number

7b I can do calculations involving powers and brackets in the numerator and denominator

Now try this!

A Puzzled order

Use brackets, + − × ÷ and the numbers 3 5 7 and 28.
Try to make the number 7.
Make up your own puzzles to challenge your friends.

B 166?

Use brackets, squaring, cubing, + − and the numbers 2 3 7 and 8.
Try to make the number 166.

inverse order of operations power square squared square root

12.4 Written and mental methods of calculation

- Mentally multiply integers and decimals
- Do mental calculations with fractions, decimals and percentages
- Use written methods for addition, subtraction, multiplication and division

Why learn this?

You use mental maths when playing board games, card games and some sports such as snooker.

What's the BIG idea?

- To find 10% of an amount, simply divide by 10. You can then use this to find other **percentages**.
  For example 30% = 10% × 3 and 5% = 10% ÷ 2. **Level 5**
- You can use **doubling** and **halving** strategies and **partitioning** to carry out mental multiplication. **Level 5**
- You can use known facts to derive unknown facts.
  For example $\frac{1}{4} = 0.25$, so $\frac{1}{8} = 0.25 \div 2 = 0.125$. **Level 5 & Level 6**
- You can use standard column methods to add or subtract **integers** and **decimals** with varying numbers of digits. **Level 5 & Level 6**
- When subtracting decimals with different numbers of digits, you can use a zero place holder. **Level 5 & Level 6**
- You can use standard column methods to multiply or divide integers and decimals. **Level 5 & Level 6**
- You can also use **equivalent** calculations to multiply and divide a decimal by a decimal. For example 42.8 ÷ 0.7 = 428 ÷ 7. **Level 5 & Level 6**
- You can use **estimation** to check the answer to a calculation. **Level 5 & Level 6**

Learn this

$\frac{1}{4} = 0.25 = 25\%$
$\frac{1}{2} = 0.5 = 50\%$
$\frac{3}{4} = 0.75 = 75\%$
$\frac{1}{3} = 0.333... = 33\frac{1}{3}\%$
$\frac{1}{10} = 0.1 = 10\%$
$\frac{1}{5} = 0.2 = 20\%$
$\frac{1}{100} = 0.01 = 1\%$

Practice, practice, practice!

1 Use a mental method to work out

a 10% of 350 **b** 5% of 350 **c** $2\frac{1}{2}\%$ of 350 **d** $17\frac{1}{2}\%$ of 350

2 Use a mental method to work out

a 9.4 × 32 **b** 4.4 × 2.5 **c** −19 × 2.5 **d** 87 × 31

3 a Find sets of equivalent fractions, decimals and percentages from the cloud.

$\frac{1}{10} = 0.1 = 10\%$

b Three sets are incomplete. Complete them.

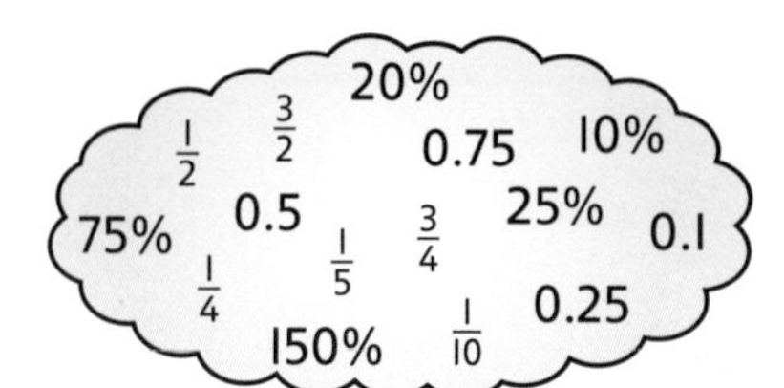

4 Use a written method to work out

a 58.7 + 963.41 + 97.34 **b** 1.07 + 2.5 + 14 + 0.79
c 21 − 5.27 + 6.31 **d** 15.47 + 3.6 − 17.43 + 3.05

Level 5

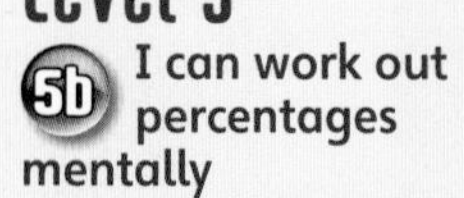

5b I can work out percentages mentally

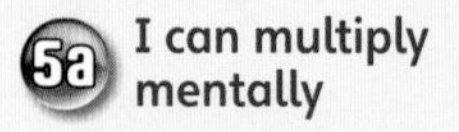

5a I can multiply mentally

5a I can recall equivalent fractions, decimals and percentages

5a I can add and subtract integers and decimals with up to two decimal places

decimal double estimate equivalent fraction

5 $2.84 \times 32 = 90.88$

Use this fact to work out

a 28.4×32 **b** 284×32 **c** 28.4×3.2 **d** 284×0.32

6 **a** A plank of wood 236.8 cm long needs to be divided into four equal pieces. How long will each piece be?

Hint: Always estimate the answer first.

b The perimeter of a regular hexagon is 504.6 cm. What is the length of each side?

Hint: Regular means all the sides are of equal length.

Level 5

5a I can position the decimal point by considering a given calculation

5a I can divide decimals by a single-digit number

7 Use a mental method to work out

a $\frac{4}{5}$ of 30 **b** 0.75 of 280 g **c** $\frac{2}{5}$ of 32.5

d 0.1 of £83 **e** $1\frac{1}{2}$ of 18 **f** $\frac{7}{8}$ of 560 kg

8 Use a written method to work out these. Give your answers to one decimal place if appropriate.

a $196.8 \div 0.6$ **b** $3.15 \div 0.07$ **c** $574.4 \div 1.7$

d Compound A needs to be divided into samples for testing. Each testing dish can hold 3.2 g. Compound A has a mass of 18.9 kg. How many sample dishes are needed?

For worded problems, make sure your answer fits the context of the problem.

9 **a** Use a written method to work out the volume of this cuboid.

b Another cuboid has a volume of 35.52 m³. Its length is 4 m and its width is 2.4 m. What is its height?

3.6 cm
9.6 cm
4.2 cm

10 A factory makes garden fences from sheets of metal. The factory checks the length of metal wasted each week. One week the total length of waste was 346.37 units. The factory produced 52.025 units more waste on Tuesday than on Friday. Use a written method to find the amount of waste on Tuesday and on Friday.

Day	Waste
Monday	57.265
Wednesday	89.9
Thursday	40.78

Level 6

6b I can work out fractions and decimals mentally

6b I can divide by a decimal

6a I can multiply and divide with decimals

6a I can add and subtract integers and decimals of any size

Now try this!

A Which flooring material?

50 cm by 50 cm carpet tiles cost £1.69 each. Carpet from a 4.5 m wide roll costs £26.49 per metre. Which flooring type is the better buy for a room measuring

a 4 m by 4.5 m **b** 3.5 m by 4.2 m?

B Can you make it?

Use digit cards 0 to 9. Place them face down. Select three cards and make a number. Use brackets, + − × ÷ · and the other six cards to try and make your number. If you cannot make it exactly, how close can you get?

alve integer partition percentage (%) to one decimal place (to 1 d.p.)

12.5 Metric measures

- Recognise and use metric units of measure
- Convert between metric units
- Solve problems involving metric and imperial units

Why learn this?

When producing and reading drawings, engineers and architects need to be able to understand and use scales and metric measures.

What's the BIG idea?

- **Converting** to a larger unit means fewer of them, so divide. Converting to a smaller unit means more of them, so multiply. **Level 5**
- Metric units of length are **millimetres (mm)**, **centimetres (cm)**, **metres (m)** and **kilometres (km)**. Metric units of mass are **kilograms (kg)** and **grams (g)**. Metric units of capacity are **litres (*l*)**, **millilitres (*ml*)** and **centilitres (*cl*)**. Another metric unit of mass is the **tonne** (1 tonne = 1000 kg) **Level 5**
- You can convert units of **volume** to equivalent units of **capacity**.
  1 m^3 = 1000 litres 1000 cm^3 = 1 litre 1 cm^3 = 1 *ml* **Level 5**
- You can use the following **approximations** for converting imperial to metric units.
  1 **mile** ≈ 1.6 km 1 **foot** (ft) ≈ 30 cm 1 **pound** (lb) ≈ 0.5 kg
  1 **ounce** (oz) ≈ 30 g 1 **pint** ≈ 0.5 litres 1 **gallon** ≈ 4.5 litres **Level 5**
- Metric units of area are square millimetres (mm^2), square centimetres (cm^2), square metres (m^2) and square kilometres (km^2). Another metric unit of area is the **hectare**.
  1 hectare = 10 000 m^2. **Level 5 & Level 6**

Learn this

1 km = 1000 m
1 m = 100 cm
1 cm = 10 mm
1 kg = 1000 g
1 litre = 1000 *ml*
10 *ml* = 1 *cl*

Practice, practice, practice!

Super fact!

In the early 1790s, the French Academy of Sciences agreed on the definition of the metre as 'one ten-millionth of the distance from the North Pole to the equator'.

Level 5

5c I can recognise equivalent metric measures of length

1 Which of these lengths are the same?

18 cm, 1800 m, 18 mm, 180 mm, 1800 cm, 1.8 km, 1800 mm, 18 m, 1.8 m, 1.8 cm, 180 cm

5c I can convert one metric unit to another

2 Convert these masses to kilograms.

550 g = 550 ÷ 1000 = 0.55 kg

a 1500 g **b** 2750 g **c** 8420 g **d** 12 875 g

3 Convert these amounts to the units shown.

a 650 g (kilograms) **b** 240 *ml* (litres) **c** 4.6 m (centimetres)
d 7 mm (centimetres) **e** 2.85 kg (grams) **f** 34.6 cm (millimetres)

4 An adult African elephant can weigh 5455 kg. How many tonnes is this?

5b I can convert between units of capacity and volume

5 A water butt has a capacity of 120 litres. Convert this to

a cubic metres **b** cubic centimetres.

approximately equal to (≈) capacity centilitres (*cl*) centimetre (cm) convert foot gallon gram (g) kilogram (kg) kilometre (km)

6 A swimming pool has a volume of 360 m³.
How many litres of water will be needed to fill it completely?

7 Convert these amounts to the units shown.

30 miles (kilometres) *1 mile ≈ 1.6 km so 30 miles ≈ 1.6 × 30 = 48 km*

a 40 gallons (litres) **b** 12 feet (centimetres) **c** 8 oz (grams)
d 35 oz (kilograms) **e** 25 feet (metres) **f** 9 pints (litres)

8 Simon needs 17 lb of potatoes.
The supermarket sells potatoes in 2.5 kg, 5 kg and 10 kg bags.
Which size bag should he choose?

9 5 miles ≈ 8 kilometres

Use a mental method to work out the approximate distance from Liverpool to Manchester in kilometres.

Liverpool–Manchester
35 miles

10 Convert the recipe to approximate metric measures.

Chocolate fudge cake
6 oz plain flour
$3\frac{1}{2}$ oz dark chocolate
4 oz butter
$\frac{1}{4}$ lb brown sugar
1 oz cocoa powder
3 eggs
$\frac{1}{4}$ pint milk

Level 5

5b I can convert between units of capacity and volume

5a I can convert imperial units to metric units

Did you know?

≈ means is 'approximately equal to'.

11 A farmer is selling a field.
The field is rectangular and measures 300 m by 200 m.
Is the farmer's sale board correct?

12 **a** A square measures 10 mm by 10 mm. What is its area?
b Another square measures 1 cm by 1 cm. What is its area?
c Look at your answers to parts **a** and **b**.
How do you convert an area in square millimetres to square centimetres?
d Convert 4550 cm² into **i** square millimetres, **ii** square metres.

Level 6

6b I can convert between metric units of area

Now try this!

A Paper sizes

The 'A series' of paper sizes ranges from A0 to A8.
The table gives the dimensions of sizes A0 to A4.

Paper sizes (inches)				
A0	A1	A2	A3	A4
33.1 × 46.8	23.4 × 33.1	16.5 × 23.4	11.7 × 16.5	8.3 × 11.7

a Use the fact that 1 inch = 2.54 cm to convert these measurements to millimetres.
b If you fold a sheet of A4 in half across its longest length you get two sheets of A5. What are the dimensions of an A5 sheet?
c What is the area, in square metres, of an A0 sheet?

B Seconds of life

How long have you been alive?
Calculate your answer
a in days
b in hours
c in minutes
d in seconds.

hectare litre (*l*) metre (m) mile millilitre (m*l*) millimetre (mm) ounce pint pound tonne volume

12.6 Using a calculator to solve problems

- Enter numbers and interpret the display of a calculator in different contexts
- Do mental calculations with time
- Solve problems involving money and measures

Why learn this?

You need to be able to use a calculator to do home finances and check bank and credit card statements.

What's the BIG idea?

- When you are working with money in pounds, [3.4] on your **calculator** means £3.40. When you are working with lengths in metres, [3.4] means 3.4 m or 3 m 40 cm. **Level 5**
- There are 60 **minutes** in 1 **hour**, so 1 hour 28 minutes is equivalent to $1\frac{28}{60}$ hours, which is a mixed number. You use the [$a\frac{b}{c}$] **key** to **enter** fractions on your calculator. To enter $1\frac{28}{60}$, press [1] [$a\frac{b}{c}$] [2] [8] [$a\frac{b}{c}$] [6] [0]. **Level 6**

learn this

60 seconds = 1 minute
60 minutes = 1 hour
24 hours = 1 day
52 weeks = 1 year
365 days = 1 year
366 days = 1 leap year

Practice, practice, practice!

Level 5

1 Interpret these calculator displays in
i metres **ii** metres and centimetres.

[117.2] *i 117.2 m* *ii 117 m 20 cm*

a [1.68] **b** [201.03] **c** [0.75] **d** [30.05]

5b I can interpret metric measures of length displayed on a calculator

2 Interpret these calculator displays in
i kilograms **ii** kilograms and grams.

a [2.16] **b** [91.05] **c** [7.026] **d** [10.098]

5b I can interpret metric measures of mass displayed on a calculator

3 Zola is working out a capacity in litres. Her calculator shows [0.45].
a What is the answer in litres?
b What is the answer in millilitres?

5b I can interpret metric measures displayed on a calculator

4 Use a mental method to convert these times into the units shown.
a $3\frac{1}{2}$ days (hours) **b** 3.25 hours (minutes)
c 38.5 days (weeks) **d** 320 minutes (hours and minutes)
e 36 hours (days) **f** 1 week (hours)

5b I can mentally convert between units of time

5 David is working on a measures problem. The answer needs to be in metres. How should he enter these lengths into his calculator?
a 2 m 35 cm **b** 375 cm **c** 82 cm **d** 6 m 6 cm

5a I can enter metric measures in an appropriate form

calculator: clear display enter key memory convert

6 Calculate these areas. Give your answers to one decimal place in the units shown.

a 4 m 68 cm × 4.265 m (in m^2) **b** 96 cm × 0.34 m (in cm^2)

c 2.15 km × 820 m (in km^2) **d** 99 cm 5 mm × 804 mm (in cm^2)

7 A factory quotes the following prices.
Which deal offers the better value for money?

Deal A:
89p for 1 kg 70 g

Deal B:
£1.89 for 2 kg 75 g

Tip
Divide the price by the weight.

Watch out!
When comparing deals, the units of comparison must be the same.

8 26 tins of biscuits cost £87.10. What does one tin of biscuits cost?
Use a written method and check your answer with a calculator.

Level 5

5a I can enter metric measures in an appropriate form

5a I can divide £.p by a two-digit number

9 Enter these measurements of time into your calculator as mixed numbers.
Use your calculator to find the equivalent decimal.

a 4 hours 30 minutes **b** 12 hours 12 minutes

c 7 hours 20 minutes **d** 2 hours 39 minutes

10 Mr Angelo works 39 hours 50 minutes and is paid £334.60.
What is his hourly rate?

11 A train travels at a constant speed and covers 500 m in 25 seconds.

a How long will it take to travel 252 km?

b What distance can the train travel in 2 hours?

12 A car's fuel tank holds 45 litres of diesel. On a full tank it travels 585 miles.
Use 1 gallon ≈ 4.5 litres and 1 km ≈ 0.625 miles.

a How many miles per gallon does the car achieve?

b Diesel costs 117.1p per litre. What is the fuel cost of travelling
i 585 miles **ii** 812.5 miles **iii** 1242.8 km?

Hint: Work out the cost of travelling 1 mile

Level 6

6b I can enter time as a mixed number into a calculator

6a I can solve problems involving distance and time

6a I can solve problems involving distance, capacity and cost

Now try this!

A Units of display

Work with a partner. You will need a calculator.
Take turns to enter a number. Each give the displayed number in as many different units as you can. For example [2.5] could be 2 hours 30 minutes.
Using the table may help. Set yourselves a one-minute time limit.

Money	Length	Mass	Capacity	Area	Time

Who can generate the most correct measurements?

B Seconds in a leap year

How many seconds are there in a leap year?

Did you know?
It is a leap year if the year can be divided exactly by 4, except at the beginning of a century, when it must be divisible by 400.

time: second minute hour day week month year

maths!

A kart-load of pirates

The Famous Daft Pirates are competing in a high-speed kart race at the world famous Grans-Thatch race course.

Driver 2

Lap 1: 35.65
Lap 2: 35.02
Lap 3: 35.45
Lap 4: 34.40

Driver 1

Lap 1: 37.40
Lap 2: 36.67
Lap 3: 35.85
Lap 4: 34.20

BB

LJS

CJR

WJ

Driver 3
Lap 1: 36.13
Lap 2: 34.35
Lap 3: 34.60
Lap 4: 33.52

Times are given as seconds with hundredths of seconds.

Driver 4
Lap 1: 37.12
Lap 2: 36.20
Lap 3: 33.85
Lap 4: 32.87

After finishing the race, the lap times for each driver are mixed up by mistake. Using the information below, match each driver with their set of lap times.

What were the final finishing positions?

Wavy Jones won the race.

The difference between Black Beard's fastest and slowest laps was only 1.25 seconds.

Long Joan Silver had an average time of 35.01 seconds.

Captain Jack Robin's robin raided the hot dog stand after the race.

Nursing calculations

Nurses use mathematics all the time. Arithmetic is used for fluid calculations, drug measurements and conversion between units – both metric and imperial. Drugs may be prescribed in grams (g), milligrams (mg), micrograms or even nanograms. The relationship between these units is multiples of 1000.
So, 1 gram = 1000 milligrams
1 milligram = 1000 micrograms
1 microgram = 1000 nanograms

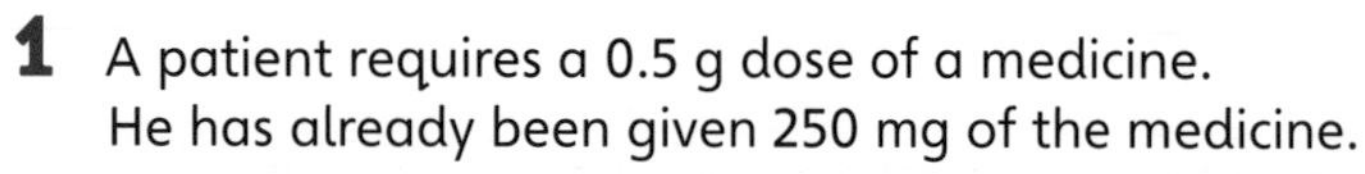

1 A patient requires a 0.5 g dose of a medicine.
He has already been given 250 mg of the medicine.

a How many more grams of medicine will he need?

b A dose of 1000 micrograms has been prepared. Will this be enough? **Level 5**

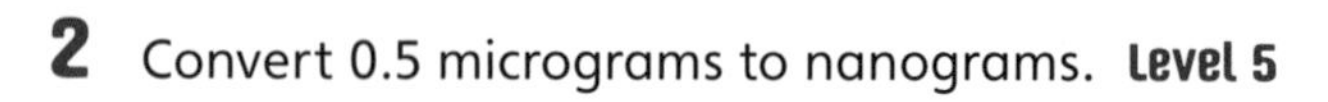

2 Convert 0.5 micrograms to nanograms. **Level 5**

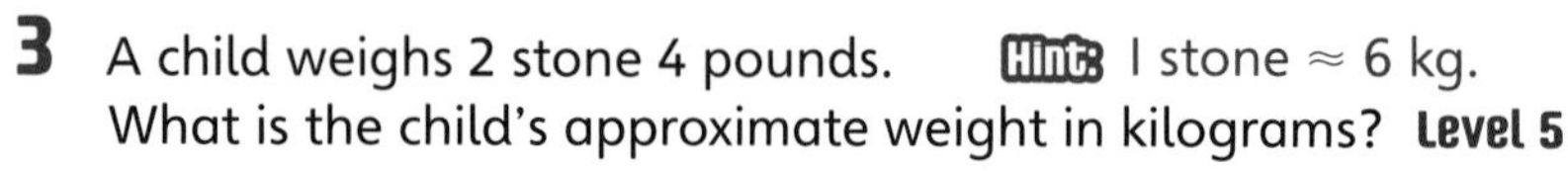

3 A child weighs 2 stone 4 pounds. **Hint:** 1 stone ≈ 6 kg.
What is the child's approximate weight in kilograms? **Level 5**

4 A newborn baby weighs 7 lb 6 oz. What is this as a metric measure? **Level 5**

5 How many litres of dextrose are contained in 3 litres of liquid that is 10% dextrose? **Level 5**

6 Drug A is supplied as 5 *ml* ampoules containing 50 mg per *ml*.
The patient requires 0.1 of the ampoule.

a How many millilitres does the patient require?

b How many milligrams of drug A will the patient receive? **Level 6**

7 To check for strength of dilution, the following calculation is done.

$$\frac{90\text{ mg}}{50\text{ m}l} = 1.8\text{ mg/m}l$$

Perform an inverse calculation to check its accuracy. **Level 6**

8 Medicine x comes in 0.02 g tablets. The patient needs a total dosage of 1800 mg, which is to be taken in 3 doses. How many tablets are required per dose? **Level 6**

9 A patient is to be given 3650 micrograms in a solution over a period of 2 hours 20 minutes. Use your calculator to work out how much he should be given per hour.
Give your answer in **a** micrograms and **b** milligrams. **Level 6**

10 A formula for calculating drug dosages is:

$$\text{dose} = \frac{\text{what you want}}{\text{what you've got}} \times \text{what you want it to be in}$$

You want a $\frac{1}{40}$ solution of medicine Y to be made up into 1 litre.
You have a $\frac{1}{10}$ solution.
What dosage of medicine Y, in millilitres, do you need? **Level 7**

The BIG ideas

- To find 10% of an amount, simply divide by 10. You can then use this to find other **percentages**. For example, 30% = 10% × 3 and 5% = 10% ÷ 2. **Level 5**
- Metric units of length are **millimetre (mm)**, **centimetre (cm)**, **metre (m)** and **kilometre (km)**. Metric units of mass are **kilogram (kg)** and **gram (g)**. Metric units of capacity are **litre (*l*)**, **millilitre (m*l*)** and **centilitre (c*l*)**. **Level 5**
- You can use the following approximations for converting **imperial** to metric units. 1 mile ≈ 1.6 km, 1 foot ≈ 30 cm, 1 pound (lb) ≈ 0.5 kg, 1 ounce (oz) ≈ 30 g, 1 pint ≈ 0.5 litres, 1 gallon ≈ 4.5 litres. **Level 5**
- **Dividing** by 0.1 is the same as dividing by $\frac{1}{10}$ or multiplying by 10. **Level 6**
- There are 60 minutes in 1 hour, so 1 hour 28 minutes is equivalent to $1\frac{28}{60}$, which is a **mixed number**. You use the $a\frac{b}{c}$ key to enter fractions on your calculator.
  To enter $1\frac{28}{60}$, press 1 $a\frac{b}{c}$ 2 8 $a\frac{b}{c}$ 6 0 **Level 6**
- To divide fractions, **invert** the dividing fraction (turn it upside down) and change the division sign to multiplication. **Level 7**

Practice SATs-style questions

Level 5

Q1 **a** Copy and complete

10% of £60 = ___

___ % of £60 = £3

b Use part **a** to work out 35% of £60.

Q2 Write in the missing numbers.

250 mm = ___ cm

250 cm = ___ m

250 m = ___ km

Level 6

Q3 Work out

a $\frac{1}{6} + \frac{3}{4}$

b $\frac{5}{6} - \frac{3}{18}$

Q4 **a** Copy and complete

32.6 ÷ 0.1 = 32.6 × ___

32.6 ÷ ___ = 32.6 × 100

b Following a chemical reaction, the mass of substance A is 0.01 times greater. The original mass of substance A was 28.25 g. What is the increase in the mass of substance A?

Level 7

Q5 Work out these. Give each answer in its simplest form.

a $\frac{2}{7} \times \frac{3}{8}$

b $\frac{3}{8} \div \frac{2}{7}$

Q6 Work out

a $3 - 3^2$

b $3 + (-3)^2$

Q7 Aramen Council has a list of people waiting for an allotment. A piece of land that is to be used for allotments has an area of $4\frac{2}{7}$ km². It is to be divided into allotments of area $\frac{5}{14}$ km². How many people will be allocated an allotment this time?

13 The plot thickens

This unit is about graphs and equations.

Simon works for video game developer *Rare* making games for the Xbox 360. He specialises in programming artificial intelligence (AI) to capture the thought processes of the characters in the game. AI makes the characters respond realistically to their environment.

Simon often has to work out where a character is in relation to other objects in the game world, so that the character can decide the route to take to reach his/her goal. Simon uses coordinates to represent the positions of objects in the game world, and to represent the route (between two positions) that the character travels along, he uses the equation of a straight line.

In his current game, Simon is writing code for a vehicle that is trying to collect treasure scattered about the game world.

Activities

A On Simon's coordinate grid, the vehicle is centred over the point (2, 4) and there is a pot of gold at (12, 9).
The vehicle travels along a straight line with equation $y = \frac{1}{2}x + 3$.
- Plot the graph of $y = \frac{1}{2}x + 3$ on a coordinate grid with x-axis from 0 to 15 and y-axis from 0 to 10.
- Will the vehicle arrive at the treasure?

B At the treasure, the vehicle makes a 90° clockwise turn and travels in a straight line towards the jigsaw piece.
- Draw the vehicle's new line of travel on your axes from activity A.
- The jigsaw piece has x-coordinate 14. What is its y-coordinate?

Did you know?

It is unclear who invented the very first video game, but it is believed to have been William Higinbotham in 1958. His game, 'Tennis for Two', was created and played on an oscilloscope in Brookhaven National Laboratory, America.

Before you start this unit...

1 Draw a coordinate grid with x- and y-axes from −5 to 5.

page 76

a Plot these points: (−2, 1), (3, −1), (−5, −4), (0, −2).

b Draw these straight-line graphs.
i $x = 4$ ii $y = -1$

2 a What is the value of $3x - 4$ when $x = 2$?

b What is the value of $3x - 4$ when $x = -2$?

Level Up Maths 4-6 page 92

3 Find the value of x in each of these equations.

page 172

a $x - 2 = 3$ b $3x = 21$
c $2x - 5 = 13$

4 A mystery number is s. Write an expression for 4 more than double s.

Level Up Maths 4-6 page 16

World's Greatest Maths

Plus digital resources

Did you know?

An English mathematician, Alan Turing, may have been the first person to begin research work on artificial intelligence. Turing argued that if a machine could successfully pretend to be human to a knowledgeable observer, then the machine should be considered intelligent.

13.1 More graphs

- Read and plot coordinates in all four quadrants
- Generate coordinate pairs that satisfy a linear rule
- Recognise straight-line graphs which are parallel to the x- or y-axis
- Plot graphs of linear functions in all four quadrants where y is given in the form $y = mx + c$

What's the BIG idea?

→ A graph of the **equation** $x = a$ is a line **parallel** to the y-axis. It crosses the x-axis at $(a, 0)$
A graph of the equation $y = b$ is a line parallel to the x-axis. It crosses the y-axis at $(0, b)$. **Level 5**

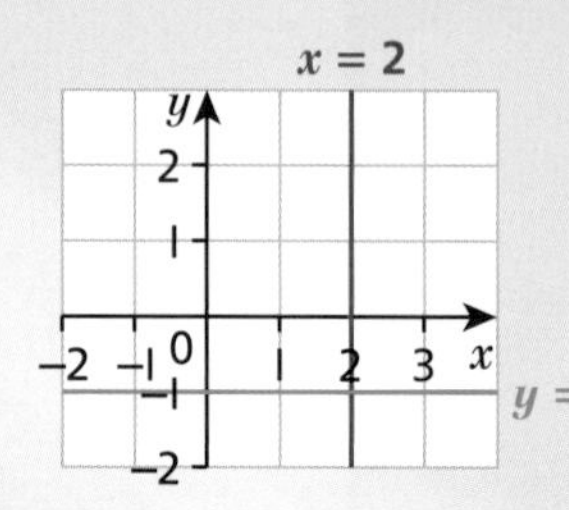

→ You can plot a **function** by working out a set of **coordinates** for it.

x	−2	0	2	4
$y = \frac{1}{2}x - 1$	−2	−1	0	1

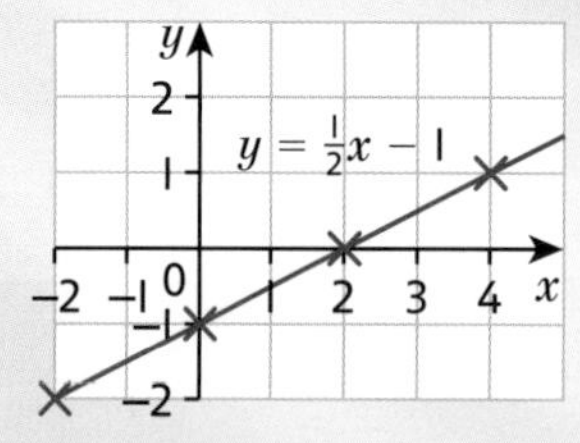

Level 6

→ A **linear function** has the form $y = mx + c$.
Its graph has a **gradient** m and **intercepts** (crosses) the y-axis at $(0, c)$.

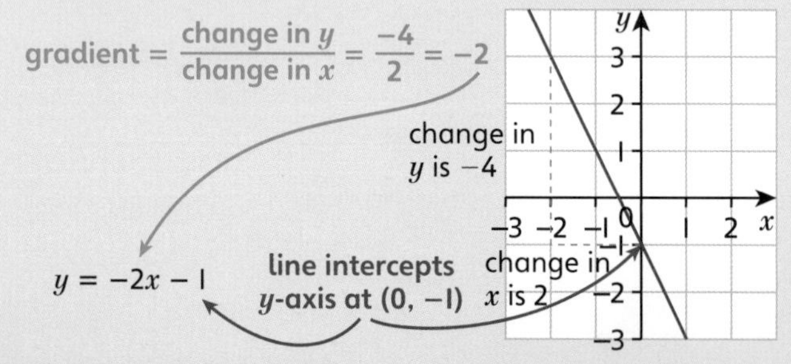

Level 6 & Level 7

Why learn this?

Functions can be used to create wire frame models and computer images.

Learn this

A positive gradient goes from low to high. A negative gradient runs from high to low.

Practice, practice, practice!

1 **a** Write the equation of a line parallel to the x-axis that passes through (5, 3).

b Write the equation of a line parallel to the x-axis that passes through (−3, −2).

c Write the equation of a line parallel to the y-axis that passes through (6, 7).

d Write the equation of a line parallel to the y-axis that passes through (−5, −1).

Level 5

5a I can write equations of straight-line graphs that are parallel to the x- or y-axis

coordinates equation function gradient intercept

2 **a** Copy and complete this table of values for the function $y = 4x - 3$.

x	−6	−4	−2	0	2	4	6
y							

b Draw a graph of the function on squared paper.

c Write the equation of a line which is parallel to this one.

d Create a table of values and plot the line.

e How could you plot the second line without creating a table of values?

3 Repeat Q2 for the function $y = 5 - 2x$.

Level 6

6b I can generate and plot coordinates that satisfy a linear function in all four quadrants

4 Find the gradient of lines A and B.

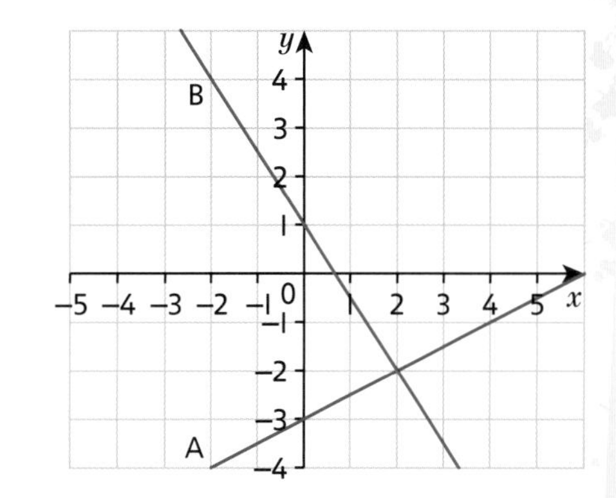

5 Look at these linear functions.

A $y = 5 - 3x$ B $y = 4x + 5$ C $y = -3(2 + x)$ D $y = 2(2x + 1)$

a Which have the same gradient?

b Which intercept the y-axis at the same point?

6 **a** Draw graphs of $y = 3x$ and $y = \frac{1}{3}x$.

b Write the equation of a line of reflection that reflects one line onto the other.

7 **a** Draw the graphs of $y = 3x + 2$ and $y = \frac{1}{3}x + 2$.

b Where do they intersect?

c Write the equation of a line of reflection that reflects one line onto the other.

8 The base of an isosceles triangle is parallel to the x-axis and passes through (0, −5). The triangle has a vertex at (0, 7).
Write any three linear functions whose graphs form the isosceles triangle described.

Level 7

7c I can find the gradient of a line from its graph

7b I can recognise and compare features of linear functions

7b I can use and understand $y = mx + c$

Now try this!

A Throw a line!

Work with a partner. You need a dice and a coin. Roll the dice and flip the coin to give a value for m in the function $y = mx + c$, and again to decide c. Heads is positive, tails is negative. For example, if you get 3 and tails, then 4 and heads, the function is $y = -3x + 4$. Sketch the graph of your function. See how many graphs you can generate and sketch in five minutes.

B Octagon

Write eight linear functions that form a regular octagon with its centre at the origin and that is made up of four pairs of parallel lines. (The sides don't all have to be the same length.)

linear function parallel quadrant regular

13.2 Other functions and graphs

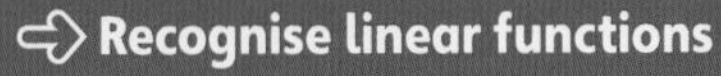

- Recognise linear functions
- Rearrange linear functions into the form $y = mx + c$
- Plot graphs of linear functions using ICT

Why learn this?

Both patterns are made from the same pieces. The same linear function can also be written in different ways. Reorganising linear functions in the form $y = mx + c$ lets you compare them.

What's the BIG idea?

→ A **linear function** can be written in the form $y = mx + c$. Its graph is a straight line.
  ✓ $y = 3x - 10$ is a linear function.
  ✗ $y = 5x^2 + 3x - 10$ is *not* a linear function. **Level 7**

→ The same linear function can be written in more than one way. For example, $4 = y - 3x$ and $y - 4 = 3x$ can both be rewritten as $y = 3x + 4$. **Level 7**

→ You can rearrange a linear function into the form $y = mx + c$ by doing the same operations to both sides.

For example $\qquad y - 4 = 3x$

Add 4 to both sides $\qquad y - 4 + 4 = 3x + 4$

$\qquad y = 3x + 4$

For example $\qquad 7(2x + y) = 28$

Divide both sides by 7 $\qquad \frac{\not{7}(2x + y)}{\not{7}} = \frac{\not{28}^{\,4}}{\not{7}}$

Subtract $2x$ from both sides $\qquad 2x + y - 2x = 4 - 2x$

$\qquad y = 4 - 2x$ **Level 7**

Practice, practice, practice!

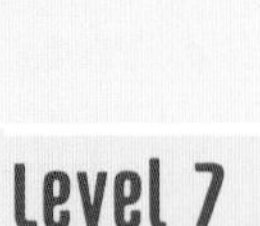

Level 7

7a I can rearrange a linear function by performing one operation on both sides

1 Rearrange each of these functions into the form $y = mx + c$.

a $y - 7 = 6x$ **b** $4x + y = 7$ **c** $0 = 10x - y - 8$

d $4y = 8x + 4$ **e** $\frac{1}{2}y = 4x - 3$ **f** $y - x = 3$

Watch out!

When you rearrange a function, if you do an operation on one side, you must do the same operation on the other side.

2 Rearrange each of these functions into the form $y = mx + c$.

a $10 + y = -7x$ **b** $5x + y = 8$

c $3y = 6x + 9$ **d** $0 = 9 - y - 2x$

7a I can rearrange a linear function by performing several operations on both sides

3 Rearrange each of these functions into the form $y = mx + c$. Write the value of m and c for each one.

a $5x + y + 3 = 5$ **b** $2(2 + y) = 10x$ **c** $y - 3 - x = 3 + 4x$

d $2(3 - y) = x$ **e** $2y + 1 + 3 - 4x = 4$ **f** $2(4 - y) = 6(x + 4)$

intercept linear function

4 Rearrange each of these functions into the form $y = mx + c$.

a $4y = 8x + 12$ **b** $5y - 10 = 5x$ **c** $2y - 5 = 3 - 4x$

d $4(x - 2y) = 16$ **e** $3(y - 2x) = 4y - 8x - 3$

f $3 - y = 4x$ **g** $7 + 6x + y = 3$ **h** $8 - 3x - y = 7$

Which of **a–h** have the same y-intercept?

5 For each of these functions, say whether or not it is a linear function.

a $3y = 4x - 9$ **b** $32 = 5y - 2x$ **c** $4x(x - 1) = 2y$

d $4(y - 2x) = 56$ **e** $y = (3x + 2)^2$ **f** $6(7x - y) = 24$

6 Four linear functions have each been written in two different ways. Match the functions into pairs and write each in the form $y = mx + c$.

A $3(y - 5x) = 12$ B $-12 = 3y + 6x$

C $2y - 6 = x$ D $0 = 10x - 2y + 8$

E $\frac{3}{2} = 4x - y$ F $x = -\frac{1}{2}(y + 4)$

G $8x = 2y + 3$ H $3y - \frac{3}{2}x = 9$

Functions A and D can both be rewritten as $y = 5x + 4$.

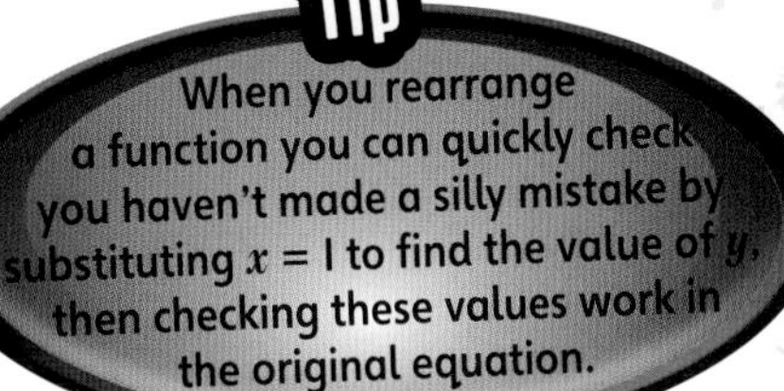

7 Two linear functions have each been written in three different ways. Match the functions into sets.

A $4(y - 7) = 6x$ B $3(x + y) = 2x - 1$ C $4(y - x - 5) = 2(x + 4)$

D $x + 3(y - 2) = -7$ E $2(y + 1) = -(y + x - 1)$ F $3x + y - 1 = 3y - 15$

8 Use ICT to plot graphs of the four linear functions in Q6.

9 **a** Use ICT to plot a graph of the function $y - 2x - 2 = 0$.

b Plot a graph of the function where the gradient is twice as large, and the intercept with the y-axis is the same.

10 **a** Use ICT to plot a graph of the function $2(y + 3) = x$.

b Plot a graph of the function with the same gradient that intercepts the y-axis at (0, 1).

Level 7

7a I can rearrange a linear function by performing several operations on both sides

7a I can recognise whether a function is linear

7a I can recognise the same linear function written in different ways

7a I can use ICT to draw a graph of a linear function where y is given implicitly in terms of x

Now try this!

A Match that function!

Work with a partner. Write four different linear functions that are not in the form $y = mx + c$. Write each function on a separate piece of paper. Using ICT, draw a graph of each function. Now swap functions and graphs with another pair and try to match each other's functions with their graphs.

B Function triplets

Work with a partner. Write a linear function in the form $y = mx + c$. Now rearrange it into three different forms. Write each one on a separate piece of paper. Repeat for another two linear functions. Now mix up your nine pieces of paper. Swap functions with another pair and try to sort each other's functions into the three different sets.

13.3 Direct proportion

- Understand what it means for two variables to be in direct proportion
- Use graphs to solve problems involving direct proportion

Why learn this?

Physical laws often involve proportion – the acceleration of this car is in direct proportion to the force being applied to it.

What's the BIG idea?

- Two **variables** are in **direct proportion** if they increase and decrease in the same ratio.
  This means that if one quantity doubles, so does the other quantity. **Level 6**
- If two variables are in direct proportion, when one variable is zero, so is the other. This means that a graph of two variables in direct proportion will be a straight line that goes through the origin. **Level 6**

Did you know?

Mathematicians sometimes use the symbol $\propto$ to represent direct proportion. So $y \propto x$ means that 'y is directly proportional to x'.

Practice, practice, practice!

Level 6

6c I can interpret graphs for simple problems involving direct proportion

1 This graph shows the costs of different numbers of toilet rolls at a cash and carry store.

Cost: £1, £2, £3

Number of rolls: 0 1 2 3 4 5 6 7 8 9 10 11 12 13 14 15 16 17 18

a How much does it cost to buy five toilet rolls?

b **i** How much does it cost to buy 10 toilet rolls?

ii The number of toilet rolls has doubled. What has happened to the price?

c **i** How much does it cost to buy 15 toilet rolls?

ii The number of toilet rolls has tripled. What has happened to the price?

d How much does it cost to buy 100 toilet rolls?

2 The gravitational force on an object is directly proportional to its mass. A laboratory obtains the following results in an experiment.

Mass (kg)	Force (newtons)
10	98
20	196
30	294

Work out the force in newtons on an object with a mass of

a 40 kg **b** 5 kg **c** 25 kg **d** 55 kg

direct proportion gradient

3 In a chemical reaction, the amount of product B formed is directly proportional to the original amount of material A. Part of the graph is shown. Use the graph to deduce the amount of B produced when

a A = 35 g

b A = 20 g

c A = 100 g

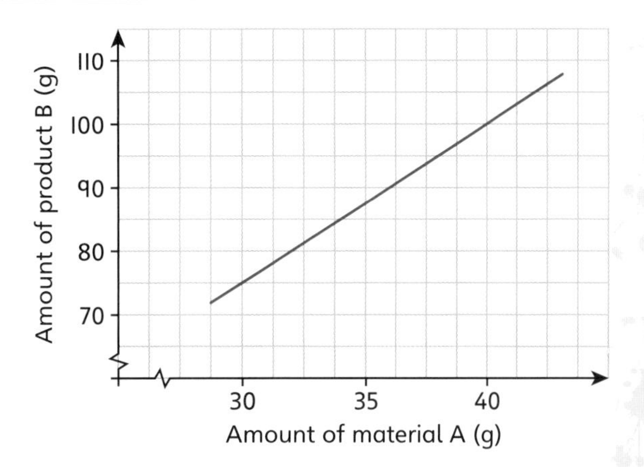

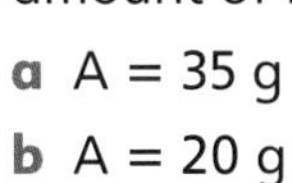

Level 6

6c I can interpret graphs for simple problems involving direct proportion

4 An emergency plumber charges a £30 call-out fee, and then £20 an hour.

a How much would the plumber charge for two hours' work?

b How much would the plumber charge for four hours' work?

c Are the plumber's charges in direct proportion to the number of hours he works? Explain your answer.

6b I can identify whether a statement describing a relationship is describing a relationship of direct proportion

5 The circumference of a circle is equal to π times the diameter of the circle. Are the length of the diameter and the length of the circumference in direct proportion? Explain your answer.

6 Which of these six graphs show two variables in direct proportion?

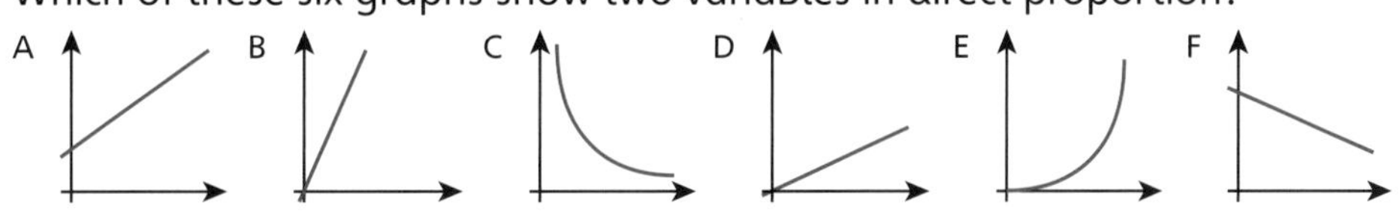

6a I can find out by drawing a graph whether two values are in direct proportion

Learn this

If two variables are in direct proportion their graph will be a straight line that goes through the origin.

7 A laboratory measures three pairs of variables. Draw a graph of each pair of variables and use the graphs to decide which pairs are in direct proportion.

a

x	3.5	4.5	8
y	21	27	48

b

x	2	5	6.5
y	13	25	31

c

x	4	6.5	7
y	12	19.5	21

8 a What is the value of the y-intercept of any graph that shows two variables in direct proportion?

b Find the equation of each graph that represented a directly proportional relationship in Q7.

Level 7

7b I can identify the gradient and y-intercept of any straight-line graph

Now try this!

A All in proportion

There are three variables x, y and z. x and y are in direct proportion. y and z are in direct proportion. Are x and z in direct proportion? Explain your reasoning.

B Squared away

Some physical laws involve more complicated proportional relationships.

x	1	2	3	4
y	3	12	27	48
x^2				

In this table of values, x and y are not proportional, but they are related. Copy and complete this table. Can you spot a directly proportional relationship now? Try and deduce a formula that connects the variables x and y.

intercept variable

13.4 Solving problems involving direct proportion

- Understand that if variables are in direct proportion, then the ratios of corresponding values are equal
- Use algebra to solve problems involving variables that are in direct proportion

Why learn this?

You use direct proportion when exchanging currency.

What's the BIG idea?

- Two **variables** are in **direct proportion** if they increase and decrease in the same **ratio**. Their graph will be a straight line through the origin. **Level 6**
- In a table of values for variables that are in direct proportion, the value of $\frac{y}{x}$ is always the same.
- If you know the ratio $y : x$, you can work out y if you know x, or x if you know y. **Level 7**

x	5	8	13	15
y	30	48	78	90
$\frac{y}{x}$	6	6	6	6

Level 7

- If $y : x$ is 6 : 1, this means that $\frac{y}{x} = 6$.
  You can write y **in terms of** x, as $y = 6x$, or x in terms of y, $x = \frac{y}{6}$ **Level 7**

Tip

In science, if one pair of results isn't directly proportional and the others are, check to see if you made a mistake.

Practice, practice, practice!

1 This graph converts pounds to euros.

a Use the graph to create a table of values for £20, £40, £60, £80 and £100 and their corresponding values in euros.

b Extend your table to show the ratio of euros to pounds for each pair of corresponding values.

c Is the number of euros in direct proportion to the number of pounds?

d Copy and complete: € = ☐ × £

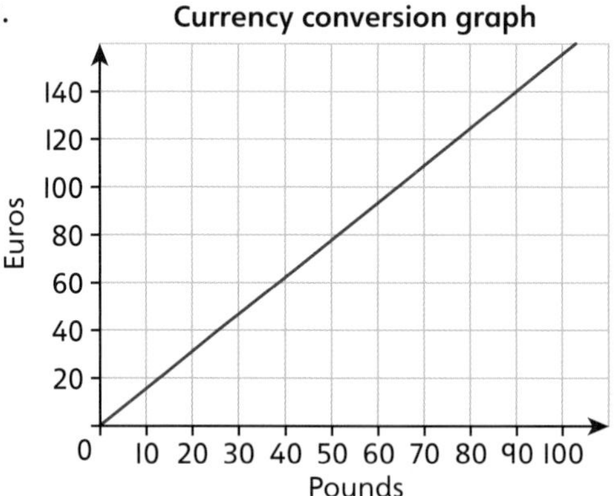

2 This table of values converts pounds to dollars.

Pounds	20	50	70	90
Dollars	39	97.5	136.5	175.5

a What is the ratio of dollars to pounds for each pair of values?

b Express the relationship between the variables in terms of pounds.

c Is the number of dollars in direct proportion to the number of pounds?

d Describe what a graph showing the number of dollars on the y-axis and the number of pounds on the x-axis would look like.

Level 7

7C I can understand that variables that are in direct proportion can be written as ratios

Did you know?

Currency trading has a long history and can be traced back to the ancient Middle East and the Middle Ages when foreign exchange started to take shape after the international merchant bankers devised bills of exchange (bank notes).

direct proportion   in terms of

3 For each table, work out the ratios of the second-row values to the first-row values. Which variables are in direct proportion?

a

x	2	7	15	33
y	5	17.5	37.5	80.5

b

m	6	20	42	90
n	13.2	44	92.4	198

c

a	15	27	44	72
b	19.5	35.1	57.2	93.6

d

s	24	32	45	60
t	38.4	51.2	74.5	96

4 This function machine is a currency converter.

amount in pounds → $\times m$ → amount in foreign currency

a Choose a value for m and create a table of values for £10, £20, £50, £70, £100 and their foreign currency values.

b Express the foreign currency value in terms of the number of pounds using algebra.

c What is the ratio of foreign currency to pounds?

d Are they in direct proportion?

e What would a graph of this foreign currency against pounds look like? What is its gradient?

5 Ethan and Mia travel to Denmark. Mia gets 237.5 Danish kroner (DKK) for £25.

a Write this as a ratio of Danish kroner to pounds.

b Use an algebraic method to work out how many kroner Ethan gets for
i £90 **ii** £35 **iii** £120

c When they get back, Ethan has 95 DKK left and Mia has 304 DKK left. Use an algebraic method to find out how many pounds they each get when they exchange this for pounds.

6 Argent and Bailey want to travel from Calais to Toulouse by motorbike. They won't travel quickly, but know that they can cover 300 km in 8 hours.

a Write this as a ratio of distance to time.

b Toulouse is 1000 km from Calais. How much travelling time will it take?

c How far can they go in 15 hours?

7 On the return journey they have a faster bike. They can cover 390 km in 6 hours.

a Write this as a ratio of distance to time.

b How long does it take them to go from Toulouse to Calais?

c How far can they go in 8 hours?

Level 7

7c I can understand that variables that are in direct proportion can be written as ratios

7b I can solve a problem of direct proportion if I know the ratio of the variables

Now try this!

A Journey converter

Work with a partner. Kilometres and miles are in direct proportion. Their ratio is 8 to 5. Create a table of values to show the approximate distances from your school to local towns and landmarks, in miles and in kilometres.

B What's that in yuan?

The ratio of pounds to Chinese yuan is 5 : 64. Take the prices of ten different items in pounds and use an algebraic method to work out their cost in yuans.

ratio variable

13.5 Constructing and solving equations

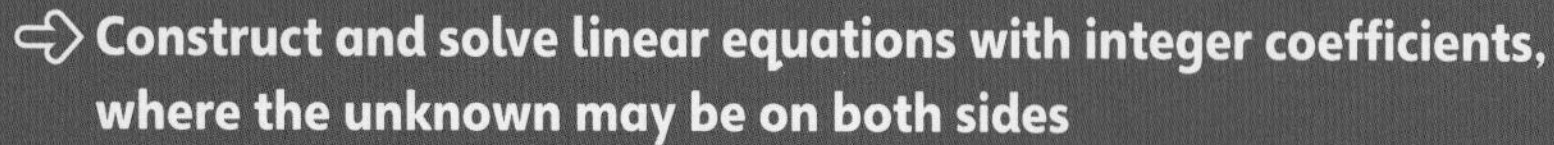

- Construct and solve linear equations with integer coefficients, where the unknown may be on both sides
- Solve simple equations involving x^2

Why learn this?

Equations can be useful for working out perimeters. For instance, you could write an equation to work out how many barriers of a particular size you need.

What's the BIG idea?

→ You can solve **linear equations** of the form $ax + b = c$ in one or two steps.

For example, to solve	$7x + 5 = 47$
Subtract 5 from both sides	$7x + 5 - 5 = 47 - 5$
Divide both sides by 7	$\frac{7x}{7} = \frac{42}{7}$
Therefore	$x = 6$ **Level 5**

→ You can also solve equations where the unknown is on both sides by doing the same operations to both sides.

For example	$4(3x - 3) = 2(2x + 2)$
Divide both sides by 2	$\frac{^{2}\cancel{4}(3x - 3)}{\cancel{2}} = \frac{\cancel{2}(2x + 2)}{\cancel{2}}$
Multiply out the brackets	$6x - 6 = 2x + 2$
Subtract $2x$ from both sides	$6x - 6 - 2x = 2x + 2 - 2x$
	$4x - 6 = 2$
Add 6 to both sides	$4x - 6 + 6 = 2 + 6$
	$4x = 8$
Therefore	$x = 2$ **Level 6**

→ When solving equations involving x^2, first rearrange the equation to find what x^2 equals. Then remember that there will be two solutions for x, one positive and one negative. For example $x^2 - 6 = 30$ can be rearranged to give $x^2 = 36$, which has solutions $x = 6$ and $x = -6$ **Level 7**

Super fact!

It would take over 56 000 barriers 1.5 m long to line both sides of a marathon course.

Tip

Remember to do the same to both sides.

Practice, practice, practice!

Level 5

5b I can solve a one-step equation

5a I can solve a two-step equation

1 Find the value of x in each of these equations.

a $3x = 24$ **b** $5x = 45$ **c** $8x = 104$ **d** $14x = 56$

2 Find the value of x in each of these equations.

	$3x + 1 = 10$
Subtract 1 from both sides	$3x + 1 - 1 = 10 - 1$
	$3x = 9$
Divide both sides by 3	$\frac{\cancel{3}x}{\cancel{3}} = \frac{^{3}\cancel{9}}{\cancel{3}}$
Therefore	$x = 3$

a $2x + 3 = 15$ **b** $5x + 3 = 28$ **c** $7x + 5 = 47$ **d** $15x - 12 = 93$

bracket expression linear equation

3 **a** Write an algebraic expression for the perimeter of this shape, and simplify it.

b Work out the value of x for each of these perimeters.

i 40 m **ii** 94 cm **iii** 166 m

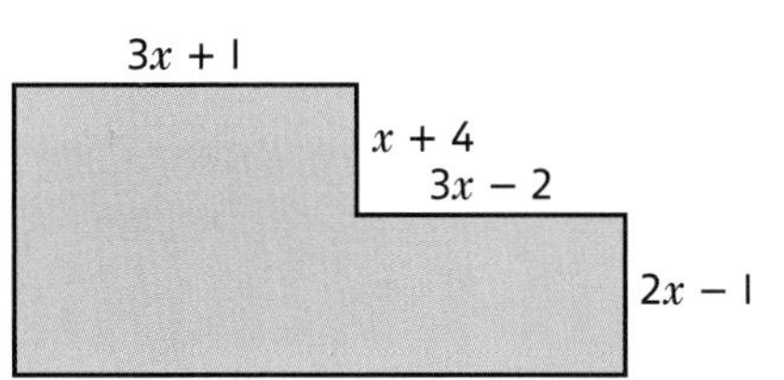

4 Solve these equations.

$4x + 2 = 2x + 6$

Subtract 2 from both sides $4x + 2 - 2 = 2x + 6 - 2$

$4x = 2x + 4$

Subtract $2x$ from both sides $4x - 2x = 2x + 4 - 2x$

$2x = 4$

Divide both sides by 2 $\frac{2x}{2} = \frac{4}{2}$

Therefore $x = 2$

Tip To check your solution, substitute the value for the unknown back into the original equation.

a $3x + 1 = 2x + 7$ **b** $5x - 4 = 3x + 2$ **c** $12 - x = 4x - 8$

d $10x - 2 = 10 - 2x$ **e** $-3x + 8 = 3x - 4$ **f** $7 + 5x = -x + 1$

5 **a** Write an algebraic expression for the perimeter of this shape, and simplify it.

b Find the perimeter for each value of x.

i $x = 3$ m **ii** $x = 6$ mm

iii $x = 11$ cm **iv** $x = 20$ m

c Work out the value of x for each of these perimeters.

i 58 m **ii** 118 cm **iii** 142 m **iv** 370 m

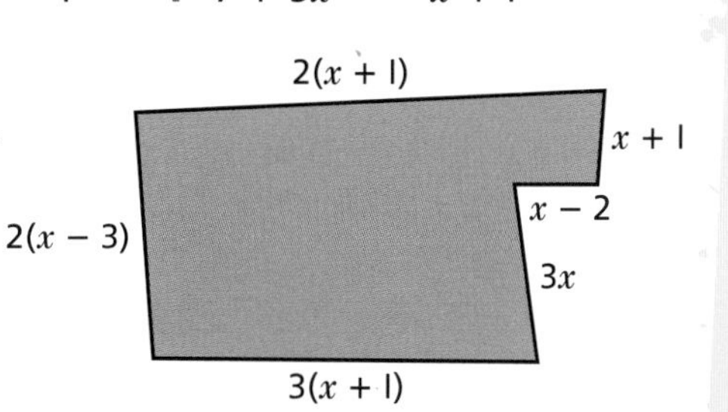

Level 6

6c I can write and solve two-step equations

6b I can solve equations with x on both sides

6b I can write and solve an equation which involves brackets

6 Solve these equations.

a $4(x + 3) = 3x + 19$ **b** $5(7 - 2x) = 2x - 1$ **c** $-2(1 - 5x) = 30 + 2x$

7 Solve these equations involving x^2.

a $x^2 = 25$ **b** $2x^2 = 32$

c $3x^2 + 6 = 18$ **d** $39 - 2x^2 = 21$

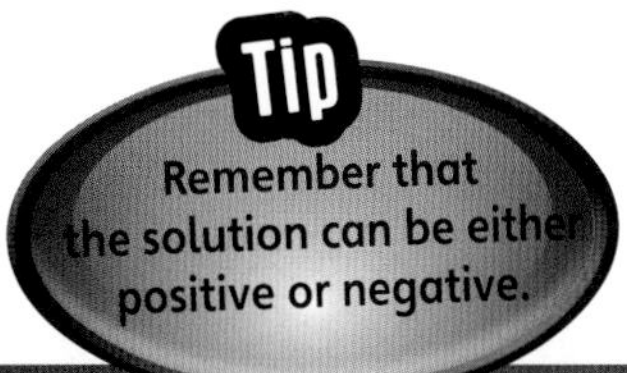

Level 7

7c I can solve two-step equations which involve brackets and have x on both sides

7c I can solve an equation involving x^2

Now try this!

A Where do you live?

Work with a partner. Each make up an equation where the solution is the number of your house or of a relative's house. For example, if you live at number 12 your equation could be $5x + 3 = 63$. Challenge your partner to solve it.

B Desk dimensions

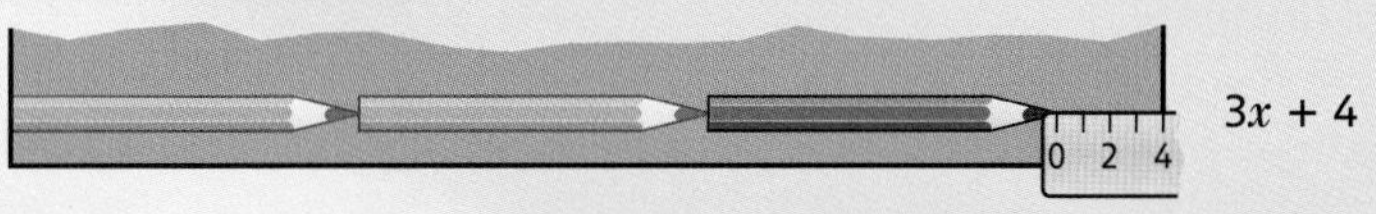

Work with a partner.

1 Measure the length and width of your desk in pencil lengths, measuring any remaining distance that is less than a pencil length with a ruler.

2 Write equations for the length, width and perimeter of your desk using x to represent the pencil length.

3 Measure the actual width of your desk, and find x using your width equation from step 2.

4 Use your value of x to find the perimeter of your desk.

5 Compare your results with another pair sitting at a similar desk.

perimeter

13.6 Writing and solving complex linear equations

- Write and solve equations involving brackets and division
- Find alternative ways of solving equations

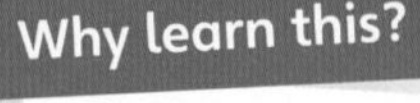

In science, equations are often used to express the relationship between variables.

What's the BIG idea?

- Use the correct **order of operations** when you form and solve equations.
  Brackets → Powers (e.g. squaring) → × ÷ → + −
  Level 5 & Level 6
- Check your solutions by substituting back into the original equation.
  For example, if you think the solution to $2(3x - 1) = 3x + 7$ is $x = 2$:
  Substitute 2 into the left-hand side of the equation $2(3 \times 2 - 1) = 10$
  Substitute 2 into the right-hand side of the equation $3 \times 2 + 7 = 13$
  $10 \neq 13$, so $x = 2$ is wrong. **Level 6 & Level 7**
- There is often more than one way to simplify and solve an equation. **Level 7**
- You can **simplify** equations involving division by multiplying both sides by the same amount.

  For example $\frac{3x - 1}{2} = \frac{3x + 7}{4}$

  Multiply both sides by 4 $\frac{4(3x - 1)}{2} = \frac{4(3x + 7)}{4}$

  Then $2(3x - 1) = 3x + 7$ **Level 7**

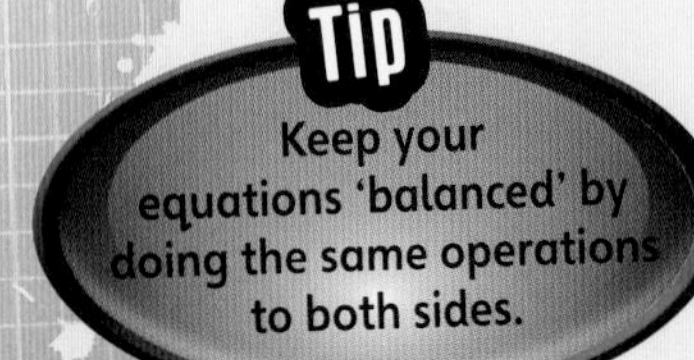

Practice, practice, practice!

Level 6

6a I can write and solve equations involving division

1 Eric thinks of a number, multiplies it by 3, adds 5 and halves the result.
Jodie takes the same number, subtracts 3 and multiplies the result by 5.
Their answers are the same.

a Write an equation for this situation.

b Solve it to find the original number.

2 Rahim buys food for a picnic. He calculates how many packs of cakes he needs by multiplying the number of people coming by 4, then subtracting 3 because some people won't eat much, and finally dividing by 5 because there are five cakes in a pack.
Later he realises this number of packs is the same as number of people minus 2.

a Write an equation for this situation.

b Solve the equation to find how many people are coming.

c How many packs of cakes does Rahim need?

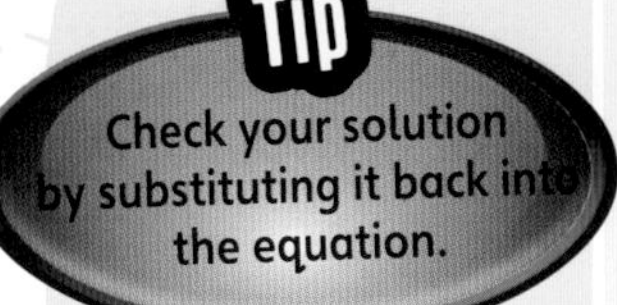

bracket equation order of operations

3 Solve these equations.

a $3(2x + 1) = 5(x - 1)$ b $4(3x + 2) = 5(3x + 1)$

c $8(x - 1) = 4(x + 2)$ d $6(2x - 4) = 3(2x + 2)$

Tip

Check your solution by substituting it back into the original equation.

Level 7

7c I can solve equations involving brackets and with the unknown on both sides

4 Sophie and Emma both had the same number of beads.
Sophie had two boxes, each with three full compartments and two extra beads.
Emma had four boxes, each with one full compartment and six extra beads.

a Express this as an equation involving brackets.

Hint: Use c for the number of beads in a full compartment.

b How many beads are in a full compartment?

c How many beads did Sophie and Emma each have?

5 Solve these equations.

7b I can solve equations involving brackets and negative multiples

a $4(3a - 6) = 100 - 2(a - 1)$ b $86 - 2(2p + 1) = 9(3p - 1)$

c $-2(6x + 5) = 54 - 2(2x + 12)$ d $40 - 2(t + 6) = -2(4 - 2t)$

6 Solve these equations.

7a I can solve equations involving division, brackets and negative numbers

$\frac{5x + 6}{3} = \frac{30 - x}{2}$ Multiply both sides by 6

$2(5x + 6) = 3(30 - x)$

$10x + 12 = 90 - 3x$

$10x + 3x = 90 - 12$

$13x = 78$

$x = 6$

a $\frac{5x + 3}{2} = \frac{10x - 18}{3}$ b $\frac{11s - 5}{4} = \frac{13s - 1}{5}$ c $\frac{70 - 2b}{5} = \frac{15b + 9}{7}$

7 Josh has four full packets of pencils and four extra. He puts half of them into his pencil case. Marcus has four pencils short of eight full packets. He puts one third into his pencil case. When they check, they find that they both have the same number of pencils in their pencil cases.

7a I can write and solve equations involving division, brackets and negative numbers

a Write an equation to express this.

b Solve the equation to find the number of pencils in a full packet.

c How many pencils does Josh have in his pencil case?

8 a Solve $3(x - 2) = 6x + 3$ by

7a I can find alternative ways of solving equations

i first multiplying out the brackets ii first dividing both sides by 3.

b Solve $15 - 3(x + 1) = 2(x + 1)$ by

i first multiplying out the brackets ii first adding $3(x + 1)$ to both sides.

Now try this!

A Stay balanced!

Work with a partner. One of you writes a true statement, for example $24 - 4 = 2 \times 10$. The other writes four simple instructions, such as 'multiply by 5' or 'add 3'. Together, apply the instructions in the same order to both sides of the statement.
At each stage, check whether the statement is still true.

B An age-old riddle

Work out this riddle. The sum of the ages of a brother and sister is 28. In four years' time the sister will be half the age of her brother. How old are they now? Make up your own riddle for a partner to solve.

simplify

World's Greatest Maths!

13.7 Scrapyard skittles

It's the grand final of this year's Scrapyard Challenge competition. To win you will need to build a giant motorised catapult! Your catapult will fire a watermelon at a target of skittles, and you need to knock over as many as possible.

But building mechanical marvels out of scrap metal isn't an exact science! You'll have to use trial and improvement to solve these problems.

Fuel tank

Your motorised catapult needs a fuel tank. The fuel tank needs to be cube-shaped, with a capacity of 2 m^3.

Trial for x	x^3	Too big or too small?
1	1	Too small
2	8	Too big
1.5		

- Copy and complete this table to find the length of one side of the fuel tank using trial and improvement.
- Give your answer correct to one decimal place.

The volume of a cube of side length x is x^3 or $x \times x \times x$.

Stacks of skittles

The skittles you're aiming at are arranged in the shape of a rectangle with length 2 more than its width.

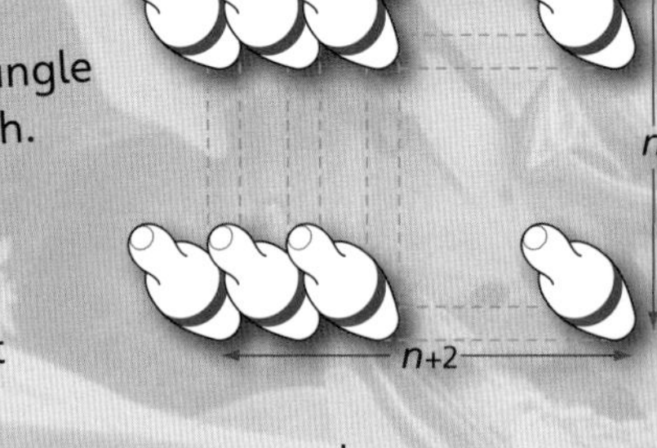

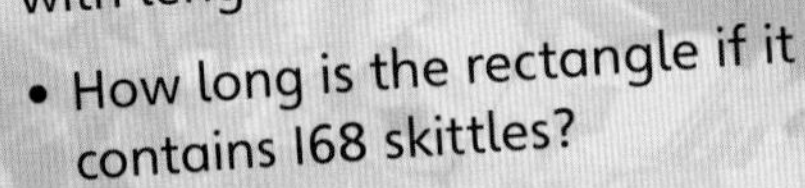

- How long is the rectangle if it contains 168 skittles?

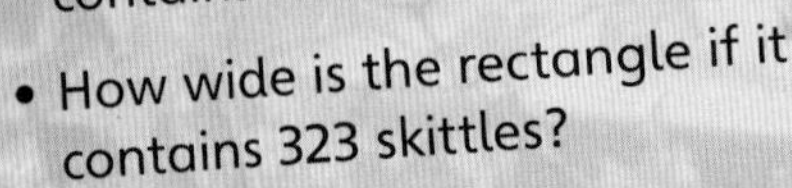

- How wide is the rectangle if it contains 323 skittles?
- A different target is made from skittles formed into a rectangle twice as long as it is wide. How long is this rectangle if it contains 98 skittles?

Hurry up!

You will lose points if it takes you a long time to build your catapult.

The number of points lost is calculated using the formula

points lost = $t^3 + 50t$

where t is the time in hours taken to build the catapult.

To win the competition, you must lose no more than 1000 points.

- What is the longest you can take to build your catapult? Use a table like this to record your trials. Give your answer in hours to one decimal place.

Trial for t	$t^3 + 50t$	Too big or too small?
10		

- Write your answer in hours and minutes.

Range-finder

The range of the catapult depends on the size of the counter-weight.
If you use a w kg counter-weight the catapult will fire a distance of $w^2 + 4w$ m.

- How far will the cannon fire if you use a 10 kg counter-weight?
- You need to fire the catapult a distance of 300 m. What size counter-weight should you use? Give your answer correct to two decimal places.

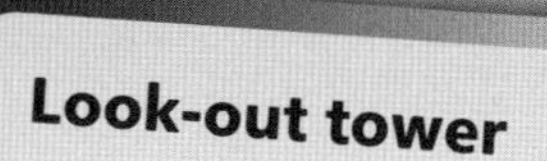

Look-out tower

You need a good view to aim your catapult at the target. This look-out tower is a cuboid of height 10 m. It has a square base with side length x m.

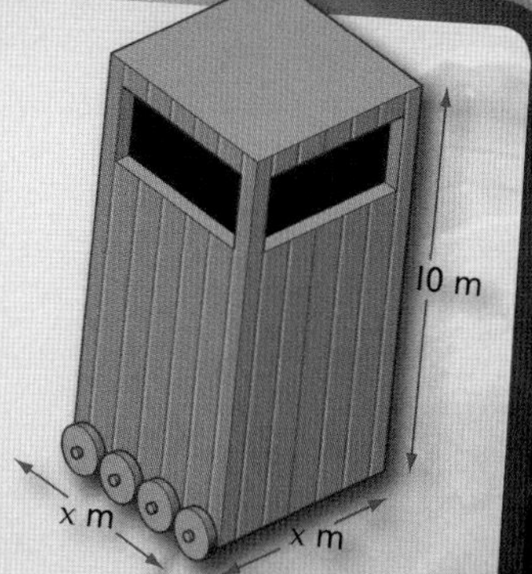

- Write an expression for the surface area of the cuboid in terms of x.
- Use trial and improvement to find the value of x if the surface area is 220 m^2. Give your answer correct to two decimal places.

Finishing touches

The base of your catapult is an open box which needs to have a capacity of 17 m^3. It is made by cutting squares out of a 6 m by 7 m sheet of wood. This diagram shows the net of the box.

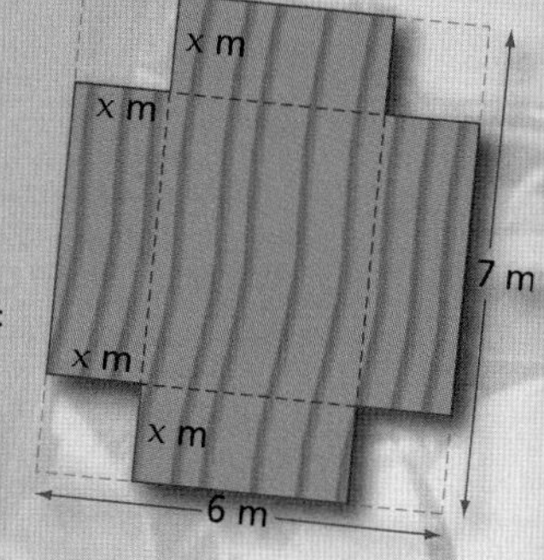

- Use trial and improvement to find a value of x between 0 and 1, correct to the nearest cm.

Trial for x	Capacity of box (m³)	Too big or too small
0.5	15	Too small

- There is another value of x, between 1 and 2, which gives the same capacity. Use trial and improvement to find this value, correct to the nearest cm.

Bonus points!

Your team captain wants you to redesign the base unit of your catapult so that it has the largest capacity possible.

- Using the same net as before, can you find a value of x which gives a capacity greater than 17 m^2?
- Use a graphical calculator or graph plotting program to find the value of x which gives the greatest possible capacity. Give your answer correct to one decimal place.

13.8 Applying mathematics and solving problems

- Solve problems involving number and algebra
- Break complex problems into simpler steps
- Choose and use efficient techniques for algebraic manipulation
- Use trial and improvement methods where a more efficient method is not obvious

Why learn this?

Maths problems and puzzles come in many different forms. Solving them can be challenging but fun.

What's the BIG idea?

- Extract the numbers before you tackle a word problem. Level 6
- **Logically** organise the information you've been given. Level 6
- Sometimes it helps to break down a problem into simpler steps or tasks. Level 6 & Level 7
- **Simplify** equations as much as possible. Think about
  - collecting like terms
  - finding a **common factor**
  - multiplying out brackets. Level 6 & Level 7
- Consider which techniques to use.
  For example
  - Can you solve the equation?
  - Does plotting a graph help?
  - Is **trial and improvement** a good approach? Level 6 & Level 7

Super fact!

Sudoku means 'single number' in Japanese.

Did you know?

Sudoku is related to magic squares and can be traced back to China in the 8th century.

Practice, practice, practice!

Level 6

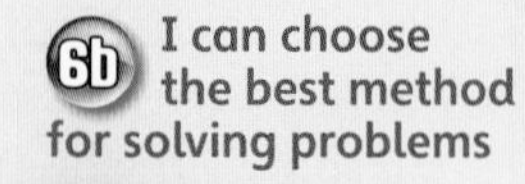

6b I can choose the best method for solving problems

1 Find the missing digits.

a $(3\square)^2 = \square 3 \square 9$ b $(\square 2)^3 = \square\square 2 \square$

c $2\square \times \square = \square 40$ d $\square^2 + 2^2 = 4\square$

2 In a geography test, the teacher gives three marks for a right answer and deducts one mark for a wrong answer. April attempted all 25 questions and scored 47 marks. How many right answers did she get?

Tip

With a word problem, extract the numbers before you tackle the problem.

3 The product of three consecutive numbers is 97 290. What are the numbers?

4 I spend £50 in a shop. I buy trainers which normally cost £29.50, but they have a 20% discount. I spend £12.30 on a sweatshirt. I also buy a pair of jeans. How much did the jeans cost?

common factor logically simplify

5 Use the numbers 1 to 9 to complete these magic squares so that every row, column and diagonal adds up to 15.

a

$3x$	$2x + 3$	x
y		
$y + 7$		

b

a		
	$a + 1$	
$b^2 - 2$	$3b + 1$	$5b - b^2$

Level 6

6a I can break down a problem into simpler steps

6 Penny is 21 years older than her daughter.
Today, Penny is six times as old as her granddaughter.
In 12 years' time she will be three times as old as her granddaughter.
How old are Penny, her daughter and her granddaughter now?

Level 7

7b I can break down a complex problem into simpler steps

7 A straight-line graph goes through (0, −3). It also goes through the point (5, 7).

a Without plotting a graph, write the function of the graph in the form $y = mx + c$.

b Where does the line cross the x-axis?

8 The dimensions of a large room are shown in the diagram. The total area of the room is 511 m^2. Find a positive value for s.

$s + 2$, $s + 3$, $s + 2$, $s + 1$

9 The dimension sum (height + width + depth) of a box for a courier company must be no more than 1.5 m. The depth of a box is twice its width.
What height (to the nearest centimetre) will the courier company allow that gives the greatest volume?

Now try this!

A Your birthday colour

Take the day in the month of your birthday. Add 56 to this number. Add the difference between your day and 32. Divide the result by 4, then add 3 to your answer. The result is your key number.

a If $a = 1$, $b = 2$, $c = 3$ and so on, what letter matches your key number? Choose a colour that begins with that letter.

b Explain why you chose yellow.

B Weigh up the facts

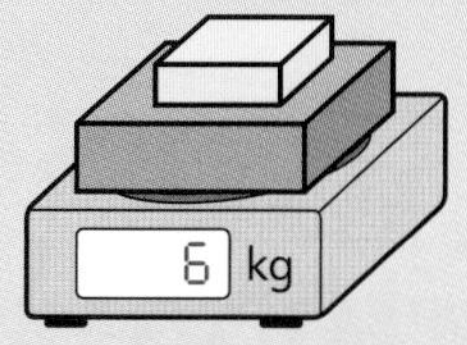

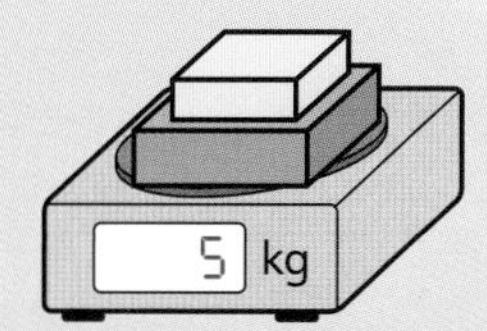

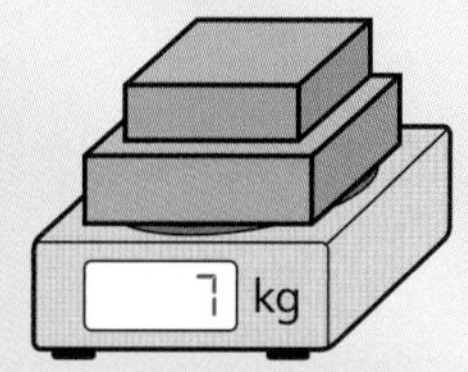

a What is the mass of each parcel?

b Create your own puzzle like this for a partner to solve.

trial and improvement

Creating a game world

Javinder has just started work as a games designer. Her first solo project will involve working with coordinates and straight line graphs. With these she will be able to design elements within the game world.

1 Javinder's first job is to use coordinates to create a treasure chest in the shape of a cuboid.
These are the coordinate points that she is using:

$A(3, 4)$, $B(7, 7)$, $C(11, 7)$, $D(6, 4)$, $E(3, 2)$, $F(6, 2)$, $G(10, 5)$

a Draw a set of axes with the x-axis from 0 to 12 and the y-axis from 0 to 8.
Plot the coordinate points.
Join the points with a straight line in the following order:
$A\ B\ C\ D\ A$
$A\ E\ F\ G\ C$

Are Javinder's coordinates correct? If not, correct her data.

b What is the equation of line AE?

c What is the equation of line BC? **Level 5**

2 Javinder's next task is to create a ski slope for Bob, the game world character, to use.
She has created two slopes using the equations of straight lines:

Slope 1: $y = 2x - 1$
Slope 2: $y = \frac{1}{2}x + 1$

a Create a table of values for each function.

b Draw the graph of each function on the same set of axes.

c Which slope would be the better choice for a ski slope if a 'gentle' gradient is needed?

d Could you have answered part **c** by simply looking at the equation of the line? Explain your answer fully. **Level 6**

3 In a different game world level, another ski slope is required. However, it needs to be sloping down from left to right.

a How would you amend the equation $y = 2x - \frac{1}{2}$ to achieve this sloping direction?

b Check your adjustment by creating a table of values and plotting the line. **Level 7**

4 A pair of rockets take off in accordance with the following functions.

Rocket 1: $x = \frac{1}{2}(y - 4)$
Rocket 2: $x - \frac{1}{2}y - 2 = 0$

Rearrange these functions into the form $y = mx + c$. **Level 7**

5 When working out the optimum distance from the ski slope for Bob, Javinder has formed this equation.

$16 - 2(a + 2) = -6(3a - 4)$

Solve it to find Bob's optimum distance in metres. **Level 7**

The BIG ideas

- A graph of the **function** $x = a$ is a line **parallel** to the y-axis. It crosses the x-axis at a. **Level 5**
- A graph of the function $y = b$ is a line parallel to the x-axis. It crosses the y-axis at b. **Level 5**
- You can plot a function by working out a set of **coordinates** for it. **Level 6**
- You can solve equations where the unknown is on both sides by doing the same operations to both sides. **Level 6**
- A **linear function** has the form $y = mx + c$. Its graph has a **gradient** m and **intercepts** (crosses) the y-axis at c. **Level 6 & Level 7**
- A linear function can be written in the form $y = mx + c$. Its graph is a straight line. For example, $y = 3x - 10$ is a linear function. **Level 6 & Level 7**
- You can rearrange a linear function into the form $y = mx + c$ by doing the same operations to both sides (the same as for linear equations). **Level 7**

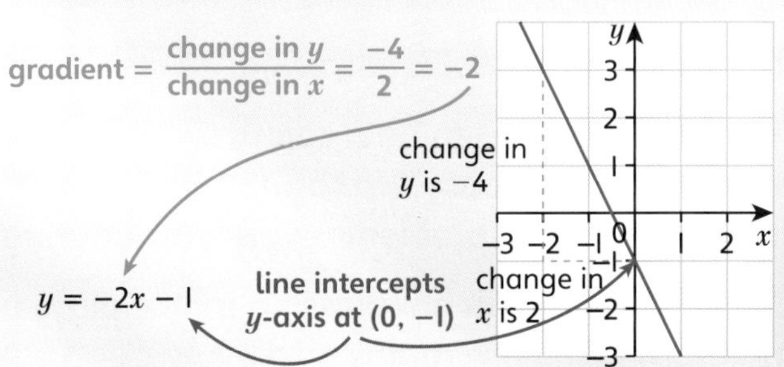

Practice SATs-style questions

Level 5

Q1 **a** When $a = 4$, what is the value of $8 + a$?

b When $b = 5$, what is the value of $5b$?

Q2

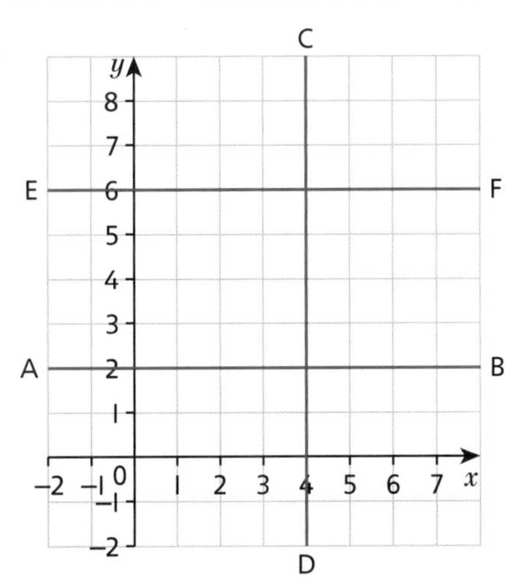

The line AB has equation $y = 2$.
Find the equation of line

a CD **b** EF

Level 6

Q3 Multiply out this expression. Write your answer as simply as possible.

$3(x + 3) + 4(5 + x)$

Q4 Solve this equation.

$3x + 8 = 5x + 5$

Q5 Complete the table of values for the equation $y = 2x + 3$.

x	0	2	4
y			

Level 7

Q6 Solve this equation. Give both possible solutions.

$2x^2 - 15 = 35$

Q7 Find the gradients of the lines through the points

a (1, 2) and (4, 5)

b (2, 4) and (6, 2)

Q8 The equation $x^3 + x = 16$ has a solution between 2 and 2.5.
Find the solution to 1 decimal place.

14 Putting things in proportion

This unit is about problem solving.

Courtney is training to be a colour technician with the international company ***Mahogany Hairdressing***, and is faced with solving problems every day. Courtney says:

'I have learnt that in hairdressing maths plays a very important role. I use maths with every client who comes to see me. If someone decides they want their hair to be lighter, or darker, I have to decide how to achieve this.

'Our range of colours comes in 60 m*l* tubes. Each tube of colour is graded according to depth – dark or light, numbered from 2 to 10 – and tone – cool or warm colour, numbered from 2 to 9. Peroxide has to be added to activate the colour. This comes in strengths of 6%, 9% and 12% – the higher the percentage of the peroxide, the more it will lighten the colour. I must choose which strength to use and measure out just the right amount.

'Colours and peroxide can be mixed in different ratios. 1 : 1 means I mix 60 m*l* of colour with 60 m*l* of peroxide, and 2 : 3 means 60 m*l* of colour and 90 m*l* of peroxide.

'Sometimes only a fraction of a tube is used and it is very important to work out the correct amount of peroxide to add.'

Activities

A Colour and peroxide are to be mixed in the ratio 2 : 3. Which of these amounts are not correct?

	Colour (ml)	Peroxide (ml)
a	20	30
b	30	40
c	50	75
d	70	115
e	100	150

B A colour technician needs 180 m*l* of colour and peroxide in total. The ratio of peroxide to colour is 3 : 2.

a How much colour (m*l*) is needed?

b How much peroxide (m*l*) is needed?

c If the ratio was 5 : 4, how much of each would be required? How many tubes of colour would be required?

Did you know?

Hair colouring has been known for centuries. Ancient cultures around the world used natural dyes, derived from plants, such as henna, indigo and camomile. Roman women used a mixture of boiled walnut leaves and leeks to make their hair beautifully dark and shiny.

Before you start this unit...

1 **a** What percentage of this pattern is red?

b Copy and colour this pattern so that 70% is green.

Level Up Maths 4-6 page 190

2 Three pens cost 90p. How much would two pens cost?

Level Up Maths 4-6 page 190

3 All the houses in the village of Malltraeth are painted either yellow or pink. There are 3 yellow houses for every 2 pink houses. In total, there are 40 houses in the village. How many houses are pink?

Level Up Maths 4-6 page 186

4 Write each fraction in its simplest form.

a $\frac{4}{6}$ **b** $\frac{12}{16}$ **c** $\frac{21}{35}$

Level Up Maths 4-6 page 54

5 Which pack of batteries is better value?

Level Up Maths 4-6 page 194

Plus digital resources

Did you know?

The symbol : is thought to have originated in England in the early seventeenth century. It was used in a text entitled *Johnson's Arithmetik; In two Bookes* in 1633, but it was used to indicate fractions, for example $\frac{3}{4}$ was written as 3 : 4.

14.1 Proportion and ratio

- Understand the relationship between ratio and proportion
- Understand and use ratio and proportion to solve problems
- Use the unitary method to solve word problems involving ratio and direct proportion

Why learn this?

Proportion is useful for identifying trends. A nation's development can be measured by a variety of factors such as the proportion of the population who are literate or who have access to clean water or to health care.

What's the BIG idea?

→ You can use the **unitary method** to solve **ratio** and **proportion** problems. This means finding out the value of one part first.
For example, the ratio of pineapple to melon in a fruit salad is 2 : 3.
If there are 80 g of pineapple, how many grams of melon are there?
80 g pineapple is 2 parts, so 1 part is $80 \div 2 = 40$ g.
Melon is 3 parts, that is $3 \times 40 = 120$ g. **Level 5**

→ Two variables are in direct proportion if they increase and decrease in the same ratio. For example, the weight of flour needed and the number of cakes baked. **Level 5**

→ The unitary method can only be used if the variables are in **direct proportion**. **Level 6**

Did you know?

In 2004 1 in 3 people in India lived on less than US$1 per day.

Practice, practice, practice!

Level 5

5c I can use direct proportion in simple contexts

1 Which of these currency exchange adverts represents direct proportion?

Travel agent	Bank
€1.20 per £1, commission free	€1.30 per £1 with £3 charge

5c I can use ratio notation

2 Orange paint is made with one part red paint and three parts yellow paint.

a Write the ratio of red paint to yellow paint.

b Copy and complete the table to show the amount of each colour needed to make different quantities of orange paint.

Red	Yellow
1	3
2	
	9
5	
	24

5a I can understand the relationship between ratio and proportion (convert proportions to ratios)

3 Three fifths of the pupils in a school are boys.

a What fraction of pupils are girls?

b Write the ratio of boys to girls.

5a I can use proportional reasoning to solve simple problems

4 The sides of a triangle are in the ratio 3 : 4 : 5.
How long are the other sides

a if the shortest side is 9 cm

b if the middle side is 16 cm?

direct proportion proportion

5 The price charged for pens is directly proportional to the number bought.
The price charged for three pens is £1.20.

- **a** Calculate the price of these and explain your working.
  i 9 pens **ii** 12 pens **iii** 1 pen **iv** 4 pens
- **b** If you have £2.00 to spend, how many pens can you buy?

Tip
When solving ratio and proportion problems, it can help to find the value of one item first (the unitary method).

Level 5

5a I can use the unitary method to solve simple word problems involving ratio and direct proportion

6 Meryl is going to France.
The currency conversion rate is £1 = €1.42.

- **a** Meryl has £100. How much is that in euros?
- **b** Her aunt gave Meryl another £50.
  How many euros does she have now?
- **c** Meryl came home with €60. How much is this in pounds?

Hint: Find out how many pounds you get for one euro

7 Downloading 40 tunes from a music website costs £12.
How much does it cost to download eight tunes?

8 Four chocolate bars cost £1.84.

- **a** Calculate the cost of seven chocolate bars.
- **b** How many chocolate bars can you buy for £5.60?

9 Here are the ingredients to make six pancakes.
Sophie is organising a party for herself and seven friends. She wants enough ingredients so that each person, including herself, has three pancakes.

Pancakes (makes 6)
120 g plain flour
2 eggs
300 mℓ milk

- **a** Write the recipe so that Sophie has the correct amounts of ingredients.
- **b** Sophie has 1 kg of flour. How many pancakes can she make?

10 Jamie is paid £52 for 8 hours work.

- **a** Jamie works for 30 hours. How much does he earn?
- **b** Jamie is paid double for overtime. Jamie works 5 hours of overtime in addition to his normal 30 hours. How much does he earn?

Level 6

6b I can use proportional reasoning to solve problems

Now try this!

A Missing numbers

Make up a table of values that are in direct proportion. Rub out some of the values in the table. Challenge your partner to find the missing values.

B Holiday money

- **a** Look at the currency exchange adverts in Q1.
  Which is the better deal if you want to exchange **i** £100 **ii** £25?
- **b** George exchanged some money at the travel agent. He received €60.
  How much would he have received if he had gone to the bank?

Learn this
When two variables are in direct proportion, they increase or decrease in the same ratio.

ratio unitary method

14.2 Simplifying ratios

- Reduce a ratio to its simplest form
- Simplify a ratio expressed in fractions or decimals
- Compare ratios by changing them to the form 1 : m or m : 1

Why learn this?

You can use ratios to compare similar things, such as sports teams.

What's the BIG idea?

- **Simplifying** a **ratio** is similar to simplifying **fractions**. You need to divide each part of the ratio by a **common factor**. For example

  20 : 12 (÷4, ÷4) → 5 : 3 **Level 5**

- When ratios involve different **units**, you need to change all the parts to the same units before simplifying them. **Level 5**
- Ratios that are written with fractions and **decimals** need to be changed to whole numbers before they can be simplified. **Level 6**
- You can compare ratios by changing them into the form 1 : m or m : 1. **Level 6**

Practice, practice, practice!

Level 5

5a I can simplify a three-part ratio

1 Copy and complete.

- **a** 16 : 10 : 8 = 8 : 5 : ☐
- **b** 35 : 40 : 20 = 7 : ☐ : 4
- **c** 28 : 12 : 16 = ☐ : 3 : 4
- **d** 36 : 54 : 27 = ☐ : 6 : ☐

2 In a spelling quiz, Rani scored 20, Sean scored 12 and Thomas scored 16.

- **a** Write the ratio of Rani's, Sean's and Thomas's scores.
- **b** Write the ratio in its simplest form.

Watch out!

Check that you've divided both parts of the ratio by the highest common factor.

3 This season, Cyber City football team won 24 matches, lost 9 and drew 12. Write the ratio of winning games to drawn games to losing games in its simplest form.

4 Write these ratios in their simplest form.

- **a** £6 : £2 : 120p
- **b** 50 cm : 2 m : 300 mm
- **c** 5 kg : 3 kg : 8000 g
- **d** 4 hours : 3 hours : 200 minutes

Tip

Change all values to the same units before simplifying.

common factor decimal equivalent fraction

5 Match the equivalent ratios.

0.25 : 3	$\frac{1}{3}$: 5	$\frac{1}{2}$: 2	2 : 30
1 : 4	3 : 36	24 : 3	4 : 0.5
1 : 12	10 : 40	8 : 1	1 : 15

0.25 : 3, 1 : 12, 3 : 36

6 **a** The ratio of pupils who have a packed lunch to those who have school dinners is 0.8 : $\frac{3}{10}$. Calculate the fraction of pupils who have a packed lunch.

b The ratio of pupils who travel to school by bus to those who walk is $\frac{2}{5}$: 0.9. Calculate the fraction of pupils who walk to school.

7 Paul, Saima and Claire share a pizza in the ratio 0.4 : 0.5 : 0.6.

a What fraction of the pizza did Paul get?

b What fraction of the pizza did Saima get?

8 Jamie and Paul share a bar of chocolate in the ratio 0.3 : $\frac{1}{8}$.
What fraction of the chocolate bar did Jamie get?
Write the fraction in its simplest form.

9 Write these ratios in the form 1 : m.

a 2 : 5 **b** 40 mm : 7 cm

c 40 cm : 6 m **d** 5 kg : 300 g

10 Write the ratios in Q9 in the form m : 1.

11 Carl and Sarah practised high jump.
The ratio of cleared jumps to failed jumps was 12 : 20 for Carl, and 8 : 12 for Sarah.
Compare the ratios to find out who had the better record of clearing jumps.

Level 6

6b I can simplify a ratio expressed in fractions or decimals

6a I can compare ratios by changing them to the form 1 : m or m : 1

Now try this!

A Simplifying ratios challenge

- Roll an ordinary dice twice. Write the two numbers as a ratio and reduce it to its simplest form. How many different ratios can you find?
- How many different ratios will there be with an eight-sided dice?

B What did you do?

- Think about yesterday. How many hours did you sleep, watch TV, spend at school, play sport, talk to friends, do other things?
- Choose three of yesterday's activities and write the ratio of times spent on them. Write the ratio in its simplest form.
- Repeat for other sets of three activities. Compare your ratios with a partner's.

ratio simplify units

14.3 Ratio problems

➪ Divide a quantity into a number of parts to solve problems
➪ Use ratio to solve problems in different contexts

What's the BIG idea?

→ **Ratios** can be used to **divide** and share different **quantities**. Level 5 & Level 6

→ Ratio can be used to solve a variety of problems in different contexts. Level 6

Why learn this?

When you make a drink you might use a ratio of various ingredients.

Practice, practice, practice!

Level 6

6C I can divide a quantity into more than two parts in a given ratio

1 Divide the number in the middle of the diagram into the ratios given.

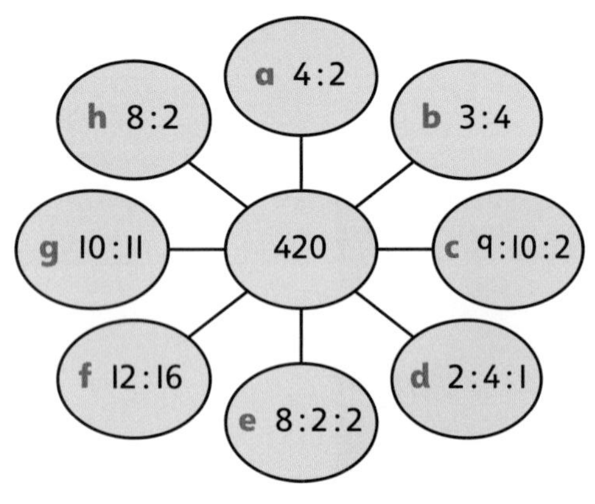

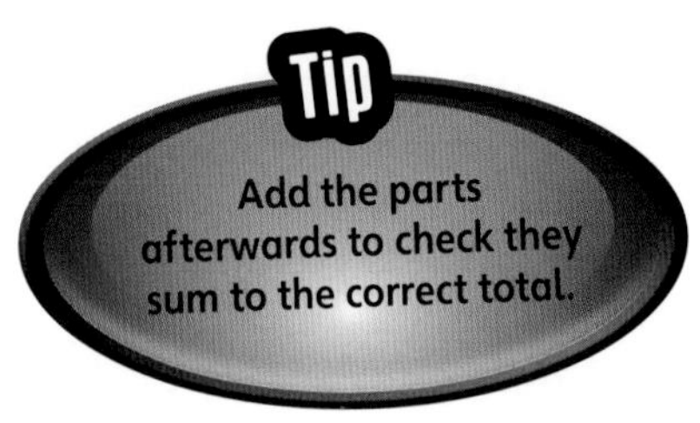

2 Divide these quantities into the ratios given.

a £360 in the ratio 3 : 6 : 9

b 45 cm in the ratio 2 : 4 : 3

c 400 g in the ratio 3 : 2 : 5

d 55 minutes in the ratio 4 : 5 : 2

Tip

The first question to ask yourself is 'How many parts are there altogether?'

6C I can interpret and use ratio in a range of contexts

3 Three sisters are given £210 by their aunt. They share the money in the ratio of their ages. Angela is 12 years old, Samantha is 16 years old and Sharon is 14 years old. How much money does each sister get?

4 The ratio of the width of a rectangle to its length is 2 : 3. The perimeter of the rectangle is 70 cm.

a Calculate the length of each side.

b Calculate the area of the rectangle.

divide quantity

5 Orange Sparkle is a drink made from orange, lemon and fizzy water in the ratio 5 : 1 : 8.

a Calculate how much of each ingredient is needed to make 840 ml.

b Calculate how much of each ingredient is needed to make 1.12 litres.

6 A plan of a building has a scale of 2 cm to 5 m.

a Write this scale as a ratio in its simplest form.

b The length of a room is 3 cm on the plan.
Calculate the real length of the room.

7 The angles in a triangle are in the ratio 4 : 6 : 8.
Find the size of each angle.

8 A business made a profit of £80 000.
The profit was shared between the three owners in the ratio 5 : 3 : 2.
Calculate how much profit each owner received.

9 A shopkeeper bought cans of fizzy orange, lemonade and ginger beer in the ratio 4 : 5 : 3. He bought 360 cans altogether.
How many cans of each drink did he buy?

10 A particular shade of green paint is made using two parts blue paint to four parts yellow paint and one part white paint.
How much blue, yellow and white paint is needed to make

a 21 litres of green paint b 63 litres of green paint c 3.5 litres of green paint?

11 Mr Clarke sells pears at 50p per kilogram.
Mrs Robinson sells pears at 30p per pound.
Who sells the cheaper pears? Explain your answer.

Level 6

6C I can interpret and use ratio in a range of contexts

Learn this

1 kilogram is roughly 2.2 pounds

Now try this!

A Ratio game 1

A game for two players. You need an ordinary dice.

- Player 1 chooses an amount from the table.

£1000	£2600	£300	£450
£870	£500	£600	£720
£9000	£10 000	£100	£50
£850	£3500	£200	£3200

- Player 2 rolls the dice twice and writes the two numbers as a ratio.
- Divide Player 1's amount into this ratio.
Player 1 gets the first part of the ratio and Player 2 gets the second part.
- Swap roles and repeat. Record how much you each win.
The winner is the person with the higher total after five turns each.

B Ratio game 2

Repeat Activity A with three or four players (rolling a dice three or four times, respectively). Divide the chosen amount into a three- or four-part ratio.

ratio

maths!

Packing it in

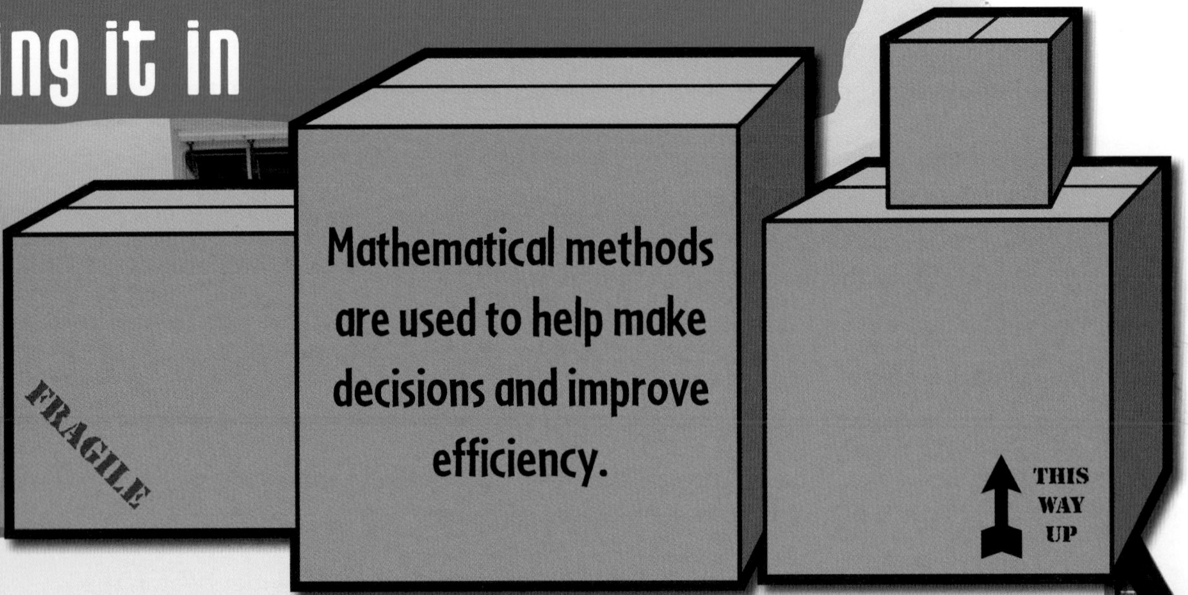

Mathematical methods are used to help make decisions and improve efficiency.

FRAGILE

THIS WAY UP

Survival

Roxanne is preparing for a survival trip, but her rucksack can only hold 10 kg of food. She has 6 food packs, each with a different weight. What combination of these food packs should she choose in order to survive for the longest time?

6 kg
8 days

4 kg
6½ days

2 kg
3 days

5 kg
6 days

3 kg
4 days

1 kg 1½ days

The packing problems faced by real organisations are often more complicated – for example, to load boxes on to a lorry you would need to consider the sizes of the boxes as well as the weight of the boxes.

Bryan's Ferries

A packing problem arises for ferry companies when, for efficiency, they need to load as many vehicles as possible on to the ferry. A ferry deck is divided up into lanes. Each lane is 10 units long. Explain why Bryan's Ferries would need a minimum of five lanes to fit on all of the vehicles shown.

The manager of Bryan's Ferries needs a quick and efficient mathematical rule for loading vehicles on to his ferries. Try using each of these three rules by drawing a diagram. How many lanes does each method need? Which method would you recommend? Why?

Rule 1: Full Lane Loading
Choose vehicles that add up to 10 and then load them on to one lane. Repeat this process until you can't make any more full lanes and then load any vehicles left over.

Rule 2: First Fit Loading
Place each vehicle in the first lane that has room for it. If there is no room open up a new lane for the vehicle.

Rule 3: First Fit Decreasing Loading
Put the vehicles in order from longest to shortest, and then follow Rule 2.

14.4 Logic and proof

- Solve problems
- Use logical argument to establish whether a statement is true or untrue

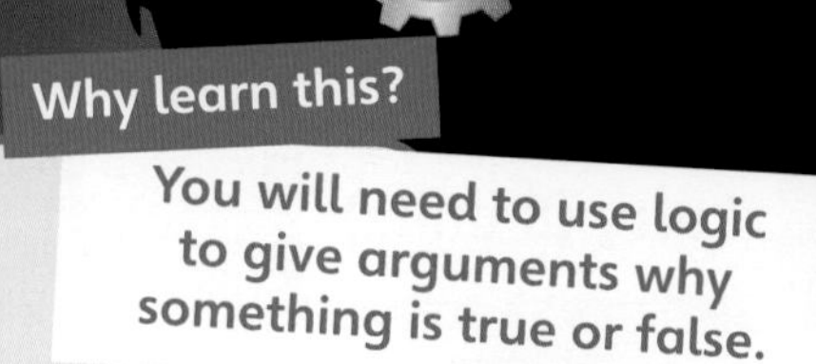

What's the BIG idea?

- A **counter example** is an example that disproves a statement or rule. **Level 6**
- **Logical** arguments are formed by building on something that we know is true. For example, Milton Keynes is in Buckinghamshire. Buckinghamshire is a county in England. Therefore, Milton Keynes is in England. **Level 6**
- Some rules and arguments can be proved using algebra.
  For example, you can prove that the sum of two consecutive numbers is odd.
  Represent the two numbers by n and $n + 1$. The sum is $n + (n + 1) = 2n + 1$.
  $2n$ will always be an even number because it is a multiple of 2. Adding 1 makes an odd number.
  Therefore, you have proved that the sum of two consecutive numbers is an odd number. **Level 7**

Super fact!
Computers use Boolean logic (developed by George Boole) to make them work.

Practice, practice, practice!

Level 6

6c I can understand the significance of a counter example

6c I can use logical argument to solve a problem

6b I can use logical argument to establish the truth of a statement

1 Peter said, 'Multiplication always makes a number larger.'
Give a counter example to show that Peter is wrong.

2 Peter is having a birthday party and needs to deliver some invitations to his friends. He knows the addresses but has forgotten who lives where.

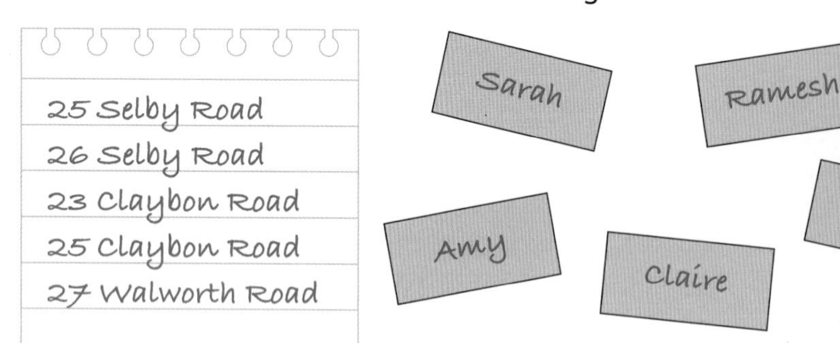

Use these clues to match each address to the correct person.

- Amy lives on the same road as Ramesh.
- The door number of Ramesh's house is an odd number.
- Sarah lives on a different road to the others.
- Claire and Ben have consecutive door numbers.
- Claire and Ramesh have the same door number but live on different roads.

3 Jamie said, 'Square numbers have an odd number of factors.'
Is this true? Justify your answer.

counter example explanation

4 True or false?
For each false statement, find a counter example to disprove it.
For each true statement, explain why it is true.

- **a** A number with four digits is larger than a number with three digits.
- **b** Squaring a number makes it larger.
- **c** An odd number added to an odd number makes an even number.
- **d** An even number multiplied by an even number makes an even number.
- **e** All prime numbers are odd numbers.
- **f** All numbers that are divisible by 8 are also divisible by 2.

Level 6

6b I can use logical argument to establish the truth of a statement

5 Look at this 100 square.
The sum of the numbers in the 2 by 2 square is $4 + 5 + 14 + 15 = 38$.

1	2	3	4	5	6	7	8	9	10
11	12	13	14	15	16	17	18	19	20
21	22	23	24	25	26	27	28	29	30
31	32	33	34	35	36	37	38	39	40
41	42	43	44	45	46	47	48	49	50
51	52	53	54	55	56	57	58	59	60
61	62	63	64	65	66	67	68	69	70
71	72	73	74	75	76	77	78	79	80
81	82	83	84	85	86	87	88	89	90
91	92	93	94	95	96	97	98	99	100

- **a** Investigate the sum of the numbers in other 2 by 2 squares.
- **b** Explain why the sum of the numbers in any 2 by 2 square in a 100 square is always even.
- **c** Copy this general square taken from the 100 square and write expressions for the other numbers in it.

n	?
?	?

- **d** Find the sum of the expressions in the general 2 by 2 square to prove that the sum of the numbers in any 2 by 2 square will always be even.

6 **a** Using the 100 square in Q5, investigate the sum of the numbers in a 3 by 3 square.
b Use algebra to prove that the sum of the numbers in any 3 by 3 square will always be divisible by 9.

7 Prove that the sum of three consecutive numbers is always divisible by 3.

8 Prove that the sum of four consecutive numbers is always twice the sum of the two numbers in the middle.

Level 7

7b I can present a concise, reasoned argument using symbols

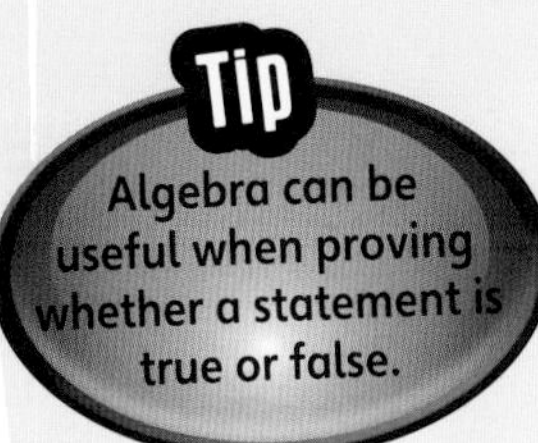

Now try this!

A Sudoku

In this Sudoku puzzle, each row and column contains the numbers 1 to 4. Each of the dark outlined squares also contains the numbers 1 to 4. Copy and complete the puzzle.

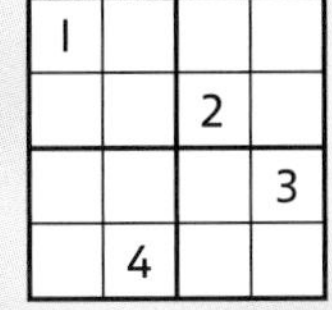

B Futoshiki

In this Futoshiki puzzle, each row and column contains the numbers 1 to 4. Copy and complete the puzzle, using the inequality signs to help you.

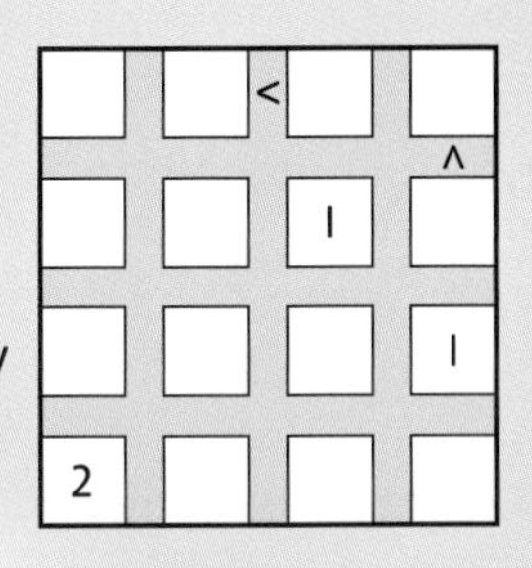

14.5 Problem solving

- Solve problems involving number and measures
- Break complex problems into simpler steps
- Solve increasingly demanding problems and evaluate solutions
- Investigate in a range of contexts

What's the BIG idea?

Why learn this?

How much food should you cook for a BBQ with your friends?

- Before trying to find the **solution** to a problem you must identify the key information. Ask yourself
  - What do I need to find out?
  - What area of maths am I going to use?
  - What calculations do I need to do? **Level 5 & Level 6**
- It is important to identify the best **method** for solving a problem. **Level 5 & Level 6**
- Solving some problems will help you to compare value for money. **Level 6**
- Sometimes a problem needs to be broken down into simpler steps to make it easier to solve. **Level 7**

Practice, practice, practice!

Level 5

5a I can choose the best method for solving problems involving number and measures

1 A lift can carry a maximum of 12 people.

  a Write the calculation you would use to work out the minimum number of trips the lift needs to make to carry 36 people from the ground floor to the top floor. Do not work out the answer.

  b Calculate the minimum number of trips that the lift needs to make if it is to carry 50 people. Show your working.

Watch out! Think carefully about whether to round up or down in real-life situations.

2 The price of a drink and a packet of crisps is 90p. The price of two drinks and a packet of crisps is £1.40. What is the price of one packet of crisps?

Tip Before tackling a word problem, work out what mathematical calculations you will use.

3 Bob and four friends are going ten-pin bowling. Each game will cost them £15 in total.

  a They have £10 each. How many games can they play?

  b If they play this many games, how much money will they each have left if they split the change equally?

4 Lucy was given £40 for her birthday. She saved four times as much as she spent. How much did she save?

5 Find three consecutive odd numbers that sum to 99.

estimate explanation

6 Adam is 12 years older than his sister Emily. The sum of their ages is three times Emily's age. How old is Adam?

7 The distance from the Earth to the Sun is approximately 93 000 000 miles. The distance from Mars to the Sun is approximately 227 000 000 km.
Calculate the distance between the Earth and Mars when they are at their closest.
Give your answer in both miles and km.

Learn this

There are roughly 1.6 km in a mile.

8 Jamie went shopping to buy a new pair of trainers.
In Tom's sports shop, the trainers normally cost £45 and were reduced by 35%.
In Sally's sports shop, the trainers usually cost £42.50 and had $\frac{1}{3}$ off.
Which shop was selling the trainers at the cheaper price?

Level 6

6b I can choose the best method for solving more difficult problems involving number and measures

9 A chocolate bar weighs 120 g. Shelly ate the first 1.5 cm piece of the bar.
The bar then weighed 90 g.
What was the length of the original chocolate bar?

10 Jessica went shopping to buy a computer. She had £450 to spend and came home with £35. The price of the computer she bought had been reduced by 20%.
What was the original price of the computer before the reduction?

11 Sanjiv was given £150 for his birthday and decided to save it. If he invests it at SuperSaver he will get 5% interest on his original amount each year. If he invests it at TopSaver, he will get 4.5% compound interest.

a In which account should he invest his money? Explain your reasoning.

b How much money would be in each account after 5 years if no further deposits or withdrawals were made?

Tip

Compound interest is calculated using the total amount of money in the account, including previous interest earned.

Level 7

7c I can break down a complex problem into simpler steps

7b I can solve increasingly demanding problems and evaluate my solutions

Now try this!

A What size?

An airline will only allow a bag as hand luggage if the dimension sum (length + depth + height) of the bag is less than 105 cm.
Work out the dimensions of the bag that will give the largest volume.

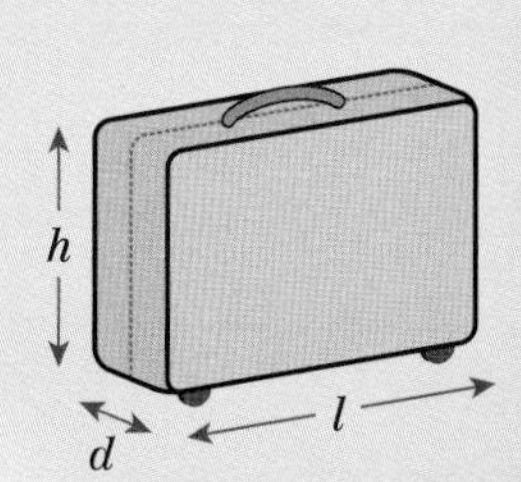

B More space!

If you travel business or first class you are sometimes allowed a larger bag.
Use a spreadsheet to investigate the dimensions of a bag that has length + depth + height

a less than 120 cm **b** less than 150 cm **c** less than 165 cm.

Explain how you can work out the length of each of the sides to maximise the volume.

Tip

Always check your answer to make sure it is sensible.

method solution

14.6 More problem solving

- Find the necessary information to solve a problem
- Evaluate solutions to find the best one
- Solve increasingly demanding problems

Why learn this?

Most jobs require you to apply maths in different contexts.

What's the BIG idea?

- Sometimes you will need to convince someone else of the **reasons** why one solution is better than another. **Level 6**
- Remember to check your solution to make sure it makes sense. **Level 6**
- When finding the answer to a problem you can sometimes find other questions to ask. **Level 7**

Level 5

5a I can identify the necessary information to solve a problem

1 Mr Carlton is 80 years old. Each birthday since he was born, he has had the same number of candles on his birthday cake as his age. How many candles has Mr Carlton had on his birthday cakes during his life so far?

Lucy's scooter budget

Lucy is thinking of buying a scooter. She will use it just for getting to work and back, which is a 24-mile return journey.

	Miles per litre	Yearly road tax	Yearly insurance
Scooter A	6	£32	£180
Scooter B	8	£47	£250

2 At Motors petrol station, unleaded petrol costs £1.21 per litre.

a How much will it cost Lucy in petrol per day for each scooter?

b Lucy works five days per week.
How much will it cost Lucy in petrol per week for each scooter?

3 Lucy has four weeks' holiday per year.
How much will it cost Lucy in petrol each year for each scooter?

Level 6

6b I can solve increasingly demanding problems and evaluate solutions

4 Petrol prices range from £1.19 per litre to £1.32 per litre.

a Calculate the minimum and maximum petrol costs for each scooter per year.

b Including road tax and insurance, which scooter is cheaper to run?
Explain your reasoning.

compare reason solve

Jamie's mobile phone dilemma

Jamie is thinking of changing his mobile phone provider.
Here is the mobile phone tariff from Moby Mobiles.

	Monthly line rental	Cost per minute, m	Cost per text, t
Option A	£10	12p	10p
Option B	£15	10p	8p
Option C	£20	10p	6p

5 At the moment, Jamie makes on average 200 minutes of telephone calls and 300 texts each month. You are a sales person for Moby Mobiles. Find the best price plan for Jamie and prepare a presentation to show Jamie why he should choose this plan.

6 Jamie increases his telephone calls by 30% and decreases his texts by 20%. Which price plan would you advise him to choose now?

7 Jamie chooses Option A. He has budgeted for a monthly bill of £43.

- **a** What is the maximum number of minutes of calls he can make?
- **b** What is the maximum number of texts he can send?
- **c** If the number of minutes of calls is the same as the number of texts he sends, how many texts can he send?

Level 6

6b I can present a concise, reasoned argument

6b I can solve increasingly demanding problems and evaluate solutions

8 Jamie decides that he will no longer make telephone calls as it is too expensive. He would rather text instead.

- **a** Investigate the cost of each price plan.
- **b** Use graphs and charts to convince Jamie which price plan he should choose.

9 Jamie's sister, Claire, also wants to buy a phone from Moby Mobiles. Claire only needs the phone for making calls.

- **a** Jamie tells Claire that either Option A or B will be better than Option C. Explain why Jamie is correct.
- **b** Draw a graph to compare the cost of making up to 500 minutes of calls with Options A and B.
- **c** Claire usually makes 280 minutes of calls per month. Which Option should she choose?

Level 7

7c I can present a concise, reasoned argument using graphs

Now try this!

A What will it cost?

Look back at Q2. Set up a spreadsheet to show the cost of petrol for scooter A over different distances if the price of petrol is £1.21 per litre.

B Calls and texts

Find someone in your class who uses a mobile phone. Ask them how many minutes they use their phone to make telephone calls and how many texts they send on average each month.
Work out which option from Moby Mobiles would be best for them.

A beautiful ratio

The golden ratio is used to divide an object into two parts so that the ratio of the larger to the smaller part (g : 1) is the same as the ratio of the whole object to the larger part. The number g is considered to be special and is approximately equal to 1.62. The simplest example of the golden ratio is the golden rectangle. There are many examples of the golden ratio in architecture because it is considered that division in the golden ratio produces an object more beautiful to look at. It is thought that the Parthenon, an ancient temple in Greece, was built with the golden rectangle proportions.

A: 6 m by 2 m
B: 8 m by 5 m
C: 12 m by 4 m
D: 150 cm by 50 cm
E: 48 cm by 30 cm

1 Identify the rectangles that are in direct proportion. **Level 5**

2 Write the ratio of length to width for each rectangle. Give your answers in their simplest form. **Level 5**

3 Work out 'length ÷ width' for each rectangle. Are any of them golden rectangles? **Level 5**

4 Construct these rectangles.
Rectangle F: length 6.5 cm, width 4 cm
Rectangle G: length 7 cm, width 2 cm
Which do you think is the golden rectangle?
Check to see if you are correct by working out the length divided by width.
Do you think that the golden rectangle is more 'beautiful' than the other rectangle? **Level 5**

5 The ratio of the width to length of a rectangle is 5 : 8. The perimeter of the rectangle is 78 cm.
a What are the length and width of the rectangle?
b What is the area of the rectangle? **Level 6**

6 An architect has decided to use the golden ratio to design a new structure. As part of the design, columns are to be constructed around a central rectangle. The area of the rectangle has to be 60 m^2.
What length and width dimensions should the architect use? **Level 6**

7 **a** Construct an accurate triangle with base angles of 72°. Make sure your construction has a base length greater than 8 cm.
b Using a pair of compasses, bisect one of the 72° angles.
c What can you say about the smallest triangle and the largest triangle?
d Show that $\frac{a}{b} = \frac{a+b}{a}$

e What is the ratio of the longer to the shorter side of the isosceles triangle? **Level 7**

The BIG ideas

- Simplifying a **ratio** is similar to simplifying fractions. You need to divide each part of the ratio by a common factor. For example,

$$20 : 12 \xrightarrow{\div 4} 5 : 3$$

Level 5

- Ratios can be used to divide and share different quantities. Level 5 & Level 6
- Some **rules** and **arguments** can be proved using algebra. For example, the sum of two consecutive numbers is odd. Represent these numbers by n and $n + 1$. The sum is $n + (n + 1) = 2n + 1$. $2n$ will always be an even number. Adding 1 makes it an odd number. Therefore, you have proved that the sum of two consecutive numbers is an odd number. Level 7
- Sometimes a problem needs to be broken down into simpler steps to make it easier to solve. Level 7

Practice SATs-style questions

Level 5

Q1 8 pens cost 96p. What is the cost of

a 4 pens

b 6 pens

c 10 pens?

Q2 Teabags are sold in boxes of 40 and 60.

Which pack gives you better value for money?

Level 6

Q3 At the travel agents, Sajid changes £120 for 150 euros.

a How many euros would he get for £200?

b When Sajid returns from his holiday, he has 24 euros remaining. If he is offered the same rate of exchange, how many pounds will he get?

Q4 Business Brains is a new company that has three directors. Mr A, Mr B and Mrs C own 2, 4 and 6 parts of the company respectively. In a week, the company makes £768 profit.
How much of the profit will each director receive?

Level 7

Q5 The compound interest formula is

$$A = P\left(1 + \frac{R}{100}\right)^n$$

where A is the amount in the bank, P is the amount deposited, R is the annual interest rate and n is the number of years.

a Use the formula to calculate the amount of money in a bank account when £250 is invested for 5 years at an annual compound interest rate of 5.6%.

b Which of the following investments would give the better return?

A: £3500 invested for 1.2 years at a rate of 5.5%

B: £3500 invested for 6 months at a rate of 9.5%

C: £3500 invested for 9 months at a rate of 7.2%

15 Back to the drawing board

This unit is about 2-D and 3-D shapes and scale drawings, in a variety of contexts.

You have already learned lots of facts about shapes, lines and angles. These facts were first written down by Euclid, a Greek mathematician born around 300 BC. His 13-volume book, *Elements*, is probably the most famous maths book ever. It was first printed in 1482 and has been reprinted many times since – in fact, parts of it were still used in maths textbooks in the early twentieth century.

Euclid starts by defining facts that we now take for granted. For example,

'It is possible to draw a straight line between any two points.'

From this he deduces that it is possible to draw shapes such as triangles, quadrilaterals and polygons, as they are all made from straight lines.

Euclid also described the methods for constructing accurate drawings using a straight edge and compasses, methods which are still taught in schools today.

Did you know?

One of the craters on the Moon has been named after Euclid.

Activities

A Book I of *Elements* starts with 23 'definitions'. Here are some of them:

A point is that which has no part.
A line is a breadthless length.
The extremities of lines are points.

Work out what he means by each one. Do you agree with his definitions?

B One of Euclid's basic 'rules' for number is:

Things equal to the same thing are also equal to one another.

What does he mean by this? Use number or algebraic statements to show how this works. Does it always work?

Before you start this unit...

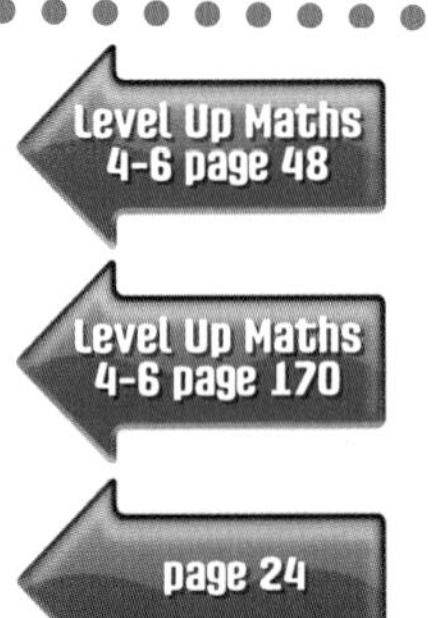

1 Draw a line that is exactly 8.7 cm long.

2 Use a protractor to draw an angle of 187°.

3

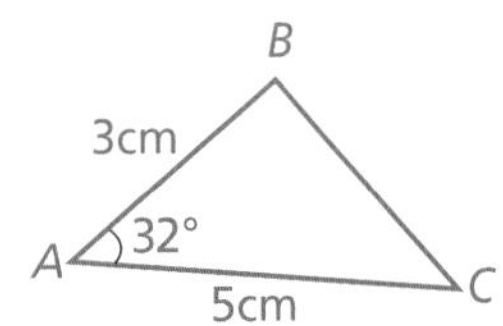

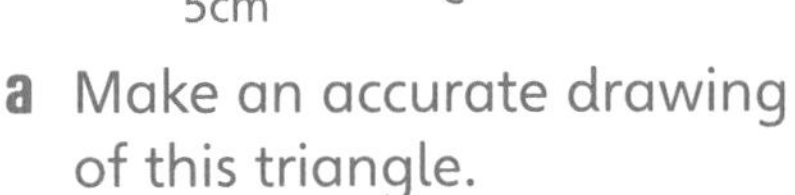

a Make an accurate drawing of this triangle.

b What is the length of side *BC*?

4 Draw a set of x- and y-axes from 0 to 10.

page 26

a Plot these coordinate points. *A*(9,7), *B*(5, 7), *C*(4,5)

b Complete the parallelogram by adding point *D*.

c Identify one pair of parallel sides.

5 Sketch one possible net for each of these shapes.

Level Up Maths 4-6 page 298

a Cube **b** Cuboid

World's Greatest Maths

Plus digital resources

Did you know?

Euclid is the most successful textbook writer of all time. *Elements* has gone through more than 1000 editions since the invention of printing.

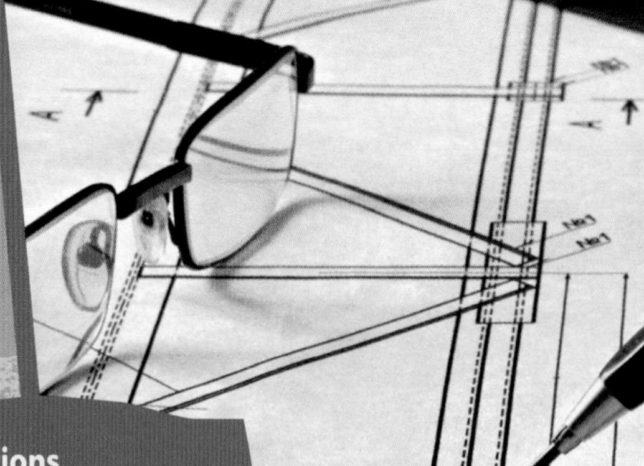

15.1 3-D shapes

- Deduce properties of 3-D shapes from 2-D representations
- Know and use geometric properties of cuboids and shapes made from cuboids
- Visualise and use a wide range of 2-D representations of 3-D objects
- Analyse 3-D shapes through 2-D representations

Why learn this?

A product designer uses 2-D representations of 3-D objects to tell a manufacturer how a product is to be made.

What's the BIG idea?

- To show a **3-D** object using a drawing in **2-D** you can use **isometric** paper. **Level 6**
- To describe a 3-D shape you can count the number of **faces** (flat surfaces), **edges** (where two faces meet) and **vertices** (where three or more edges meet). For example, this shape has six faces, 12 edges and eight vertices. **Level 6**

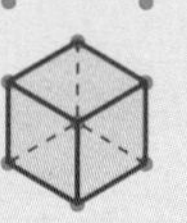

Super fact!

There are five solid shapes where all of the faces are congruent – these are called Platonic solids or regular polyhedrons. Statues of the solids have been found in Scotland and are over 4000 years old.

Practice, practice, practice!

Level 5

5c I can work out properties of 3-D shapes from their 2-D representations

5b I can describe and use geometric properties of cuboids

1 Here is one way to arrange four cubes.
Draw three other arrangements on isometric paper.

2 Look at this cuboid.

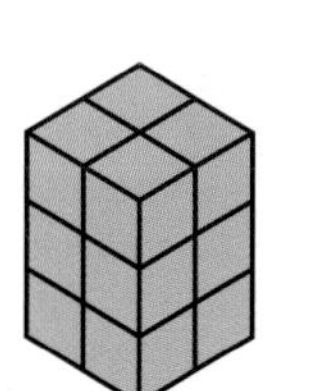

a Draw three ways to divide the cuboid into two identical shapes.

b Draw two ways to divide the cuboid into two non-identical shapes.

3 Opposite faces of this cuboid are the same colour.

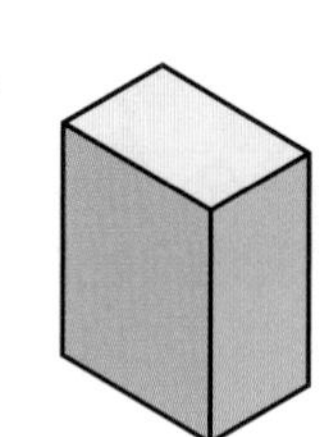

a How many edges does it have?

b How many edges are there where

i a yellow face meets a blue face

ii a green face meets a blue face

iii a yellow face meets a green face?

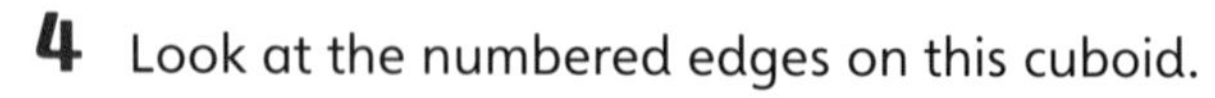

4 Look at the numbered edges on this cuboid.

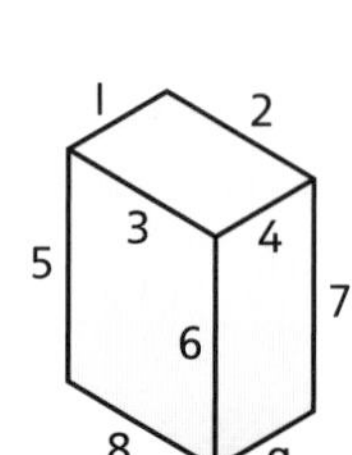

a Write two sets of parallel edges.

b Write two sets of perpendicular edges.

c Write two sets of three edges that meet at a vertex.

d How many edges can you *not* see?

2-D 3-D edge

5 Sketch nets of these solids.

a

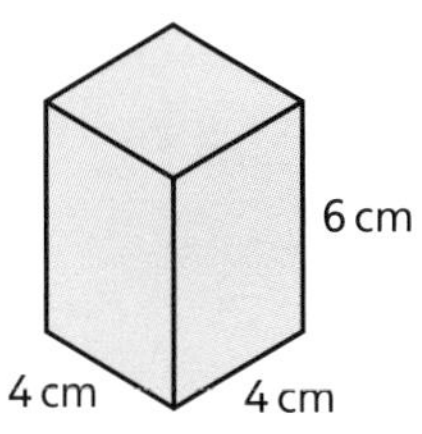

b

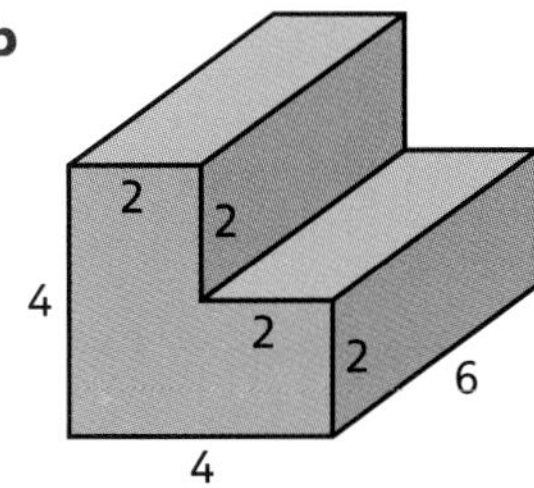

c

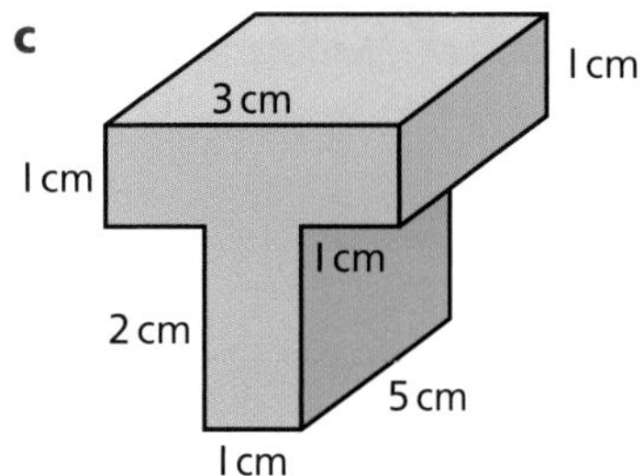

6 Look at the numbered edges on this prism.

a Write three sets of parallel edges.

b Write three sets of perpendicular edges.

c Write two sets of three edges that meet at a vertex.

d How many faces can you *not* see?

e How many edges can you *not* see?

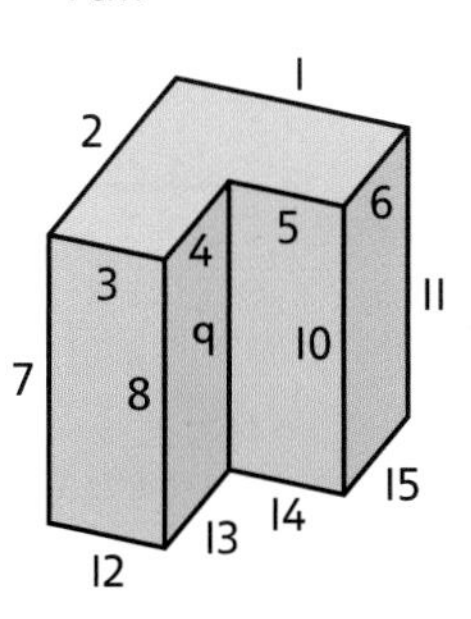

Level 5

5a I can sketch nets of 3-D shapes

5a I can describe and use geometric properties of shapes made from cuboids

7 Here are two views of the same solid made from cubes.
Another cube is added to create two new shapes.
This is what they look like this when viewed from A.

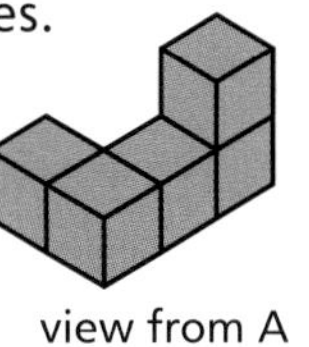
view from A

view from B

a

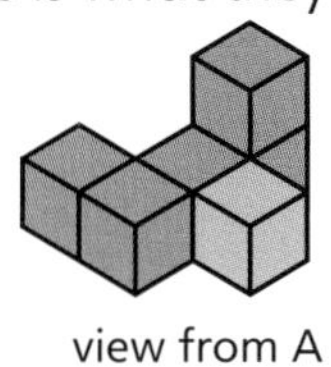
view from A

b

view from A

Using isometric paper draw the view from B of each of the new shapes.

8 The diagrams show three views of the same cube.
Which symbols are opposite each other?

9 These are the silhouettes of some 3-D solids.
Which solid can be represented by each silhouette?

a 
b 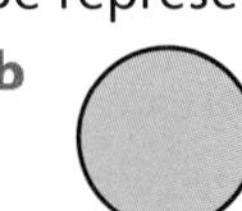
c 
d 

Hint: There may be more than one answer.

Level 6

6c I can visualise and use a variety of 2-D representations of 3-D objects

6b I can analyse 3-D shapes by looking at informal 2-D representations, like shadows

Now try this!

A Representations of 3-D shapes

Work with a partner. You need multilink cubes and isometric paper. Each secretly build a shape out of five blocks and draw a 2-D representation of the shape. Swap pictures with your partner. Who can build the correct shape quicker?

B Faces, edges and vertices

Count the number of faces, edges and vertices for each solid.
Copy and complete the table.

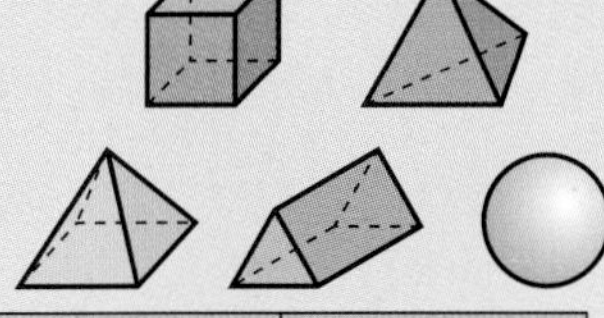

Shape	Faces	Edges	Vertices	Link
Cube				

Can you find a link between the numbers for each shape?

face isometric vertex (vertices)

15.2 Plans and elevations

- Begin to use plans and elevations
- Analyse 3-D shapes through cross-sections, plans and elevations

Why learn this?

Architects use plans and elevations when they develop ideas for buildings.

What's the BIG idea?

→ You can use 2-D representations of 3-D shapes to help visualise them.

The **front elevation** is the view looking from the front.
The **side elevation** is the view looking from the side.
The **plan** is the view looking down from above.

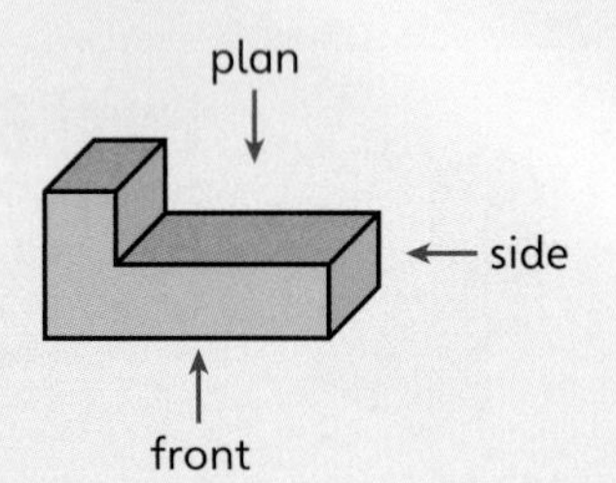

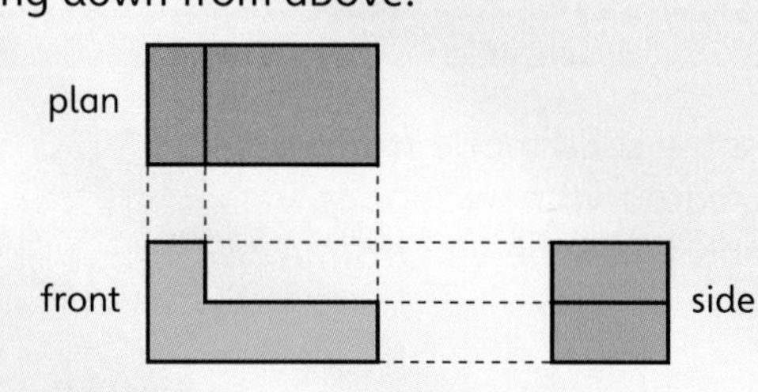

Level 6

Practice, practice, practice!

Level 6

6C I can make basic use of plans and elevations

1 a Build three different solids using four cubes.
b For each solid, sketch the plan, side elevation and front elevation.

2 Sketch the plan, side and front elevation for each of these shapes.

a
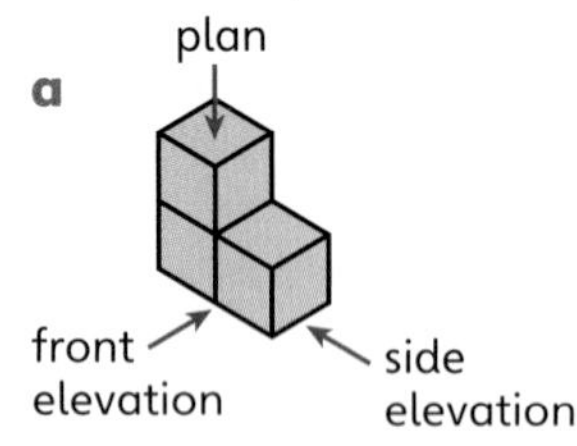

b
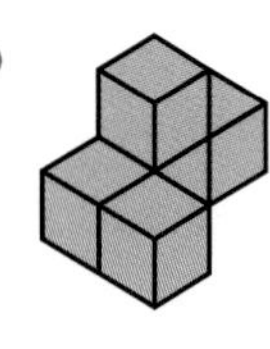

c
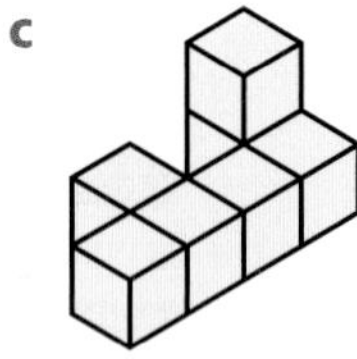

3 Use cubes to build each of these solid shapes.

a plan, front elevation, side elevation

b plan, front elevation, side elevation

c

plan, front elevation, side elevation

d
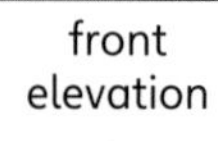
plan, front elevation, side elevation

cross-section front elevation plan

4 Each diagram shows a plan of a solid made from cubes. The numbers show how many cubes are on the base. Sketch the solid in each case.

a

b

c

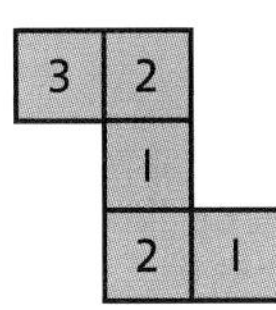

5 For each set of views, sketch the 3-D shape and a net of the solid.

a

plan

front elevation

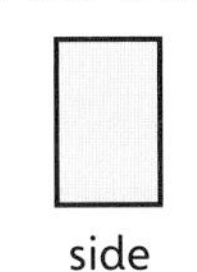
side elevation

b

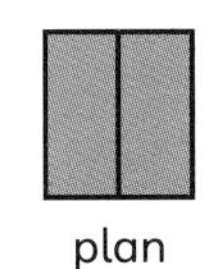
plan

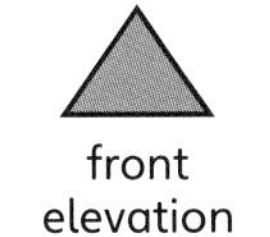
front elevation

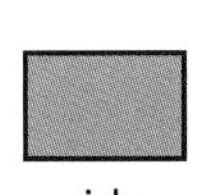
side elevation

c

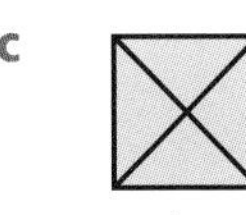
plan

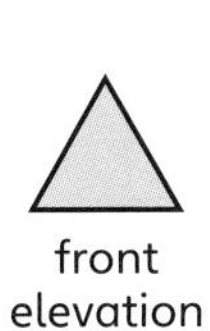
front elevation

side elevation

d

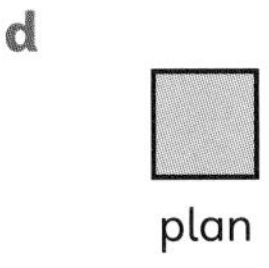
plan

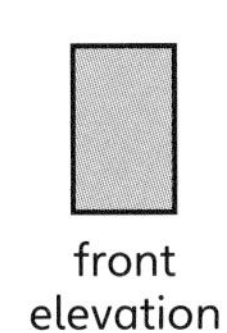
front elevation

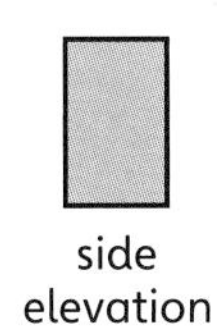
side elevation

6 Name and sketch the shape from each of these descriptions.

a The front elevation and the plan are equilateral triangles.

b The front elevation is a hexagon and the plan is a rectangle.

c The front and side elevations and the plan are all squares.

d The front elevation is a circle and the plan is a rectangle.

7 Sketch the two parts of this solid if it is cut so that the new face of each part is

a rectangular

b circular

c oval.

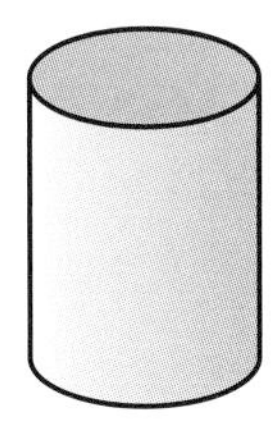

8 Sketch the two parts of these solids if they are cut along the dotted line.

a

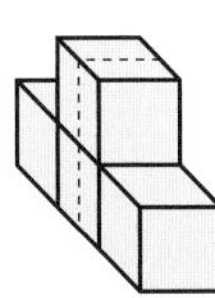

b

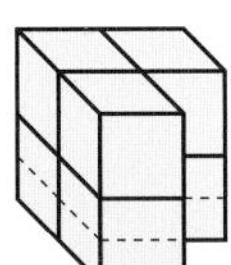

Level 6

6a I can analyse 3-D shapes by looking at cross-sections, plans and elevations

Now try this!

A Bedroom plan views

Draw a plan of your bedroom including the main pieces of furniture.
If you don't know the exact lengths of items in the room, estimate them.

B Design a cereal box

- Design a cereal box with a volume of 400 cm^3. Draw a plan, front elevation and side elevation of the box. Mark on the measurements.
- The manufacturer needs a box that holds 10% more cereal. Draw a plan, front elevation and side elevation of the new box, including the revised measurements.

15.3 Nets and constructions

- Identify nets of 3-D shapes
- Use a ruler and protractor to construct simple nets of 3-D shapes
- Use a ruler and protractor to construct triangles
- Use a ruler and compasses to construct triangles

Why learn this?

To create this box, you must first create an accurate net of the 3-D shape.

What's the BIG idea?

→ A **net** is made up of all the faces of a shape joined together so that they fold to make a 3-D shape.

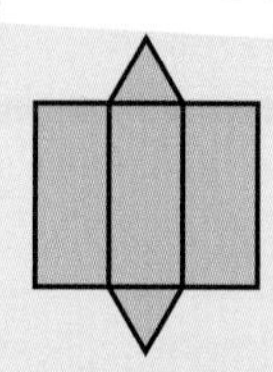

triangular prism

net of triangular prism **Level 5**

→ The minimum information needed to **construct** a triangle is either the lengths of two sides and an included angle (SAS), two angles and the included side (ASA) or all three sides (SSS).

ASA

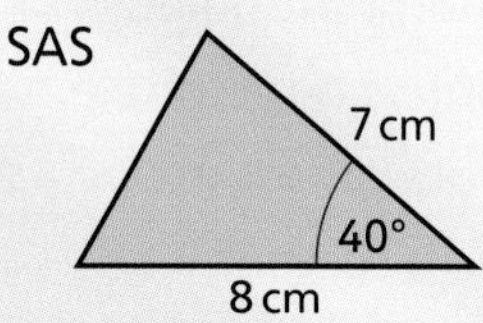

SSS

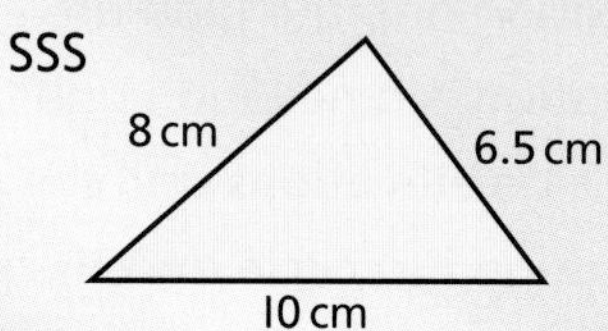

Level 5 & Level 6

→ You can use a ruler and compasses to construct a right-angled triangle if you know the lengths of the hypotenuse and one other side (RHS). **Level 7**

Practice, practice, practice!

Level 5

5c I can identify simple nets of regular polyhedra

1 Which of these are nets of a tetrahedron?

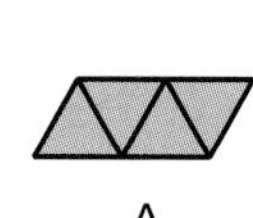

A

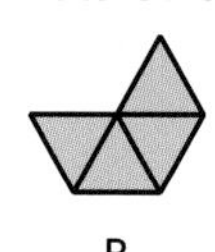

B

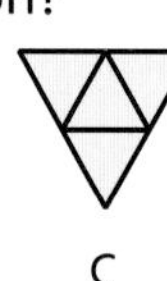

C

5b I can identify more complex nets of 3-D shapes including irregular polyhedra

2 Sketch and name the solids made from these nets.

a

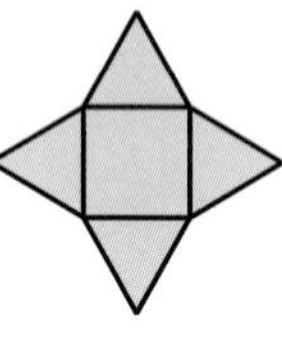

b

c

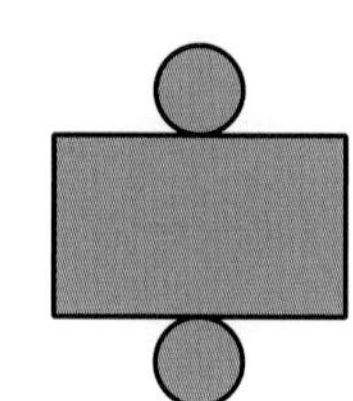

5b I can use a ruler and protractor to construct simple nets of 3-D shapes

3 Construct accurate nets of these solids.

a

6 cm
3 cm
4 cm

b

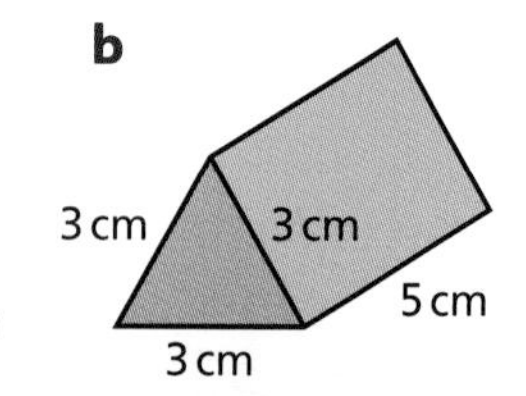

c

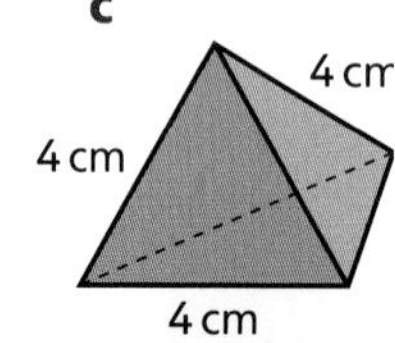

Tip

Always use a sharp pencil when drawing shapes accurately.

construct measure net

4 Construct these triangles accurately.

a sides 8 cm and 5 cm, included angle 47°

b sides 7.5 cm and 3.6 cm, included angle 34°

5 Construct these triangles accurately.

a

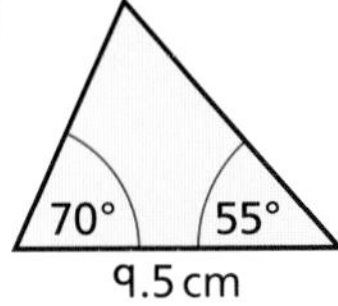

b

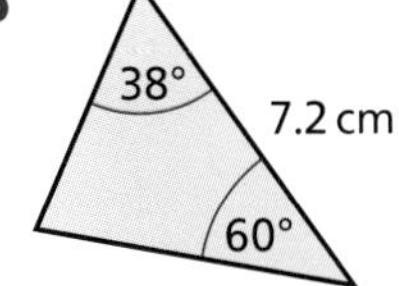

c

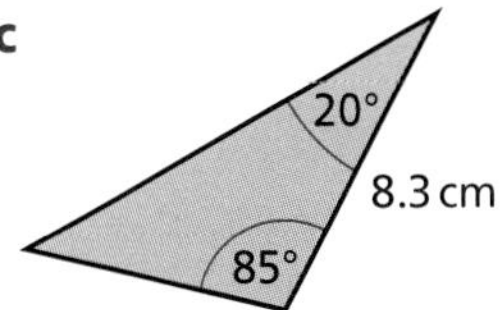

d triangle ABC, with $\angle BAC = 60°$, $CA = 8$ cm and $\angle BCA = 75°$

e Triangle XYZ, with $XY = 7.5$ cm, $\angle XYZ = 35°$ and $\angle ZXY = 71°$

Level 5

5b I can use a ruler and protractor to construct a triangle, given two sides and the included angle (SAS)

5a I can use a ruler and protractor to construct a triangle given two angles and the included side (ASA)

6 Construct these triangles accurately.

a triangle ABC, with $AC = 6$ cm, $CB = 8$ cm and $AC = 5$ cm

b triangle DEF, with $DE = 7.5$ cm, $EF = 10.1$ cm and $FD = 8.6$ cm

c triangle XYZ, with $XY = 7.5$ cm, $YZ = 4.5$ cm and $XZ = 4.5$ cm

Level 6

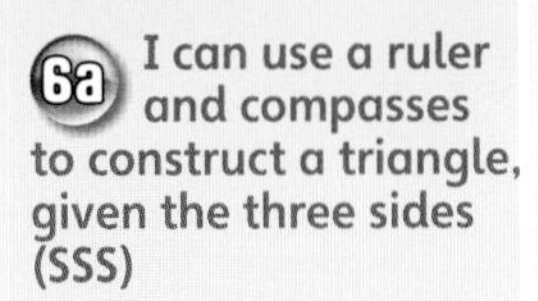

6a I can use a ruler and compasses to construct a triangle, given the three sides (SSS)

7 Draw these triangles accurately using compasses and a ruler to construct the right angle.

a

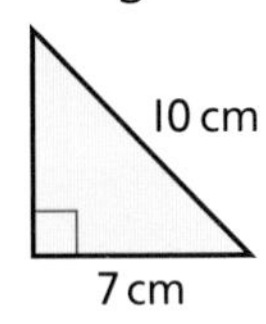

b

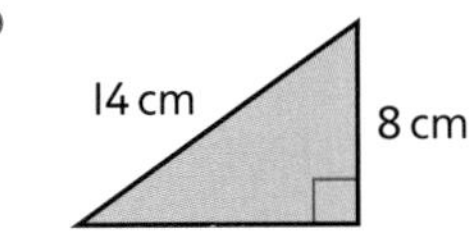

c

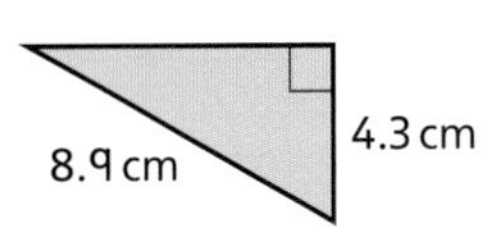

8 Which of these triangles can you construct from the information given? If you cannot construct them, explain why.

a

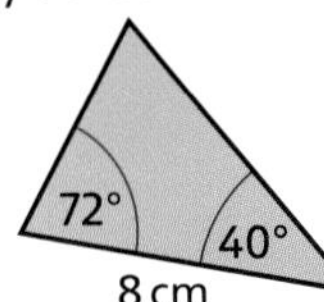

b

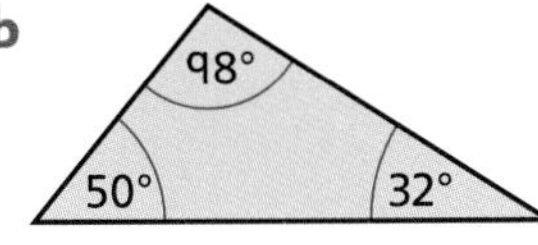

c

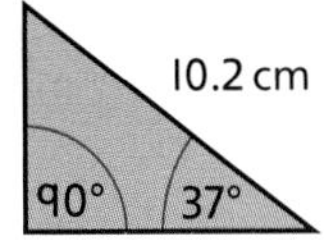

d triangle GHI, with $HI = 6$ cm, $GH = 7$ cm and $GI = 12$ cm.

e triangle LMN, with $LM = 5.5$ cm, $MN = 4.1$ cm and $LN = 10.6$ cm.

f triangle PQR, with $PQ = 6$ cm, $QR = 6$ cm and $PR = 12$ cm.

Level 7

7c I can use a ruler and compasses to construct a right-angled triangle (RHS)

7c I can identify the information needed to construct a triangle

Now try this!

A Design a net 1

You have been asked to design a packet or box for a new type of sweet. Design the box using plan, front and side elevations. Then make the net.

B Design a net 2

a Repeat Activity A for a box that is a pyramid.

b The cardboard for the box costs 56p per square metre. How much is this per net? How many nets could you actually get out of each square metre?

15.4 Maps and scale drawings

- Draw diagrams to scale
- Use scales in maps and plans
- Use and interpret maps and scale drawings

Why learn this?

Civil engineers and builders use scale diagrams in construction projects – the scale diagrams give them the dimensions of the item being built.

What's the BIG idea?

→ You can use **scales** to make accurate drawings of objects that are much bigger in real life. **Level 5 & Level 6**

→ You can use the scale on a map to tell you the distance between two places in real life. **Level 6 & Level 7**

Practice, practice, practice!

Level 5

5a I can make simple scale drawings

1 Make an accurate scale drawing of each garden using the scale given.

a 12 m, 5 m
Scale: 1 cm represents 2 m

b 30 m, 20 m, 40 m
Scale: 1 cm represents 10 m

c 40°, 25 m
Scale: 1 cm represents 5 m

2 Measure your desk. Choose a suitable scale and make an accurate drawing, clearly stating the scale used.

Level 6

6c I can use scales on maps and plans

3 Tammy is using a map with a scale of 1 : 50 000.
What are these map distances in real life?

a 3 cm **b** 5 cm **c** 10.5 cm **d** 8 cm

4 Use the map to estimate the distance from

a Siparia to Mayaro
b Port of Spain to Pitch Lake
c Devil's Woodyard to Matelot
d Icacos Point to Sangre Grande.

east estimate north perimeter

5 Look at the map of Tokyo.
How far is it, in a straight line, between

a the imperial Palace and the Fukagawa Edo Museum

b the Sony Building and the Hama Rikyū Detached Palace Garden

c the Tokyo National Museum and the Imperial Palace?

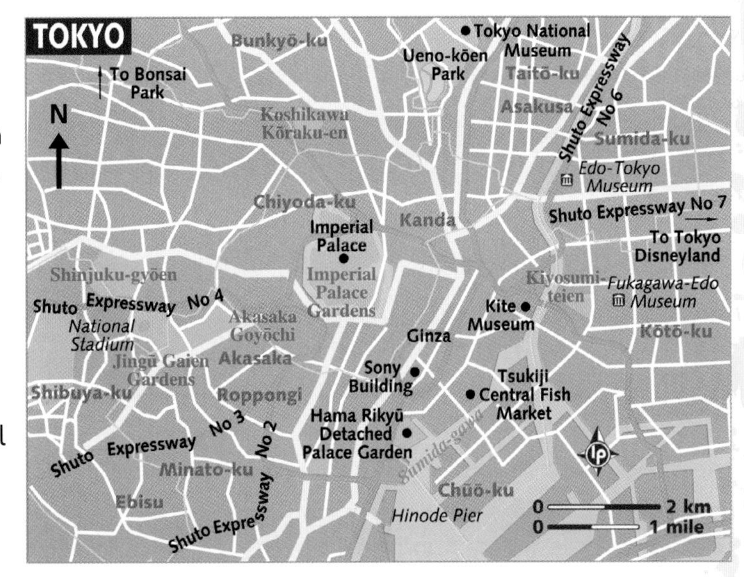

6 Follow these directions. Where do they take you?

a From the Tokyo National Museum go due south for 6 km.

b From the Hama Rikyū Detached Palace Garden follow the river north-east for about 3.5 miles.

c From the Edo-Tokyo Museum follow the Shuto Expressway No 6 southwards for about 3 km.

Level 6

6a I can use and interpret maps

7 Look at the scale drawing of Olympic Park in London. Stratford International Station is 1100 m long.

a Estimate the distance, in a straight line, from the Handball Arena to the centre of the Olympic Stadium.

b Estimate the distance from the Basketball Arena to the Spectator Services.

c Estimate the perimeter of the Warm up Athletics Track & Throws Area.

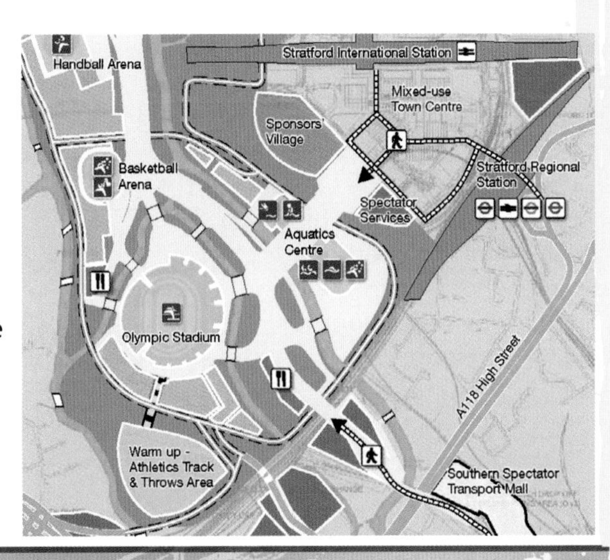

Level 7

7c I can use and interpret scale drawings

Now try this!

A Add your own landmarks

On centimetre squared paper draw a map of an island. Use a sensible scale of your own choice and write directions between different landmarks on the island.

B Personal scale drawings

Work with a partner. Draw scale drawings of each other using different scales, for example 1 : 20, 1 : 10 or even 1 : 100.

scale south west

15.5 Bearings

- Use a protractor to draw angles to the nearest degree
- Understand and use the language associated with bearings
- Use bearings to specify direction
- Draw diagrams to scale

Why learn this?

Bearings are used by the crew of ships to help them steer where they want to go. There are very few landmarks to go by on the open sea!

What's the BIG idea?

→ A **bearing** is the **direction** of one object from another. **Level 5**

→ Bearings are measured in degrees clockwise from north, and are always three-figure numbers. For example, the bearing of Alltown from Brumville is 066°. **Level 5**

→ You can draw **scale diagrams** using bearings to solve problems. **Level 6**

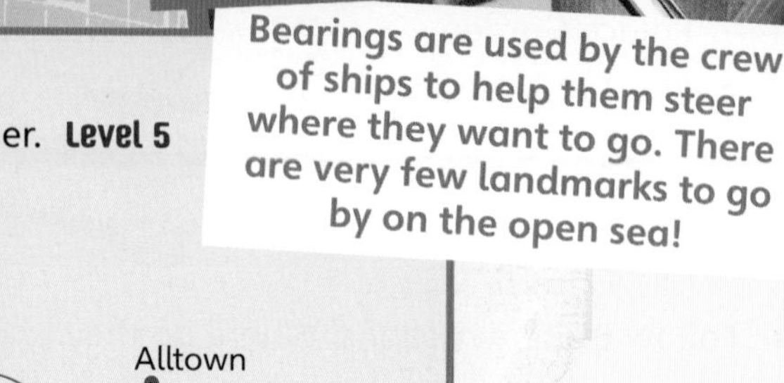

Practice, practice, practice!

1 Draw these angles accurately using a ruler and protractor.

a 136° **b** 93° **c** 171° **d** 145°

2 Draw these angles accurately using a ruler and protractor.

a 256° **b** 305° **c** 191° **d** 275°

3 Andy, a helicopter pilot, can see his troop of soldiers below him. He needs to describe to them what he can see. Using bearings, write instructions for Andy to radio to his troop.

farm
mountains
reservoir
N
Andy's troop
village
enemy

4

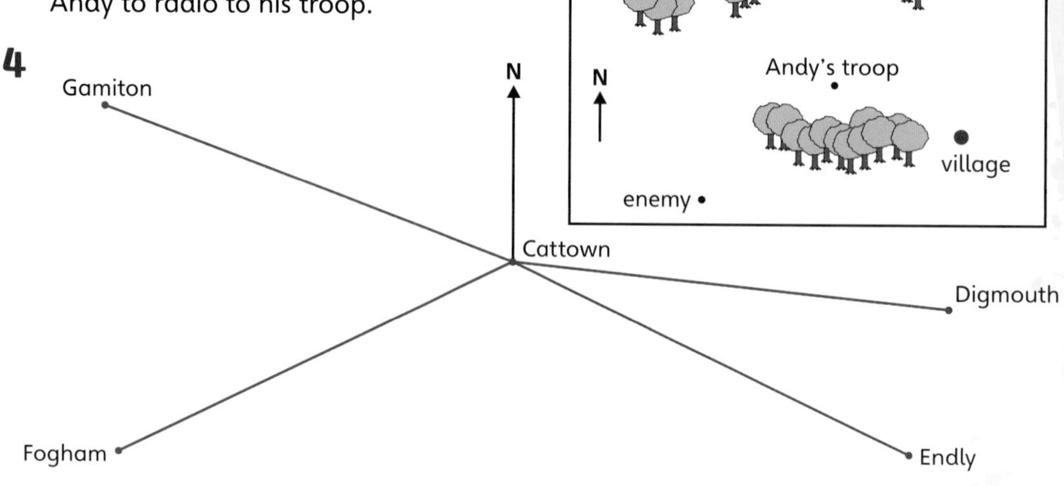

Use the diagram to find the bearing of each town from Cattown.

a Digmouth **b** Endly **c** Fogham **d** Gamiton

Level 5

5c I can use a protractor to draw obtuse angles to the nearest degree

5c I can use a protractor to draw reflex angles to the nearest degree

5a I can use bearings to describe a direction

angle bearing direction east north

5 Use a scale of 1 cm : 1 km to accurately draw the following.

a Liverton is 7.5 km from Mudford on a bearing of 045°.

b Nuttyford is 6 km from Oranville on a bearing of 137°.

c Pea Greene is 8.2 km from Quinton on a bearing of 306°.

d Rusty is 11 km from Seaborn on a bearing of 233°.

Level 5

5a I can make simple scale drawings, with lengths and angles drawn accurately

6 An aircraft flies on a bearing of 110° for 50 miles and then on a bearing of 225° for 80 miles.

a Draw an accurate scale drawing to represent this.

b What is the distance of the aircraft from where it started?

7 A ship is near the coast. A lighthouse is on a bearing of 065° and a castle is on a bearing of 340° from the ship. The ship's captain knows that the lighthouse is exactly 8 km from the castle, on a bearing of 90°.

a Use a scale of 1 cm : 1 km to show the ship's position.

b Estimate how far the ship is from the coast.

8 A ship sails 20 km on a bearing of 105° from point X to point Y. The ship then changes course and sails 26 km on a bearing of 062° to point Z.

a Use a scale of 1 cm : 4 km to show the ship's journey between points X, Y and Z.

b What bearing should the ship use to sail directly back to point X?

c What is the distance between points X and Z?

9 A yacht sails 20 km on a bearing of 110°. It then sails 25 km on a bearing of 190°. Finally, the yacht sails 10 km due west to its destination.

a Draw an accurate scale drawing to represent this.

b Write instructions for the return journey along the same path.

Level 6

6b I can draw diagrams to scale

Now try this!

A Treaure island

Draw a map of an island. Include the pirate's landing spot and lots of obstacles like a swamp, giant spiders and so on. Write instructions using bearings to get from the landing spot to the treasure. Swap maps and instructions with a partner to try and find each other's treasure.

B Losing your bearings

From Westby you need to walk 5 km on a bearing of 075° to reach an old fort.

- If you used your protractor inaccurately and walked for 5 km on a bearing of 077°, how far from the fort would you end up? Draw a map with a scale of 1 cm to 2 km to find out.
- Investigate how larger errors in measuring the bearing would affect your distance from the fort.

Watch out!

Always remember that bearings are measured clockwise from north.

scale scale diagram south west

15.6 Coordinates

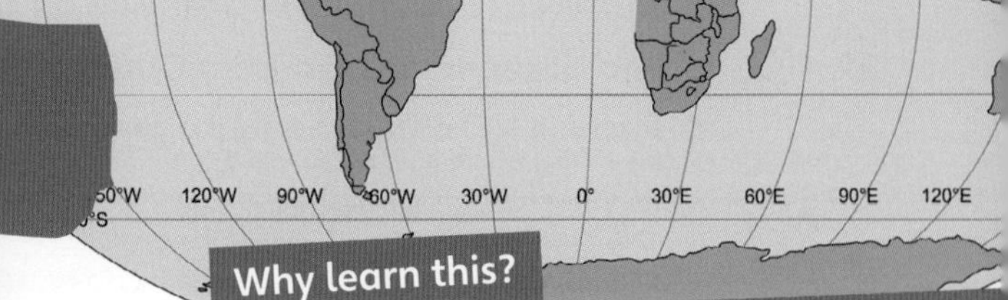

- Read and plot coordinates in all four quadrants
- Find the mid-point of a line segment

Why learn this?

Coordinates are a way of describing position. Latitude and longitude on maps are a form of coordinates.

What's the BIG idea?

- The **mid-point** is exactly halfway along a **line segment**. **Level 5**
- You can find the mid-point by using the coordinates of the end points of the line segment.
  The mid-point of the line segment joining $A(x_1, y_1)$ to $B(x_2, y_2)$ is $\left(\frac{x_1 + x_2}{2}\right), \left(\frac{y_1 + y_2}{2}\right)$
  Level 6

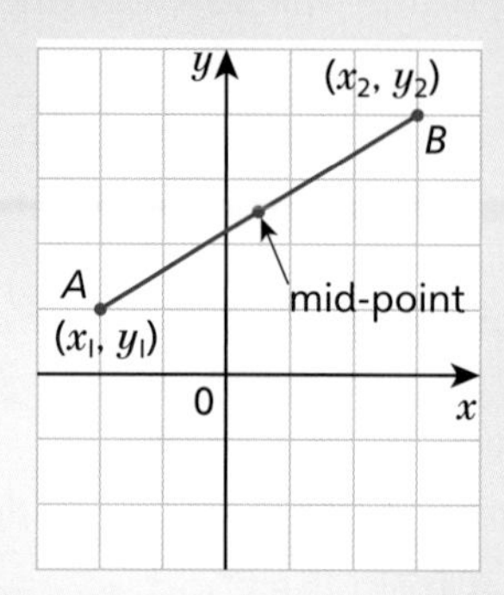

Practice, practice, practice!

Level 5

5a I can plot all the points of a shape from geometric information about the shape

1 Here are the coordinates of three corners of some squares.
Find the coordinates of the fourth corner of each square.

a (1, 0), (5, 0), (5, 4) **b** (1, 2), (−3, 2), (−3, −2)

c (1, 5), (5, 6), (4, 10) **d** (3, 1), (1, −1), (5, −1)

2 Here are the coordinates of two points: (−1, 4) and (−4, 7).
Write down the coordinates of two more points to make each of these shapes.

a square **b** rectangle

c parallelogram **d** kite

5a I can find the mid-point of a line segment

3 For each line segment, write down the coordinates of the two end points and the mid-point.

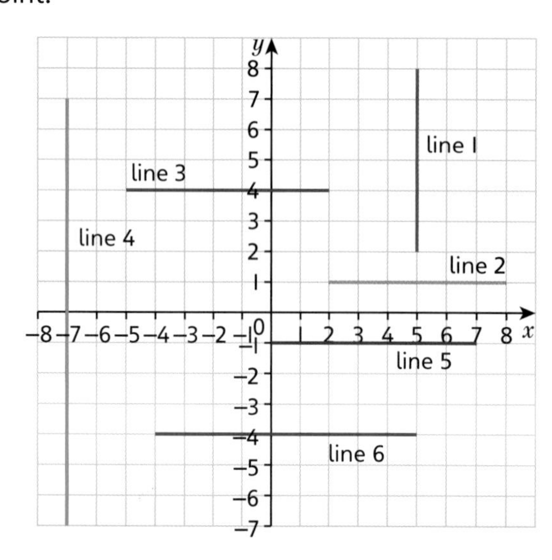

coordinates line segment

4 These coordinate pairs are the ends of line segments.
Write down the coordinates of the mid-point of each line segment.

a (3, 1), (3, 7) **b** (5, 2), (11, 2) **c** (−7, −3), (1, −3)
d (−2, 4), (−6, 4) **e** (0, 7), (3, 7) **f** (−3, −6), (4, −6)

5 For each line segment, write the coordinates of the end points and the mid-point.

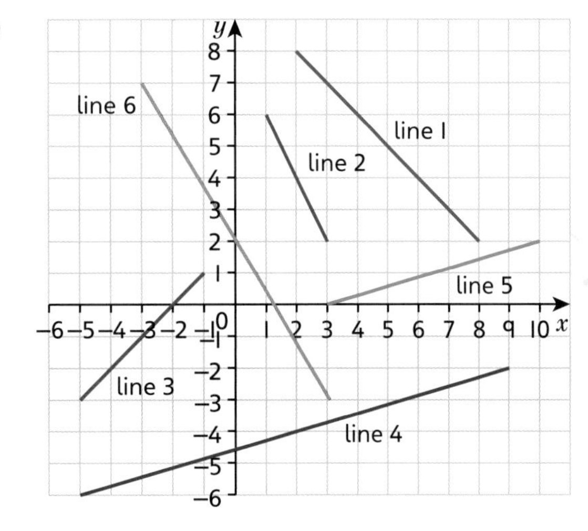

6 Find the mid-point of the line segment with these end points.

a (3, 7), (11, 3) **b** (0, 7), (2, 3) **c** (1, 1), (11, 5)
d (−6, 1), (−4, 3) **e** (3, −2), (5, 5) **f** (0, −4), (2, 11)

7 Here are the mid-points of some lines.
Find two possible end points for each line.

a (6, 3) **b** (0, 10) **c** (−1, 3) **d** (6, −4)

8 The coordinates of the mid-point of a line segment AB are (1, 2).
Find the coordinates of B when A has the following coordinates.

a (1, 4) **b** (−1, 2) **c** (6, 2) **d** (1, −3)

Level 6

6c I can find the mid-point of a vertical or horizontal line segment using coordinates

6b I can find the mid-point of a diagonal line segment

6b I can find the mid-point of a diagonal line segment using coordinates

Now try this!

A Coordinates and squares

A game for two players.
Take turns to mark a point with whole-number coordinates on a grid.
You must not mark a point that has already been taken.
The winner is the first person to mark four corners of a square.

B 3-D coordinates

Coordinates can be used in 3-D.
What are the coordinates of the other vertices of this cube?

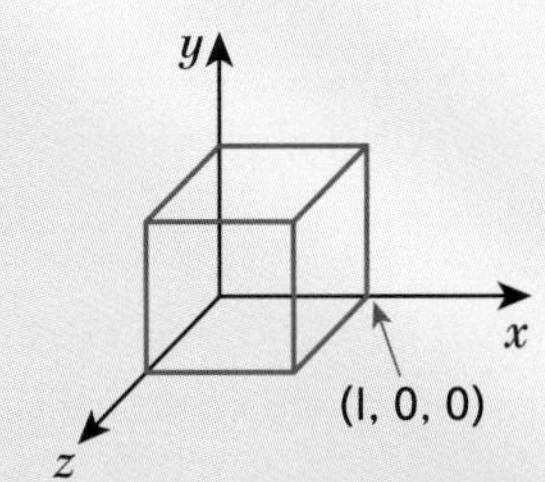

mid-point origin

15.7 Loci

- Describe familiar routes
- Draw loci
- Draw shapes and paths by using descriptions of loci

What's the BIG idea?

→ A **locus** is a set of points that follows a rule or a set of conditions called **constraints**.
For example this circle is the locus of all points that are exactly 3 cm from point *A*. **Level 7**

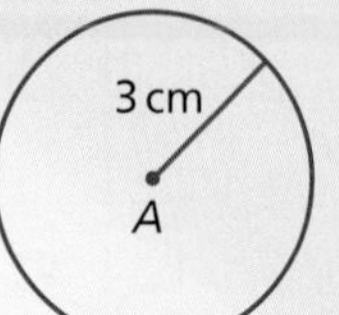

Why learn this?

Fast food outlets often have a free delivery area. The limit of this free delivery area is often described as a locus.

Practice, practice, practice!

Level 6

6a I can describe familiar routes

1 Julie walks to the Youth Club. She turns right on leaving her front gate and walks to the end of the street, where she turns left. She then takes the second left, goes straight on at the traffic lights and then turns right.
Describe Julie's route home, assuming she comes back the same way.

2 Describe the route to your next lesson or form room.

Level 7

7c I can draw a locus equidistant between two points or from a point

3 Mark a point and label it '*B*'.

a Mark six points that are exactly 4 cm from *B*.

b Use a pair of compasses to complete the locus of all points that are exactly 4 cm from *B*.

4 Copy this diagram.

A ——————————— B

a Mark six points that are the same distance from *A* as from *B*.

b Use compasses and a ruler to complete the locus of points that are the same distance from *A* as from *B*.

5 Two towns, Sefton and Rugmere, are 10.4 km apart.
The secondary school must be built exactly the same distance from both towns.
Using a scale of 1 cm to 1 km, draw a scale drawing showing the locus of positions where the school can be built.

6 Adam only delivers newspapers to houses that are 2 km or closer to the newsagent's shop. Using a scale of 2 cm to 1 km, draw a scale drawing to show the locus of Adam's delivery area.

constraints equidistant locus (loci)

7 There are two sprinklers in opposite corners of a lawn. Each can spray water up to 5 m in any direction. The lawn is a 6 m by 10 m rectangle. Using a scale of 1 cm to 1 m, draw the locus of the area that can be watered by the sprinklers.

8 Draw a 3 cm by 4 cm rectangle.

a For each side, mark three points that are exactly 2 cm away from it.

b For each corner, mark three points that are exactly 2 cm away from it.

c Complete the locus of points that are exactly 2 cm away from the rectangle.

9 Draw a 3-D sketch of each of these loci.

a all points that are the same distance from opposite faces of a cube

b all points that are exactly 5 cm, in any direction, from a point in mid air

10 This is a view looking into a room. In the far top two corners are heat detectors that can detect body heat up to a distance of 2 m away.

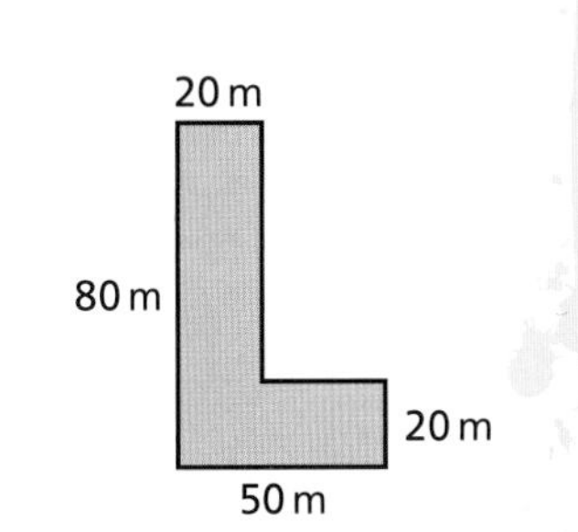

a Draw the loci of the areas where the sensors can detect body heat.

b Where would you place two additional sensors in order to cover as much of the room as possible?

11 Using a scale of 1 cm to 10 m, make an accurate scale drawing of this building plan. A path surrounds the building. Draw the route of the path around the building by finding the locus of points 10 m from the edge.

20 m

80 m

20 m

50 m

Level 7

7c I can draw a locus equidistant between two points or from a point

7b I can draw a locus equidistant from a line or around a rectangle

7a I can visualise loci in 3-D

7a I can draw shapes and paths by using descriptions of loci

Now try this!

A Jolly hockey sticks

Look at the diagram of part of an ice hockey pitch.

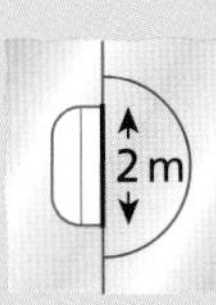

a The goal mouth is shown by the black line. Using an appropriate scale, sketch the diagram and mark all the points from where a shot of 15 m can be taken.

b Are all points from where the shot can be taken as good as each other?

B Rolling polygons

a Imagine an equilateral triangle being rolled along a flat surface. There is a red dot on the corner of the triangle. Plot the locus of the red dot as the triangle is rolled one full rotation.

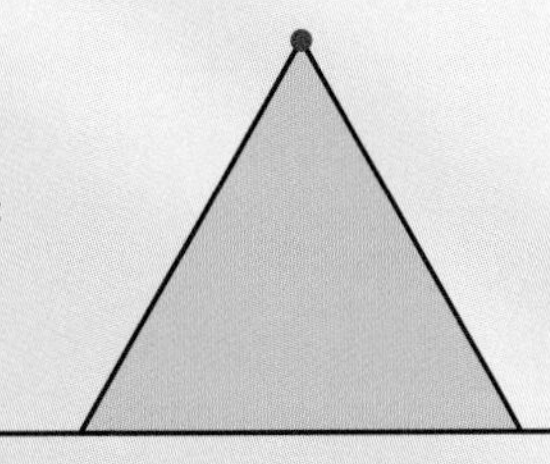

b Now imagine a square rolling along, with a red dot on the corner. Plot the locus of the red dot.

c Choose different regular polygons with a red dot on one corner. Plot the locus of the red dot as the polygon rolls.

World's Greatest Maths! 15.8

BEYOND MARS

Year: 2051
Mission classification: Phoenix 11
Destination: Alpha Centauri
Objective: Design and build an interstellar ship

The European Space Agency's Mars base has been in operation for four years and you're nearly ready to launch the first manned mission to another solar system. The Phoenix 11 starship will be built in orbit around Mars.

Can you use your 3-D skills to complete the calculations necessary to finish the starship?

Design notes

Cube
Volume = x^3
Surface area = $6x^2$

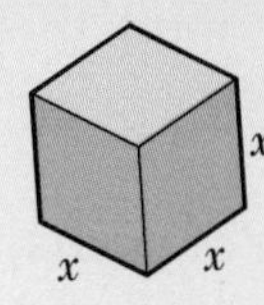

Cuboid
Volume = lwh
Surface area = $2(lw + wh + lh)$

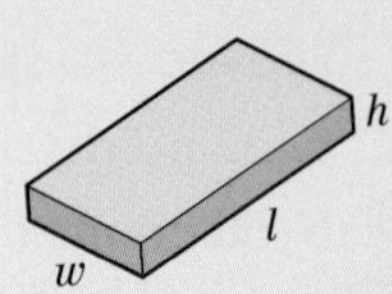

Prism
Volume = Cross-sectional area x height = Ah

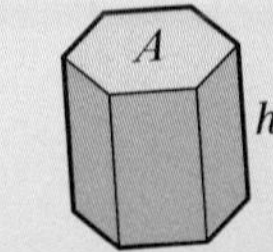

Primary fuel pods

The fuel pods will be cubes made from carbon fibre. Here is a net of one of the primary fuel pods.

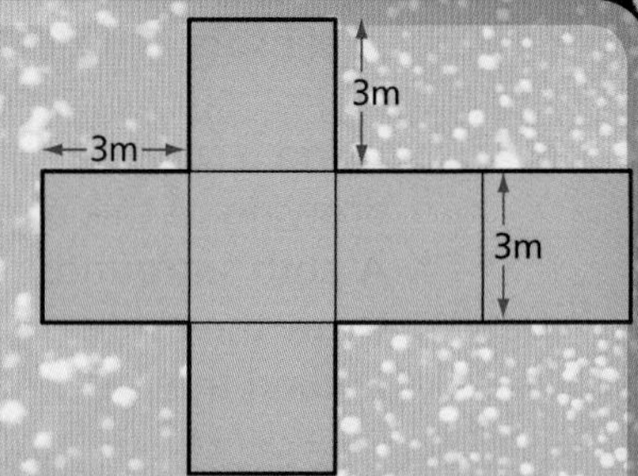

- What area of carbon fibre is needed to make this fuel pod?
- Carbon fibre costs £620 per square metre. What is the cost of the carbon fibre needed to make one fuel pod?
- What volume of fuel can be stored in each fuel pod?

Living section

The living section of the Phoenix 11 is a cuboid with the dimensions shown.

3m
12m
8m

- Sketch a net of this cuboid. On each face of your net write the area of that face.
- Write down the surface area of the cuboid.
- The living section needs to be painted with a special radiation-resistant coating. This coating costs £300 per square metre. How much will it cost to paint the living section?
- What volume of air is contained in the living section?
- The living section is used to transfer fuel pods into orbit. How many fuel pods can be stored inside the empty living section?

Landing struts

The Phoenix 11 is designed to be able to land on any new planets it discovers. This landing strut is drawn on 1 m isometric dotty paper.

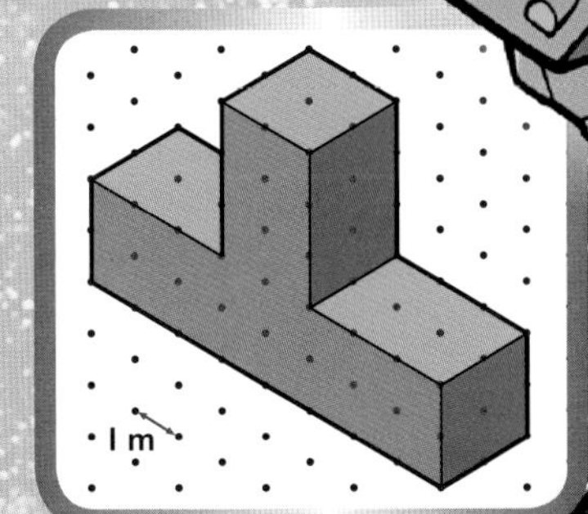

- How many faces does a landing strut have?
- Find the area of each face of the landing strut, and work out the surface area of the landing strut.
- By dividing it into two cuboids, find the volume of the landing strut.
- The landing strut will be filled with cushioning foam which weighs 120 kg per cubic metre. What is the total weight of the foam in the two landing struts?

Plasma prisms

The faster-than-light drive uses two plasma prisms. This is the blueprint for one plasma prism.

- Work out the area of each face of the plasma prism.
- What is the surface area of the plasma prism?
- What volume of plasma can be stored in each plasma prism?

Main bridge

The main bridge is the control centre for Phoenix 11. The main bridge is a prism, and its cross-section is a trapezium.

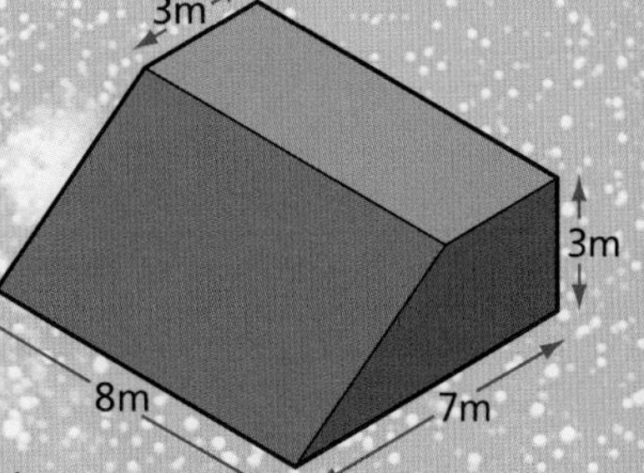

- Work out the area of the cross-section of the main bridge.
- Calculate the surface area and volume of the main bridge.

The completed starship is made up of the following components:

- 2 primary fuel pods
- 1 Living section
- 2 Landing struts
- 2 Plasma prisms
- 1 Main bridge

Work in a group to construct a scale model of the Phoenix 11 starship. You should use a scale of 1 m = 1 cm. Construct a net of each component using thin card. Draw designs and colour your nets before you make them into 3-D shapes.

Remember to add tabs to your nets to help you glue them together.

You can use a copy of resource sheet 15.8A to help you build the plasma prisms and a copy of resource sheet 15.8B to help you build the landing struts.

What is the volume of the finished starship?

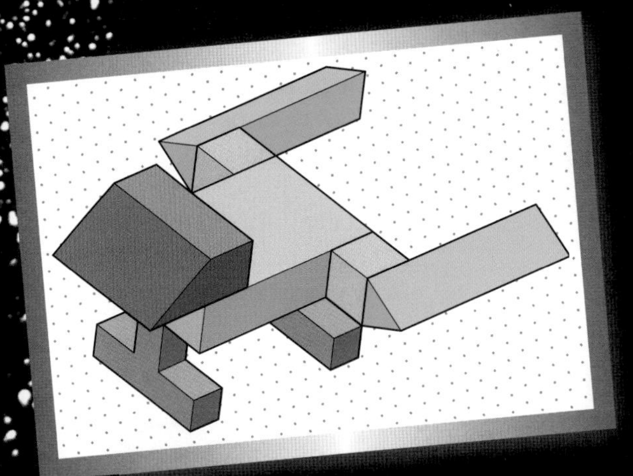

15.9 Solving problems 2

- Solve problems involving shape, space and measures
- Use logical argument

What's the BIG idea?

- Before you start to solve a problem
  - make a note of all the information you've been given
  - think about the different methods you could use – your first idea may not be your best one.
  Level 5, Level 6 & Level 7
- When you have solved a problem, look at your answer.
  - Does it look sensible?
  - Can you check your answer by **substituting** it back into the original problem?
  - Have you used the correct units? **Level 5, Level 6 & Level 7**

Why learn this?

Each figure in China's army of 8000 terracotta warriors is at least six feet tall. Twenty were transported from China to London for an exhibition at the British Museum. Good problem-solving skills are essential to plan the packaging and journey of any large object.

Practice, practice, practice!

Level 5

5c I can visualise a cube from its net

5a I can solve problems involving the area of rectangles

1 Archie's Sweets pack their chocolate buttons in a cubic box. The managing director wants the box to have a stripe printed on it that looks like a ribbon going all the way round. Which of these nets are suitable?

A

B

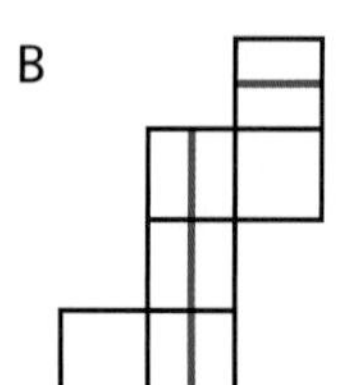

C

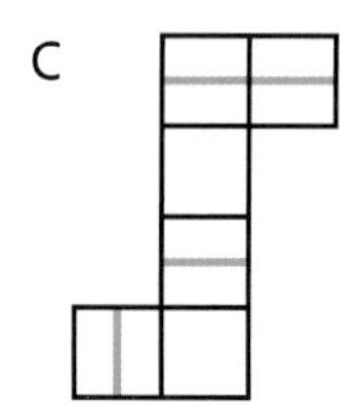

D

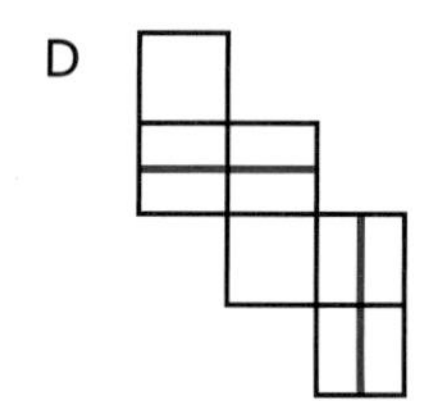

2 Susan lays a small patio in the garden. She uses 10 identical paving stones arranged as shown. The patio has an area of 2.1 m^2.

What are the side lengths of a single paving stone, in centimetres?

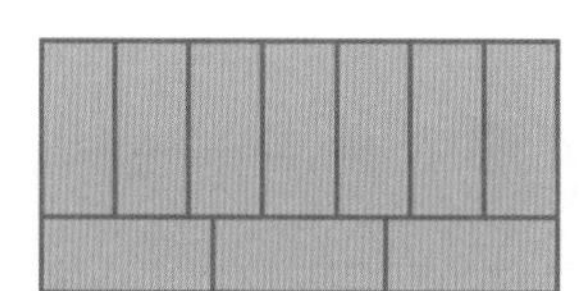

Level 6

6b I can solve problems about the volume of a cuboid

6a I can solve problems involving the perimeter of a circle

3 A tap drips every second into a square sink with 40 cm sides and a depth of 17 cm. Thirty drips have a volume of 10 *ml*. With the plug in, how long does it take to fill the sink? Give your answer in hours and minutes.

4 **a** The Level-up Knights have a round table at which they can all just sit. It has a radius of 1.25 m. The knights sit on chairs that are 75 cm wide. How many knights are there?

b When visitors come, they extend the table with a square extension. How many visitors can join them at the table?

cubic cuboid net

5 **a** Nadia is planning a trip. To start with she uses a map with a scale of 1 : 250 000. When she measures her route, it is 16.8 cm long.
She transfers her route to a 1 : 50 000 map. How long is her route now?

b How far is she planning to travel in kilometres? What is this to the nearest mile?

Level 6

6a I can solve problems involving map scales

6 **a** Each box of Archie's Sweets contains 50 cm^3 of sweets, plus about 10% air. Here are three designs for the box. Which design is the most suitable? Why?

A

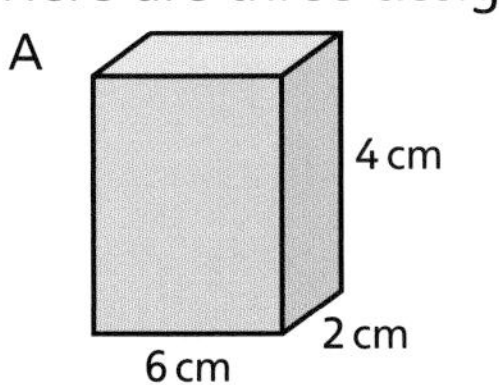

B

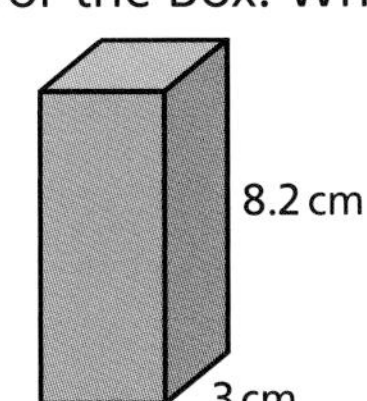

C

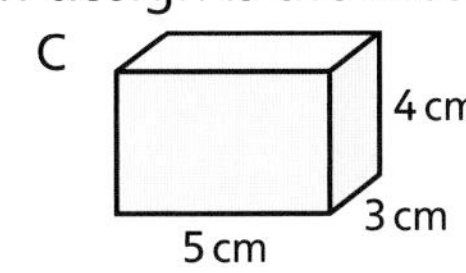

b Work out the sizes of three more boxes with the correct volume.

c Without using a calculator, work out the side length of a cubic box that has the correct volume to one decimal place.

7 **a** Work out the volume of this box.

b Design a new box that has a volume 10% larger than the original box.

c Calculate the percentage increase in the surface area of the new box.

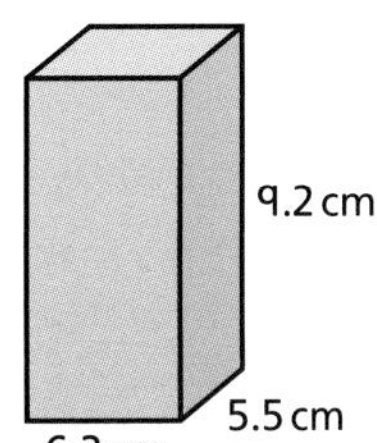

Level 7

7c I can solve more difficult problems involving the volume of a cuboid

8 **a** Six friends share a square cake which has 15 cm sides. The top and sides are covered with icing. How can they divide up the cake so they each get the same amount of cake and icing?

b Prove that this is true for each piece.

7b I can develop a logical argument for problems involving area and volume

9 Archie's Golden Triangle sweets are packed in triangular prism boxes. Which of these designs would you use? Why?

A

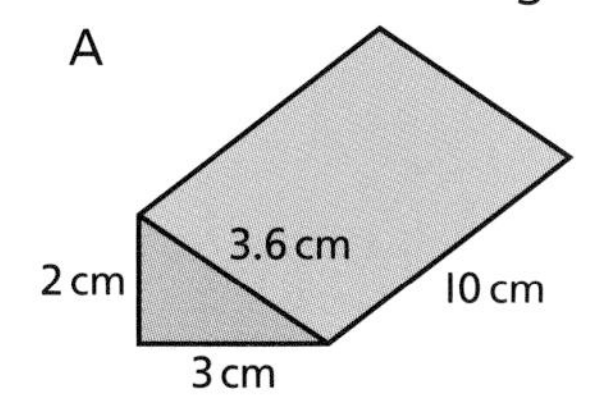

B

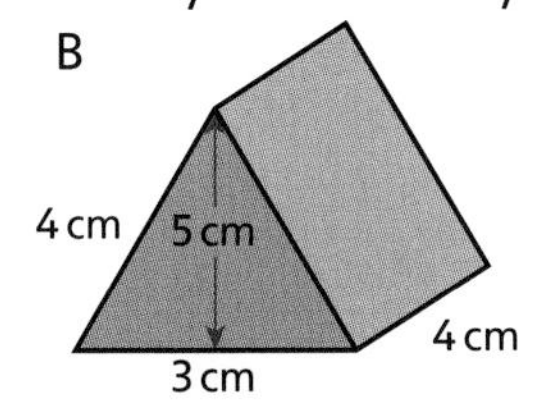

C

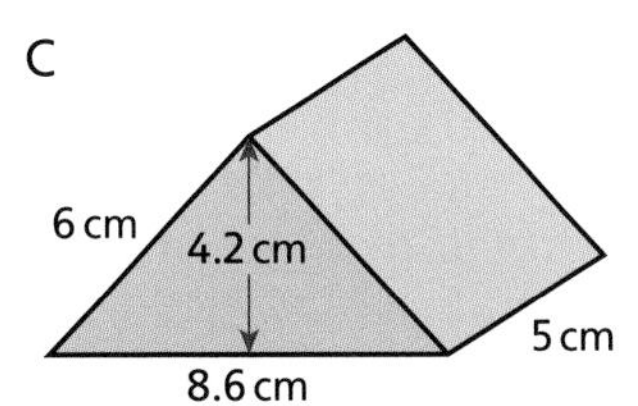

Now try this!

A **Box it up!**

Design a net for a box that will fold out into a display stand to put on the counter in a sweet shop.

B **Roll up, roll up!**

a An 11 cm by 7 cm piece of paper can be rolled into a cylinder in two ways. What is the volume of the larger cylinder?

b For a rectangular piece of paper with the longer side of length l and the shorter side of length h, work out the ratio of the larger volume to the smaller volume.

Tip

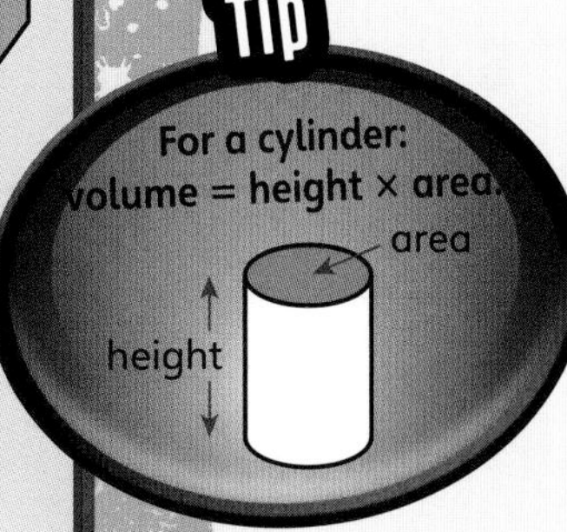

scale substituting

Postulates revisited

In the opener to this unit you were introduced to Euclid and his book *Elements*. Some of the 'rules' Euclid introduced in the book were called postulates. Euclid used these postulates, along with his other 'rules' and definitions, to prove many theorems about geometrical figures.
The first four postulates are given below.

Euclid's postulates

1. A straight line can be drawn from any point to any other point.
2. A straight line can be extended indefinitely in any direction.
3. It is possible to describe a circle with any centre and radius.
4. All right angles are equal.

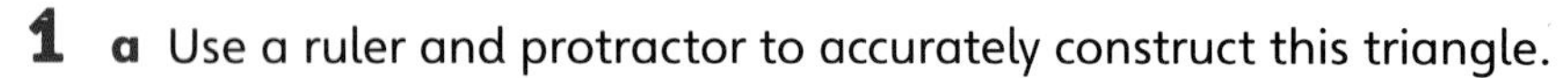

1 **a** Use a ruler and protractor to accurately construct this triangle.
b Which postulate did you use in this construction? **Level 5**

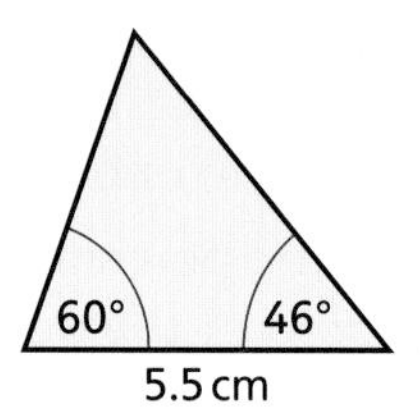

2 A square shed of side length 6 m is to be built in the top left-hand corner of a garden plot. The plot is rectangular with length 18 m and width 9 m. There is a flower bed, of width 3 m, on the left-hand side of the plot. It runs from the bottom left-hand corner up to the shed. Draw an accurate scale drawing of the garden plot using the scale 2 cm : 3 m. **Level 5**

3 Draw a line segment (AB) of length 8 cm.
Using a pair of compasses and Euclid's postulate number 3, construct an equilateral triangle with a base AB.
Check your construction to confirm that all angles equal 60°. **Level 6**

4 Use a geometric construction, or set of constructions, to show that postulate number 4 is true. **Level 7**

5 Mark a point and label it A. Mark four points that are exactly 5.8 cm from point A.
Use a pair of compasses to complete the locus of all points that are 5.8 cm from A.
What dimension is the length 5.8 cm describing?
What postulate(s) have you used in your work? **Level 7**

6 When would Euclid have used postulate number 2? **Level 7**

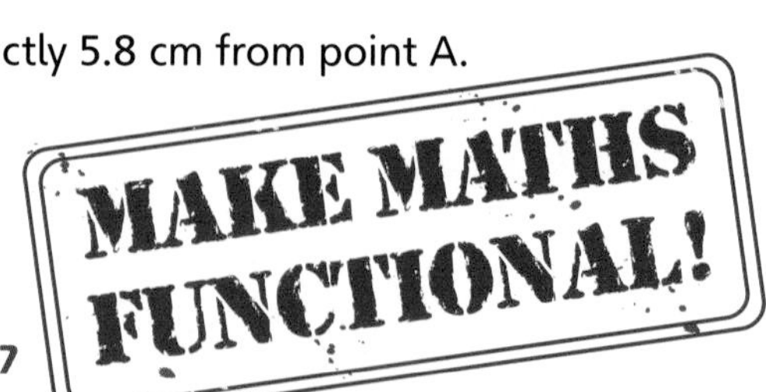

The BIG ideas

- → You can use **scales** to make accurate drawings of objects that are much bigger in real life. **Level 5 & Level 6**
- → The minimum information needed to draw a triangle is either the lengths of two sides and an included angle (**SAS**), two angles and the included side (**ASA**) or all three sides (**SSS**). **Level 6**
- → You can use a ruler and compasses to construct a **right-angled triangle** if you know the length of the **hypotenuse** and one other side. **Level 7**
- → A **locus** is a set of points that follows a rule or a set of conditions called constraints. For example, this circle is the locus of all points that are exactly 9 mm from point A. **Level 7**

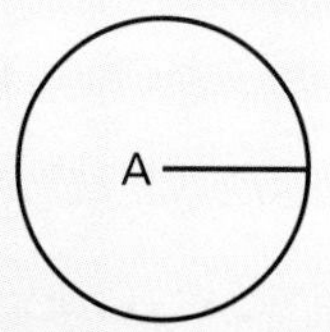

Practice SATs-style questions

Level 5

Q1 Use a protractor to draw an angle of 123°.

Q2 This box is a cuboid. Draw an accurate net of this box.

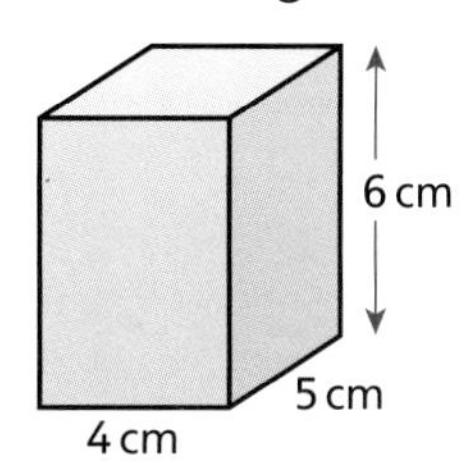

Level 6

Q3 Draw a plan, side and front elevation for both shapes shown.

a

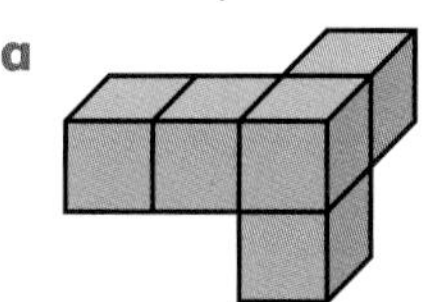

b

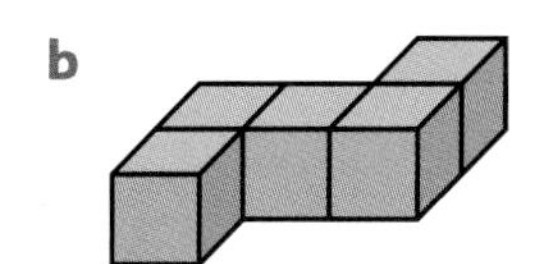

Q4 Sammi-jo is designing a section of garden for the Chelsea Flower Show. She has decided on a triangular plot. The base is to be 12 m and the two sloping sides 9 m and 15 m.

a Draw a sketch of how the plot may look.

b Using the scale 1 cm = 3 m, use a ruler and compasses to draw an accurate drawing of your sketch.

Level 7

Q5 Manymore supermarket is planning to build a new store. The store is to be equidistant from the towns of Burlam and Malurb. The towns are 8.44 km apart. Using a scale of 2 cm to 1 km, draw a scale drawing showing the locus of positions at which the store can be built.

Q6 The diagram shows a field ABCD. A treasure map shows that a treasure chest has been buried in the field. The chest is the same distance from side AB as it is from side BC. It is also equidistant from both B and C.

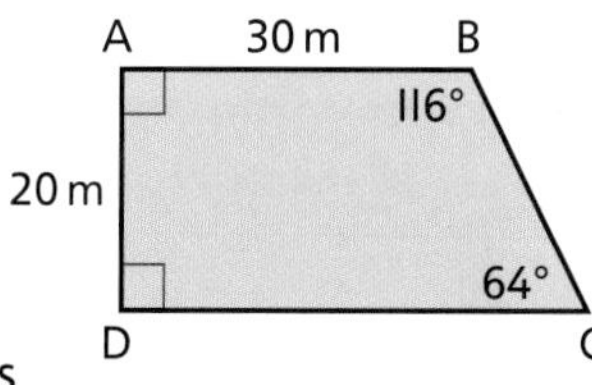

a Use a ruler and protractor to construct an accurate drawing of the field.

b Use a ruler and compasses to find X, the position of the treasure chest.

16 Statistically speaking

This unit is about collecting and using data.

Jonathan Moorse is a renewable energy consultant. He helps advise companies on how they can use renewable energy, such as wind or solar power.

Recently he has been writing a wind report for a factory that wants to use a wind turbine to generate some of its electricity.

To begin with, Jonathan collected data on the wind speeds at the factory site. He then calculated an estimate of the mean annual wind speed.

Jonathan used the mean to work out how much electricity different-sized wind turbines would be able to generate for the factory in a year – and how much money this would save the company on their electricity bills.

Activities

A Look at the wind speed data that Jonathan has collected for the Shetland Isles and the Isle of Wight.

Use his values to calculate an estimate for the mean annual wind speed for each place. Which place is the windiest? What patterns can you see in the data? How can you explain them?

Monthly average wind speed – 10 m above ground, in metres per second		
	Shetland Isles	Isle of Wight
Jan	8.6	7.3
Feb	7.8	6.4
Mar	8.2	5.9
Apr	6.7	5.3
May	6.3	5.2
Jun	5.8	5.3
Jul	5.8	5.5
Aug	5.5	5.9
Sept	6.9	6.1
Oct	7.7	7.0
Nov	7.8	6.6
Dec	8.5	7.2

B A medium-sized wind turbine can produce about $2 \times (\text{mean annual wind speed})^3$ kilowatt hours per day of electricity.

Work out an estimate of the amount of electricity a medium-sized wind turbine could produce in one year on

a the Shetland Isles **b** the Isle of Wight.

Did you know?
It takes roughly 1 kilowatt hour of electricity to run a 40 watt light bulb for 24 hours.

So, turn off lights when they aren't being used!

Before you start this unit...

1 Find the mode, median, mean and range of this set of data.

13, 12, 14, 12, 13, 15, 16, 13, 14, 19

2 The bar chart shows some types of books in Beth's room.

a How many cook books are in her room?

b How many books are not fiction?

c What is the total number of books?

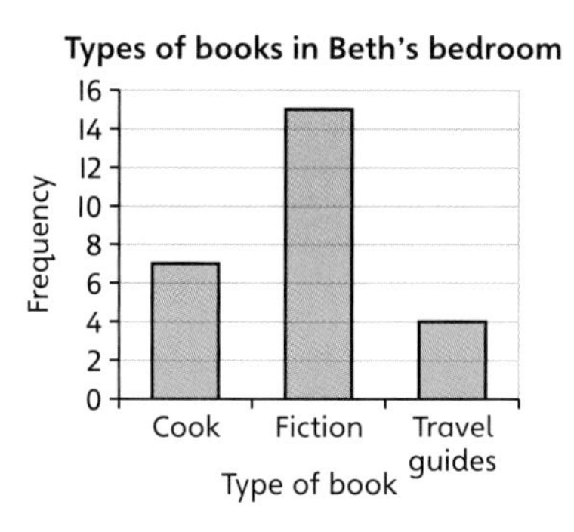

3 A fair dice is thrown. What is the probability of throwing

a a 1 **b** an odd number

c a number other than 5 or 6?

4 List all the possible outcomes of tossing two fair coins.

Plus digital resources

The Bahrain World Trade Center has large-scale wind turbines integrated within its design. The three turbines, each with a diameter of 29 metres, are supported by struts between the building's two towers. The turbines are expected to provide 10-15% of the energy needs of the building.

16.1 Frequency tables

- Record data in a grouped frequency table
- Select an appropriate level of accuracy for data
- Use inequalities to describe class intervals

internet

Why learn this?

Some websites track users by putting data into a frequency table.

What's the BIG idea?

- You can use **tallies** to help you complete a **frequency table**. Bundle the tallies in fives like this: ~~||||~~ **Level 5**
- It is usually best to have four or five groups in a frequency table. The groups should be of equal width and they should not overlap. **Level 5 & Level 6**
- The **class interval** 150 cm ⩽ height < 155 cm includes all the heights from 150 cm up to, but not including, 155 cm. **Level 6**

Practice, practice, practice!

Level 5

1 Makszi has drawn this frequency table.

Number of apples	Frequency
1–10	27
11–20	31

His teacher says it would be better to use more than two groups.
What equal class intervals could Makszi use?

5b I can choose suitable groups for a frequency table

2 Laura is investigating how well pupils can estimate angles.
She asked 16 pupils to draw an angle of 50° without using a protractor.
These are the sizes of the angles they drew.

49° 53° 59° 42° 58° 54° 51° 52°

48° 54° 56° 48° 52° 57° 49° 56°

Copy and complete this frequency table.
Choose suitable groups for the data.

Angle	Tally	Frequency

3 Kate, Alex and Chun are all investigating favourite colours.

Kate says, 'I asked 10 people and the most popular colour was green.'
Alex says, 'I asked 20 people and the most popular colour was green.'
Chun says, 'I asked 100 people and the most popular colour was red.'

What do you think the most popular colour was? Explain your answer.

5b I can choose a sample size from a number of options

4 Here are the running times of 20 films (in hours and minutes).

1:37 2:05 1:58 1:43 2:17 2:34 3:01 1:41 1:39 1:27
1:59 1:45 2:14 1:32 2:10 1:29 1:56 1:50 2:12 1:49

Construct a frequency table.

5a I can construct a simple frequency table

class interval continuous discrete

5 Suggest a suitable sample size for each of these investigations.

a testing whether a coin is biased

b investigating how long Year 9 pupils spend on homework

c gauging people's opinions on the construction of a new road

6 What is an appropriate level of accuracy for recording these?

a times spent watching TV in a week

b masses of textbooks for different subjects

c distances to pupils' holiday destinations

Level 5

5a I can choose a sample size that is sensible for my investigation

5a I can select an appropriate level of accuracy for data

7 Gareth is investigating how well pupils can estimate length.
He asked 20 pupils to cut a piece of string into 10 cm lengths without measuring.
These are the lengths of string (in centimetres) they cut.

7.4 10.5 8.7 9.8 9.3 11.1 10.9 12.4 8.2 11.6
9.0 8.5 7.6 11.7 9.3 11.8 8.4 10.2 7.8 9.6

Construct a frequency table to show the data.

8 In which class does 150 cm go in each of these frequency tables?

a

Height h, (cm)	Frequency
$140 \leqslant h < 160$	
$160 \leqslant h < 180$	
$180 \leqslant h < 200$	

b

Height h, (cm)	Frequency
$130 \leqslant h < 140$	
$140 \leqslant h < 150$	
$150 \leqslant h < 160$	

c

Height h, (cm)	Frequency
$140 < h \leqslant 145$	
$145 < h \leqslant 150$	
$150 < h \leqslant 155$	

Watch out!
Check the inequality signs carefully to make sure you know which group a value on the boundary goes in.

Level 6

6c I can construct a frequency table with equal class intervals for continuous data

6b I can identify where boundary data would go for groups described with inequalities

Now try this!

A Dice products

- Roll two dice and record the product of their scores. Do this 25 times.
- Record your data in a grouped frequency table with the class intervals 1–6, 7–12, 13–18, 19–24, 25–30, 31–36.
- Which group has the highest frequency?

B Random numbers

- Use the random number generator on your calculator to generate 30 random numbers.
- Record your data in a grouped frequency table with five equal-sized class intervals.
- Which group has the highest frequency?

Tip
The random number generator is usually a 'second function' Ran#.

frequency table grouped data interval sample tally

16.2 Collecting data and calculating statistics

- Collect data using a questionnaire
- Calculate the mean using an assumed mean
- Find the modal class for grouped data
- Know when it is appropriate to use the modal class

Why learn this?

Radio stations like to know the modal age group of their listeners and their competitors' listeners. This helps them choose the music to play.

What's the BIG idea?

- A **data collection sheet** can be used to quickly record a variety of data. **Level 5**
- Using an **assumed mean** can make calculating the mean easier.
  mean = assumed mean + mean of the differences from the assumed mean **Level 6**
- The **modal group** or **modal class** is the group with the highest frequency. **Level 6 & Level 7**

Super fact!

It is possible to cheat at the card game Black Jack by counting cards, in a method similar to using an assumed mean. Casinos don't allow this though!

Practice, practice, practice!

Level 5

5a I can complete a data collection sheet, using data generated by a questionnaire

1 **a** Design a data collection sheet to find out what your classmates had for breakfast this morning.

b Try filling in your data collection sheet by asking a few people what they had for breakfast.
If any answers are given that do not fit anywhere on your collection sheet, make a suitable adjustment to the design.

Watch out!

Make sure your data collection sheet covers all the options for the questions you ask.

Level 6

6c I can find the mean using an assumed mean from a small data set

2 Find the mean cost of a computer game using an assumed mean of £15.

Cost of a computer game (£)	11	12	24	18	15
Difference from assumed mean of £15	−4	−3	9	3	0

Total difference = £5 Mean difference = £5 ÷ 5 = £1
Mean = assumed mean + mean difference = £15 + £1 = £16

a Find the mean length of a phone call using an assumed mean of 10 minutes.

Length of phone call (minutes)	4	24	16	7	9
Difference from assumed mean of 10 minutes					

b Find the mean weight of a suitcase using an assumed mean of 19 kg.

Weight of suitcase (kg)	18.9	19.4	18.6	19.2	19.9
Difference from assumed mean of 19 kg					

assumed mean   average   class interval   data collection sheet   grouped data   mean

3 Use a suitable assumed mean to help you find the mean of each data set.

a 1008, 1001, 999, 1007, 850, 975, 1010, 1004, 1017, 990

b 4.8, 5.2, 5.7, 5.3, 4.6, 4.1, 5.3, 4.6, 4.9, 4.6

4 Petra asked her classmates how much pocket money they get.
These are her results.

Pocket money	£0 to £2.99	£3 to £5.99	£6 to £8.99	£9 or more
Boys	3	4	4	5
Girls	2	2	6	4

What is the modal class for

a boys **b** girls?

5 Look again at your answers to Q4. Is the modal class a suitable average to use for

a boys **b** girls?

Level 6

6b I can find the mean using an assumed mean from a larger data set

6b I can find the modal class of a small set of data

6a I can decide when it is appropriate to use a modal class

6 The table shows the projected UK population for 2010.

Age	Population (thousands)
0–4	3836
5–9	3444
10–14	3560
15–19	3897
20–24	4326
25–29	4337
30–34	3905
35–39	4222
40–44	4643
45–49	4554

Age	Population (thousands)
50–54	3979
55–59	3572
60–64	3743
65–69	2926
70–74	2475
75–79	2002
80–84	1492
85–89	940
90+	458

(Source: Office for National Statistics)

a What is the modal class of this data?

b Re-group the data in 15-year intervals (0–14, 15–29, ...).

c What is the modal class now?

7 What is the missing number if

a the mode is 14?

b the median is 16 and the range is 8?

c the mean is 14.6?

14	12	18	16	?

Level 7

7c I can find the modal class of a larger set of data

7c I can find a missing data value given different averages and the range

Now try this!

A II numbers

There are 11 numbers. All of them are different.
The median of the numbers is 5.
The range is 10.

a What are the 11 numbers?

b What is the mean of the 11 numbers?

B Mean scores

a Roll two dice and record the product of their scores. Do this ten times.

b Without using a calculator, calculate the mean score

i using an assumed mean of 12

ii without using an assumed mean.

c Which way was easier?

median modal class/group mode questionnaire range

16.3 Frequency diagrams

- Construct and interpret frequency diagrams
- Interpret population pyramids

What's the BIG idea?

- **Frequency diagrams** can be used to show **grouped continuous data**. A frequency diagram looks a bit like a bar chart, but there are no gaps between the bars. Level 6
- A **population pyramid** shows the distribution of age groups within a population. It looks like two back-to-back frequency diagrams. Level 6

Why learn this?

Population pyramids can be used to predict future populations of countries.

Practice, practice, practice!

Level 6

6C I can construct a simple frequency diagram when given equal class intervals for continuous data

1 This frequency table shows the lifespans of a sample of house flies.

Lifespan of fly D, (days)	$0 \leqslant D < 7$	$7 \leqslant D < 14$	$14 \leqslant D < 21$	$21 \leqslant D < 28$
Frequency	3	6	20	9

Use the data to complete a frequency diagram.

2 A post office manager recorded the weights of the last 25 items sent. The data is shown in the table.

Weight, W (grams)	$0 < W \leqslant 250$	$250 < W \leqslant 500$	$500 < W \leqslant 750$	$750 < W \leqslant 1000$
Frequency	12	7	4	2

Draw a frequency diagram for the data.

6C I can construct a frequency diagram with equal class intervals for continuous data

3 These are the temperatures at the centre of 12 potatoes after being cooked in a microwave oven.

114°C 102°C 109°C 119°C 122°C 139°C
131°C 114°C 121°C 127°C 117°C 118°C

Draw a frequency diagram to show the data. Use four groups.

6C I can read information from a frequency diagram

4 The frequency diagram shows the share prices of 100 companies traded on the London Stock Exchange.

a How many of these companies have a share price of 50p or less?

b How many of these companies have a share price of more than £1?

c David says that the diagram shows that the range of the data is £2. Is he correct? Explain your answer.

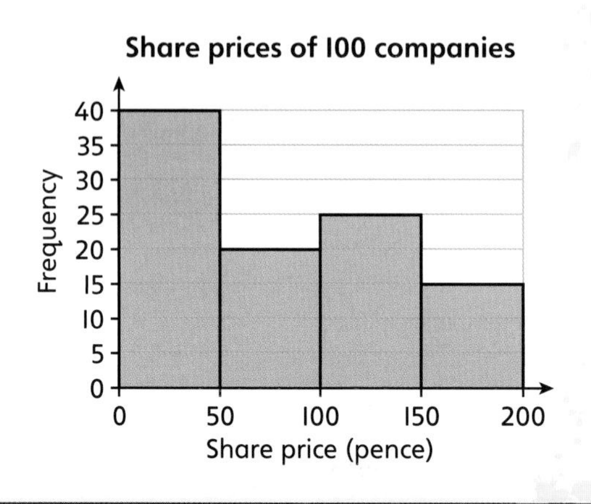

class interval continuous discrete frequency

5 These population pyramids show the populations of Germany and Ethiopia.

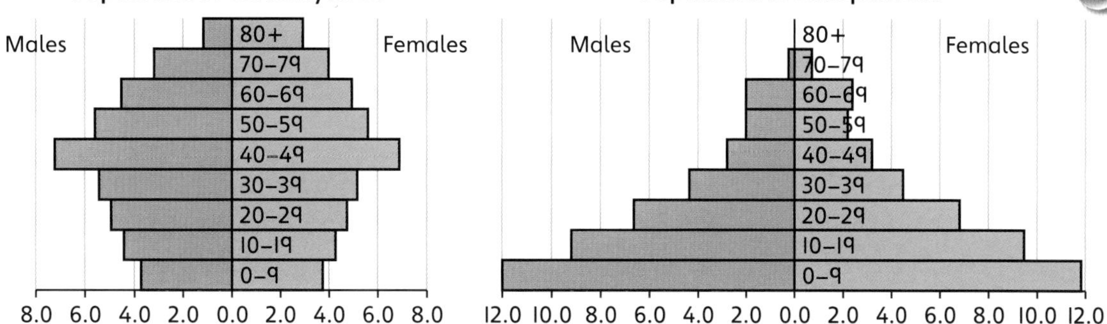

(Source: U.S. Census Bureau, International)

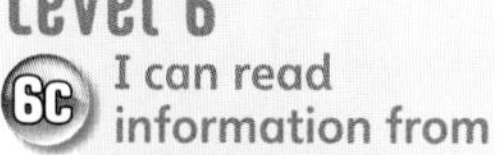

I can read information from a population pyramid

a How many males are there aged over 60 in
  i Germany **ii** Ethiopia?

b How many people are there aged under 20 in
  i Germany **ii** Ethiopia?

c Both countries have a total population of roughly 80 million.
Which do you think will have the larger population in 20 years time?

6 These are the times (in seconds) that 33 adults took to complete a memory game.

6a I can construct a frequency diagram with equal class intervals for larger sets of continuous data

491	111	363	129	473	472	149	398	612	213	106
571	253	279	505	433	302	183	412	583	389	683
242	223	471	89	197	346	500	629	202	699	592

a Draw a frequency diagram for the data using six equal groups.
Label the horizontal axis in minutes.

b How many adults took between 4 and 6 minutes?

c How many adults took longer than 6 minutes?

Now try this!

A Bag colour

Draw a bar chart to show what colour your classmates' school bags are.

B 20 years

a Draw a frequency diagram to show the population of the country in the table below.

Age A (years)	$0 \leqslant A < 20$	$20 \leqslant A < 40$	$40 \leqslant A < 60$	$60 \leqslant A < 80$
Population (millions)	30	20	10	3

b Draw a frequency diagram for 20 years later. Assume that:
- everyone aged 20–39 has had one child (two per couple)
- 10% of each existing age group has died, and all new babies live
- everyone aged 60 and over has died.

c Has the total population increased?

d What will happen to the population if these trends continue?

Did you know?

Up to two thirds of the population of Europe died from the Black Death in 1348–1350.

frequency diagram grouped data population pyramid

16.4 Interpreting graphs

- Read information from bar charts, frequency diagrams, pie charts, stem-and-leaf diagrams and line graphs
- Compare distributions

Why learn this?

Holiday brochures often contain graphs and diagrams, for example temperature charts. Understanding these could help you choose your holiday.

What's the BIG idea?

→ Make sure you understand the diagram before you start answering questions about it. Look at the title, the labels on the axes and the key if there is one. **Level 6**

Practice, practice, practice!

Level 6

6c I can read information from a frequency diagram

1 PC Jones has been operating a speed camera in a 60 mph zone. The frequency diagram shows the speeds he recorded.

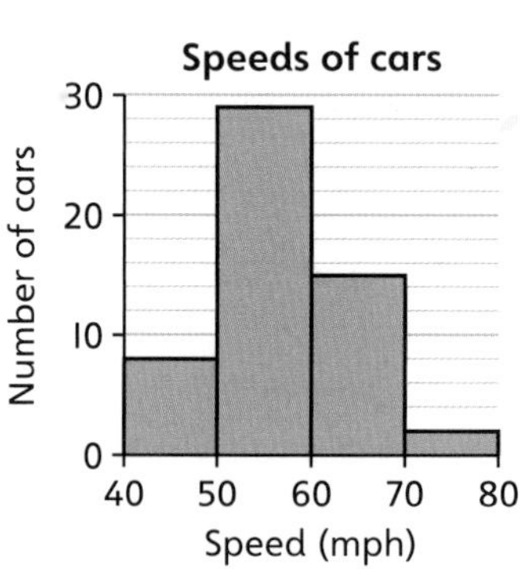

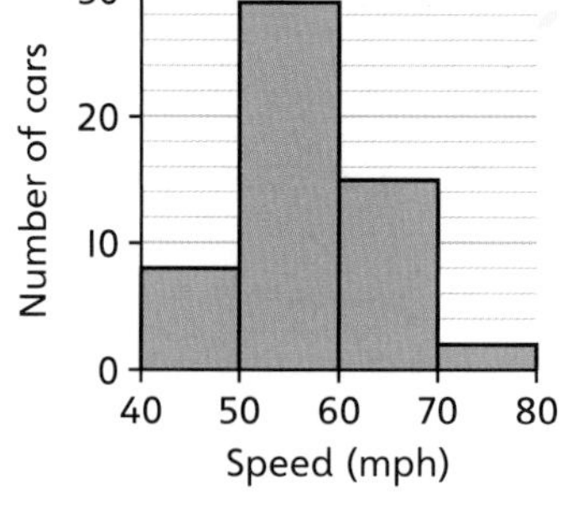

- **a** How many cars were travelling between 40 and 50 mph?
- **b** How many cars were breaking the speed limit?
- **c** Drivers are prosecuted if they are doing at least 66 mph. Is it possible to tell from the frequency diagram how many drivers will be prosecuted?
  Explain your answer.

6b I can read information from a stem-and-leaf diagram

2 This stem-and-leaf diagram shows the engine capacity of cars in litres.

- **a** What is the smallest engine capacity?
- **b** What is the largest engine capacity?
- **c** What is the most common engine capacity?
- **d** How many of the cars have an engine capacity of less than 2 litres?

Stem	Leaf
0	6 6 9
1	0 0 1 2 2 2 2 4 4 5 6 8
2	0 1 4 4 6 8
3	0 0 0 2 6
4	4

Key: 1|6 represents 1.6 litres

Watch out!

Check the key before reading off a stem-and-leaf diagram. 3|5 could mean 35 or 3.5.

6b I can answer questions about pie charts

3 The pie chart shows the favourite games of the pupils at Poindexter Academy.

20 pupils chose Monopolygon.

- **a** How many pupils are at Poindexter Academy?
- **b** How many pupils chose Noughts & Crosses?

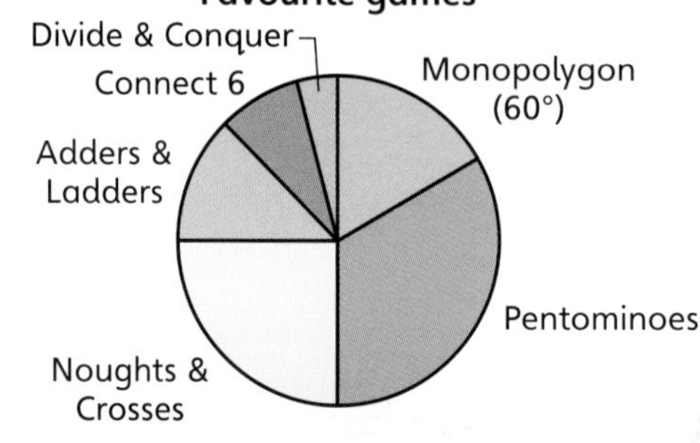

bar chart frequency diagram line graph

4 The curator at a museum has drawn this graph to show the numbers of visitors in a two-week period.

a On which day of the week is the museum closed?

b How many people visited the museum on the first Friday?

c Which week had more visitors in total?

Level 6

6b I can answer questions about line graphs

5 The diagrams show the eye and hair colours of the pupils in class 9C.

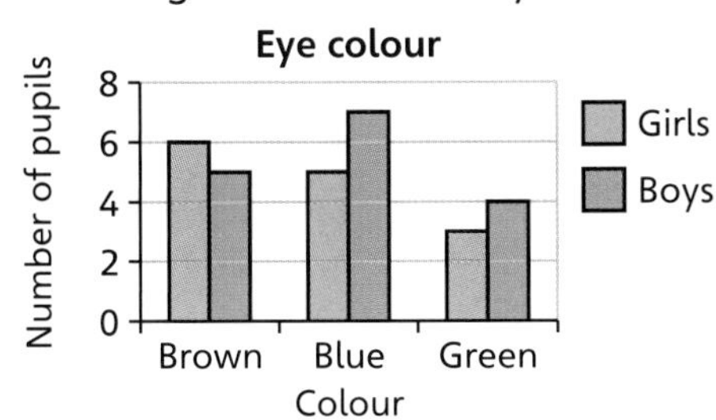

a How many boys have blue eyes?

b How many girls are in class 9C?

c How many pupils have brown hair?

d How many pupils have green eyes?

6a I can use information from different graphs to answer questions

6 The diagrams show the resting heart rates of a group of police officers and a group of call centre workers.

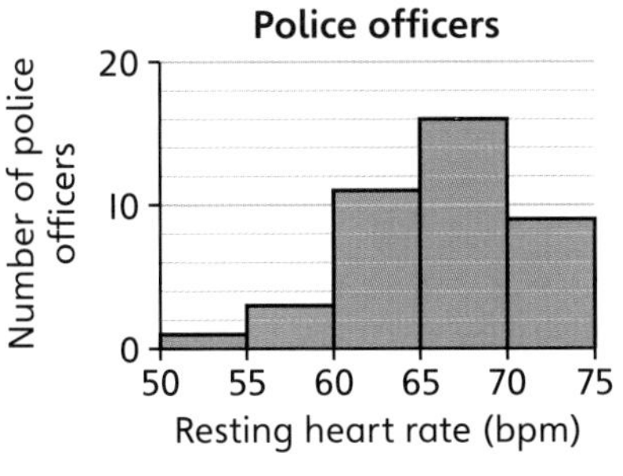

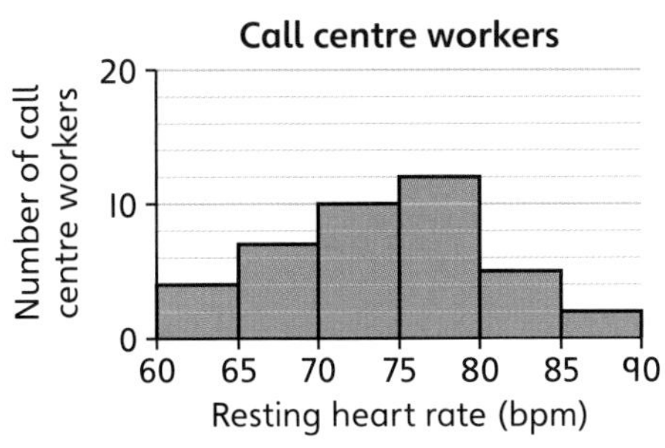

a What is the occupation of the person with the **i** highest **ii** lowest resting heart rate?

b What is the modal class for **i** police officers **ii** call centre workers?

c Which class contains the median for **i** police officers **ii** call centre workers?

6a I can use statistics to compare the graphs of two distributions

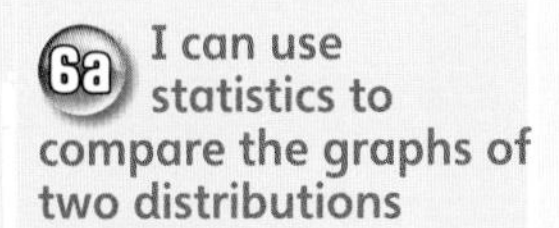

Miguel Indurain, a cyclist who won the Tour de France five times, had a resting heart rate of 28 beats per minute, one of the lowest ever recorded.

Now try this!

A Holiday weather

Look at a holiday brochure or website that contains temperature charts.

- Which holiday destination has the highest maximum temperature?
- In which month does this maximum occur?
- What is the average daily number of hours of sunshine during this month?
- How does the weather compare with the weather in the UK?

B Conversion graph

You will need Resource sheet 16.5. Use the conversion graph to answer the question on the sheeet. Write two similar questions of your own.

pie chart stem-and-leaf diagram

16.5 Comparing sets of data

➩ Compare two sets of data using an average and the range

What's the BIG idea?

- → The **median** is the middle value when a set of data is arranged in order of size. If there is an even number of data items, there will be two middle values. The median is halfway between the two. **Level 5**
- → To find the **mean**, add up all the data and divide by the number of data items. **Level 5**
- → The **range** tells you how variable a set of data is.
  range = maximum value − minimum value **Level 5**
- → It is useful to compare two sets of data using one **average** and the range. **Level 5 & Level 6**

Why learn this?

Averages can be used to compare data across many years, for example the numbers of runs scored in cricket.

Practice, practice, practice!

Level 5

5c I can compare two sets of data using the range and the median

1 The table shows the heights, in metres, of the 11 highest mountains in Ecuador and Peru.

Ecuador	5790	6268	4790	5897	5320	5248	4784	3914	5753	5230	5023
Peru	5960	5947	6089	6768	6094	5991	6040	5870	6127	6635	6344

a Find the median height and the range for each country.

b Use your answers from part **a** to make a comparison of the mountains in the two countries.

5b I can compare two sets of data using the range and the mean

2 The table shows the prices two companies charge for different internet domain names.

	.com	.co.uk	.org	.net	.org.uk	.info	.biz	.eu
webHoster	£15	£10	£9	£13	£13	£10	£19	£13
ePage	£5	£6	£5	£22	£5	£24	£19	£28

a Calculate the mean price of a domain name from each company.

b Compare the two companies' prices using the mean and the range.

3 The table shows the numbers of pairs of trainers owned by some pupils.

Pairs of trainers owned	Frequency of girls	Frequency of boys
0	2	0
1	6	8
2	4	7
3	4	3
4	3	1

a Calculate the mean number of pairs of trainers owned by **i** girls **ii** boys.

b Use the mean and the range to compare the numbers of pairs of trainers owned by girls and boys.

average mean median range

4 David is trying to decide which type of battery to buy for his digital camera. He has found a website that tested the two most popular brands to see how many pictures they can take before the battery goes flat. The mean, median and range for the two brands are shown in the table.

	Brand A	Brand B
Mean	333	290
Median	320	295
Range	128	35

Both brands of battery cost the same.
Which brand of battery would you advise David to buy?

Watch out!

Be careful when comparing data with extreme values. The mean can be distorted, so it is better to use the median.

Level 6

6b I can compare two sets of data given only the averages and the range

5 The table shows the median, mean and range of the distances, in metres, thrown by two shot-putters.

	Median	Mean	Range
Moira Spin	17.8	17.7	0.35
Kathy Lobb	18.1	17.9	0.95

If you were a selector for the Olympics, which athlete would you choose for the team? Bear in mind that each athlete will have six throws at the games.

6 A standard triathlon is made up of a 1500 m swim, a 40 km cycle and a 10 km run. The statistics in the table show the performances of two tri-athletes, over the course of a year. Use the values to compare the two tri-athletes.

6a I can compare two sets of data in more complex situations

Event	Tri-athlete	Median	Mean	Range
Swimming (minutes)	Don Walker:	33	34	3
	Jose Corredor:	37	36	4
Cycling (minutes)	Don Walker:	75	77	9
	Jose Corredor:	72	73	12
Running (minutes)	Don Walker:	49	50	5
	Jose Corredor:	45	44	4

Now try this!

A Five numbers

a Write down five different whole numbers between 1 and 100.

b Work out the median and range for your five numbers.

c Can you find a completely different set of five numbers that have exactly the same median and range as those in part **b**?

B Eight numbers

a Write down eight different numbers between 1 and 1000 (at least one of them should not be a whole number).

b Work out the median, mean and range for your eight numbers.

c Can you find a completely different set of eight numbers that have exactly the same median, mean and range as those in part **b**?

16.6 Misleading graphs

- Choose which type of chart is appropriate for a given situation
- Decide whether a graph is misleading and explain why

Why learn this?

An inappropriate scale can distort results.

What's the BIG idea?

→ A **pie chart** is a circle displaying data to show how something is shared or divided. **Level 5**

→ Different graphs and charts are used for different types of data.

- **Pictograms** and **bar charts** are useful for **discrete** data.
- Grouped-data bar charts and **line graphs** are useful for **continuous** data.
- Pie charts can be used for discrete data or grouped continuous data.
- **Scatter graphs** can be used to show the relationship between two sets of data. **Level 6**

→ Graphs can give a misleading impression if

- the scale on the vertical axis doesn't start at zero
- an uneven scale is used on the horizontal axis
- discrete data points are joined
- a small sample was used. **Level 7**

Learn this

Remember that categorical data is described in words, discrete data is counted, and continuous data is measured.

Watch out!

Line graphs should not be used to display categorical data.

Practice, practice, practice!

Level 6

6b I can choose the best graph to use with different data

1 Which type of diagram would you use for these sets of data?

a numbers of visitors to a café over the course of one year.

b types of drinks ordered in a café one lunchtime.

c distances jumped by pupils in a long jump competition.

d pupil's test marks in English and maths pupils

2 Janine has asked the girls at her tennis club their shoe size.
Here is her graph of the data she collected.

What is wrong with Janine's graph?

bar chart continuous discrete frequency diagram

Level 7

7c I can identify which graphs are misleading

3 Decide whether each graph is misleading.
If it is misleading, choose one or more of these reasons.
A The diagram needs labels or a title.
B The title is misleading.
C The scale on the vertical axis is misleading.
D The scale on the horizontal axis is uneven.

a

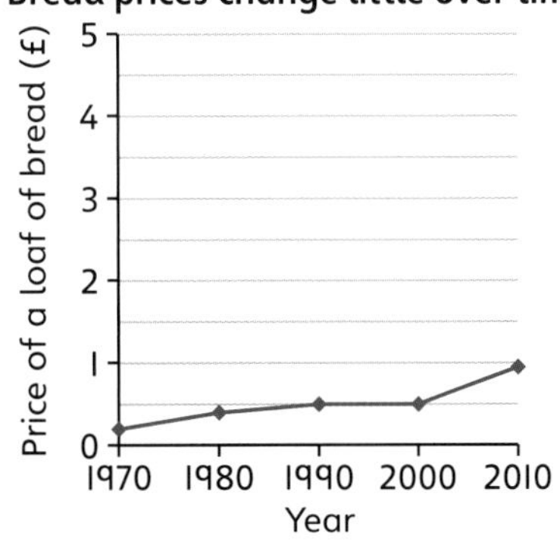

b

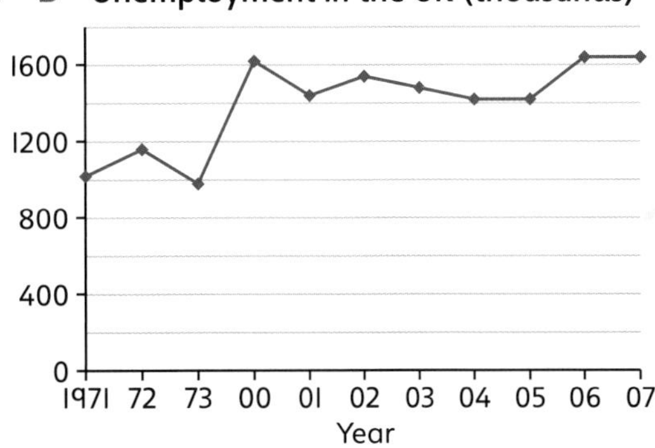

7b I can identify which graphs are misleading, and give reasons for why they are misleading

4 Suki has asked some pupils at her school what their favourite type of film is.
Her results are shown in the bar chart.
Suki concludes from her graph that the pupils at her school prefer science fiction. Why might she be wrong?

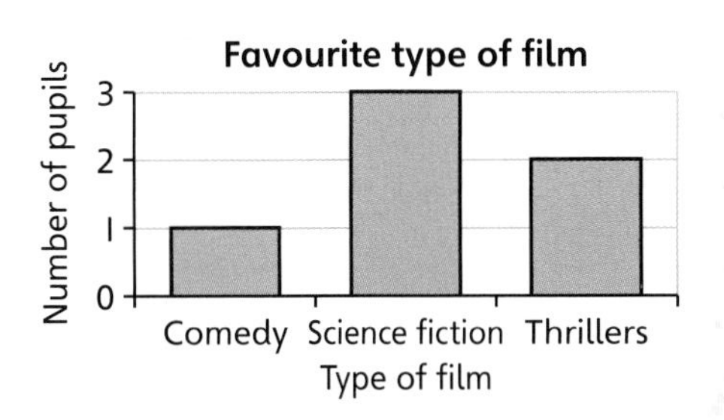

5 An athletics club is investigating how quickly members of different ages can run 100 m.
David has drawn a scatter graph for the data. He has extended the line of best fit so that he can estimate times for older members.
Why will his conclusions be unreliable?

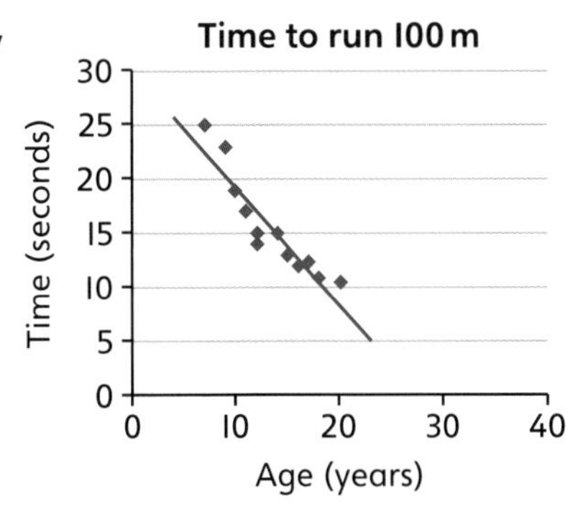

Now try this!

A Bar charts

Draw two bar charts to show the data in the table: one that is realistic and one that gives the impression that batteries last much longer in Brite Lite torches than in other brands.

Brand of torch	Battery life (hours)
Super Rays	8.7
Xpower	9.2
Brite Lite	9.9
Spotlight Max	8.6

B Be misleading

Great Britain got fewer gold medals than France or Italy in the 2004 Olympics.

Country	GB	France	Italy
Number of gold medals	9	11	10

By experimenting with ICT, try to produce a misleading graph that makes Great Britain's performance appear better than it was.

line graph pictogram pie chart scatter graph

maths!

Mind the gap

Working with real-life statistics can be tricky. You have to decide what figures are important, and what type of graph is best to display the facts.

The gender gap

Statistics show that there are definite differences between the wages of men and women in the UK. People argue over whether this is because of the types of jobs that each gender holds, or whether there is discrimination in the way that people are paid. The 'gender gap' seems to occur in lots of countries' statistics, although some countries have a bigger gap than others.

The data below shows the average gross (before tax) weekly wages of women and men working full-time and part-time in the UK over ten years. Does this data tell you anything about the gender gap?

	Male				Female			
	Full Time Median	Full Time Mean	Part Time Median	Part Time Mean	Full Time Median	Full Time Mean	Part Time Median	Part Time Mean
2007	498	606	138	198	394	463	146	178
2006	484	590	128	188	383	450	140	169
2005	471	568	122	181	371	436	135	163
2004	460	548	121	172	357	417	132	158
2003	445	539	113	165	343	400	125	150
2002	430	523	110	161	331	387	118	142
2001	416	499	99	137	314	367	112	134
2000	398	472	96	134	298	345	108	130
1999	384	453	96	138	289	331	105	124
1998	373	438	86	130	277	315	99	118

Source: www.statistics.gov.uk

Investigating data

Use the data opposite to perform a statistical investigation. You might like to use the following headings:

- **Hypothesis**
- **Plan**
- **Graphs and tables**
- **Conclusion**
- **Evaluation**

What are you investigating? What do you think the data will show?

What data are you going to use? Why did you choose this data? What type or types of graph are you going to use? Why?

Was your hypothesis right? Did you find out anything you didn't expect?

What could you do next to improve?

16.7 Experimental probability

- Complete a data collection sheet
- Apply the probabilities from experimental data

What's the BIG idea?

- A **data collection sheet** allows you to record and process data quickly. **Level 5**
- You can estimate **probabilities** from experimental data.

  $$\text{experimental probability} = \frac{\text{number of successful trials}}{\text{total number of trials}}$$

  A greater number of trials gives a more accurate estimate of the probability. **Level 6**
- **Theoretical** and **experimental probabilities** should be similar, but are unlikely to be exactly the same. **Level 6**

Why learn this?

Football managers use football statistics software to help them choose players and tactics that give their team a high probability of winning.

Practice, practice, practice!

Level 5

5c I can complete a data collection sheet, using data generated by an experiment

1 Here is a game for two players.
- Roll two dice.
- Player 1 wins a point if the sum of the two scores is a prime number.
- Player 2 wins a point if the product is a multiple of 5.

a In pairs, play a few rounds of the game. Who seems to win most often?

b Complete a data collection sheet like this for 20 rounds.

Scores on dice	Sum	Product	Player 1 wins a point?	Player 2 wins a point?
3, 5	8	15	No	Yes

Level 6

6a I can apply the probabilities from experimental data in a more complex situation

2 **a** Use your completed data collection sheet from **Q1** to estimate the probability of each player winning a point in any one round.

b Copy and complete these sample space diagrams to show the possible sums and products when two dice are rolled.

+	1	2	3	4	5	6
1	2	3	4			
2	3					
3						
4						
5						
6						

×	1	2	3	4	5	6
1	1	2	3			
2	2	4				
3						
4						
5						
6						

c Use completed diagram from part **b** to calculate the theoretical probability of each player winning a point in any one round.

d Compare your answers from parts **a** and **c**. How good were your estimates?

e Suggest a multiple that Player 2 could use that would make the game fair.

Watch out!

If your probability is greater than 1 you've made a mistake.

data collection sheet experimental probability probability

3 A football manager is trying to pick a player to take penalties. The best two players to choose between are Bob Smashford and Tony Headering. Both players are more likely to score a penalty if they scored the previous one, due to increasing confidence.
The probabilities of the players scoring are shown in the table.

	Bob Smashford	Tony Headering
Probability of scoring first penalty	$\frac{1}{2}$	$\frac{2}{3}$
Probability of scoring if scored previous penalty	$\frac{2}{3}$	$\frac{5}{6}$
Probability of scoring if missed previous penalty	$\frac{1}{2}$	$\frac{1}{6}$

Players take ten penalties each in a season.

a Explain how you could carry out a probability experiment using a dice to simulate a player taking ten penalties.

b By rolling a dice 50 times for each player, simulate their performance over five seasons.

c Draw a line graph to show the performance of the two players over the course of the five seasons.

d Work out the mean, median and range for the number of penalties scored in a season for each player.

e Which player should the football manager choose? Explain your answer.

4 The speed limit on Carlton Avenue is 40 mph. A speed camera records these speeds:
37 39 45 38 39 42 51 38

a Use the data to estimate the probability that a car selected at random is breaking the speed limit.

b Estimate how many of the next 24 cars to pass the speed camera are likely to be speeding.

Level 6

6a I can apply the probabilities from experimental data in a more complex situation

Did you know?

TV pundit Matt Le Tissier is probably the Premiership's best ever penalty taker, scoring an amazing 48 out of 49 times.

Now try this!

A What do you expect?

a Roll a dice ten times. Use a tally chart to record the scores.

b Work out the experimental probability of rolling a 6.

c Combine your results with a partner.
What is the experimental probability using your combined results?

d Combine your results with another pair.
What is the experimental probability now?

e Compare your results from parts **b** to **d** with the theoretical probability of rolling a 6.

B Random numbers

a Use the random number generator on your calculator to generate a random number. Square it, and record the result.

b Estimate the probability that the answer is less than $\frac{1}{2}$ by carrying out 30 trials.

c Now try calculating 'random number' × 'random number'. Investigate whether the probability of an answer less than $\frac{1}{2}$ is the same as in part **a**.

theoretical probability

Sunny or windy or both?

When deciding whether to install a wind turbine or solar panels, it is vital to look at the weather conditions over a period of a year or more.
The table shows collected data for Texas, USA, and south-west Ireland.

Hint: m/s stands for metres per second and kWh/m²/d is a measure of energy.

	Monthly average solar radiation – on a horizontal surface (kWh/m²/d)	Monthly average wind speed – 10 m above ground (m/s)	Monthly average solar radiation – on a horizontal surface (kWh/m²/d)	Monthly average wind speed – 10 m above ground (m/s)
	Texas, USA		south-west Ireland	
January	3.47	3.2	0.67	10.2
February	4.54	3.6	1.30	9.6
March	5.86	4.4	2.50	9.0
April	7.09	4.4	4.15	7.7
May	7.83	4.1	5.21	6.5
June	8.03	3.6	5.28	6.1
July	7.36	3.2	4.84	6.3
August	6.76	3.0	4.32	6.5
September	5.87	2.9	3.14	7.1
October	4.93	2.9	1.75	8.4
November	3.80	3.1	0.87	8.9
December	3.21	3.0	0.53	9.4

1 **a** Calculate the approximate annual mean solar radiation for both Texas and south-west Ireland.
b Compare the solar radiation figures for each area using the mean and the range. **Level 5**

2 This table shows the median, mean and range of wind speeds (in metres per second) for two areas. If you were asked to build a wind turbine, where would you build it? Give reasons for your choice. **Level 6**

	Shetland Isles	south-west Ireland
Mean	7.1	8.0
Median	7.3	8.05
Range	3.1	4.1

3 **a** Construct a frequency table with five equal class intervals for the wind speed data for south-west Ireland.
b Draw a frequency diagram to show the wind speed data for south-west Ireland.
c What is the modal class of this data? **Level 6**

4 Choose a suitable assumed mean and then use it to find the mean wind speed for Texas. **Level 7**

5 **a** Construct a frequency table, with equal class intervals, for the solar radiation data for south-west Ireland.
b What is the modal class of this data?
c Is the modal class a suitable average to use for this data? Explain your reasons fully. **Level 7**

6 If you draw a line graph to represent the solar radiation data for south-west Ireland, what trends would you expect? Draw the line graph to see if your predictions are correct. **Level 7**

The BIG ideas

- The **median** is the middle value when a set of data is arranged in order of size. If there is an even number of data items, there will be two middle values. The median is halfway between the two. **Level 5**
- To find the **mean**, add up all the data and divide by the number of data items. **Level 5**
- The **range** tells you how variable a set of data is:
  range = maximum value − minimum value. **Level 5**
- It is usually best to have four or five groups in a **frequency table**. The groups should be of equal width and they should not overlap. **Level 5 & Level 6**
- It is useful to compare two sets of data using one average and the range. **Level 5 & Level 6**
- **Frequency diagrams** can be used to show grouped **continuous** data. A frequency diagram looks a bit like a bar chart, but there are no gaps between the bars. **Level 6**
- The interval $150 \leq$ height < 155 includes all the heights from 150 cm up to but not including 150 cm. **Level 6**
- A **line graph** is a series of points joined by straight lines. **Level 6**
- Line graphs are often used to show **trends** over periods of time. These are called **time series graphs**. Time goes on the horizontal axis. **Level 6**
- Using an **assumed mean** can make calculating the mean easier:
  mean = assumed mean + mean of the differences from the assumed mean **Level 6 & Level 7**
- The **modal class** is the group with the highest frequency. **Level 6 & Level 7**

Practice SATs-style questions

Level 5

Q1 **a** Find the mean of this data set.
12, 5, 6, 8, 5, 6, 4, 9, 15, 2

b Josh says the mode of this data set is 6. Is he correct?

Q2 Best Bank recorded these waiting times, in seconds, of their customers.
~~22~~, ~~43~~, 15, 45, 52, 110, 63, 28, 55, 60, 115, 89, 45, 32

Copy and complete this frequency table for the data.

Waiting times (s)	Tally	Frequency
0–24	|	
25–49	|	

Level 6

Q3 The graph opposite shows the share price of a company over a 10-year period. Use the graph to decide whether each statement is true or false, or if it is not possible to be certain. Give a reason for each answer.

a The share price fell by more than half over the 10 years.

b In 2010 the share price will be 240p.

Q4 Some pupils conducted an experiment to investigate whether a spinner was biased. The results of their experiment are shown in the table.

Number of spins	Colour spinner landed on			
	red	green	blue	yellow
590	198	189	97	106

a Do you think the spinner is biased? Explain your answer.

b From the data, work out the probability of the spinner landing on blue. Give your answer as a decimal, to 2 decimal places.

Level 7

Q5 Four numbers have a mean of 8. Two of the numbers are 5 and 7. The two missing numbers have a difference of 4. What are the missing numbers?

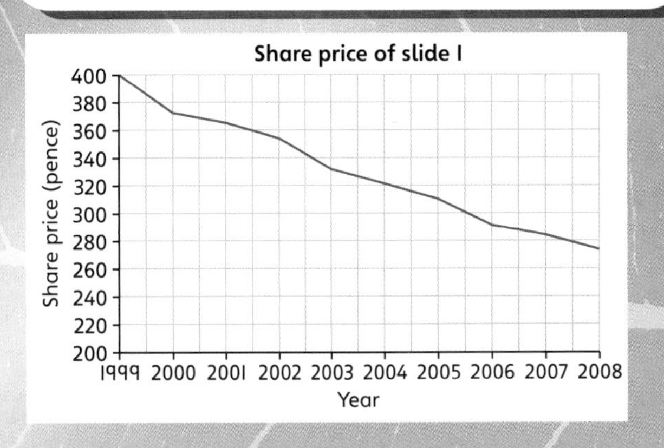

Revision 3

Quick Quiz

Q1 Work out

a $\frac{1}{4}$ of 60 kg

b $\frac{2}{5}$ of £30

→ *See 12.1*

Q2 Use the fact that $3.72 \times 24 = 89.28$ to work out

a 372×24

b 37.2×0.24

→ *See 12.4*

Q3 The sides of a triangle are in the ratio 2 : 3 : 5.
How long are the other sides if the shortest side is 12 cm?

→ *See 14.1*

Q4 Calculate mentally $(4 + 5)^2 - 3 \times 7$.

→ *See 12.3*

Q5 Convert 360 cm^2 into square millimetres.

→ *See 12.5*

Q6 Rearrange the function $2y - 6 = 8x$ into the form $y = mx + c$.

→ *See 13.2*

Q7 The diagram shows three views of the same cube.
Which letters are opposite each other?

→ *See 15.1*

Q8 Solve this equation $3(4x + 5) = 2(3x - 1) + 5$.

→ *See 13.6*

Q9 Sally bought a pair of shoes in a sale. The shoes were reduced by 10%.
She went shopping with £55 and came home with £19.
What was the original price of the shoes before the sale?

→ *See 14.5*

Q10 Here are five number cards.

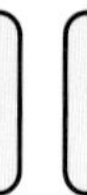

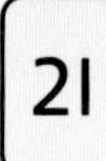

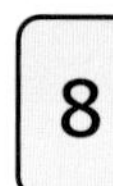

What is the missing number if

a the mode is 4?

b the mean is 12?

c the median is 8 and the range is 19?

→ See 16.2

Activity

You are planning a walking and camping holiday in France with two friends.
You buy the following equipment.

Equipment	Weight	Price
Tent	2.35 kg	£74.52
Rucksack	2200 g	£63.55
Sleeping bag	820 g	£45.99

LEVEL 5

Q1 What is the total weight of the tent, rucksack and sleeping bag?

Q2 You share the cost of the tent equally between the three of you.
How much do you each pay?

This map shows part of the route you are going to walk.

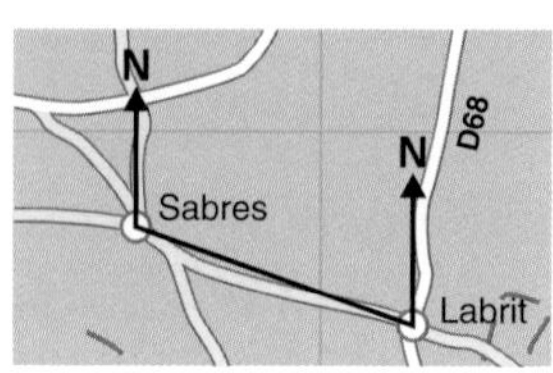

Q3 What is the bearing of Labrit from Sabres?

LEVEL 6

Q4 The scale of the map is 1 : 800 000.
What is the distance on the ground from Sabres to Labrit?

LEVEL 7

Q5 The owner draws this bar chart to show the number of flapjacks bought each day by men and women.

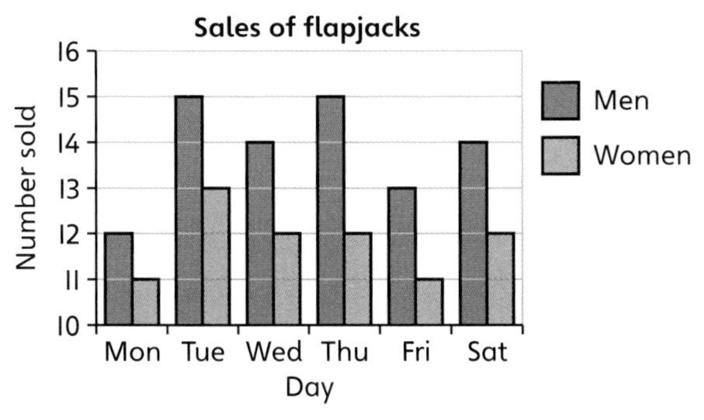

She says 'Men buy about twice as many flapjacks as women every day!' Is she correct?

Q6 Before the holiday you change £120 into euros. The ratio of pounds to euros is £1 : €1.25. After the holiday, you change the euros you haven't spent back into pounds. The ratio of pounds to euros is now £1 : €1.19 and you get £27 back. How many euros did you spend on holiday?

Practice SATs-style questions

LEVEL 5

Q1 Here are two containers and their capacities.

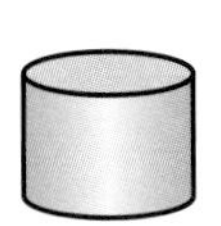
50 centilitres

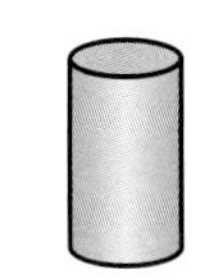
650 millilitres

a Which container holds the greater amount?

b How much more does it hold? Give your answer in millilitres.

Q2 Fred buys 24 toilet rolls. He buys them in packs of four. Each pack costs £1.92. Harry buys 24 toilet rolls. He buys them in packs of 12. Each pack costs £4.75.
Fred pays more for his 24 toilet rolls than Harry pays for his 24 toilet rolls.
How much more?

LEVEL 6

Q3 The diagrams show the nets of two dice.
Each dice has six faces numbered 1 to 6.
Copy and complete the nets so that the numbers on opposite faces add to 7.

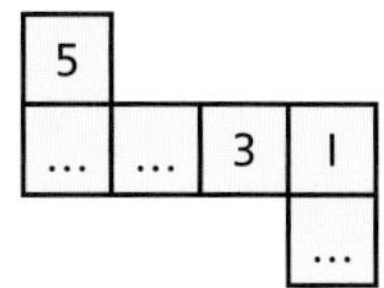

1 4
2 ... ...
...

Q4 A teacher asked 15 pupils to estimate the weight of a bag of apples.
This stem-and-leaf diagram shows all 15 results.

0 | 8 represents 0.8 kg

0 | 8 8 9
1 | 1 5 5 5 6 7 8 9
2 | 0 1 1 2

a Show that the range of estimated weights was 1.4 kg.

b What was the median estimated weight?

c The actual weight of the bag was 1.5 kg. What percentage of pupils correctly estimated the weight?

LEVEL 7

Q5 During the week before exams Huw revised for $25\frac{1}{2}$ hours.
He revised for the same length of time on Monday, Wednesday and Friday.
On Tuesday, Thursday, Saturday and Sunday he revised for two hours more than on Monday.
How long did he spend revising on Wednesday?

Q6 In a quiz, two teams each have to answer a total of 50 questions.
They score 1 point for each correct answer.
The quiz has not yet finished. Each team has answered 40 questions.
The table shows the results so far.

Team A	Team B
40% of the first 40 questions correct	55% of the first 40 questions correct

Can Team A win the game? Explain your answer.

Index